when the phase of a 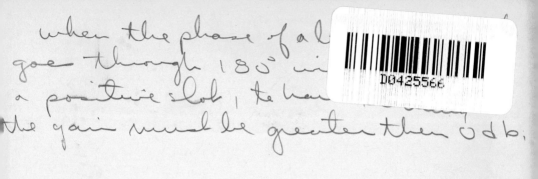 goes through 180° in a positive slot, to have this the gain must be greater than 0 db.

D0425566

CONTROL SYSTEM DESIGN

CONTROL SYSTEM DESIGN

STANLEY M. SHINNERS

Research Section Head for Advanced Studies,
Sperry Gyroscope Company
Division of Sperry Rand Corporation
Great Neck, New York

and Lecturer in Electrical Engineering
Polytechnic Institute of Brooklyn
Farmingdale, New York

JOHN WILEY & SONS, INC., NEW YORK · LONDON · SYDNEY

Copyright © 1964 by John Wiley & Sons, Inc.

All Rights Reserved
This book or any part thereof
must not be reproduced in any form
without the written permission of the publisher.

Library of Congress Catalog Card Number: 64-17152
Printed in the United States of America

To my wife
Doris
and to my children
Sharon and Walter

FOREWORD

Throughout its history, the technological field of automatic feedback control engineering has evolved from an intimate relationship between theory and practice. The early work by Minorsky on the steering control of naval battleships, the subsequent developments in feedback amplifier design, and the early applications of industrial process controlled directly into the explosive growth of the field during World War II. Since 1945 control engineering has played a vital role in the development of industrial automation and military and space systems.

Since 1957 this dual emphasis on theory and applications has been reinforced by the activities of the International Federation on Automatic Control—both by the technical congresses every three years and by the expanding work of the Committees on Theory, Applications, and Components. The basic theme adopted for the Third International Congress of IFAC in London in 1966 is the transition between theory and applications.

In the light of this historical parallelism, a modern control text emphasizing the aspects of theory that have found most significant application in real engineering practice is particularly welcome. In any text, the author's most important contribution is his selection of material and the relative emphasis he decides to place on particular topics. This book is consistently characterized by the strong industrial experience of the author—a background that is coupled with extensive teaching experience in both industrial and university programs. Because of this personal interpretation, the book represents a significant contribution and a welcome addition to the library of control books which reflect primarily either the academic or the industrial background of the authors.

The contribution of the book is highlighted by the author's coverage of a variety of topics of recent importance. The recognition of the importance of computers in control system design and the discussion of optimizing and adaptive systems are particularly significant. Throughout the text the development of theoretical topics is coupled with clear indications of the application of the theory in engineering design and system evaluation—that very coupling which has encouraged such rapid growth of control engineering in the past.

JOHN G. TRUXAL

Brooklyn, New York
January 20, 1964

PREFACE

In this book I have attempted to fill a rather large gap in the literature on feedback control system design by presenting a unified treatment of all the classical and modern concepts of control system theory. I hope, further, that this book will serve as a catalyst in unifying all the current knowledge in the rapidly growing field of control system design.

The material on which this book is based has developed from the courses on feedback control system design that I have been teaching for a number of years at the Polytechnic Institute of Brooklyn and at the Sperry Gyroscope Company. In my approach to the subject, I have emphasized an orderly and sequential presentation in order to help the reader to understand and to apply the principles discussed.

I have omitted much of the detailed introductory mathematical information usually found in books on control system design on the assumption that my audience will have the required mathematical background and that the space devoted to this material will be better spent on a wider and more detailed treatment of the subject at hand. Consistent with this objective, the book covers basic feedback concepts, linear systems, nonlinear systems, sampled-data systems, statistical design, optimal control systems, and adaptive control systems as well as a review of the advanced mathematical concepts required to understand the presentation.

Another feature to which I have given emphasis is the use of analog and digital computers as aids in solving control system problems. This strong orientation toward computing techniques is a natural development attendant upon the inclusion of material on nonlinear systems, statistical analysis, sampled-data systems, optimization, and adaptivity. The emphasis of this book, that of applying theory to practical problems through the use of modern techniques, should contribute to the growth of students as control system engineers and increase the capability of practicing engineers in this field.

Chapter 1 introduces the concept of open-loop and closed-loop control systems. Chapter 2 reviews important features of the Laplace transform theory and the signal flow diagram. Certain definitions and nomenclature, together with the derivation of the transfer function for several common devices found in feedback control systems, are presented in Chapter 3.

ix

Chapter 4 treats various performance criteria, while Chapter 5 offers a comprehensive treatment of stability criteria, together with several useful and practical examples. The concepts of stability, presented in Chapter 5, are applied in great detail to the design of linear systems in Chapter 6. Chapter 7 discusses and presents examples for the design of nonlinear systems. Chapter 8 illustrates the application of statistical techniques for the design of systems having random inputs and, in addition, reviews probability theory. Chapter 9 discusses the design of sampled-data control systems. The z-transform theory is also presented in this chapter, as are certain elements of information theory. Chapters 10 and 11 are devoted to a discussion of optimal control systems and adaptive control systems, respectively. Although adaptive control systems appeared first in the literature, in my opinion the control engineer cannot fully understand adaptive control theory until he fully understands optimal control theory. Therefore I present optimal control system theory first. Appendix A reviews matrix and determinant analysis. Conversion factors and mathematical relationships useful to the control engineer are presented in Appendices B and C, respectively. A full set of problems for all the chapters, chosen specifically to enhance the presentation and to emphasize salient points, concludes the text.

A chapter devoted specifically to components has not been included. Despite this, components do receive a great deal of attention throughout the text as part of the overall system. I chose this method of presentation in the interest of maintaining a unified treatment.

I wish to express my sincere appreciation to Dr. John G. Truxal, Vice President for Educational Development, Polytechnic Institute of Brooklyn, for his thorough review of the manuscript and for his valuable suggestions. A debt of gratitude is also owed to Mr. S. Adelman and Mr. P. M. Lowitt, colleagues of mine at the Sperry Gyroscope Company with whom I have co-authored a series of twelve papers in this field, for their assistance and suggestions. In addition, Mr. K. E. Forsberg, Mr. R. V. Gould, Mr. G. W. Jacob, Mr. P. Miller, and Mr. E. M. Thyberg of the Sperry Gyroscope Company deserve particular mention for their interest in this project. I wish also to thank Mr. A. Cincotta, Miss C. Doman, Mr. J. J. Reid, Mr. L. S. Roseo, and the many others who assisted me.

I am most grateful to my wife, Doris, for her encouragement, understanding, patience, and assistance throughout this endeavor. In addition, I wish to express thanks and appreciation to my parents for their efforts, encouragement, and inspiration.

STANLEY M. SHINNERS

Great Neck, L.I.
January 1964

CONTENTS

CONTROL SYSTEM DESIGN

1

THE GENERAL CONCEPT

OF CONTROL SYSTEM DESIGN

1-1. INTRODUCTION

Throughout history, man has attempted to control nature's forces in order to help him perform physical tasks which were beyond his own capabilities. Science fiction writers have tried to describe man's imagination of and quest for unusual devices which perform strange and desirous tasks. During the dynamic and highly motivated twentieth century, many of man's imagined devices have turned into reality. The ability of scientists and engineers to control nature's forces successfully has been the catalyst for progress from the time of the industrial revolution.

The quest for survival during the last two decades has resulted in a very rapid growth in the knowledge and concept of control system design. During World War II, the needs of the military resulted in the design of automatic fire control systems, autopilots, and other types of automatic control equipment. Since World War II, the needs of the military have resulted in complex guided missile weapon systems, precision tracking radars, and adaptive autopilot systems. In addition, the knowledge of automatic control theory has been applied to industrial uses for machines in automated factories and process plants. Today, the field of automatic control ranks as one of the most promising fields in industry; its growth potential appears unlimited.

Control systems can be defined as devices which regulate the flow of energy. Their arrangement, complexity, and appearance vary with their purpose and function. In general, control systems can be categorized as being either open-loop or closed-loop. The distinguishing feature between these two types of control systems is the use of feedback comparison for closed-loop operation.

Properties characteristic of open-loop and closed-loop control systems are discussed in this chapter. We shall give several examples of each type so that the reader may gain a thorough understanding and a good foundation for further studies in this book. A qualitative, philosophical comparison between the behavior of closed-loop control systems and that of living creatures will conclude the discussion of this chapter.

1

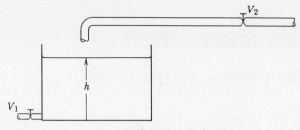

Figure 1–1.   Tank level control system.

1–2. OPEN-LOOP CONTROL SYSTEMS

Open-loop control systems represent the simplest and least complex form of controlling devices. Their concept and functioning are illustrated by several simple examples in this section.

Figure 1–1 illustrates a simple tank level control system. We wish to hold the tank level, h, within reasonable acceptable limits even though the outlet flow through valve V_1 is varied. This can be achieved by manual adjustment of the flow rate of valve V_2. This system is not a precision system since it does not have the capability of accurately measuring the output flow rate through valve V_1, the input flow rate through valve V_2, or the tank level. Figure 1–2 shows the simple relationship which exists in this system between the input (the desired tank level) and the output (the actual tank level). This signal flow representation of the physical system is called a "block diagram." Arrows are used to show the input entering and the output leaving the control system. This control system does not have any feedback comparison, and the term "open-loop" is used to describe its absence.

The angular position of a gun turret being controlled from a remote source is illustrated in Figure 1–3. Commands from a potentiometer located at a remote location activate the positioning of the gun turret. The control signal is amplified and drives a motor which is geared to the gun turret. The block diagram shown in Figure 1–2 is also applicable to this system. The input would be the desired angular position, the output would be the actual angular position, and the control system would consist of the amplifier and motor. For accurate positioning the gun turret should be precisely calibrated with the angular position of the potentiometer, and the characteristics of the potentiometer, amplifier, and

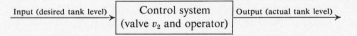

Figure 1–2.   Tank level control system block diagram.

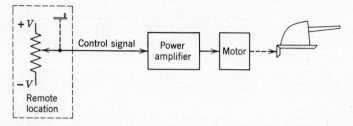

Figure 1–3.   *Controlling the position of a gun turret from a remote location.*

motor should remain constant. Except for the potentiometer, the components that comprise this open-loop control system are not precision devices. Their characteristics can easily change and result in false calibration and poor accuracies. In practice, simple open-loop control systems are never used for the accurate positioning of fire control systems due to the inherent possibility of inaccuracies and the stakes involved.

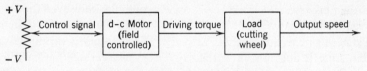

Figure 1–4.   *Field-controlled d-c motor.*

Figure 1–4 illustrates a field-controlled d-c motor turning a cutting wheel at a constant speed. When a piece of wood is applied to the surface of the cutting wheel, it acts as a disturbing torque to the driving torque and results in slowing down the speed of the cutting wheel, assuming that the control signal remains constant. This situation can be represented as shown in Figure 1–5. The symbol appearing between the motor and the load represents a subtractor.

The effect of disturbance torques, or other secondary inputs, is detrimental to the accurate functioning of an open-loop control system. It has no way of automatically correcting its output since there is no feedback comparison. We must resort to changing the input manually in order to compensate for secondary inputs.

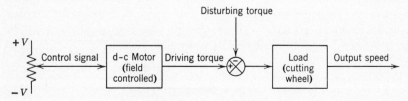

Figure 1–5.   *Field-controlled d-c motor having a disturbance torque.*

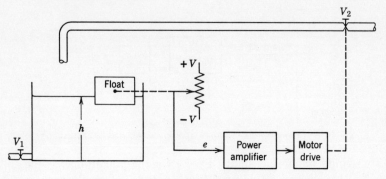

Figure 1-6. Automatic tank level control system.

1-3. CLOSED-LOOP CONTROL SYSTEMS

Closed-loop control systems derive their valuable accurate reproduction of the input from feedback comparison. An error detector derives a signal proportional to the difference between the input and output. The closed-loop control system drives the output until it equals the input and the error is zero. Any differences between the actual and desired output will be automatically corrected in a closed-loop control system. Through proper design, the system can be made relatively independent of secondary inputs and changes in component characteristics. This section illustrates the closed-loop control system versions of the open-loop control systems considered in Section 1-2.

Figure 1-6 illustrates an automatic tank level control version of the system shown in Figure 1-1. It can maintain the desired tank level h within quite accurate tolerances even though the outlet flow rate through valve V_1 is varied. If the tank level is not correct, an error voltage, e, is developed. This is amplified and applied to a motor drive which adjusts valve V_2 in order to restore the desired tank level by adjusting the inlet flow rate. A block diagram analogous to this system is shown in Figure 1-7. Because feedback comparison is present the term closed-loop is used to describe the system's operation.

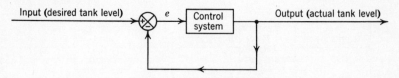

Figure 1-7. Block diagram of a closed-loop system.

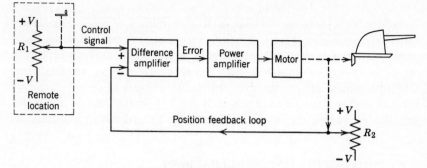

Figure 1–8.   An automatic positioning system for a gun turret.

Figure 1–8 illustrates an automatic gun turret position control version of the system shown in Figure 1–3. This feedback system can position the gun turret quite accurately on commands from potentiometer R_1. Potentiometer R_2 feeds a signal back to the difference amplifier, which functions as an error detector. Should an error exist, it is amplified and applied to a motor drive which adjusts the output shaft position until it agrees with the input shaft position, and the error is zero. The block diagram shown in Figure 1–7 is also applicable to this system. The input would be the desired angular position, the output would be the actual angular position, and the control system would consist of the amplifier and the motor.

An automatic speed control version of the field-controlled d-c motor, which was shown in Figure 1–4, is illustrated in Figure 1–9. This feedback system has the capabilities of maintaining the output speed relatively constant even though disturbing torques may occur. A tachometer, which functions as a transducer that transforms speed to a voltage, is the feedback element for this control system. Should the output speed differ from the desired speed, the difference amplifier develops an error signal which adjusts the field current of the motor in order to restore the desired output speed.

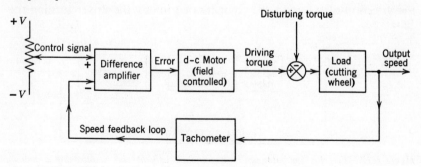

Figure 1–9.   Automatic speed control for a field-controlled d-c motor.

Feedback control systems used to control position, velocity, and acceleration are very common in industrial and military applications. They have been given the special name of "servomechanisms." With all their many advantages, feedback systems have a very serious disadvantage since the closed-loop system may inadvertently act as an oscillator. Through proper design, however, all the advantages of feedback can be utilized without having an unstable system. A major task of this book is to determine how this may be accomplished for several types of systems.

1-4. PHILOSOPHICAL CONSIDERATIONS

The relation between the behavior of living creatures and the functioning of feedback control systems has recently gained wide attention. Norbert Weiner in his book *Cybernetics* implied that all systems, living and mechanical, are both information and feedback control systems. He suggested that the most promising techniques for studying both systems are information theory and feedback control theory.

Several characteristics of feedback control systems can be linked to human behavior. Feedback control systems can "think" in the sense that they can replace, to some extent, human operations. These devices do not have the privilege of freedom in their thinking process and are constrained by the designer to some predetermined function. Adaptive feedback control systems, which are capable of modifying their functioning in order to achieve optimum performance in a varying environment, have recently gained wide attention. These systems are a step closer to the adaptive capability of human behavior.

The human body is, indeed, a very complex and highly perfected adaptive feedback control system. Consider, for example, the human actions required to steer an automobile. The driver's object is to keep the automobile traveling in the center of a chosen lane on the road. Changes in the direction of the road are compensated for by the driver turning the

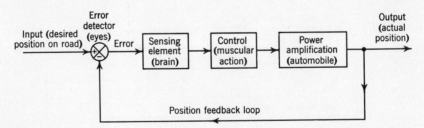

Figure 1–10. Steering an automobile—a feedback control system involving a human transfer function.

steering wheel. His object is to keep the difference between the output (the actual path of the car) and the input (the desired path of the car) as close to zero as is possible.

Figure 1–10 illustrates the block diagram of the feedback control system involved in steering an automobile. The error detector in this case is the driver's eyes. This in turn activates the brain's sensing elements. Signals are then transmitted from the brain to the driver's muscles which control the steering wheel. Power amplification is provided by the automobile's steering mechanism, which controls the position of the front wheels.

It is important to emphasize, at this point, that the approximations which are inherently necessary in order to express complex human transfer functions often result in large practical errors. The differential equations which describes the driver's response will have variable coefficients, since his performance is adaptive. In addition, learning, fatigue, motivation, and familiarity with the road he is traveling on will have an effect on the driver's response.

2

MATHEMATICAL TOOLS
FOR THE CONTROL ENGINEER

2-1. INTRODUCTION

The design of linear, continuous, feedback control systems is dependent on mathematical tools such as the Laplace transformation and the signal flow graph. In addition to these techniques, the design of linear, sampled-data, feedback control systems requires a knowledge of the z-transformation and some segments of information theory. The design of linear continuous systems having random inputs requires a knowledge of probability theory and statistical theory. The scope of this book does not permit a detailed discussion of all these mathematical devices. The philosophy followed here is to review the theory of these techniques and to focus attention on the specific application of these mathematical tools to feedback control systems.

This chapter reviews the theory and application of the Laplace transformation and the signal flow graph. Elements of probability theory and statistical theory are presented in Chapter 8 when we discuss statistical design of feedback control systems having random inputs. Chapter 9 will discuss the z-transformation and certain segments of information theory when sampled-data systems are presented. Matrix algebra is reviewed in Appendix A. Common and useful conversion factors and mathematical relationships are presented in Appendices B and C, respectively.

2-2. REVIEW OF THE LAPLACE TRANSFORMATION[1,2]

The Laplace transformation is very helpful in the solution of ordinary differential equations describing the behavior of systems; it is based on the use of the Laplace integral. When the integral operates on a differential equation, a "transformed" equation results. It is expressed in terms of an arbitrary complex variable, s. The resulting transformed equation is in purely algebraic terms which can be easily manipulated to

8

obtain a solution of the desired quantity as an explicit function of the complex variable. In order to obtain a solution in terms of the original variable, it is necessary to perform the inverse process by replacing the complex variable. This operation is known as obtaining the "inverse Laplace transformation."

The Laplace operator $\mathscr{L}$ is defined as

$$\mathscr{L} \triangleq \int_0^\infty e^{-st}\, dt \qquad (2\text{--}1)$$

The complex variable s represents the quantity $\sigma + j\omega$. The Laplace transform $F(s)$ of a certain function of time $f(t)$ is defined as

$$F(s) \triangleq \mathscr{L}[f(t)] \qquad (2\text{--}2)$$

In general, the variable need not be limited only to time. Time is, however, the variable quantity encountered in most control system problems, and hence it is used in this discussion.

A more explicit definition of the Laplace transform is obtained by substituting equation 2–1 into equation 2–2:

$$F(s) = \int_0^\infty f(t)e^{-st}\, dt \qquad (2\text{--}3)$$

Therefore, the Laplace transform of any function may be obtained by multiplying that function by e^{-st} and then integrating the product from $t = 0$ to $t = \infty$. The only requirements are that the variable t be defined for all values of time greater than zero and that the complex variable s be sufficiently large for the integral of equation 2–3 to converge (a limit exists for the integral as $t \to \infty$).

2–3. USEFUL LAPLACE TRANSFORMS

The Laplace transforms for various types of time function will now be considered. These are readily obtainable through a direct application of equation 2–3. Attention will be focused on the type of function that is common to feedback control systems. Several examples will illustrate the techniques of application prior to our tabulation of several useful transform pairs.

a. The Laplace Transform of a Unit Step

$$f(t) = 1 \qquad [f(t) = 0 \text{ for } t \leqslant 0]$$

$$\mathcal{L}[f(t)] = \mathcal{L}(1) = \int_0^\infty (1)\, e^{-st}\, dt$$

$$= \int_0^\infty e^{-st}\, dt = \left[-\frac{1}{s} e^{-st} \right]_0^\infty$$

$$= -\frac{1}{s} (e^{-\infty} - e^{-0})$$

$$\therefore \quad \mathcal{L}(1) = \frac{1}{s} \tag{2-4}$$

b. The Laplace Transform of an Exponential Decay

$$f(t) = e^{-\alpha t}$$

$$\mathcal{L}[f(t)] = \mathcal{L}(e^{-\alpha t}) = \int_0^\infty e^{-\alpha t}\, e^{-st}\, dt$$

$$= \int_0^\infty e^{-(s+\alpha)t}\, dt = \left[-\frac{1}{s+\alpha} e^{-(s+\alpha)t} \right]_0^\infty$$

$$= -\frac{1}{s+\alpha} (e^{-\infty} - e^{-0})$$

$$\therefore \quad \mathcal{L}(e^{-\alpha t}) = \frac{1}{s+\alpha} \tag{2-5}$$

c. The Laplace Transform of a Unit Ramp

$$f(t) = t$$

$$\mathcal{L}[f(t)] = \mathcal{L}(t) = \int_0^\infty t\, e^{-st}\, dt \tag{2-6}$$

The application of equation 2–3 for the Laplace transform of a unit ramp function requires integration by parts. Applying the well-known mathematical relation for integration by parts, given in equation 2–7, results in a solution for equation 2–6.

$$\int u\, dv = uv - \int v\, du \tag{2-7}$$

Let

$$u = t, \qquad dv = e^{-st}\, dt$$

$$du = dt, \qquad v = \frac{e^{-st}}{-s}$$

$$\therefore \int_0^\infty t\, e^{-st}\, dt = \left[t\, \frac{e^{-st}}{-s} \right]_0^\infty - \int_0^\infty \frac{e^{-st}}{-s}\, dt$$

$$= 0 - \left(\frac{e^{-\infty}}{s^2} - \frac{e^{-0}}{s^2} \right)$$

$$\therefore \ \mathscr{L}(t) = \frac{1}{s^2} \tag{2-8}$$

d. The Laplace Transform of a Sinusoidal Function

$$f(t) = \sin \omega t$$

$$\mathscr{L}[f(t)] = \mathscr{L}(\sin \omega t) = \int_0^\infty \sin \omega t\, e^{-st}\, dt \tag{2-9}$$

The solution to equation 2–9 is simplified by using the exponential form of sin ωt, given by equation 2–10.

$$\sin \omega t = \frac{e^{j\omega t} - e^{-j\omega t}}{2j} \tag{2-10}$$

$$\therefore \int_0^\infty \sin \omega t\, e^{-st}\, dt = \int_0^\infty \frac{e^{j\omega t} - e^{-j\omega t}}{2j}\, e^{-st}\, dt$$

$$= \frac{1}{2j} \int_0^\infty (e^{-(s-j\omega)t} - e^{-(s+j\omega)t})\, dt$$

$$= \frac{1}{2j} \left[-\frac{e^{-(s-j\omega)t}}{s - j\omega} + \frac{e^{-(s+j\omega)t}}{s + j\omega} \right]_0^\infty$$

$$= \frac{1}{2j} \left(-\frac{e^{-\infty}}{s - j\omega} + \frac{e^{-\infty}}{s + j\omega} + \frac{e^{-0}}{s - j\omega} - \frac{e^{-0}}{s + j\omega} \right)$$

$$= \frac{1}{2j} \left(\frac{1}{s - j\omega} - \frac{1}{s + j\omega} \right)$$

$$\therefore \ \mathscr{L}(\sin \omega t) = \frac{\omega}{s^2 + \omega^2} \tag{2-11}$$

Once the Laplace transform for any function $f(t)$ is obtained and tabulated, it need not be derived again. The foregoing results and other transform pairs useful to the control engineer appear in Table 2–1. In addition, the location of poles of the transformed function in the complex plane is listed.

Table 2–1.   Common Laplace transform pairs

Name of Function	Time Function, $f(t)$	Laplace Transform, $F(s)$	Location of Poles in s Plane
1. Unit Impulse at $T = 0$	$\delta(t)$	1	None
2. Unit Step for $t > 0$	1	$\dfrac{1}{s}$	One pole at the origin
3. Unit Ramp	t	$\dfrac{1}{s^2}$	Double pole at the origin
4. Parabolic	t^2	$\dfrac{2}{s^3}$	Triple pole at the origin
5. nth-Order Ramp	t^n	$\dfrac{n!}{s^{n+1}}$	$n + 1$ multiple poles at the origin
6. Exponential Decay	$e^{-\alpha t}$	$\dfrac{1}{s + \alpha}$	One pole on the real axis at $-\alpha$
7. Sine Wave	$\sin \omega t$	$\dfrac{\omega}{s^2 + \omega^2}$	Two poles on the imaginary axis at $\pm j\omega$
8. Cosine Wave	$\cos \omega t$	$\dfrac{s}{s^2 + \omega^2}$	Two poles on the imaginary axis at $\pm j\omega$
9. Exponentially Decaying Sine Wave	$e^{-\alpha t} \sin \omega t$	$\dfrac{\omega}{(s + \alpha)^2 + \omega^2}$	Two complex poles located at $-\alpha \pm j\omega$
10. Exponentially Decaying Ramp	$\omega t \, e^{-\omega t}$	$\dfrac{\omega}{(s + \omega)^2}$	Two poles on the real axis at $-\omega$

2–4.   IMPORTANT PROPERTIES OF THE LAPLACE TRANSFORM

The Laplace transformation has been introduced in order to simplify several mathematical operations that occur in control system design. These operations center about the solution of linear differential equations. The following discussion will enumerate several basic properties of the Laplace transformation which are required for the solution of such equations.

a.   Addition and Subtraction.   If the Laplace transforms of $f_1(t)$ and $f_2(t)$ are $F_1(s)$ and $F_2(s)$ respectively, then

$$\mathscr{L}[f_1(t) \pm f_2(t)] = F_1(s) \pm F_2(s) \qquad (2\text{–}12)$$

b.   Multiplication by a Constant.   If the Laplace transform of $f(t)$ is $F(s)$, then multiplication of the function $f(t)$ by a constant K results in a Laplace transform of $KF(s)$.

c.   Direct Transforms of Derivatives.   If the Laplace transform of $f(t)$ is $F(s)$, the transform of the time derivative $f'(t)$ of $f(t)$ is given by

$$\mathscr{L}[f'(t)] = SF(s) - f(0^+) \qquad (2\text{–}13)$$

where $f(0^+)$ is the initial value of $f(t)$, evaluated as $t \to 0$ from the positive region.

d. Direct Transforms of Integrals. If the Laplace transform of $f(t)$ is $F(s)$, the transform of the time integral of $f(t)$ is given by

$$\mathscr{L}\left[\int f(t)\, dt\right] = \frac{F(s)}{s} + \frac{1}{s}\left[\int f(t)\, dt\right]_{t=0^+} \tag{2-14}$$

where $[\int f(t)\, dt]_{t=0^+}$ signifies that the integral is evaluated as $t \to 0$ from the positive region.

e. The Initial-Value Theorem. If the Laplace transform of $f(t)$ is $F(s)$, and if the $\lim_{s \to \infty} sF(s)$ exists, then the initial value of the time function is given by

$$\lim_{t \to 0} f(t) = \lim_{s \to \infty} sF(s) \tag{2-15}$$

f. The Final-Value Theorem. If the Laplace transform of $f(t)$ is $F(s)$, and if $sF(s)$ is analytic on the imaginary axis and in the right half plane, then the final value of the time function is given by

$$\lim_{t \to \infty} f(t) = \lim_{s \to 0} sF(s) \tag{2-16}$$

2-5. THE INVERSE LAPLACE TRANSFORMATION

The time response is the quantity of ultimate interest to the control system designer. Therefore it is necessary to retransform the solution, which is in terms of the complex variable s, back into terms of the time domain. The mathematical process of going from the complex-variable expression to that of time is called the inverse Laplace transformation and is denoted symbolically by

$$\mathscr{L}^{-1}F(s) = f(t) \tag{2-17}$$

In general, the transformed solution of an nth-order differential equation is of the form

$$F(s) = \frac{A_X s^X + A_{X-1} s^{X-1} + \cdots + A_1 s + A_0}{s^Y + B_{Y-1} s^{Y-1} + \cdots + B_1 s + B_0} \tag{2-18}$$

In practical systems, the order of the polynomial in the denominator is equal to, or greater than, that of the numerator. For the cases where $Y > X$, partial fraction expansion is directly applicable. When $Y = X$, it is necessary to perform longhand division of the denominator into the numerator in order that $F(s)$ be in the form of a proper fraction.

The simplest method for obtaining inverse transformations is to use a table of transforms. Unfortunately, many forms of the $F(s)$ equation are not found in the usual table of Laplace transform pairs. When the form of the solution cannot be readily reduced to a form available in a table, we must use Heaviside's expansion theorem. This theorem permits the expansion of the algebraic equation into a series of simpler terms whose transforms are available from a table. It is then possible to obtain the inverse transformation of the original algebraic expression by adding together the inverse transformations of the terms in the Heaviside expansion. Equation 2–19 expresses this operation symbolically. The function $F(s)$ represents the original algebraic expression and $F_1(s)$, $F_2(s)$, $F_3(s)$, . . . , $F_n(s)$ are terms of the partial fraction expansion.

$$\mathscr{L}^{-1}[F(s)] = \mathscr{L}^{-1}[F_1(s)] + \mathscr{L}^{-1}[F_2(s)] + \cdots + \mathscr{L}^{-1}[F_n(s)] \quad (2\text{–}19)$$

A large variety of functions of interest to the control engineer can be written as

$$F(s) = \frac{As + B}{(s + C)(s + D)} \quad (2\text{–}20)$$

In this second-order equation A, B, C, and D represent numerical constants. By means of Heaviside's expansion theorem, this function can be expanded into partial fractions:

$$\frac{As + B}{(s + C)(s + D)} = \frac{K_1}{s + C} + \frac{K_2}{s + D} \quad (2\text{–}21)$$

This expansion can be carried out regardless of the number of factors in the denominator. In order to identify the constants, both sides of equation 2–21 are multiplied by $s + C$.

$$\frac{As + B}{s + D} = K_1 + \frac{K_2(s + C)}{s + D} \quad (2\text{–}22)$$

By substituting $s = -C$, the last term vanishes and a numerical value for K_1 can be obtained. An analogous procedure leads to the value for K_2.

$$K_1 = \frac{B - AC}{D - C} ; \qquad K_2 = \frac{B - AD}{C - D} \quad (2\text{–}23)$$

An expression for the expanded form of $F(s)$, in terms of known constants, can now be obtained by substituting this result into equation 2–21:

$$F(s) = \frac{B - AC}{D - C} \cdot \frac{1}{s + C} + \frac{B - AD}{C - D} \cdot \frac{1}{s + D} \quad (2\text{–}24)$$

It is now a simple process to obtain the inverse Laplace transform from this last equation. The corresponding time function can be obtained by merely inspecting the terms and comparing them with transform pairs listed in Table 2–1:

$$f(t) = \frac{B - AC}{D - C} e^{-Ct} + \frac{B - AD}{C - D} e^{-Dt} \qquad (2\text{-}25)$$

The control engineer occasionally encounters functions with two or more equal roots, as

$$F(s) = \frac{As + B}{(s + C)^2(s + D)} \qquad (2\text{-}26)$$

In this equation A, B, C, and D represent numerical constants. The transient response of this third-order equation must contain three constants. Simple algebraic properties lead to the partial fraction expansion

$$\frac{As + B}{(s + C)^2(s + D)} = \frac{K_1}{(s + C)^2} + \frac{K_2}{(s + C)} + \frac{K_3}{(s + D)} \qquad (2\text{-}27)$$

In order to identify the constants, both sides of equation 2–27 are multiplied by $(s + C)^2$.

$$\frac{As + B}{s + D} = K_1 + K_2(s + C) + \frac{K_3(s + C)^2}{s + D} \qquad (2\text{-}28)$$

The constant K_1 can now be evaluated by simply substituting $s = -C$.

$$K_1 = \frac{B - AC}{D - C} \qquad (2\text{-}29)$$

In order to determine the constant K_2, both sides of equation 2–28 must be differentiated with respect to s, and s is then set equal to $-C$:

$$\left[\frac{d}{ds}\frac{As + B}{s + D}\right]_{s=-C} = K_2 + K_3\left[\frac{d}{ds}\frac{(s + C)^2}{s + D}\right]_{s=-C} \qquad (2\text{-}30)$$

The resulting numerical value for K_2 is given by

$$K_2 = \left[\frac{d}{ds}\frac{As + B}{s + D}\right]_{s=-C} = \frac{AD - B}{(D - C)^2} \qquad (2\text{-}31)$$

The constant K_3 can be obtained by the same procedure used in evaluating the expression given by equation 2–20. Its value is

$$K_3 = \frac{B - AD}{(C - D)^2} \qquad (2\text{-}32)$$

2–6. THE TRANSFER FUNCTION CONCEPT

Control systems can be easily described by a set of differential equations. A block diagram is a simplified device for the same purpose. The physical elements appearing in block diagrams are described by a term called the "transfer function." This is defined as the element's ratio of output to input in the s plane. The system is assumed to be in equilibrium prior to excitation, and all initial values are assumed to be zero when determining the transfer function.

Consider the block diagram of the simple linear system shown in Figure 2–1. The only assumption made concerning this linear system is that the input and output are related by a linear differential equation whose coefficients are constant and can be written in the form

$$A_n \frac{d^n c}{dt^n} + \cdots + A_1 \frac{dc}{dt} + A_0 c(t) = B_m \frac{d^m r}{dt^m} + \cdots + B_1 \frac{dr}{dt} + B_0 r(t)$$

$$(2\text{–}33)$$

The Laplace transform of equation 2–33, assuming zero initial conditions, can be written as

$$(A_n s^n + \cdots + A_1 s + A_0) R(s) = (B_m s^m + \cdots + B_1 s + B_0) C(s) \quad (2\text{–}34)$$

The ratio $C(s)/R(s)$ is called the transfer function of the element and completely characterizes its performance. It is usually designated as $G(s)$.

$$G(s) = \frac{C(s)}{R(s)} = \frac{A_n s^n + \cdots + A_1 s + A_0}{B_m s^m + \cdots + B_1 s + B_0} \quad (2\text{–}35)$$

Therefore the Laplace transform of the output is the product of the transfer functions of the input and the element, assuming that the initial conditions are zero:

$$C(s) = G(s) R(s) \quad (2\text{–}36)$$

In general, the function $G(s)$ is the ratio of two polynomials in s:

$$G(s) = \frac{P(s)}{Q(s)} \quad (2\text{–}37)$$

The characteristic equation of the system is obtained by setting $Q(s)$ equal

Input, $r(t)$ → | System $g(t)$ | → Output, $c(t)$

Figure 2–1.   Block diagram of a simple linear system.

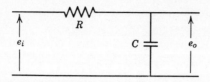

Figure 2–2. An integrating or phase-lag network.

to zero. The roots of the characteristic equation, the zeros of $Q(s)$, are the poles of $G(s)$ and determine the stability of the element, or system.

2–7. TRANSFER FUNCTIONS OF COMMON NETWORKS

The control engineer depends heavily on simple passive networks to perform three main functions in feedback control systems:

1. Modify the phase characteristics.
2. Modify the gain characteristics.
3. Filter noise and other undesirable signals.

The first two types of network assist in modifying the transfer function of the feedback control system in order to promote stability and improve closed-loop performance. The last characteristic is used to minimize the effects of noise and other undesirable signals of practical control systems.

Figure 2–2 represents an electrical network which is used for integration or providing a phase lag. This circuit obtains its integrating property from the fact that the voltage across the capacitor is proportional to the integral of the current through it. To determine the performance of this network we must determine the transfer function relation which exists between the input and output signals. The differential equation describing the performance of this network is given by the two equations

$$e_i = Ri + \frac{1}{C} \int i\, dt \qquad (2\text{–}38)$$

$$e_o = \frac{1}{C} \int i\, dt \qquad (2\text{–}39)$$

These differential equations can be solved for the relation between e_o and e_i by means of the Laplace transform. $e_o(0^+)$ is assumed equal to zero. Equations 2–40 and 2–41 are the Laplace transforms of equations 2–38 and 2–39, respectively.

$$E_i(s) = RI(s) + \frac{I(s)}{Cs} \qquad (2\text{–}40)$$

$$E_o(s) = \frac{I(s)}{Cs} \qquad (2\text{–}41)$$

Eliminating $I(s)$ between these last two equations results in the transfer function

$$\frac{E_o(s)}{E_i(s)} = \frac{1}{RCs + 1} \tag{2-42}$$

Notice from equation 2–42 that integration is possible only for those frequencies where $RCs \gg 1$. It is important to note that this same transfer function can be obtained quite simply by obtaining the ratio of the Laplace transforms of the output to input voltages.

$$\frac{E_o(s)}{E_i(s)} = \frac{1/Cs}{1/Cs + R} = \frac{1}{RCs + 1} \tag{2-43}$$

The impedance of the network's capacitor approaches a short circuit at very high frequencies, and ultimately it will have no output. This circuit is

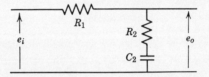

Figure 2–3.   An integrating network with fixed high-frequency attenuation.

basically a low-pass filter whose high-frequency response is attenuated to a very large degree. Very often it is undesirable to have such a large attenuation at high frequencies. The circuit of Figure 2–3 limits this attenuation to a value of $R_2/(R_1 + R_2)$. The transfer function of the network is obtained in an analogous manner.

$$\frac{E_o(s)}{E_i(s)} = \frac{R_2 + 1/C_2s}{R_1 + R_2 + 1/C_2s} = \frac{R_2C_2s + 1}{(R_1 + R_2)C_2s + 1} \tag{2-44}$$

A tabulation of the foregoing results, together with other useful transfer functions which the control engineer will most likely encounter in his profession, is shown in Table 2–2. Network 1 is known as a differentiating or phase-lead network. Notice that it is basically a high-pass filter possessing very large attenuation at low frequencies. This attenuation can be limited to a finite value of $R_2/(R_1 + R_2)$ by network 3. A lag-lead network, which provides a phase lag at low frequencies and a phase lead at high frequencies, is shown as network 5. Networks 6 and 7 possess slight modifications to the low-frequency and high-frequency responses, respectively. Network 8 is used for eliminating unwanted frequency bands. Network 9 is used for passing signals in a narrow band of frequencies.

2–8. TRANSFER FUNCTIONS OF SYSTEMS

In order to determine the transfer function of complex systems, it is necessary to eliminate intermediate input and output variables of the system's elements. This will enable the control engineer to obtain a relation between the input and output of the overall system. This section will consider the transfer functions of cascaded elements, single-loop feedback systems, and multiple-loop feedback systems.

A cascaded system is shown in Figure 2–4. The transfer function of the overall system can be obtained from a solution to the following set of equations:

$$E_2(s) = G_1(s)E_1(s) \tag{2–45}$$

$$E_3(s) = G_2(s)E_2(s) \tag{2–46}$$

$$E_4(s) = G_3(s)E_3(s) \tag{2–47}$$

$$E_5(s) = G_4(s)E_4(s) \tag{2–48}$$

By inspection, it can be seen that the transfer function of the cascaded system is the product of the transfer functions of the individual elements:

$$E_5(s) = G_1(s)G_2(s)G_3(s)G_4(s)E_1(s) \tag{2–49}$$

Consider the elementary linear feedback system shown in Figure 2–5. $G(s)$ and $H(s)$ represent the transfer functions of the direct-transmission and feedback portions of the loop, respectively. They may be individually composed of cascaded elements and minor feedback loops.

The following three equations are required in order to compute the overall system transfer function:

$$B(s) = H(s)C(s) \tag{2–50}$$

$$E(s) = R(s) - B(s) \tag{2–51}$$

$$C(s) = G(s)E(s) \tag{2–52}$$

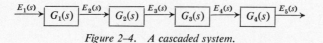

Figure 2–4.   A cascaded system.

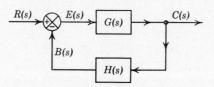

Figure 2–5.   General block diagram of a single-loop feedback system.

Table 2–2.   Transfer functions of common networks

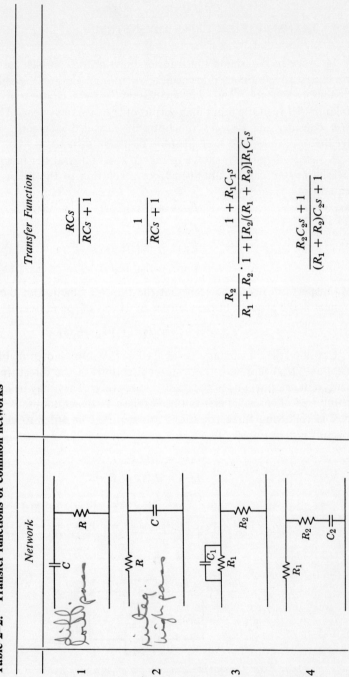

Network	Transfer Function
1	$\dfrac{RCs}{RCs + 1}$
2	$\dfrac{1}{RCs + 1}$
3	$\dfrac{R_2}{R_1 + R_2} \cdot \dfrac{1 + R_1 C_1 s}{1 + [R_2/(R_1 + R_2)]R_1 C_1 s}$
4	$\dfrac{R_2 C_2 s + 1}{(R_1 + R_2)C_2 s + 1}$

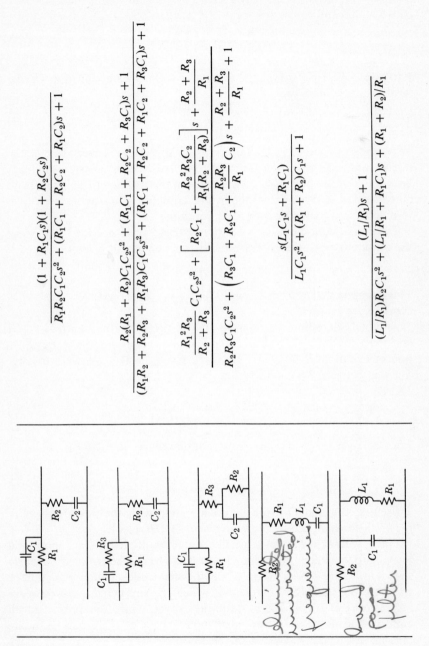

5

$$\frac{(1 + R_1C_1s)(1 + R_2C_2s)}{R_1R_2C_1C_2s^2 + (R_1C_1 + R_2C_2 + R_1C_2)s + 1}$$

6

$$\frac{R_2(R_1 + R_2)C_1C_2s^2 + (R_1C_1 + R_2C_2 + R_3C_1)s + 1}{(R_1R_2 + R_2R_3 + R_1R_3)C_1C_2s^2 + (R_1C_1 + R_2C_2 + R_1C_2 + R_3C_1)s + 1}$$

7

$$\frac{\dfrac{R_1^2R_3}{R_2 + R_3}C_1C_2s^2 + \left[R_2C_1 + \dfrac{R_2^2R_3C_2}{R_1(R_2 + R_3)}\right]s + \dfrac{R_2 + R_3}{R_1}}{R_2R_3C_1C_2s^2 + \left(R_3C_1 + R_2C_1 + \dfrac{R_2R_3}{R_1}C_2\right)s + \dfrac{R_2 + R_3}{R_1} + 1}$$

8

$$\frac{s(L_1C_1s + R_1C_1)}{L_1C_1s^2 + (R_1 + R_2)C_1s + 1}$$

9

$$\frac{(L_1/R_1)s + 1}{(L_1/R_1)R_2C_1s^2 + (L_1/R_1 + R_1C_1)s + (R_1 + R_2)/R_1}$$

Solution of these three equations results in the following transfer function between $R(s)$ and $C(s)$:

$$\frac{C(s)}{R(s)} = \frac{G(s)}{1 + G(s)H(s)} \tag{2-53}$$

For cases where $G(s)H(s) \gg 1$, the closed-loop transfer function can be written in the form

$$\frac{C(s)}{R(s)} \approx \frac{1}{H(s)} \tag{2-54}$$

This implies that the closed-loop transfer function is independent of the direct transmission transfer function $G(s)$, and only depends on the feedback transfer function $H(s)$. Use is made of this characteristic in feedback amplifier design in order that the overall amplifier gain may be insensitive to tube and/or transistor parameter variations.

The characteristic equation for the system can be obtained by setting the denominator of the system transfer function equal to zero:

$$1 + G(s)H(s) = 0 \tag{2-55}$$

This equation determines system stability, and it will receive much attention in later chapters.

Another interesting relationship that is useful to the control system engineer is between the system error $E(s)$ and the given input $R(s)$. Solution of equations 2–50, 2–51, and 2–52 results in the following transfer function between $R(s)$ and $E(s)$:

$$\frac{E(s)}{R(s)} = \frac{1}{1 + G(s)H(s)} \tag{2-56}$$

For cases when $G(s)H(s) \gg 1$, this relation reduces to the form

$$\frac{E(s)}{R(s)} \approx \frac{1}{G(s)H(s)} \tag{2-57}$$

Therefore, the system error varies inversely with the open-loop gain, $G(s)H(s)$, for that frequency range where $G(s)H(s) \gg 1$.

Practical feedback systems usually contain multiple feedback loops and several inputs. All multiple-loop systems can be reduced to the basic form shown in Figure 2–5 by means of step-by-step feedback loop reduction or by means of "signal flow diagrams," which are considered in the concluding sections of this chapter. Multiple inputs, which are present in all control systems because unwanted inputs, such as noise and drift, are present, can occur anywhere in the feedback system. Successive block diagram reduction techniques permit the control engineer to determine

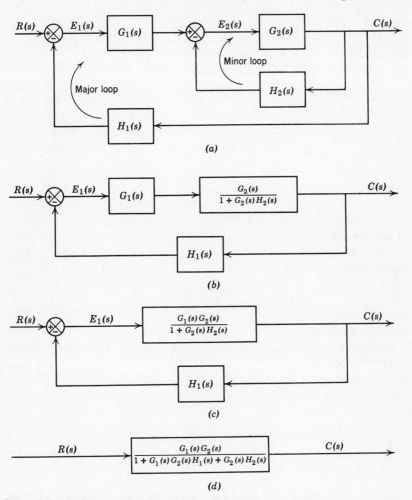

Figure 2–6. Reducing a feedback system containing two feedback paths. (a) The original system. (b) Reducing the minor feedback loop. (c) The equivalent feedback system. (d) The system transfer function.

their effect on the overall feedback system. The technique of multiple feedback loop reduction can best be understood by means of a few simple illustrations.

Figure 2–6 illustrates a multiple-loop feedback system containing an outer, or major, feedback loop and an inner, or minor, feedback loop. The original feedback system is illustrated in Figure 2–6a. In Figure 2–6b, the minor feedback loop has been reduced by utilizing equation 2–53. The reduced minor feedback loop, in cascade with element $G_1(s)$, is combined

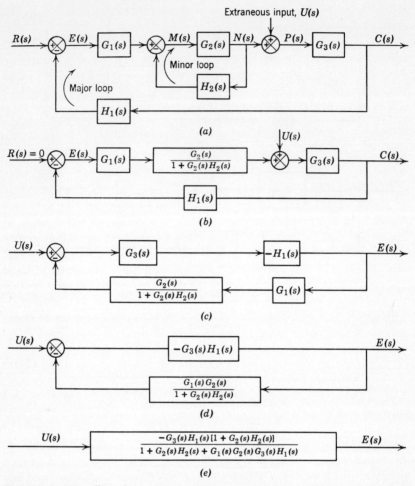

Figure 2–7.   The effect of an extraneous input on system error.   (a) The original system.
(b) Reducing the minor feedback loop.   (c) Rearranging the system.   (d) The equivalent
feedback system.   (e) The system transfer function.

into one equivalent transfer function in Figure 2–6c, which is of the same
form as Figure 2–5. Figure 2–6d shows the closed-loop transfer function.

Figure 2–7 illustrates a feedback system containing a minor feedback
path and an extraneous input, $U(s)$, which may represent an unwanted
signal as noise. In order to determine the effect of this input, the feedback
elements are rearranged showing $U(s)$ as the input to the system and $E(s)$
as the output. The solution should be quite obvious from the step-by-step
procedure illustrated in Figures 2–7a, 2–7b, 2–7c, and 2–7d. Figure 2–7d

is equivalent to the form shown in Figure 2–5. Figure 2–7e shows the closed-loop transfer function.

Block diagram reduction techniques get very tedious and time consuming as the number of feedback paths increases, as is illustrated in Figures 2–8 and 2–9. In order to solve complex problems, it is much simpler to make use of the theorems and properties of "signal flow graphs," which permit a solution almost by inspection.

2–9. THE SIGNAL FLOW DIAGRAM

Signal flow graphs enable the control engineer to formulate the response of a complicated linear, multiloop system to an input applied anywhere much more rapidly than the conventional block diagram reduction techniques do. S. J. Mason of M.I.T. focuses attention on signal flow graphs in his articles published in the *Proceedings of the IRE* of September 1953[3] and July 1956.[4] His first article discusses some basic properties of these graphs. His second presents a generalized theorem which permits writing the desired answer practically by inspection.

A signal flow graph is a topological representation of a set of linear equations having the form

$$y_i = \sum_j^n a_{ij} x_j, \qquad i = 1, \ldots, n \tag{2–58}$$

This equation expresses each of the n variables in terms of the others and themselves. A signal flow graph represents a set of equations of this type by means of branches and nodes. A node is assigned to each variable of interest in the system. For example, node i represents variable y_i. Branches are used to relate the different variables. For example, branch ij relates variable y_i to y_j where the branch originates at node i and terminates at node j. Consider the following set of linear equations:

$$y_2 = ay_1 + by_2 \qquad + cy_4 \tag{2–59}$$

$$y_3 = \qquad dy_2 \tag{2–60}$$

$$y_4 = ey_1 \qquad + fy_3 \tag{2–61}$$

$$y_5 = \qquad gy_3 + hy_4 \tag{2–62}$$

The signal flow graph which represents this set of equations is shown in Figure 2–10. Here y_1 can be interpreted as the input to the system and y_5 as its output. The control engineer would be interested in obtaining the ratio of y_5/y_1.

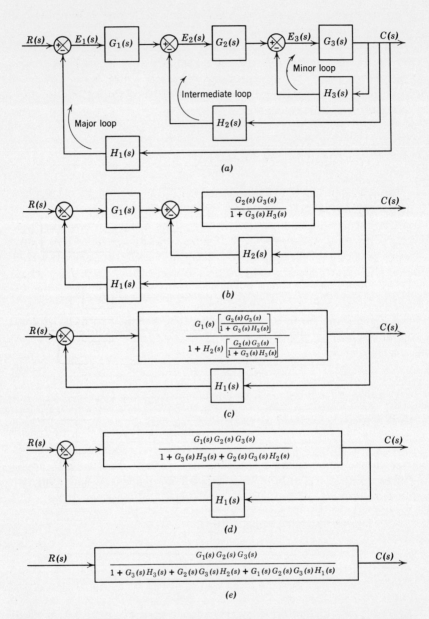

Figure 2–8. Reducing a feedback system containing three feedback paths. (a) The original system. (b) Reducing the minor feedback loop. (c) Reducing the intermediate feedback loop. (d) The equivalent feedback system. (e) The system transfer function.

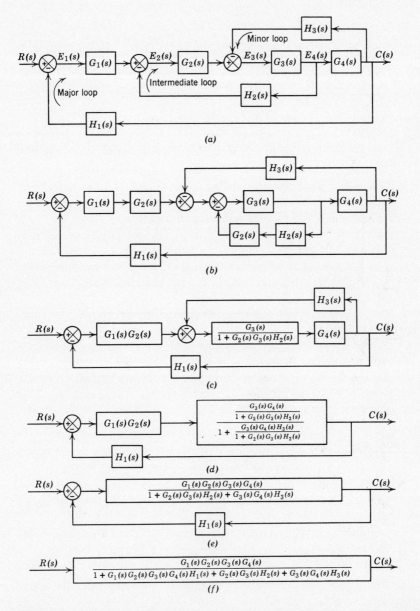

Figure 2–9. Reducing a multiple-loop system containing complex paths. (a) The original system. (b) Rearranging the summing points of the intermediate and minor loops. (c) Reducing the equivalent intermediate loop. (d) Reducing the equivalent minor loop. (e) The equivalent feedback system. (f) The system transfer function.

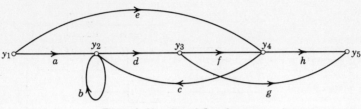

Figure 2–10.   Signal flow diagram.

Before proceeding further, several terms used in signal flow diagrams must be defined.

a. *Source* is a node having only outgoing branches, as y_1 in the preceding illustration.

b. *Sink* is a node having only incoming branches, as y_5.

c. *Path* is a group of connected branches having the same sense of direction. In the preceding illustration, *eh*, *adfh*, and *b* are paths.

d. *Forward paths* are paths which originate from a source and terminate at a sink along which no node is encountered more than once, as *eh*, *adg*, and *adfh*.

e. *Path gain* is the product of the coefficient associated with the branches along the path.

f. *Feedback loop* is a path originating from a node and terminating at the same node. In addition, a node cannot be encountered more than once. In the preceding example *b* and *dfc* are feedback loops.

g. *Loop gain* is the product of the coefficients associated with the branches forming a feedback loop.

2–10. REDUCTION OF THE SIGNAL FLOW DIAGRAM

Several preliminary simplifications can be made to the complex signal flow graph of a system by means of the following signal flow graph algebra.

a. Addition. 1. The signal flow diagram in Figure 2–11a represents the linear equation

$$y_3 = ay_1 + by_2 \qquad (2\text{–}63)$$

2. The signal flow diagram in Figure 2–11b represents the linear equation

$$y_2 = (a + b)y_1 \qquad (2\text{–}64)$$

b. Multiplication. The signal flow diagram in Figure 2–11c represents the linear equation

$$y_4 = abcy_1 \qquad (2\text{–}65)$$

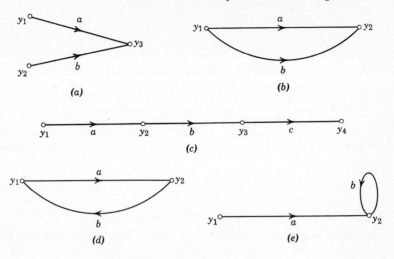

Figure 2–11. Signal flow graph algebra.

c.   Feedback Loops. 1. The signal flow diagram in Figure 2–11*d* represents the linear equation

$$y_2 = \frac{a}{1 + ab}\, y_1 \tag{2–66}$$

2. The signal flow in Figure 2–11*e* represents the linear equation

$$y_2 = \frac{a}{1 + b} \tag{2–67}$$

It is possible to apply the preceding signal flow diagram algebra to a complicated graph and reduce it to one containing only a source and a sink. This process requires repeated applications until the final desired form is obtainable. An interesting property of network and system topology permits the writing of the desired answer almost by inspection. The general expression for signal flow graph gain[4] is given by equation 2–68.

$$G = \frac{\sum_K G_K \Delta_K}{\Delta} \tag{2–68}$$

where G_K = gain of the Kth forward path

$$\Delta = 1 - \sum_n P_{n_1} + \sum_n P_{n_2} - \sum_n P_{n_3} + \cdots$$

P_{n_r} = gain product of the nth possible combination of r non-touching loops

Δ_K = the value of Δ for that part of graph not touching the Kth forward path

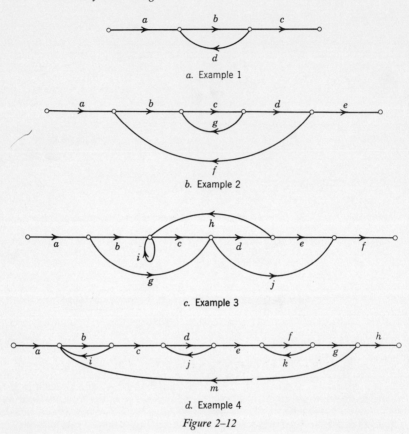

a. Example 1

b. Example 2

c. Example 3

d. Example 4

Figure 2–12

Δ is known as the determinant of the graph and Δ_K as the cofactor of the forward path K. Basically, Δ consists of the sum of the products of loop gains taken none at a time (1), one at a time (with a minus sign), two at a time (with a plus sign), etc. Δ_K basically contains the products of the nontouching loops. The proof of this general gain expression is contained in Ref. 4. A few examples follow in order to show how this general gain expression may be used.

Example 1. For Figure 2–12*a*,

$$\Delta = 1 - bd$$
$$G_1 = abc$$
$$\Delta_1 = 1$$
$$\therefore \quad G = \frac{abc}{1 - bd}$$

Example 2. For Figure 2–12*b*,

$$\Delta = 1 - cg - bcdf$$
$$G_1 = abcde$$
$$\Delta_1 = 1$$
$$\therefore \quad G = \frac{abcde}{1 - cg - bcdf}$$

Example 3. For Figure 2–12*c*,

$$\Delta = 1 - (i - cdh)$$
$$G_1 = abcdef$$
$$G_2 = agdef$$
$$G_3 = agjf$$
$$G_4 = abcjf$$
$$\Delta_1 = 1, \qquad \Delta_3 = 1 - i$$
$$\Delta_2 = 1 - i, \qquad \Delta_4 = 1$$
$$\therefore \quad G = \frac{abcdef + agdef(1 - i) + agjf(1 - i) + abcjf}{1 - (i - cdh)}$$

Example 4. For Figure 2–12*d*,

$$\Delta = 1 - (bi + dj + fk + bcdefgm)$$
$$+ (bidj + bifk + djfk) - bidjfk$$
$$G_1 = abcdefgh$$
$$\Delta_1 = 1$$
$$\therefore \quad G = \frac{abcdefgh}{1 - (bi + dj + fk + bcdefgm)}$$
$$+ (bidj + bifk + djfk) - bidjfk$$

2–11. APPLICATION OF THE SIGNAL FLOW DIAGRAM TO MULTIPLE FEEDBACK SYSTEMS

It is important at this point to differentiate between signal flow diagrams and block diagrams. Basically, the signal flow diagram represents a detailed picture of a system's behavior whereas the block diagram shows the manner of interconnection of the various elements of the system. The signal flow diagram is useful in analyzing multiple-loop feedback systems and in determining the effect of a particular element or parameter in an overall feedback system, whereas the block diagram is useful in the design and analysis of sections of a feedback system.

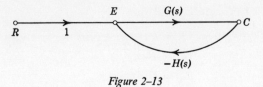

Figure 2–13

The signal flow diagram and block diagram usually present the same information for simple systems. The signal flow diagram for the block diagram shown in Figure 2–5 is shown in Figure 2–13. Using signal flow graph theory, the system's closed-loop response is obtained as follows.

$$\Delta = 1 + G(s)H(s)$$
$$G_1 = G(s)$$
$$\Delta_1 = 1$$
$$\therefore \quad \frac{C(s)}{R(s)} = G = \frac{G(s)}{1 + G(s)H(s)}$$

This result agrees with equation 2–53. For more complicated systems, however, the signal flow diagram can save a great deal of time in deriving the desired answers. In order to illustrate this point, the signal flow diagram approach will be used to solve the problems posed in Figures 2–6 through 2–9.

   a. The signal flow diagram for Figure 2–6 appears in Figure 2–14*a*. By inspection, the overall system transfer function is

$$\Delta = 1 + G_1(s)G_2(s)H_1(s) + G_2(s)H_2(s)$$
$$G_1 = G_1(s)G_2(s)$$
$$\Delta_1 = 1$$
$$\therefore \quad \frac{C(s)}{R(s)} = G = \frac{G_1(s)G_2(s)}{1 + G_1(s)G_2(s)H_1(s) + G_2(s)H_2(s)}$$

This result agrees with the transfer function shown in Figure 2–6*d*.
   b. The signal flow diagram for Figure 2–7 appears in Figure 2–14*b*. By inspection, the overall system transfer function is

$$\Delta = 1 + [G_2(s)H_2(s) + G_1(s)G_2(s)G_3(s)H_1(s)]$$
$$G_1 = -G_3(s)H_1(s)$$
$$\Delta_1 = 1 + G_2(s)H_2(s)$$
$$\therefore \quad \frac{E(s)}{U(s)} = G = \frac{-G_3(s)H_1(s)[1 + G_2(s)H_2(s)]}{1 + G_2(s)H_2(s) + G_1(s)G_2(s)G_3(s)H_1(s)}$$

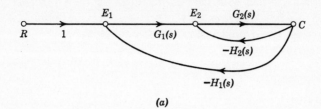

(a)

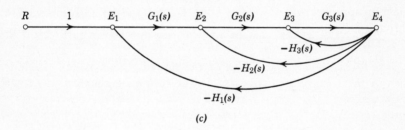

(b)

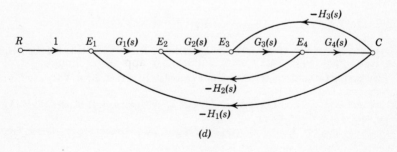

(c)

(d)

Figure 2–14

This result agrees with the transfer function shown in Figure 2–7*e*.

c. The signal flow diagram for Figure 2–8 appears in Figure 2–14*c*. By inspection, the overall system transfer function is

$$\Delta = 1 + G_3(s)H_3(s) + G_2(s)G_3(s)H_2(s) + G_1(s)G_2(s)G_3(s)H_1(s)$$

$$G_1 = G_1(s)G_2(s)G_3(s)$$

$$\Delta_1 = 1$$

$$\therefore \quad \frac{C(s)}{R(s)} = G = \frac{G_1(s)G_2(s)G_3(s)}{1 + G_3(s)H_3(s) + G_2(s)G_3(s)H_2(s) + G_1(s)G_2(s)G_3(s)H_1(s)}$$

This result agrees with the transfer function shown in Figure 2–8*e*.

d. The signal flow diagram for Figure 2–9 is shown in Figure 2–14*d*. By inspection, the overall system transfer function is

$$\Delta = 1 + G_1(s)G_2(s)G_3(s)G_4(s)H_1(s)$$
$$+ G_2(s)G_3(s)H_2(s) + G_3(s)G_4(s)H_3(s)$$

$$G_1 = G_1(s)G_2(s)G_3(s)G_4(s)$$

$$\Delta_1 = 1$$

$$\therefore \quad \frac{C(s)}{R(s)} = G = \frac{G_1(s)G_2(s)G_3(s)G_4(s)}{\begin{array}{c}1 + G_1(s)G_2(s)G_3(s)G_4(s)H_1(s)\\ + G_2(s)G_3(s)H_2(s) + G_3(s)G_4(s)H_3(s)\end{array}}$$

This result agrees with the transfer function shown in Figure 2–9*f*.

The foregoing examples illustrate the simplifications made possible by use of the signal flow diagrams. In the remaining chapters, the signal flow diagram approach will be used in order to simplify the solutions of problems. In addition, further properties and applications of this powerful tool will be demonstrated.

REFERENCES

1. *Modern Operational Mathematics in Engineering*, R. V. Churchill, McGraw-Hill Book Co., New York, 1944.
2. *Transients in Linear Systems*, M. F. Gardner and J. L. Barnes, John Wiley and Sons, New York, 1942, Vol. 1.
3. Feedback Theory: Some Properties of Signal Flow Graphs, S. J. Mason, *Proc. IRE*, **41**, No. 9, 1144 (Sept. 1953).
4. Feedback Theory: Further Properties of Signal Flow Graphs, S. J. Mason, *Proc. IRE*, **44**, No. 9, 920 (July 1956).

3 TRANSFER FUNCTION REPRESENTATION

OF PHYSICAL SYSTEMS

3–1. DEFINITION OF NOMENCLATURE AND SYMBOLS

The nomenclature and symbols described in this section are based on the proposed standards issued by the AIEE subcommittee on Terminology and Nomenclature of the Feedback Control Systems Committee.[1] Figure 3–1 represents a general feedback control system. It uses standard symbols and notations. It would be well worth the reader's time to memorize the nomenclature and symbols, and the definitions of these terms, since they are employed universally by the practicing control system engineer.

The *command*, v, is an input which is developed externally and is independent of the feedback control system.

The *reference input elements*, a, produce a signal proportional to the command.

The *reference input*, r, is the signal input to the system which is proportional to the command.

The *primary feedback*, b, is a signal that is a function of the controlled variable and is compared with the reference input in order to obtain the actuating signal.

The *actuating signal*, e, equals the difference between the reference input and the primary feedback.

The *control elements*, g_1, develop the manipulated variable from the actuating signal.

The *manipulated variable*, m, is the quantity obtained from the control elements and applied to the controlled system.

The *disturbance*, u, represents undesired signals that attempt to affect the value of the controlled variable c.

The *controlled system*, g_2, is the device to be controlled.

The *controlled variable*, c, is the quantity of the feedback system that is controlled.

The *indirectly controlled system*, z, is outside the feedback loop and relates the indirectly controlled variables to the controlled quantity.

The *indirectly controlled variable*, q, is related to the controlled variable

35

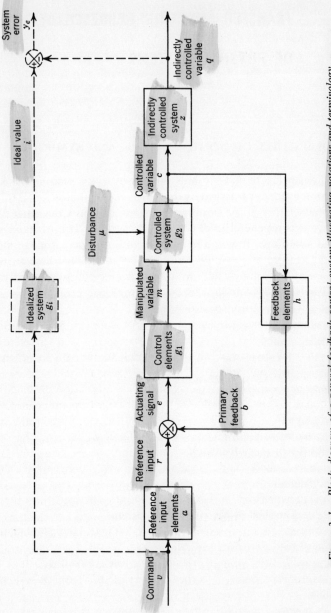

Figure 3–1. Block diagram of a general feedback control system illustrating notations and terminology.

through the indirectly controlled system. It is outside the feedback system and is not directly measured for control.

The *feedback elements*, *h*, produce the primary feedback from the controlled variable.

The *idealized system*, g_i, is a system whose performance results in a response with an ideal value from the command.

The *ideal value*, *i*, is the value of the indirectly controlled variable which would result from an idealized system operating from the same command as the actual system.

The *system error*, y_e, is the difference between the ideal value and the indirectly controlled variable.

The dashed-line portion of the block diagram represents an idealized system. It is used to compare the indirectly controlled variable of the system to the ideal, or desired, value. The system error is the difference between these two values. For systems that have unity feedback the ideal system would also equal unity.

The reference input elements and feedback elements usually consist of devices known as "transducers." These devices convert various types of input signals into electrical output signals. Many examples of transducers are used in industry. The potentiometer is probably the simplest form. Its prime function is to convert a shaft position into a proportional electrical signal. Transducers that convert velocity and acceleration into proportional electrical signals are tachometers and accelerometers, respectively. Pressure and temperature transducers convert pressure and temperature changes, respectively, into proportional electrical signals.

The primary functions of the control elements are to provide amplification to the actuating signals and to modify the frequency characteristics of the signal in order to insure stability. Electronic, electromechanical, magnetic, hydraulic, and pneumatic devices are used for this purpose.

The controlled system is the portion of the system that responds to the manipulated variable and develops the controlled variable. The controlled system may represent a gun mount, an aircraft's frame, or a chemical process.

At this stage it is desirable to give the reader an idea of the form of the transfer functions for some elementary and common devices which might be used in a feedback control system. Although this book does not have a specific chapter on components, extensive coverage is given to system components in this and succeeding chapters. We have chosen to treat components as part of the overall system in order to emphasize a unified system approach.

The following four sections of this chapter derive the transfer functions for several elementary and common mechanical, electrical, hydraulic, and thermal configurations. Section 3–6 then divides the transfer functions into "types" on the basis of form. In the last section of this chapter we determine the characteristic responses for several types of systems.

3–2. TRANSFER FUNCTION REPRESENTATION OF TYPICAL MECHANICAL CONTROL SYSTEM DEVICES

The purpose of this section is to illustrate the procedure used for deriving the transfer function representation of some typical mechanical control system devices from their basic differential equations. The control engineer must master this very important step before he can fill in the transfer function properly for the blocks of a feedback control system. We limit our discussions to mechanical systems which can be represented by linear equations over their useful operating range. Nonlinear mechanical devices are discussed in Chapter 7.

Mechanical control system devices can generally be classified as being either translational or rotational. The major difference between the two is that we talk of forces and translational units in the former, and torque and angular units in the latter. Newton's three laws of motion[2] govern the action of both types of mechanical system. Basically, these laws state that the sum of the applied forces, or torques, must equal the sum of the reactive forces, or torques, for a body whose acceleration is zero. Another way of stating this is that the sum of the forces must equal zero for a body at rest or moving at a constant velocity. We shall consider some simple translational systems and then simple rotational systems. The basic concepts illustrated and developed here should be sufficient to enable the reader to handle more complex systems.

1.   Mechanical Translation Systems

The three basic characteristics of a mechanical translational system are mass, stiffness, and damping. Mass represents an element having inertia. Stiffness represents the restoring force action as that of a spring because of its property of elasticity. Damping, or viscous friction, represents a characteristic of an element that absorbs energy. Before discussing translational systems containing more than one element, we shall consider first the governing relationships for some very basic system elements.

We use the English system of units as our standard. The symbols for the various quantities together with their respective units are shown in Table 3–1.

Table 3–1. Mechanical translation symbols and units

Quantity	Symbol	English Units
Distance	y	Feet
Velocity	v	Feet/second
Acceleration	a	Feet/second^2
Force	f	Pounds
Mass	M	Slugs
Damping Factor	B	Pounds/feet/second
Stiffness Factor	K	Pounds/feet

a. Force Applied to a Mass. When a force f is applied to a mass M, it produces an acceleration of the mass. A reaction force f_M is developed; it equals the product of mass and acceleration. Its direction is opposite to the applied force. In Figure 3–2 terminal y_0 has motion of the reference, while terminal y has motion of the mass. We assume that the reference terminal is stationary. Therefore, the equation of the opposing force, in terms of mass M, displacement y, velocity v, and acceleration a, is

$$f_M = M \frac{d^2y}{dt^2} = M \frac{dv}{dt} = Ma \qquad (3\text{–}1)$$

b. Force Applied to a Spring. When a force f is applied to a spring and stretches it the spring tries to contract, and when the spring is compressed it tries to expand. This reaction is due to the elastic property of stiffness, which attempts to act as a restoring force. In Figure 3–3 positions y and y_0 are measured from their respective equilibrium positions, and K is defined as the stiffness factor. In accordance with Hooke's law, the restoring force f_K on the spring is given by

$$f_K = K(y - y_0) \qquad (3\text{–}2)$$

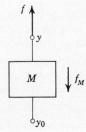

Figure 3–2. Force applied to a mass.

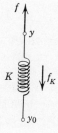

Figure 3–3. Force applied to a spring.

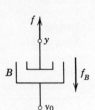

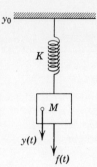

Figure 3–4. Force applied
to a damping device.

Figure 3–5. Force applied to
a spring-mass system.

If the reference terminal y_0 is placed at the origin of the coordinate system, then $y = 0$, and equation 3–2 reduces to

$$f_K = Ky \tag{3–3}$$

c. Force Applied to a Damping Device. A damping device has the property of absorbing energy. One of the most elementary types of damping devices used in translation systems is the dashpot. Basically, it can be thought of as a piston moving in a housing containing a fluid, as shown in Figure 3–4. When a force f is applied, a reaction force f_B is developed which equals the product of the damping factor B and the relative velocities of the two ends of the damping device. The magnitude of the reactive forces, in terms of damping factor, velocity, and position, is

$$f_B = B\left(\frac{dy}{dt} - \frac{dy_0}{dt}\right) = B(v_y - v_{y_0}) \tag{3–4}$$

If the reference terminal y_0 is stationary, then $v_{y_0} = 0$ and equation 3–4 reduces to

$$f_B = B\frac{dy}{dt} = Bv_y \tag{3–5}$$

d. Force Applied to a Mass and a Spring. Let us now consider the case of a force $f(t)$ applied to the mass and spring shown in Figure 3–5. It is assumed that the system has no effective damping. A displacement $y(t)$ of the mass is produced with respect to a reference terminal y_0, which is assumed to be stationary. The application of Newton's law to this system yields

$$M\frac{d^2y(t)}{dt^2} + Ky(t) = f(t) \tag{3–6}$$

A solution to this equation can easily be obtained by means of the Laplace transform.

$$Ms^2Y(s) + KY(s) = F(s)$$

$$Y(s) = \frac{F(s)}{Ms^2 + K} \tag{3-7}$$

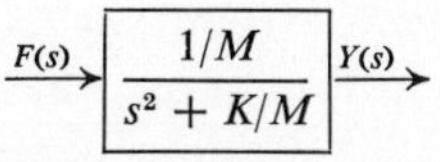

$$F(s) \rightarrow \boxed{\frac{1/M}{s^2 + K/M}} \rightarrow Y(s)$$

Figure 3–6. Block diagram for the spring-mass system.

The transfer function of this mechanical translation system, defined as the ratio of the output $Y(s)$ divided by the input $F(s)$, is given by

$$\frac{Y(s)}{F(s)} = \frac{1/M}{s^2 + K/M} \tag{3-8}$$

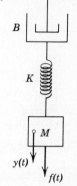

and its simple block diagram is given in Figure 3–6.

e. Force Applied to a Mechanical System Containing a Mass, Spring, and Damper. The case of a force $f(t)$ applied to a mass, spring, and damper is shown in Figure 3–7. The system produces a displacement of the mass, $y(t)$, measured from a reference terminal, y_0, which is assumed to be stationary. The application of Newton's law to this system yields

$$M\frac{d^2y}{dt^2} + B\frac{dy}{dt} + Ky(t) = f(t) \tag{3-9}$$

Figure 3–7. Force applied to a system containing a spring, mass, and damper.

A solution to this equation can easily be obtained by means of the Laplace transform.

$$Ms^2Y(s) + BsY(s) + KY(s) = F(s) \tag{3-10}$$

The transfer function of this mechanical translation system, defined as the ratio of the output $Y(s)$ divided by the input $F(s)$, is given by

$$\frac{Y(s)}{F(s)} = \frac{1/M}{s^2 + (B/M)s + K/M} \tag{3-11}$$

and its simple block diagram appears in Figure 3–8.

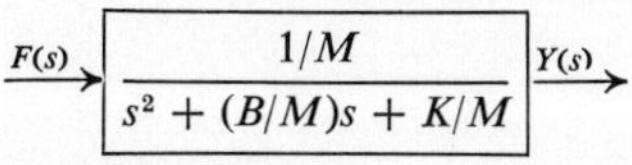

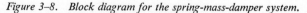

$$F(s) \rightarrow \boxed{\frac{1/M}{s^2 + (B/M)s + K/M}} \rightarrow Y(s)$$

Figure 3–8. Block diagram for the spring-mass-damper system.

2. Mechanical Rotational Systems

The three basic characteristics of a mechanical rotational system are moment of inertia, stiffness, and damping. Rotational systems are quite similar to translational systems except that torque equations are used to describe system equilibrium instead of force equations, and we use angular displacement, velocity, and acceleration quantities. Before considering rotational systems containing more than one element, we first consider the governing relationships of some very basic elements. The symbols for the various quantities and their respective units are shown in Table 3–2.

Table 3–2. Mechanical rotational symbols and units

Quantity	Symbol	English Units
Angle	θ	Radians
Angular Velocity	ω	Radians/second
Angular Acceleration	α	Radians/second^2
Torque	T	Pound-feet
Moment of Inertia	J	Slug-feet^2
Damping Factor	B	$\dfrac{\text{Pound-feet}}{\text{Radian/second}}$
Stiffness Factor	K	$\dfrac{\text{Pound-feet}}{\text{Radian}}$

a. Torque Applied to a Body Possessing a Moment of Inertia. A torque T applied to a body having a moment of inertia J produces an angular acceleration α. A reactive torque T_J is developed which equals the product of the moment of inertia and angular acceleration. It has an angular direction opposite to the applied torque. In Figure 3–9, θ is measured with respect to its equilibrium position, which is defined as zero angular position. Therefore, the equation of the opposing torque, in terms of moment of inertia J, angular displacement θ, angular velocity ω, and

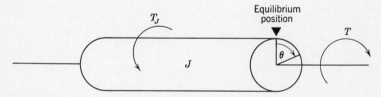

Figure 3–9. Torque applied to a body.

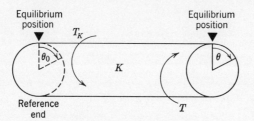

Figure 3–10. Torque applied to a spring.

angular acceleration α, is

$$T_J = J\frac{d^2\theta}{dt^2} = J\frac{d\omega}{dt} = J\alpha \tag{3-12}$$

b. Applied Torque Twisting a Shaft. When a torque T is applied to a shaft and twists it, the shaft tries to twist back with a torque T_K due to its property of stiffness. Figure 3–10 illustrates this action and reaction. Angular positions θ and θ_0 represent the positions of the two ends of the spring measured from their respective equilibrium positions, and K is defined as the stiffness factor. The restoring torque is given by

$$T_K = K(\theta - \theta_0) \tag{3-13}$$

If the reference end is stationary, then $\theta_0 = 0$, and equation 3–13 reduces to

$$T_K = K\theta \tag{3-14}$$

c. Torque Applied to a Damping Device. A disk or cylinder being rotated through some fluid, as shown in Figure 3–11, is an example of an elementary type of rotational damping device. Positions θ and θ_0 represent the angular positions of the two ends of the device measured from their respective equilibrium positions. When a torque T is applied to such a device, a reactive torque T_B is developed which equals the product of the damping factor B and the relative angular velocities at the ends of the damping device.

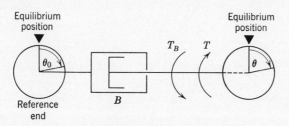

Figure 3–11. Torque applied to a damping device.

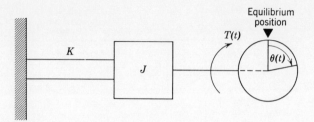

Figure 3–12.   Torque applied to a body and a springy shaft.

The magnitude of the reactive torque, in terms of the damping factor, angular velocity, and position, is

$$T_B = B\left(\frac{d\theta}{dt} - \frac{d\theta_0}{dt}\right) = B(\omega - \omega_0) \tag{3–15}$$

If the reference end is stationary, equation 3–15 reduces to

$$T_B = B\frac{d\theta}{dt} = B\omega \tag{3–16}$$

d.   Torque Applied to a Moment of Inertia at the End of a Twisting Shaft. We now consider the case of a torque $T(t)$ applied at the end of a shaft which possesses a moment of inertia J. The shaft is being twisted and has a stiffness factor K. This configuration is shown in Figure 3–12. We assume that the system has no effective damping. A displacement $\theta(t)$ of the moment of inertia is produced with respect to its equilibrium position. The reference end of the shaft is assumed to be stationary. Applying Newton's law to this system yields

$$J\frac{d^2\theta(t)}{dt^2} + K\theta(t) = T(t) \tag{3–17}$$

A solution to this equation can easily be obtained by means of the Laplace transform.

$$Js^2\theta(s) + K\theta(s) = T(s)$$

$$\theta(s) = \frac{T(s)}{Js^2 + K} \tag{3–18}$$

The transfer function of this mechanical rotational system, defined as the

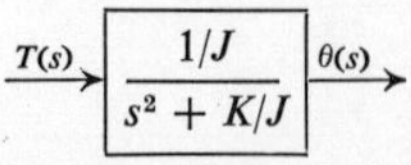

$$T(s) \rightarrow \boxed{\frac{1/J}{s^2 + K/J}} \rightarrow \theta(s)$$

Figure 3–13.   Block diagram for a moment of inertia and twisting shaft system.

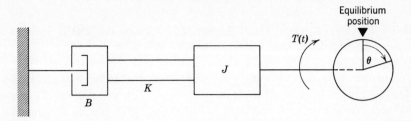

Figure 3–14. *Torque applied to a moment of inertia, a twisting shaft, and a damping device.*

ratio of the output $\theta(s)$ divided by the input $T(s)$, is given by

$$\frac{\theta(s)}{T(s)} = \frac{1/J}{s^2 + K/J} \tag{3-19}$$

and its simple block diagram is illustrated in Figure 3–13.

  e. **Torque Applied to a Body Having a Moment of Inertia, a Twisting Shaft, and a Damping Device.**   The configuration of a torque $T(t)$ applied to a body having a moment of inertia J, a twisting shaft having a stiffness factor K, and a damper having a damping factor B, is shown in Figure 3–14. The system produces a displacement, $\theta(t)$, measured from an equilibrium position θ_0, which is assumed to be zero. The reference end of the damping device is assumed to be stationary. Applying Newton's law to this system yields

$$J\frac{d^2\theta(t)}{dt^2} + B\frac{d\theta(t)}{dt} + K\theta(t) = T(t) \tag{3-20}$$

A solution to this equation can easily be obtained by means of the Laplace transform.

$$Js^2\theta(s) + Bs\theta(s) + K\theta(s) = T(s) \tag{3-21}$$

The transfer function of this mechanical rotational system, defined as the ratio of the output $\theta(s)$ divided by the input $T(s)$, is given by

$$\frac{\theta(s)}{T(s)} = \frac{1/J}{s^2 + (B/J)s + K/J} \tag{3-22}$$

and its simple block diagram is illustrated in Figure 3–15.

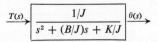

Figure 3–15. *Block diagram for a moment of inertia, twisting shaft, and damper system.*

3–3. TRANSFER FUNCTION REPRESENTATION OF TYPICAL ELECTRICAL CONTROL SYSTEM DEVICES

This section illustrates the procedure used for deriving the transfer function representation of some commonly used electrical control system devices from their basic differential equations. We specifically analyze a d-c generator, armature-controlled d-c servomotor, Ward-Leonard system, field-controlled d-c servomotor, and a two-phase a-c induction servomotor. The analysis is limited to the linear operating range of these devices; nonlinear electrical devices are covered in Chapter 7.

1. D-C Generator[3,4]

A d-c generator is commonly used in control systems for power amplification. The armature, which is driven at a constant speed n, is capable of producing a relatively large controllable current, i_a, as the field current i_f is varied. Its exact value is dependent on the load circuit, Z_L. A schematic diagram of the configuration is shown in Figure 3–16. The symbols R_f, L_f and R_g, L_g represent the resistive and inductive components of the field and armature circuits, respectively.

The voltage induced by the armature, $e_g(t)$, is a function of the speed of rotation n and the flux developed by the field, ϕ. It can be expressed as

$$e_g(t) = K_1 n \phi \qquad (3–23)$$

The flux depends on the field current and the characteristics of the iron used in the field. This is a linear relationship up to a certain saturation point and can be expressed as

$$\phi = K_2 i_f \qquad (3–24)$$

By substituting equation 3–24 into equation 3–23, and assuming that the armature rotation speed is constant, the relation between the induced

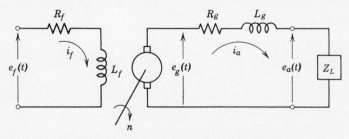

Figure 3–16.   D-C generator schematic diagram.

armature voltage $e_g(t)$ and the field current i_f can be expressed as

$$e_g(t) = K_g i_f \tag{3-25}$$

where $K_g = K_1 K_2 n$ = generator constant having units of volts/ampere. The equation relating the applied control voltage to the field, $e_f(t)$, and resulting current of the field circuit, i_f, can be expressed as

$$e_f(t) = R_f i_f + L_f \frac{di_f}{dt} \tag{3-26}$$

The field current can be eliminated between equations 3–25 and 3–26, and an expression relating the applied control voltage to the field $e_f(t)$ and the developed armature voltage $e_g(t)$ can be obtained.

$$e_f(t) = \frac{R_f}{K_g} e_g(t) + \frac{L_f}{K_g} \frac{de_g(t)}{dt} \tag{3-27}$$

This can be expressed in terms of the Laplace transform as

$$E_f(s) = \frac{1}{K_g} (R_f + L_f s) E_g(s) \tag{3-28}$$

The transfer function of this device, defined as the ratio of the output $E_g(s)$ to the input $E_f(s)$, is given by

$$\frac{E_g(s)}{E_f(s)} = \frac{K_g/L_f}{s + R_f/L_f} \tag{3-29}$$

and its simple block diagram is shown in Figure 3–17.

If it is desired to obtain the transfer function $E_a(s)/E_f(s)$, we must first determine the nature of the actual load connected to the armature. For example, consider that the Laplace transform of the load can be represented as $Z_L(s)$. Then the transfer function $E_a(s)/E_g(s)$ can be expressed as

$$\frac{E_a(s)}{E_g(s)} = \frac{Z_L(s)}{R_g + L_g s + Z_L(s)} \tag{3-30}$$

and the overall transfer function of the d-c generator, $E_a(s)/E_f(s)$, can be expressed as

$$\frac{E_a(s)}{E_f(s)} = \frac{E_g(s)}{E_f(s)} \times \frac{E_a(s)}{E_g(s)} = \frac{K_g/L_f}{s + R_f/L_f} \times \frac{Z_L(s)}{R_g + L_g s + Z_L(s)} \tag{3-31}$$

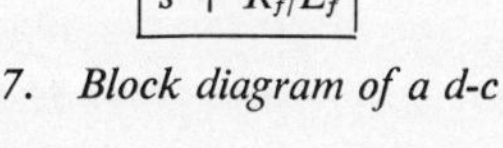

Figure 3–17.   Block diagram of a d-c generator.

2. Armature-Controlled D-C Servomotor[5]

Armature-controlled d-c servomotors are quite commonly used as the prime mover in control systems. As a matter of fact, a d-c generator driving an armature-controlled d-c servomotor is known as the Ward-Leonard system. We study this configuration next, drawing on the relations derived for the d-c generator and armature-controlled d-c servomotor.

A schematic diagram of the armature-controlled d-c servomotor is shown in Figure 3–18*a*. The symbols R_m and L_m represent the resistive and inductive components of the armature circuit. The field excitation is constant, being supplied from a d-c source. The motor is shown driving a load having an inertia J and damping B.

As the armature rotates, it develops an induced voltage e_m which is in a direction opposite to the control voltage $e_a(t)$. It is proportional to the speed of rotation n and the flux created by the field current. Since we are assuming that the field current is held constant, the flux must be constant. Therefore, the induced armature voltage is only dependent on the speed of rotation and can be expressed as

$$e_m = K_e n = K_e \frac{d\theta_0}{dt} \tag{3-32}$$

where K_e = voltage constant of the motor having units of volts/(radian/second). The voltage equation of the armature circuit is

$$e_a(t) = R_m i_a + L_m \frac{di_a}{dt} + e_m \tag{3-33}$$

Substituting equation 3–32 into 3–33 and taking the Laplace transform, we obtain

$$E_a(s) = (R_m + L_m s) I_a(s) + K_e s \theta_0(s) \tag{3-34}$$

The developed torque of the motor, T_D, is a function of the flux developed by the field current, the armature current, and the length of the conductors. Since we are assuming that the field current is held constant, the developed torque T_D can be expressed as

$$T_D = K_T i_a \tag{3-35}$$

where K_T = torque constant of the motor having units of pound-feet/ampere. The developed torque is used to drive the system having a total inertia J, and to overcome the damping B. This can be expressed as

$$T_D = J \frac{d^2\theta_0}{dt^2} + B \frac{d\theta_0}{dt} \tag{3-36}$$

Substituting equation 3–35 into equation 3–36 and taking the Laplace transform, we obtain

$$K_T I_a(s) = (Js^2 + Bs)\theta_0(s) \tag{3-37}$$

The overall system transfer function $\theta_0(s)/E_a(s)$ obtained by eliminating $I_a(s)$ between equations 3–34 and 3–37 is

$$\frac{\theta_0(s)}{E_a(s)} = \frac{K_T}{JL_m s^3 + (R_m J + L_m B)s^2 + (R_m B + K_e K_T)s} \tag{3-38}$$

Equation 3–38 can be defined in terms of an armature time constant T_a, a motor time constant T_m, and a damping factor ζ, as follows:

$$\frac{\theta_0(s)}{E_a(s)} \quad \frac{1/K_e}{s[T_a T_m s^2 + (T_m + \zeta T_a)s + (\zeta + 1)]} \tag{3-39}$$

where

$$T_a = \frac{L_m}{R_m}$$

$$T_m = \frac{JR_m}{K_e K_T} \tag{3-40}$$

$$\zeta = \frac{R_m B}{K_e K_T}$$

The simple block diagram of this system is illustrated in Figure 3–18*b*.

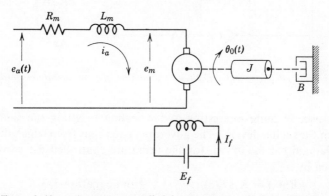

Figure 3–18a.   Armature-controlled d-c servomotor schematic diagram.

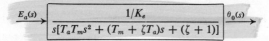

Figure 3–18b.   Block diagram of an armature-controlled d-c motor.

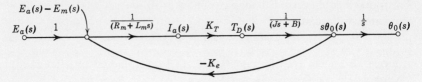

Figure 3–18c. Signal flow diagram representation for the armature-controlled d-c servomotor.

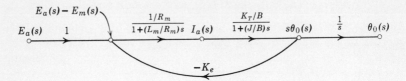

Figure 3–18d. A signal flow diagram more appropriate for analog computer simula tion

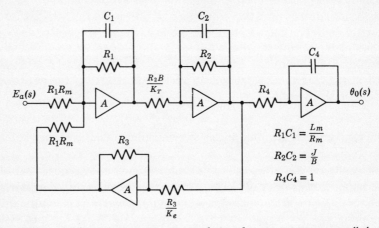

Figure 3–18e. Analog computer circuit simulation for an armature-controlled d-c servomotor.

It is usually quite interesting and revealing to study the signal flow diagram for such a device. The governing equations from which the signal flow diagram can be drawn for the armature-controlled d-c servomotor are given by

$$E_m(s) = K_e s\theta_0(s) \qquad \text{(from equation 3–32)} \qquad (3\text{–}41)$$

$$I_a(s) = \frac{E_a(s) - E_m(s)}{R_m + L_m s} \qquad \text{(from equation 3–33)} \qquad (3\text{–}42)$$

$$T_D(s) = K_T I_a(s) \qquad \text{(from equation 3–35)} \qquad (3\text{–}43)$$

$$\theta_0(s) = \frac{1}{s} \frac{T_D(s)}{(Js + B)} \qquad \text{(from equation 3–36)} \qquad (3\text{–}44)$$

The signal flow diagram is illustrated in Figure 3–18c. It clearly illustrates the inherent feedback (back electromotive force) of this device. This property is sometimes used to stabilize a feedback control system (see Problem 3–7). It is left as an exercise to the reader to prove that the transfer function of this system, as derived from the signal flow diagram, agrees with equations 3–39 and 3–40.

Since signal flow graphs represent the mathematical structure of a system, they represent a type of basic analog. Likewise, an analog computer may be thought of as the physical realization of a signal flow graph. However, any arbitrary signal flow graph is not necessarily a suitable representation as the program for an analog computer. This is due primarily to the fact that the control engineer avoids simulating differentiations which have wide bandwidths and associated noise problems. For the case of the armature-controlled d-c servomotor, a signal flow diagram more appropriate for analog simulation is shown in Figure 3–18d. The analog computer simulation circuitry is shown in Figure 3–18e.

An analog computer can be a very useful and powerful tool for analyzing a feedback control system. It is used quite frequently in this book. Problem 3–9 will provide some practice in drawing the signal flow diagram and analog computer simulation circuitry for several of the devices discussed in this section.

3. The Ward-Leonard System[6,7]

A configuration having a d-c generator driving an armature-controlled d-c motor is known as a Ward-Leonard system. The d-c generator acts as a rotating power amplifier that supplies the power which, in turn, drives the prime mover. Variations of the conventional Ward-Leonard system are known as the amplidyne, the metadyne, the Rotorol, and the Regulex. The reader is referred to more authoritative books on d-c machinery[6] for a description of these devices.

A schematic diagram of the basic Ward-Leonard system is shown in Figure 3–19. The notations used are the same as those of Figures 3–16 and 3–18. Many sophisticated variations of this basic configuration, using compensating windings, exist.[7]

To enable us to combine the transfer-function relationships derived previously for the d-c generator and armature-controlled d-c motor, we shall add the resistive and inductive components of the generator and motor and define a new armature time constant, T_a', as

$$T_a' = \frac{L_g + L_m}{R_g + R_m} \tag{3-45}$$

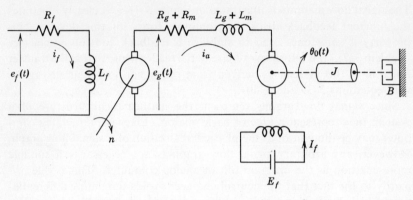

Figure 3–19.   Ward-Leonard system schematic diagram.

Assuming that the induced armature voltage $e_g(t)$ is applied directly to the armature of the motor, equation 3–39 may be rewitten as

$$\frac{\theta_0(s)}{E_g(s)} = \frac{1/K_e}{s[T_a'T_m s^2 + (T_m + \zeta T_a')s + (\zeta + 1)]} \qquad (3\text{–}46)$$

It is now relatively simple to obtain the transfer function representation of the configuration shown in Figure 3–19. Defining $e_f(t)$ as the input and θ_0 as the output of the system, we need merely to combine the transfer

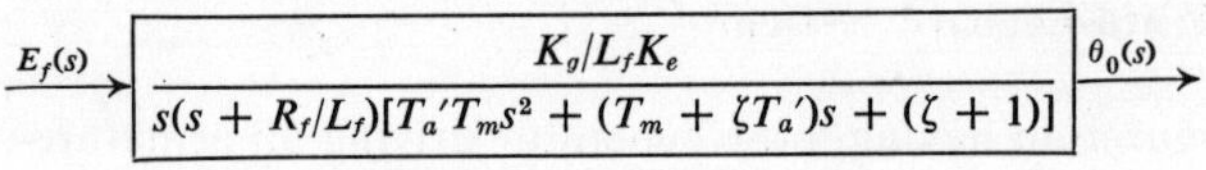

$$E_f(s) \longrightarrow \boxed{\frac{K_g/L_f K_e}{s(s + R_f/L_f)[T_a'T_m s^2 + (T_m + \zeta T_a')s + (\zeta + 1)]}} \longrightarrow \theta_0(s)$$

Figure 3–20.   Block diagram of the Ward-Leonard system.

function given by equations 3–29 and 3–46. Therefore the system transfer function is given by

$$\frac{\theta_0(s)}{E_f(s)} = \frac{K_g/L_f}{s + R_f/L_f}\cdot\frac{1/K_e}{s[T_a'T_m s^2 + (T_m + \zeta T_a')s + (\zeta + 1)]} \qquad (3\text{–}47)$$

and its simple block diagram is illustrated in Figure 3–20.

4. Field-Controlled D-C Servomotor[8]

A d-c servomotor can also be controlled by varying the field current and maintaining a constant armature current. The schematic diagram of such a configuration, known as the field-controlled d-c servomotor, is shown in Figure 3–21. The notations are the same as those of Figure 3–18.

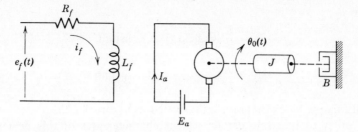

Figure 3–21. Field-controlled d-c servomotor schematic diagram.

The developed torque of the motor, T_D, is a function of the flux developed by the armature current, the field current, and the length of the conductors. Since we are assuming that the armature current is held constant, the developed torque T_D can be expressed as

$$T_D = K_T i_f \qquad (3\text{-}48)$$

where K_T = torque constant of the motor having units of pound-feet/ampere. The developed torque is used to drive the system having a total inertia J and to overcome the damping B. This can be expressed as

$$T_D = J \frac{d^2\theta_0}{dt^2} + B \frac{d\theta_0}{dt} \qquad (3\text{-}49)$$

Substituting equation 3–48 into equation 3–49, we obtain a differential equation relating the field current and the output shaft position.

$$i_f = \frac{J}{K_T} \frac{d^2\theta_0}{dt^2} + \frac{B}{K_T} \frac{d\theta_0}{dt} \qquad (3\text{-}50)$$

An expression for the value of the field current i_f can be obtained from the voltage equation of the field circuit.

$$e_f(t) = R_f i_f + L_f \frac{di_f}{dt} \qquad (3\text{-}51)$$

Substituting equation 3–50 into equation 3–51 and taking the Laplace transform, we obtain

$$E_f(s) = (R_f + L_f s)\left(\frac{J}{K_T} s^2 + \frac{B}{K_T} s\right)\theta_0(s) \qquad (3\text{-}52)$$

The transfer function of the device, defined as the output $\theta_0(s)$ divided by the input $E_f(s)$, is given by

$$\frac{\theta_0(s)}{E_f(s)} = \frac{K_T/R_f B}{s(1 + T_f s)(1 + T_m s)} \qquad (3\text{-}53)$$

where

$$T_f = \frac{L_f}{R_f} = \text{field time constant}$$

$$T_m = \frac{J}{B} = \text{motor time constant}$$

and its simple block diagram is illustrated in Figure 3–22a.

In order to illustrate certain salient characteristics of this device its signal flow diagram is considered next. The governing equations from which the signal flow diagram can be drawn for the field-controlled d-c servomotor are given by

$$I_f(s) = \frac{E_f(s)}{R_f + L_f s} \qquad \text{(from equation 3–51)} \qquad (3\text{–}54)$$

$$T_D(s) = K_T I_f(s) \qquad \text{(from equation 3–48)} \qquad (3\text{–}55)$$

$$\theta_0(s) = \frac{1}{s} \frac{T_D(s)}{Js + B} \qquad \text{(from equation 3–49)} \qquad (3\text{–}56)$$

The simple signal flow diagram of this device is illustrated in Figure 3–22b.

The signal flow diagram takes on an interesting aspect if the armature current is not held constant. In that case, the developed torque of the motor T_D is proportional to both the field and armature circuits and is given by

$$T_D(s) = K_T{}' I_f(s) I_a(s) \qquad (3\text{–}57)$$

The signal flow representation for this case requires the following additional relations for the armature circuit:

$$I_a(s) = \frac{E_a(s) - E_m(s)}{R_m + L_m s} \qquad \text{(from equation 3–33)} \qquad (3\text{–}58)$$

$$E_m(s) = K_D I_f(s)[s\theta_0(s)] \qquad (3\text{–}59)$$

It is left as an exercise to the reader to determine the signal flow diagram and transfer function for this system (see Problem 3–8).

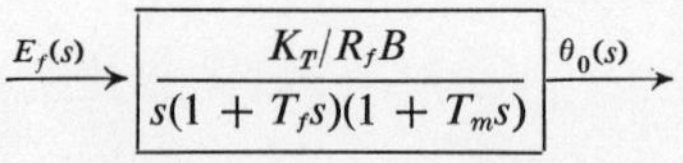

Figure 3–22a. *Block diagram of a field-controlled d-c motor.*

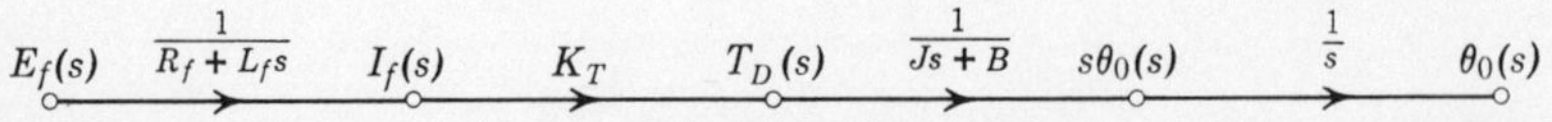

Figure 3–22b. *Signal flow diagram representation for the field-controlled d-c servomotor.*

5. Two-Phase A-C Servomotor[9-11]

The two-phase a-c servomotor is probably the most commonly used type of servomotor. Its popularity stems from the fact that many error-sensing devices, which will be covered in Chapter 6, are carrier frequency (a-c) devices. By using two-phase a-c servomotors, demodulation need not be performed and a-c amplification can be used throughout the electrical portion of the system.

It is basically a two-phase induction motor having its two stator coils separated by 90 electrical degrees. A control signal is applied to one phase (the control winding) while the other phase (the reference winding) is supplied with a fixed signal that is phase-shifted by 90° relative to the control signal. It is primarily used for relatively low-power applications. A schematic diagram of an a-c servomotor driving a load of inertia J and damping B is shown in Figure 3–23. The reference field's voltage is denoted as $e_r(t)$ and the control field's voltage is denoted as $e_c(t)$.

As the control voltage is varied, the developed torque T_D and speed n vary. A set of torque-speed curves for various values of control voltage are shown in Figure 3–24. These characteristics are obtained from conventional torque-speed curves of two-phase a-c induction motors by designing the rotor with a relatively high resistance. It is interesting to note that when the control voltage equals zero, both the torque and speed are zero. However, when the control voltage has a finite value, torque and speed are developed. Notice that these curves show a very large torque for zero speed which is desirable in developing a very rapid acceleration.

Unfortunately, the torque-speed curves are not straight lines. Therefore we cannot write a linear differential equation to represent them. However, by approximating these characteristics with those of linear curves, reasonable accuracy can be achieved. Since the developed torque T_D is a

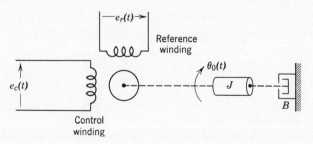

Figure 3–23. Two-phase a-c servomotor schematic diagram.

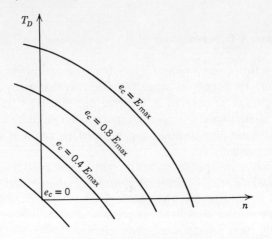

Figure 3-24.   Two-phase a-c servomotor torque-speed characteristics.

function of speed n and the control voltage $e_c(t)$, we have to write the torque equation in terms of partial derivatives.

$$\frac{\partial T_D}{\partial n} n + \frac{\partial T_D}{\partial e_c} e_c(t) = T_D(n, e_c) \tag{3-60}$$

By defining

$$\frac{\partial T_D}{\partial n} \equiv K_n \qquad \text{(where } K_n \text{ is a negative number)}$$

$$\frac{\partial T_D}{\partial e_c} \equiv K_e$$

and substituting $n = d\theta_0/dt$, we can rewrite equation 3-60 as

$$K_n \frac{d\theta_0}{dt} + K_e e_c(t) = T_D \tag{3-61}$$

The developed torque is used to drive the system having a total inertia J, and to overcome the damping B. This can be expressed as

$$T_D = J \frac{d^2\theta_0}{dt^2} + B \frac{d\theta_0}{dt} \tag{3-62}$$

Substituting equation 3-61 into equation 3-62 and taking the Laplace transform, we obtain

$$K_n s\theta_0(s) + K_e E_c(s) = Js^2\theta_0(s) + Bs\theta_0(s) \tag{3-63}$$

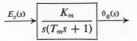

Figure 3–25. Block diagram of a two-phase a-c servomotor.

The transfer function of the device, defined as the output $\theta_0(s)$ divided by the input $E_c(s)$, is given by

$$\frac{\theta_0(s)}{E_c(s)} = \frac{K_m}{s(T_m s + 1)} \qquad (3\text{–}64)$$

where
$$K_m = \frac{K_e}{B - K_n} = \text{motor constant}$$

$$T_m = \frac{J}{B - K_n} = \text{motor time constant}$$

and its simple block diagram is illustrated in Figure 3–25.

3–4. TRANSFER FUNCTION REPRESENTATION OF TYPICAL HYDRAULIC CONTROL SYSTEM DEVICES[5,12]

Hydraulic components are commonly found in control systems that are either all hydraulic or a combination of electromechanical and hydraulic devices. The procedure used for deriving the transfer function representation of some commonly used hydraulic control system devices from their basic differential equations is illustrated in this section. We specifically consider hydraulic motors, pumps, and valves.

1. Hydraulic Motor and Pump

There is no essential difference between a hydraulic pump and motor, just as there is no essential difference between a d-c generator and a d-c motor. Basically, the hydraulic device is classified as a motor if the input is hydraulic flow or pressure and the output is mechanical position; or a pump if the input is mechanical torque and the output is hydraulic flow or pressure.

Figure 3–26 illustrates a commonly used hydraulic power transmission system. This device, which is capable of controlling large torques, consists of a variable displacement pump that is driven at a constant speed. A control stroke, which determines the quantity of oil pumped, also

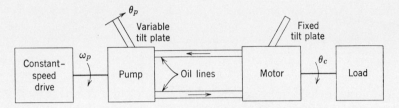

Figure 3–26.   Hydraulic power transmission system.

controls the direction of fluid flow. The angular displacement of the hydraulic motor is proportional to the volumetric flow and is in the same direction as the oil flow from the pump. Oil leakage around the valves of the pump results in the inertia of the load producing an effective time constant for the system. A functional block diagram of the hydraulic transmission is illustrated in Figure 3–27.

The amount of oil displaced per revolution of the hydraulic pump is a function of the tilt angle θ_p. When $\theta_p = 0°$, there is no flow in the oil lines. As θ_p is increased in the positive direction, more oil flows in the lines with the direction shown. When θ_p is negative, the direction of oil flow reverses.

In order to derive the differential equation relating $\theta_p(t)$ and $\theta_c(t)$, we must define certain hydraulic quantities. The volume of oil flowing from the pump, Q_p, is distributed in flow of oil through the motor, Q_m; leakage flow around the motor, Q_l; and compressibility flow, Q_c. The equation describing this process is given by

$$Q_p = Q_m + Q_l + Q_c \tag{3–65}$$

It can be shown that

$$Q_p = K_p \theta_p \tag{3–66}$$

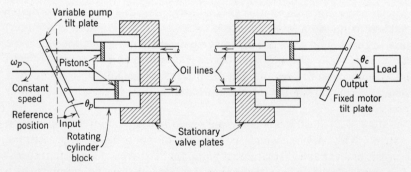

Figure 3–27.   Functional block diagram of a hydraulic power transmission system.

where K_p = volumetric pump flow per second per angular displacement of θ_p

θ_p = displacement of the pump stroke

$$Q_m = V_m \omega_c \qquad (3\text{-}67)$$

where V_m = volumetric motor displacement

ω_c = angular velocity of motor shaft

$$Q_l = L P_L \qquad (3\text{-}68)$$

where L = leakage coefficient of complete system, $(\text{ft}^3/\text{sec})/(\text{lb}/\text{ft}^2)$

P_L = load-induced pressure drop across motor, pounds per foot

and

$$Q_c = \frac{dV}{dt} = \frac{V}{K_B} \frac{dP_L}{dt} \qquad (3\text{-}69)$$

where V = total volume of liquid under compression, cubic feet

K_B = bulk modules of oil, pounds per square foot

Substituting equations 3–66 to 3–69 into equation 3–65, we obtain the relationship

$$K_p \theta_p = V_m \omega_c + L P_L + \frac{V}{K_B} \frac{dP_L}{dt} \qquad (3\text{-}70)$$

Assuming that the hydraulic motor is 100% efficient, the torque relationship of this system is given by

$$\text{Torque} = V_m P_L = J \frac{d^2\theta_c}{dt^2} \qquad (3\text{-}71)$$

Substituting equation 3–71 into 3–70, we obtain

$$K_p \theta_p = V_m \frac{d\theta_c}{dt} + \frac{L}{V_m} J \frac{d^2\theta_c}{dt^2} + \frac{V}{K_B} \frac{J}{V_m} \frac{d^3\theta_c}{dt^3} \qquad (3\text{-}72)$$

The Laplace transform of equation 3–72 is given by

$$K_p \theta_p(s) = V_m s \theta_c(s) + \frac{LJ}{V_m} s^2 \theta_c(s) + \frac{VJ}{K_B V_m} s^3 \theta_c(s) \qquad (3\text{-}73)$$

The transfer function of this device, defined as the ratio of the output $\theta_c(s)$ to the input $\theta_p(s)$, is given by

$$\frac{\theta_c(s)}{\theta_p(s)} = \frac{K_p/V_m}{s[(VJ/K_B V_m^2)s^2 + (LJ/V_m^2)s + 1]} \qquad (3\text{-}74)$$

and its simple block diagram is illustrated in Figure 3–28.

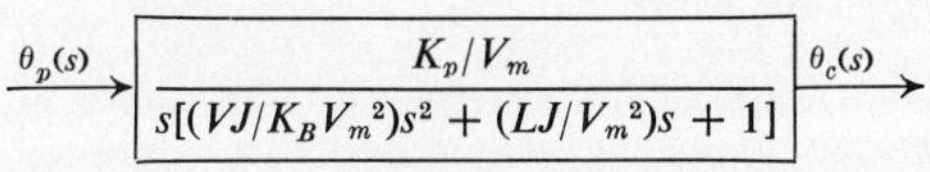

$$\theta_p(s) \longrightarrow \boxed{\frac{K_p/V_m}{s[(VJ/K_B V_m^2)s^2 + (LJ/V_m^2)s + 1]}} \longrightarrow \theta_c(s)$$

Figure 3–28. Block diagram of a pump-controlled hydraulic transmission system.

The bulk modulus K_B is usually a very large number. Therefore, equation 3–74 can usually be simplified to the following expression.

$$\frac{\theta_c(s)}{\theta_p(s)} = \frac{K_p/V_m}{s[(LJ/V_m^2)s + 1]} \tag{3–75}$$

It is important to emphasize, however, that even a relatively small amount of air in the oil lines would lower K_B. This would cause the resonant frequency of the system to decrease sharply and reduce its capabilities. In addition, a large volume of oil between the hydraulic pump and motor has a similar effect. Therefore the control engineer always attempts to keep these lines as short and narrow as possible.

2.   Hydraulic Valve-Controlled Motor

Another method of controlling a hydraulic motor is with a constant-pressure source and a valve that controls the flow of oil through it. A valve-controlled hydraulic system is usually lighter than a pump-controlled system. Therefore the time constants are greatly reduced, and the performance of the hydraulic system can be increased. Valve-controlled systems do, however, have the disadvantages associated with devices whose characteristics are nonlinear.

Figure 3–29 illustrates a valve-controlled hydraulic system. A fluid source, at constant pressure, is provided at the center of the control valve. Fluid return lines are located on each side of this pressure source. When the control valve is moved to the right, hydraulic fluid flows through line A into the hydraulic motor. This results in a pressure differential across the piston of the motor which causes it also to move to the right. This action causes fluid to be pushed back into the valve through line B which

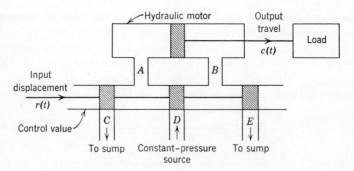

Figure 3–29.   A valve-controlled hydraulic system.

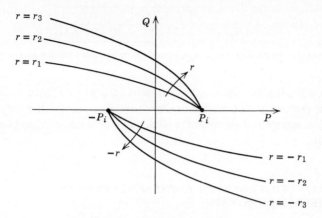

Figure 3–30. Valve characteristics.

returns it to the sump through line E. Similar operation occurs when the control valve is moved to the left. Observe that all fluid flows are blocked when the control valve is in the neutral position, as shown in Figure 3–29.

Figure 3–30 represents the characteristics for the valve-controlled hydraulic motor. The pressure between lines going to the motor is denoted by P, the flow through these lines is denoted by Q, and r denotes the displacement of the valve from its neutral position. Although these characteristics are nonlinear, it will be assumed that they are linear for small input displacements. This is basically an application of small-signal theory, used so frequently by circuit designers. For small excursions from a given quiescent operating point,

$$\Delta Q = \frac{\partial Q}{\partial P} \Delta P + \frac{\partial Q}{\partial r} \Delta r \qquad (3\text{–}76)$$

At any given quiescent operating point, it will be assumed that $\partial Q/\partial P$ and $\partial Q/\partial r$ are constants.

The transfer function relating the input r and output c can be obtained by comparing the valve-controlled hydraulic system with the pump-controlled hydraulic system. Studying these two systems carefully, it is observed that ΔQ is analogous to Q_p, ΔP is analogous to P_L, and Δr is analogous to θ_c. Using these analogies, the transfer function can easily be found to be given by

$$\frac{C(s)}{R(s)} = \frac{(1/V_m)(\partial Q/\partial r)}{s[(VJ/K_B V_m{}^2)s^2 + (J/V_m{}^2)(L - \partial Q/\partial P)s + 1]} \qquad (3\text{–}77)$$

The term $L - \partial Q/\partial P$ in the denominator of this equation is always positive since Figure 3–30 indicates that $\partial Q/\partial P$ is always negative. The

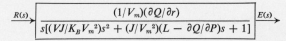

$$\xrightarrow{R(s)} \boxed{\dfrac{(1/V_m)(\partial Q/\partial r)}{s[(VJ/K_B V_m{}^2)s^2 + (J/V_m{}^2)(L - \partial Q/\partial P)s + 1]}} \xrightarrow{E(s)}$$

Figure 3–31. Block diagram of a valve-controlled hydraulic transmission system.

simple block diagram for this system is illustrated in Figure 3–31. It is left as an exercise to the reader to determine the transfer function of the system if a spring and damper are attached to the control rod (see Problem 3–10).

3–5. TRANSFER FUNCTION REPRESENTATION OF THERMAL SYSTEMS[13]

If the assumption is made that the temperature of a body is uniform, then a small number of thermal systems can be represented by linear differential equations. This approximation is reasonably correct for relatively small configurations. This section specifically considers a hot-water heating system as an example of a typical thermal system.

Figure 3–32 illustrates an electric hot-water heating system. The object of this system may be, typically, to supply hot water in a home. Any demand for hot water in the home causes hot water to leave and cold water to enter the tank. In order to reduce heat loss to the surrounding air, the tank is insulated. A thermostatic switch turns an electrical heating element on or off in order to maintain a desired reference temperature.

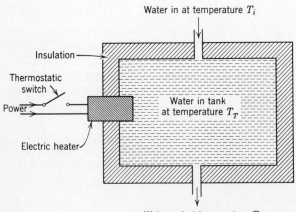

Figure 3–32. Electric hot-water heating system.

The fundamental relationship of thermal systems in equilibrium requires that the heat added to the system equals the heat stored plus the heat lost. This can be expressed by the relationship

$$Q_h = Q_c + Q_o - Q_i + Q_l \qquad (3\text{--}78)$$

where Q_h = heat flow supplied by heating element
Q_c = heat flow into water in tank
Q_o = heat flow lost by hot water leaving tank
Q_i = heat flow carried in by cold water entering tank
Q_l = heat flow through insulation
It can be shown that

$$Q_c = C\frac{dT_t}{dt} \qquad (3\text{--}79)$$

where C = thermal capacity of water in tank
T_t = temperature of water in tank

$$Q_o = VHT_t \qquad (3\text{--}80)$$

where V = water flow from tank
H = specific heat of water

$$Q_i = VHT_i \qquad (3\text{--}81)$$

where T_i = temperature of water entering tank

and
$$Q_l = \frac{T_t - T_e}{R} \qquad (3\text{--}82)$$

where T_e = temperature of air surrounding tank
R = thermal resistance of insulation
Substituting equations 3–79 to 3–82 into equation 3–78 yields the expression

$$Q_h = C\frac{dT_t}{dt} + VH(T_t - T_i) + \frac{T_t - T_e}{R} \qquad (3\text{--}83)$$

The general thermal problem presented, so far, has considered T_t, T_i, T_e, and V as variables. Three of these parameters must be specified in order to solve this problem. For the specific condition where V is a constant and $T_e = T_i$, equation 3–83 reduces to the expression

$$Q_h = C\frac{dT_r}{dt} + \left(VH + \frac{1}{R}\right)T_r \qquad (3\text{--}84)$$

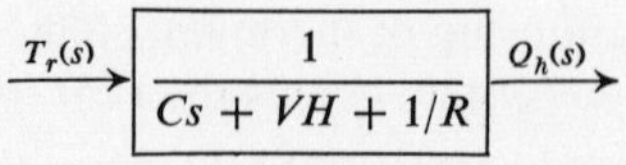

$$\xrightarrow{T_r(s)} \boxed{\dfrac{1}{Cs + VH + 1/R}} \xrightarrow{Q_h(s)}$$

Figure 3–33. Block diagram for the system shown in Figure 3–32.

where T_r = temperature above the reference T_e. The Laplace transform of equation 3–84 is given by

$$Q_h(s) = T_r(s)\left(Cs + VH + \frac{1}{R}\right) \tag{3–85}$$

The transfer function of this system, defined as the ratio of the output $Q_H(s)$ to the input $T_R(s)$ is given by

$$\frac{Q_h(s)}{T_r(s)} = \frac{1}{Cs + VH + 1/R} \tag{3–86}$$

and its simple block diagram is illustrated in Figure 3–33.

3–6. TYPES OF FEEDBACK CONTROL SYSTEMS

Several transfer functions of typical mechanical, electrical, hydraulic, and thermal configurations were derived in Sections 3–2 through 3–5. These transfer functions may be expressed by a generalized transfer function such as

$$G(s) = \frac{K(1 + A_1s + A_2s^2 + A_3s^3 + \cdots + A_es^e)}{s^n(1 + B_1s + B_2s^2 + B_3s^3 + \cdots + B_ms^m)} \tag{3–87}$$

where $A_1, A_2, A_3, \ldots, B_1, B_2, B_3, \ldots$ = constant coefficients; K = overall transfer function gain; and $n = 0, 1, 2, 3 \ldots$.

The exponent n denotes the power to which the s term in the denominator is raised. It may equal zero or any positive integer. Physically, it represents the number of series integrations present in the transfer function.

The value of the exponent n is defined as numerically equal to the "type" of system. This terminology, which is introduced in order to help predict the characteristics of control systems, determines the properties of the controlled variable that results from a constant value of actuating error. When $n = 0$, the system represented by equation 3–87 is defined as a type 0 system; when $n = 1$ it is called a type 1 system, when $n = 2$ it is called a type 2 system, when $n = 3$ it is called a type 3 system, and so on. This nomenclature should not be confused with the order of the system, which refers to the highest power of s in the denominator.

For a type 0 system, a constant actuating signal results in a constant value for the controlled variable. For a type 1 system, a constant actuating signal results in a constant velocity of the controlled variable. For a type

2 system, a constant actuating signal results in a constant acceleration of the controlled variable. For a type 3 system, a constant actuating signal results in a constant rate of change of acceleration of the controlled variable.

Most practical systems are either type 0, 1, 2, or 3, because systems of higher type are difficult to stabilize and tend to exhibit relatively large dynamic errors. However, the steady-state characteristics of higher type systems are very desirable. Chapter 4 illustrates the relation between system type and accuracy.

3–7. CHARACTERISTIC RESPONSES OF TYPICAL FEEDBACK CONTROL SYSTEMS

The purpose of this section is to describe the transient response of a typical feedback control system. We consider a very common configuration in which a two-phase a-c servomotor, whose transfer function is given by equation 3–64, is enclosed by a simple unity feedback loop. Figure 3–34 illustrates the block diagram of this type 1, second-order system. For purposes of simplicity, the reference input elements, control elements, feedback elements, and the indirectly controlled system are assumed to be unity.

The closed-loop transfer function of this system is given by

$$\frac{C(s)}{R(s)} = \frac{K_m/T_m}{s^2 + (1/T_m)s + K_m/T_m} \tag{3–88}$$

By defining the natural resonant frequency ω_n and the damping factor ζ as

$$\omega_n^{\,2} = \frac{K_m}{T_m} \quad \text{and} \quad \zeta = \frac{1}{2\omega_n T_m} \tag{3–89}$$

equation 3–88 can be rewritten as

$$\frac{C(s)}{R(s)} = \frac{\omega_n^{\,2}}{s^2 + 2\zeta\omega_n s + \omega_n^{\,2}} \tag{3–90}$$

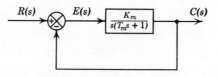

Figure 3–34. Feedback system containing a two-phase a-c induction motor.

We assume that the input to the system is a unit step. Therefore, $R(s) = 1/s$, and the Laplace transform of the output can be written as

$$C(s) = \frac{\omega_n^2}{s(s^2 + 2\zeta\omega_n s + \omega_n^2)} \tag{3-91}$$

Factoring the denominator, we obtain

$$C(s) = \frac{\omega_n^2}{s(s + \zeta\omega_n - \omega_n\sqrt{\zeta^2 - 1})(s + \zeta\omega_n + \omega_n\sqrt{\zeta^2 - 1})} \tag{3-92}$$

The exact solution of the output in the time domain is very dependent on the value of ζ. When $\zeta \geqslant 1$, the second-order system has poles which lie along the negative real axis of the complex plane. When $\zeta < 1$, however, a pair of complex conjugate poles result. We shall determine the output response to a step input for the three cases: where the damping factor equals unity, is greater than unity, and is less than unity.

Case A. Damping Factor Equals Unity. When $\zeta = 1$, equation 3-92 reduces to

$$C(s) = \frac{\omega_n^2}{s(s + \omega_n)^2} \tag{3-93}$$

The time domain response of this third-order system can be obtained by utilizing the solution obtained in equation 2-26 in Chapter 2. The partial fraction expansion of equation 3-93 is given by

$$C(s) = \frac{K_1}{(s + \omega_n)^2} + \frac{K_2}{s + \omega_n} + \frac{K_3}{s} \tag{3-94}$$

By defining the constants A, B, C, and D of equation 2-26 as

$$A = D = 0 \quad \text{and} \quad C = \sqrt{B} = \omega_n$$

the constants K_1, K_2, and K_3 of equation 3-94 can be evaluated by using the equations 2-29, 2-31, and 2-32. Therefore,

$$K_1 = \frac{B - AC}{D - C} = \frac{\omega_n^2 - 0}{0 - \omega_n} = -\omega_n \tag{3-95}$$

$$K_2 = \left[\frac{d}{ds}\frac{As + B}{s + D}\right]_{s=-C} = \left[\frac{d}{ds}\frac{(0 + \omega_n)^2}{s + 0}\right]_{s=-\omega_n}$$

$$= \left[-\frac{\omega_n^2}{s^2}\right]_{s=-\omega_n} = -1 \tag{3-96}$$

$$K_3 = \frac{B - AD}{(C - D)^2} = \frac{\omega_n^2 - 0}{(\omega_n - 0)^2} = 1 \tag{3-97}$$

Substituting these constants into equation 3–94, we obtain

$$C(s) = \frac{-\omega_n}{(s + \omega_n)^2} - \frac{1}{s + \omega_n} + \frac{1}{s} \tag{3-98}$$

The time domain response of the output, $c(t)$, may be obtained by utilizing the table of Laplace transforms given in Table 2–1.

$$c(t) = -\omega_n t\, e^{-\omega_n t} - e^{-\omega_n t} + 1 \tag{3-99}$$

Figure 3–35*a* illustrates the output response together with the unit step input. Notice that the output response exhibits no overshoots when $\zeta = 1$. This response is universally described as being critically damped.

Case B. *Damping Factor Greater than Unity.* When $\zeta > 1$, the time domain responses of the third-order system described by equation 3–92 can be obtained quite simply from its partial fraction expansion. This can be expressed as

$$C(s) = \frac{K_1}{s} + \frac{K_2}{s + \zeta\omega_n - \omega_n\sqrt{\zeta^2 - 1}} + \frac{K_3}{s + \zeta\omega_n + \omega_n\sqrt{\zeta^2 - 1}} \tag{3-100}$$

where $\zeta\omega_n - \omega_n\sqrt{\zeta^2 - 1}$ and $\zeta\omega_n + \omega_n\sqrt{\zeta^2 - 1}$ are positive real numbers. The constants K_1, K_2, and K_3 can be evaluated quite simply by the methods described in Chapter 2. Their values are

$$K_1 = 1$$
$$K_2 = [2(\zeta^2 - \zeta\sqrt{\zeta^2 - 1} - 1)]^{-1} \tag{3-101}$$
$$K_3 = [2(\zeta^2 + \zeta\sqrt{\zeta^2 - 1} - 1)]^{-1}$$

Therefore equation 3–100 can be written as

$$C(s) = s^{-1} + [2(\zeta^2 - \zeta\sqrt{\zeta^2 - 1} - 1)]^{-1}(s + \zeta\omega_n - \omega_n\sqrt{\zeta^2 - 1})^{-1}$$
$$+ [2(\zeta^2 + \zeta\sqrt{\zeta^2 - 1} - 1)]^{-1}(s + \zeta\omega_n + \omega_n\sqrt{\zeta^2 - 1})^{-1} \tag{3-102}$$

The time domain response of the output, $c(t)$, may be obtained by utilizing the table of Laplace transforms given in Table 2–1. It can be expressed as

$$c(t) = 1 + [2(\zeta^2 - \zeta\sqrt{\zeta^2 - 1} - 1)]^{-1}e^{-(\zeta-\sqrt{\zeta^2-1})\omega_n t}$$
$$+ [2(\zeta^2 + \zeta\sqrt{\zeta^2 - 1} - 1)]^{-1}e^{-(\zeta+\sqrt{\zeta^2-1})\omega_n t} \tag{3-103}$$

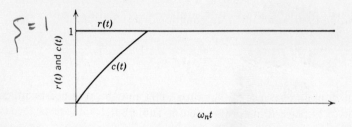

Figure 3–35a.   Input and output response for a critically damped type 1, second-order system.

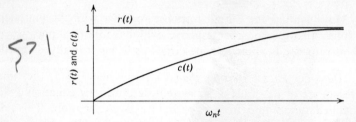

Figure 3–35b.   Input and output response for an overdamped type 1, second-order system.

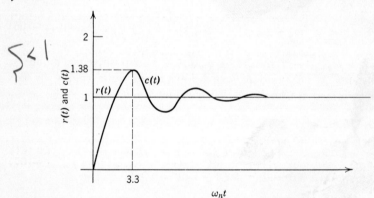

Figure 3–35c.   Input and output response for an underdamped type 1, second-order system ($\zeta = 0.3$).

Figure 3–35*b* illustrates the output response together with the unit step input. Notice that when $\zeta > 1$, the output response exhibits no overshoots and takes longer to reach its final value than when $\zeta = 1$. This response is universally described as being overdamped.

Case C.   *Damping Factor Less than Unity.*   When $\zeta < 1$, the time domain response of the third-order system described by equation 3–92 can be obtained in an analogous manner. The solution is slightly more complex, however, since we now have a pair of complex conjugate poles.

The partial fraction expression of equation 3–92 can be written as

$$C(s) = \frac{K_1}{s} + \frac{K_2}{s + \zeta\omega_n - j\omega_n\sqrt{1 - \zeta^2}} + \frac{K_3}{s + \zeta\omega_n + j\omega_n\sqrt{1 - \zeta^2}}$$

(3–104)

The constants K_1, K_2, and K_3 can be evaluated in an analogous manner by the method described in Chapter 2. The mathematics, however, becomes quite complex. In order to simplify this situation somewhat, use is made of the trigonometric relationships between the location of the conjugate complex poles in the complex plane and the damping factor ζ. The geometry of the configuration is illustrated in Figure 3–36. Notice that the distance from the origin to either pole equals ω_n. In addition, the angle α has the following trigonometric properties:

$$\cos \alpha = -\zeta$$
$$\sin \alpha = \sqrt{1 - \zeta^2}$$

(3–105)

Utilizing the relations given by equation 3–105, the constants K_1, K_2, and K_3 can be expressed as

$$K_1 = 1$$
$$K_2 = \frac{e^{-j\alpha}}{2j \sin \alpha}$$
$$K_3 = \frac{e^{j\alpha}}{2j \sin \alpha}$$

(3–106)

Therefore equation 3–104 can be written as

$$C(s) = \frac{1}{s} + \frac{e^{-j\alpha}}{2j \sin \alpha} (s + \zeta\omega_n - j\omega_n\sqrt{1 - \zeta^2})^{-1}$$

$$+ \frac{e^{j\alpha}}{2j \sin \alpha} (s + \zeta\omega_n + j\omega_n\sqrt{1 - \zeta^2})^{-1} \quad (3\text{–}107)$$

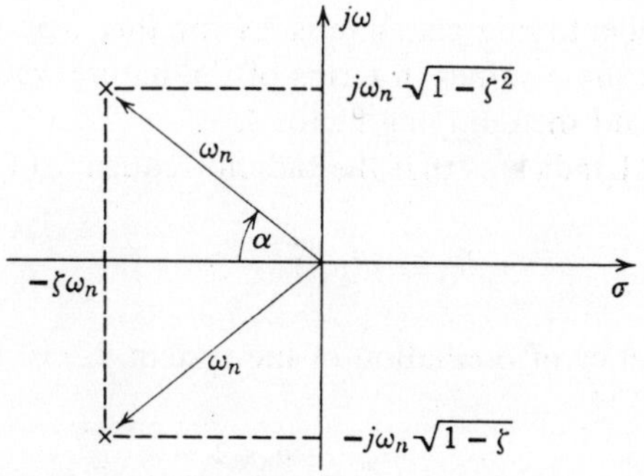

Figure 3–36. Location of the conjugate complex poles in the complex plane.

The time domain response of the output, $c(t)$, may be obtained by utilizing Table 2–1. It can be expressed as

$$c(t) = 1 + \frac{e^{-j\alpha}}{2j \sin \alpha} e^{-(\zeta\omega_n - j\omega_n\sqrt{1-\zeta^2})t} - \frac{e^{j\alpha}}{2j \sin \alpha} e^{-(\zeta\omega_n + j\omega_n\sqrt{1-\zeta^2})t} \quad (3\text{–}108)$$

This can be simplified to

$$c(t) = 1 + \frac{e^{-\zeta\omega_n t}}{\sin \alpha} \frac{e^{-j\alpha}e^{j\omega_n t\sqrt{1-\zeta^2}} - e^{j\alpha}e^{-j\omega_n t\sqrt{1-\zeta^2}}}{2j} \quad (3\text{–}109)$$

Further simplification yields

$$c(t) = 1 + \frac{e^{-\zeta\omega_n t}}{\sqrt{1-\zeta^2}} \frac{e^{j(\omega_n t\sqrt{1-\zeta^2}-\alpha)} - e^{-j(\omega_n t\sqrt{1-\zeta^2}-\alpha)}}{2j} \quad (3\text{–}110)$$

The last term of equation 3–110 is recognizable as equal to the

$$\sin (\omega_n t\sqrt{1-\zeta^2} - \alpha).$$

Therefore, equation 3–110 can be simplified to

$$c(t) = 1 + \frac{e^{-\zeta\omega_n t}}{\sqrt{1-\zeta^2}} \sin (\omega_n\sqrt{1-\zeta^2}\, t - \alpha) \quad (3\text{–}111)$$

Figure 3–35c illustrates the output response for a value of ζ approximately equal to 0.3, together with the unit step input. Notice that the output response exhibits several overshoots before finally settling out. This response, which is characteristic of an exponentially damped sinusoid, is universally described as being underdamped.

The time to the first overshoot and its value at the first overshoot are two interesting identifying characteristics for this type of response. We shall next derive these values in terms of the natural radian frequency of oscillation, ω_n, and the damping factor ζ.

Equation 3–111 indicates that the radian frequency of oscillation of the system, ω_m, is

$$\omega_m = \omega_n\sqrt{1-\zeta^2} \quad (3\text{–}112)$$

The cyclic frequency of oscillation of the system, f_m, is

$$f_m = \frac{\omega_m}{2\pi} = \frac{\omega_n\sqrt{1-\zeta^2}}{2\pi} \quad (3\text{–}113)$$

The period of oscillation of the system, t_m, is

$$t_m = \frac{1}{f_m} = \frac{2\pi}{\omega_n\sqrt{1 - \zeta^2}} \tag{3-114}$$

The first and therefore peak overshoot occurs at $t_m/2$. Therefore, the time to the first overshoot, t_r, which is commonly referred to as the rise time, is

$$t_r = \frac{t_m}{2} = \frac{\pi}{\omega_n\sqrt{1 - \zeta^2}} \tag{3-115}$$

or

$$\omega_n t_r = \frac{\pi}{\sqrt{1 - \zeta^2}} \tag{3-116}$$

For the case illustrated in Figure 3–35c, where $\zeta = 0.3$, the time to the first overshoot is approximately $3.3/\omega_n$.

Substituting the result of equation 3–116 into equation 3–111 yields the value for the maximum instantaneous value of the output, $c(t)$:

$$c(t) = 1 + \frac{\exp\left(-\zeta\pi/\sqrt{1 - \zeta^2}\right)}{\sqrt{1 - \zeta^2}} \sin\left(\pi - \alpha\right) \tag{3-117}$$

This can be simplified by substituting

$$\sin\left(\pi - \alpha\right) = \sin\alpha \quad \text{and} \quad \sin\alpha = \sqrt{1 - \zeta^2}$$

Therefore,

$$c(t) = 1 + \exp\left(-\frac{\zeta\pi}{\sqrt{1 - \zeta^2}}\right) \tag{3-118}$$

Thus the maximum value of the output response to a step input is

$$1 + \exp\left(-\frac{\zeta\pi}{\sqrt{1 - \zeta^2}}\right)$$

This is usually expressed as a percentage of the input.

Therefore, for a unit step input

$$\text{Maximum per cent overshoot} = \exp\left(-\frac{\zeta\pi}{\sqrt{1 - \zeta^2}}\right) \times 100 \tag{3-119}$$

For the case illustrated in Figure 3–35c, where $\zeta = 0.3$, the maximum per cent overshoot equals approximately 38%.

The type 1, second-order system is a very common and popular one. In order for the reader to become more familiar with its typical characteristic responses, Figures 3–37 and 3–38 are shown to illustrate the resulting transient responses and per cent maximum overshoots, respectively, for several values of damping factor.

It is interesting to compare the sketches of Figures 3–35*a*, *b*, and *c*. The critically damped system appears to be a compromise among the three systems shown. Although it does take a longer time to reach the desired value of unity than the underdamped system, it does not exhibit overshoots. The underdamped system, however, oscillates several times around the desired value before it finally settles to its steady-state value. Depending on the value of the damping factor, the underdamped system

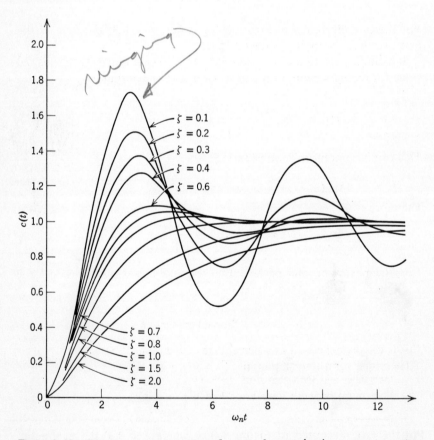

Figure 3–37. Transient response curves of a type 1, second-order system to a step input.

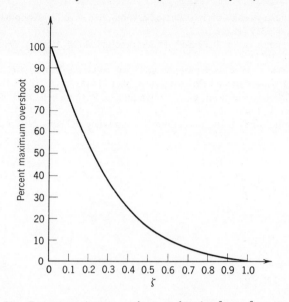

Figure 3–38. *Percent maximum overshoot vs. damping factor for a type 1, second-order system.*

may reach its final value faster than the critically damped system. Overdamped systems are hardly ever used in practice. As a matter of interest, practical systems are usually designed to be somewhat underdamped. Chapter 4 will discuss this in greater detail in terms of the various performance criteria.

REFERENCES

1. Proposed Symbols and Terms for Feedback Control Systems, AIEE Committee Report, *Elec. Eng.*, **Pt. 2, 70,** 905 (1951).
2. *Engineering Mechanics*, A. Higdon and W. B. Stiles, Prentice-Hall, New York, 1949, Chapter 9.
3. The Dynamo Electric Amplifier—Class A Operation, R. M. Saunders, *Trans. AIEE*, **68** (1949).
4. An Analysis of Rotating Amplifiers, B. Litman, *Trans. AIEE*, **Pt. 2, 68,** 1111 (1949).
5. *Servomechanisms and Regulating System Design*, H. Chestnut and R. W. Mayer, John Wiley and Sons, New York, 1959, Vol. 1, 2nd edition.
6. *Direct-Current Machinery*, R. C. Kloeffler, R. M. Kerchner, and J. L. Brenneman, The Macmillan Co., New York, 1950.
7. *Feedback Control Systems*, J. C. Gille, N. J. Pelegrin, and P. Decaulne, McGraw-Hill Book Co., New York, 1959, Chapter 33.
8. *Servomechanisms and Regulating System Design*, H. Chestnut and R. W. Mayer, John Wiley and Sons, New York, 1955, Chapter 7, Vol. 2.

9. Operating Characteristics of Two-Phase Servomotors, R. J. W. Koopman, *Trans. AIEE*, **Pt. 1, 68,** 319 (1949).
10. Transient Response of Small Two-Phase Servomotors, A. M. Hopkin, *Trans. AIEE*, **Pt. 1, 70,** 881 (1951).
11. *Electric Machinery*, M. Liwschitz-Garik and C. C. Whipple, Vol. 2, *A-C Machines*, Chapter 7, D. Van Nostrand Co., Princeton, N. J., 1946.
12. *Principles of Servomechanisms*, G. J. Brown and D. P. Campbell, John Wiley and Sons, New York, 1948.
13. *Response of Physical Systems*, J. D. Trimmer, John Wiley and Sons, New York, 1950.

4   PERFORMANCE CRITERIA

4–1. INTRODUCTION

During the dawn of control system theory, engineers were generally less fussy in rigidly defining performance criteria. We were more apt to look on the feedback control system rather qualitatively and center attention primarily on stability and static accuracy. However, modern complex control systems have demanded the development of accurate criteria of performance.

The performance of a feedback control system is generally a function of stability, sensitivity, accuracy, transient response, and residual noise jitter. The exact specifications are usually dictated by the required system performance. Certain characteristics are more important in some systems than in others.

The great amount of literature that has appeared on the subject in recent years is evidence of the increasing importance that performance criteria has been given in feedback control system design. In order to keep pace with the requirements of modern feedback control systems, several new criteria of performance have been developed.[1] It is the purpose of this chapter to review and study several classical performance criteria together with more recent and sophisticated approaches. The control literature of the past decade abounds in various criteria of performance. Unfortunately, a large amount of this material is either impractical, incomplete, or designed to solve a very specific problem. After filtering the literature, we find that the integral of time and error (ITAE) criterion for optimizing the transient response and the root-mean-square-error criterion for minimizing the effects of noise stand out as being very useful, and we present them in this chapter together with the classical criteria of performance. In addition, several of the other performance criteria are considered in the following chapters. Performance criteria are presented from the modern optimal control theory viewpoint in Chapter 10 and are extended to adaptive control systems in Chapter 11.

4-2. STABILITY

A feedback control system must be stable, even when the system is subjected to command signals, extraneous inputs anywhere within the loop, power supply variations, and changes in parameters of the feedback loop.

It is an erroneous philosophy merely to say that a system is "stable." The question of how stable the system is must also be determined. In order to answer this question adequately, we must return to equation 2–53, which is repeated below:

$$\frac{C(s)}{R(s)} = \frac{G(s)}{1 + G(s)H(s)} \tag{4-1}$$

Let us focus some attention on the denominator of this equation. Should $G(s)H(s)$ equal unity at a phase angle of 180°, the denominator would equal zero and the feedback system would oscillate. The margin by which $G(s)H(s)$ is shy of unity magnitude is known as the "gain margin," and the phase of which it is shy 180° is known as the "phase margin." These quantities indicate the degree to which the system is stable. They are used by the control engineer to determine how stable the feedback system is. Useful, qualitative, desirable design values are 60° for the phase margin and 0.25 (-12 decibels) for the gain margin. These numbers indicate that when $G(s)H(s)$ equals unity, its phase is 120°, and when $G(s)H(s)$ has 180° phase shift, its magnitude is 0.25.

4-3. SENSITIVITY

Sensitivity is a measure of the dependency of a system's characteristics on those of a particular element. The sensitivity of a system's transmittance T with respect to the characteristics of a given element K is defined as

$$S_K{}^T = \frac{d \ln T}{d \ln K} \tag{4-2}$$

A more meaningful definition can be obtained by rewriting equation 4–2 as

$$S_K{}^T = \frac{dT/T}{dK/K} \tag{4-3}$$

Equation 4–3 states that the sensitivity of T with respect to K is the percentage change in T divided by that percentage change in K which has

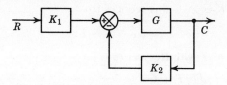

Figure 4–1. A representative control system.

caused the change in T to occur. This definition is valid only for small changes. It is important to note that an ideal system has zero sensitivity.

In order to illustrate the concept of sensitivity, consider the typical control system shown in Figure 4–1. Here K_1 represents the transfer function of the input transducer, K_2 represents the transfer function of the feedback transducer, and G represents the combined transfer function of an amplifier, stabilizing network, motor, and gear train in the forward part of the feedback loop.

The overall system transmittance T can be shown to be given by the equation

$$T = \frac{C}{R} = \frac{K_1 G}{1 + K_2 G} \tag{4-4}$$

Let us now determine the sensitivity of the overall system transmittance with respect to changes in K_1, K_2, and G.

a. Sensitivity of T with Respect to K_1

$$S_{K_1}{}^T = \frac{dT/T}{dK_1/K_1} = \frac{K_1}{T} \frac{dT}{dK_1}$$

where

$$\frac{dT}{dK_1} = \frac{(1 + K_2 G)G - 0}{(1 + K_2 G)^2} = \frac{G}{1 + K_2 G} = \frac{T}{K_1}$$

$$\therefore \quad S_{K_1}{}^T = \frac{K_1}{T} \times \frac{T}{K_1} = 1 \tag{4-5}$$

b. Sensitivity of T with Respect to K_2

$$S_{K_2}{}^T = \frac{dT/T}{dK_2/K_2} = \frac{K_2}{T} \frac{dT}{dK_2}$$

where

$$\frac{dT}{dK_2} = \frac{0 - K_1 G^2}{(1 + K_2 G)^2} = \frac{-K_1{}^2 G^2}{K_1(1 + K_2 G)^2}$$

$$\therefore \quad S_{K_2}{}^T = \frac{K_2}{T} \times \frac{-K_1{}^2 G^2}{K_1(1 + K_2 G)^2} = \frac{-K_2}{T} \times \frac{T^2}{K_1} = \frac{-K_2 G}{1 + K_2 G}$$

For cases where $K_2G \gg 1$, this reduces to

$$S_{K_2}{}^T \approx -1 \qquad (4\text{-}6)$$

c. Sensitivity of *T* with Respect to *G*

$$S_G{}^T = \frac{dT/T}{dG/G} = \frac{G}{T}\frac{dT}{dG}$$

where

$$\frac{dT}{dG} = \frac{(1 + K_2G)K_1 - K_1GK_2}{(1 + K_2G)^2} = \frac{K_1}{(1 + K_2G)^2}$$

$$\therefore \quad S_G{}^T = \frac{G}{T} \times \frac{K_1}{(1 + K_2G)^2} = \frac{1}{1 + K_2G} \qquad (4\text{-}7)$$

The results obtained in equations 4–5, 4–6, and 4–7 are quite interesting. The symbols K_1 and K_2 represent input and feedback transducers, respectively, and equations 4–5 and 4–6 illustrate that they are very critical. Any changes in their characteristics are directly reflected in an overall system transmittance change. Elements used for K_1 and K_2 must therefore possess precise and stable characteristics with temperature and time. Equation 4–7 shows that the sensitivity of the overall system transmittance with respect to *G* is divided by 1 plus the overall loop gain, K_2G. From a sensitivity viewpoint, it appears desirable to design K_2G to be as large a value as possible. However, it need not be very precise or stable.

Let us now try to extend the results derived in this section in order to determine the requirements of the various elements shown in the simple gun fire positioning device of Figure 4–2. In this system R_1, R_2, $\pm V$, and the difference capability of the difference amplifier must all be precise and stable. The gain characteristics of the difference amplifier, voltage amplifier, stability network, power amplifier, and motor need not be precise or stable. Any changes in the characteristics of these elements will be divided by 1 plus the loop gain. Let us now consider the gear train, which

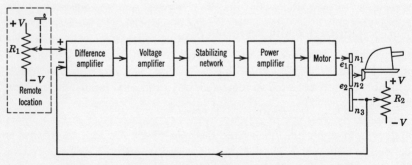

Figure 4–2.   An automatic positioning system for a gun turret.

is composed of three gears: n_1, n_2, n_3. Gear meshes can result in system errors because the tooth space exceeds the thickness of an engaging tooth. This phenomenon is commonly referred to as backlash. It can be measured by holding one gear fast and observing the amount of motion in the other gear. Figure 4–2 denotes the backlash between gears n_1 and n_2 as e_1, and that between n_2 and n_3 as e_2. By a similar analysis, it can be shown that the error produced by backlash e_1 is divided out by 1 plus the loop gain while the error produced by backlash e_2 is added practically directly into the overall system transmittance. Therefore, there is a need of precision gearing for n_2 and n_3 but not for n_1. A later chapter illustrates that backlash at e_1, however, is very important from a stability viewpoint. From a sensitivity viewpoint, however, it is not critical.

4-4. STATIC ACCURACY

Accuracy probably ranks as the next most important characteristic of a feedback control system. The control system designer strives to design this system to minimize error for a certain anticipated input. This section considers techniques which are available for determining the system accuracy.

Theoretically, it is desirable for a control system to have the capability of responding to changes in position, velocity, acceleration, and changes to higher-order derivatives with zero error. Such a specification is very impractical and unrealistic. Fortunately, the requirements of practical systems are much less stringent. For example, let us consider the automatic positioning system of a gun turret which is illustrated in Figure 4–2. Its functioning is similar to the gun positioning system in Figure 1–8. Realistically, it would be desirable for this system to respond well to inputs of position and velocity, but not necessarily to those of acceleration. In addition, it probably would be desirable for this system to respond with zero error for positional-type inputs. However, a finite following error could probably be tolerated for inputs of velocity. In contrast to this system, where the stakes are quite high, let us consider a simpler positioning system which perhaps is only required to reproduce the angular position of a dial at some remote location. Such a control system would probably be only required to reproduce any positional inputs, but not any higher-order inputs such as those of velocity and acceleration.

A method for determining the steady-state performance of any control system is to apply the final-value theorem of the Laplace transform as defined by equation 2–16. Let us reconsider the general feedback system shown in Figure 2–5. Equation 2–56, which is repeated next, describes the relation between the resulting system error, $E(s)$, for a given input $R(s)$.

$$\frac{E(s)}{R(s)} = \frac{1}{1 + G(s)H(s)} \tag{4-8}$$

The steady-state error can be expressed as

$$e(t)_{ss} = \lim_{t \to \infty} e(t) = \lim_{s \to 0} \frac{sR(s)}{1 + G(s)H(s)} \tag{4-9}$$

The control engineer is usually interested in inputs of position, velocity, and acceleration. A unit step, unit ramp, and unit paraboloid are simple mathematical expressions which represent these physical quantities, respectively. They are defined in equations 4–10 through 4–12, where the notation $U(t)$ means a unit step for $t > 0$.

A Unit Step:

$$r(t) = U(t), \qquad R(s) = \frac{1}{s} \tag{4-10}$$

A Unit Ramp:

$$r(t) = tU(t), \qquad R(s) = \frac{1}{s^2} \tag{4-11}$$

A Unit Paraboloid:

$$r(t) = t^2 U(t), \qquad R(s) = \frac{2}{s^3} \tag{4-12}$$

We next determine the steady-state error of several types of system for each of these three inputs. The unit step, unit ramp, and unit paraboloid assume that the loop transfer function $G(s)H(s)$ has the general form

$$G(s)H(s) = \frac{K(1 + T_1 s)(1 + T_2 s) \cdots (1 + T_M s)}{s^n[(T_3 s)^2 + 2\zeta\omega_n s + 1](1 + T_4 s)(1 + T_5 s) \cdots (1 + T_N s)} \tag{4-13}$$

where s^n = a multiple pole at the origin of the complex plane

K = gain factor of the expression

As discussed in Chapter 3, the exponent of s in the denominator, n, represents the system type. For example, a type 0 system indicates that $n = 0$, a type 1 system indicates that $n = 1$, and so on. We consider the specific cases of a type 0, 1, 2 and a general nth-type system.

1. Unit Step Input   *position*

An expression for the steady-state error can be obtained by substituting $R(s) = 1/s$ into equation 4–9.

$$e(t)_{ss} = \lim_{s \to 0} \frac{s(1/s)}{1 + G(s)H(s)} = \frac{1}{1 + \lim_{s \to 0} G(s)H(s)} \tag{4-14}$$

The quantity $\lim\limits_{s\to 0} G(s)H(s)$ is defined as the position constant and is denoted by K_p.

$$K_p = \lim_{s\to 0} G(s)H(s) \tag{4-15}$$

Therefore the expression of the steady-state error in terms of the position constant is

$$e(t)_{ss} = \frac{1}{1 + K_p} \tag{4-16}$$

Equation 4–16 states that the steady-state following error of a feedback control system having a unit step input equals $1/(1 + $ the position constant). We now determine K_p for a type 0, 1, 2 and a general nth-type system.

a. Type 0 System. K_p can be obtained for a type 0 system by substituting $G(s)H(s)$, as given in equation 4–13, into equation 4–15 and setting $n = 0$.

$$K_p = \lim_{s\to 0} \frac{K(1 + T_1 s)(1 + T_2 s)\cdots(1 + T_M s)}{[(T_3 s)^2 + 2\zeta\omega_n s + 1](1 + T_4 s)(1 + T_5 s)\cdots(1 + T_N s)} = K \tag{4-17}$$

b. Type 1 System ($n = 1$)

$$K_p = \lim_{s\to 0} \frac{K(1 + T_1 s)(1 + T_2 s)\cdots(1 + T_M s)}{s[(T_3 s)^2 + 2\zeta\omega_n s + 1](1 + T_4 s)(1 + T_5 s)\cdots(1 + T_N s)} = \infty \tag{4-18}$$

c. Type 2 System ($n = 2$)

$$K_p = \lim_{s\to 0} \frac{K(1 + T_1 s)(1 + T_2 s)\cdots(1 + T_M s)}{s^2[(T_3 s)^2 + 2\zeta\omega_n s + 1](1 + T_4 s)(1 + T_5 s)\cdots(1 + T_N s)} = \infty \tag{4-19}$$

d. Type n System ($n > 0$)

$$K_p = \lim_{s\to 0} \frac{K(1 + T_1 s)(1 + T_2 s)\cdots(1 + T_M s)}{s^n[(T_3 s)^2 + 2\zeta\omega_n s + 1](1 + T_4 s)(1 + T_5 s)\cdots(1 + T_N s)} = \infty \tag{4-20}$$

Equations 4–18 through 4–20 indicate that the position constant is infinity for all types of systems greater than 0. Therefore, equation 4–16 implies that all types of system greater than 0 have a theoretical steady-state positional following error of zero. Equation 4–17 indicates that the position constant is finite for a type 0 system and, therefore, its following error for a position input is finite.

2. Unit Ramp Input   *velocity*

An expression for the steady-state error can be obtained by substituting $R(s) = 1/s^2$ into equation 4–9.

$$e(t)_{ss} = \lim_{s \to 0} \frac{s(1/s^2)}{1 + G(s)H(s)} = \frac{1}{\lim\limits_{s \to 0} sG(s)H(s)} \tag{4–21}$$

The quantity $\lim\limits_{s \to 0} sG(s)H(s)$ is defined as the velocity constant and is denoted by K_v.

$$K_v = \lim_{s \to 0} sG(s)H(s) \tag{4–22}$$

Therefore the expression of the steady-state error in terms of the velocity constant is

$$e(t)_{ss} = \frac{1}{K_v} \tag{4–23}$$

Equation 4–23 states that the steady-state following error of a feedback control system having a unit ramp input equals 1 divided by the velocity constant. We now determine K_v for a type 0, 1, 2, and a general nth system:

a. Type 0 System. K_v can be obtained for a type 0 system by substituting $G(s)H(s)$, as given in equation 4–13, into equation 4–22 and setting $n = 0$.

$$K_v = \lim_{s \to 0} \frac{sK(1 + T_1 s)(1 + T_2 s) \cdots (1 + T_M s)}{[(T_3 s)^2 + 2\zeta\omega_n s + 1](1 + T_4 s)(1 + T_5 s) \cdots (1 + T_N s)} = 0 \tag{4–24}$$

b. Type 1 System ($n = 1$)

$$K_v = \lim_{s \to 0} \frac{sK(1 + T_1 s)(1 + T_2 s) \cdots (1 + T_M s)}{s[(T_3 s)^2 + 2\zeta\omega_n s + 1](1 + T_4 s)(1 + T_5 s) \cdots (1 + T_N s)} = K \tag{4–25}$$

c. Type 2 System ($n = 2$)

$$K_v = \lim_{s \to 0} \frac{sK(1 + T_1 s)(1 + T_2 s) \cdots (1 + T_M s)}{s^2[(T_3 s)^2 + 2\zeta\omega_n s + 1](1 + T_4 s)(1 + T_5 s) \cdots (1 + T_N s)} = \infty \tag{4–26}$$

d. Type n System ($n > 1$)

$$K_v = \lim_{s \to 0} \frac{sK(1 + T_1 s)(1 + T_2 s) \cdots (1 + T_M s)}{s^n[(T_3 s)^2 + 2\zeta\omega_n s + 1](1 + T_4 s)(1 + T_5 s) \cdots (1 + T_N s)} = \infty \tag{4–27}$$

Equations 4–26 and 4–27 indicate that the velocity constant is infinity for all types of system greater than 1. Therefore, equation 4–23 implies that all types of system, greater than 1, have a theoretical steady-state velocity following error of zero. Equation 4–24 indicates that a type 0 system cannot follow a velocity input. Equation 4–25 indicates that a type 1 system has a finite following error for a velocity input.

3. Unit Parabolic Input   *acceleration*

An expression for the steady-state error can be obtained by substituting $R(s) = 2/s^3$ into equation 4–9.

$$e(t)_{ss} = \lim_{s \to 0} \frac{s(2/s^3)}{1 + G(s)H(s)} = \frac{2}{\lim\limits_{s \to 0} s^2 G(s)H(s)} \tag{4–28}$$

The quantity $\lim\limits_{s \to 0} s^2 G(s)H(s)$ is defined as the acceleration constant and is denoted by K_a.

$$K_a = \lim_{s \to 0} s^2 G(s)H(s) \tag{4–29}$$

Therefore the expression of the steady-state error in terms of the acceleration constant is

$$e(t)_{ss} = \frac{2}{K_a} \tag{4–30}$$

Equation 4–30 states that the steady-state following error of a feedback control system having a unit parabolic input equals 2 divided by the acceleration constant. We now determine K_a for a type 0, 1, 2 and a general nth-type system:

a. Type 0 System. K_a can be obtained for a type 0 system by substituting $G(s)H(s)$, as given in equation 4–13, into equation 4–29 and setting $n = 0$.

$$K_a = \lim_{s \to 0} \frac{s^2 K(1 + T_1 s)(1 + T_2 s) \cdots (1 + T_M s)}{[(T_3 s)^2 + 2\zeta \omega_n s + 1](1 + T_4 s)(1 + T_5 s) \cdots (1 + T_N s)} = 0 \tag{4–31}$$

b. Type 1 System $(n = 1)$

$$K_a = \lim_{s \to 0} \frac{s^2 K(1 + T_1 s)(1 + T_2 s) \cdots (1 + T_M s)}{s[(T_3 s)^2 + 2\zeta \omega_n s + 1](1 + T_4 s)(1 + T_5 s) \cdots (1 + T_N s)} = 0 \tag{4–32}$$

c.   Type 2 System $(n = 2)$

$$K_a = \lim_{s \to 0} \frac{s^2 K(1 + T_1 s)(1 + T_2 s) \cdots (1 + T_M s)}{s^2[(T_3 s)^2 + 2\zeta\omega_n s + 1](1 + T_4 s)(1 + T_5 s) \cdots (1 + T_N s)} = K \tag{4-33}$$

d.   Type n System $(n > 2)$

$$K_a = \lim_{s \to 0} \frac{s^2 K(1 + T_1 s)(1 + T_2 s) \cdots (1 + T_M s)}{s^n[(T_3 s)^2 + 2\zeta\omega_n s + 1](1 + T_4 s)(1 + T_5 s) \cdots (1 + T_N s)} = \infty \tag{4-34}$$

Equation 4-34 indicates that the acceleration constant is infinity for all types of system greater than 2. Therefore, equation 4-30 implies that all

Table 4-1.   Summary of steady-state constants for various types of input

System Type	Type of Input		
	Unit Step	*Unit Ramp*	*Unit Paraboloid*
0	K_p	0	0
1	∞	K_v	0
2	∞	∞	K_a
3	∞	∞	∞

types of system greater than 2 have a theoretical steady-state acceleration following error of zero. Equations 4-31 and 4-32 indicate that type 0 and 1 systems cannot follow an acceleration input. Equation 4-33 indicates that a type 2 system has a finite following error for an acceleration input.

A summary of the results derived appears in Table 4-1. It is quite general and enables the reader to compare the capabilities of various types of systems. Notice from this table that the steady-state constants are zero, finite, or infinite. It is important to emphasize at this time that if the inputs are other than unit quantities the steady-state errors are proportionally increased. For example, should the input to a type 1 system be a ramp whose value is B position units (feet, yards, and so on)/second, then the steady-state error as given by equation 4-23 would be modified to read

$$e(t)_{ss} = \frac{B}{K_v} \tag{4-35}$$

It is also interesting to note that the unit of the velocity constant is 1/second and that of the acceleration constant is 1/second squared. The position constant K_p has no dimensions.

Let us now consider an input composed of position, velocity, and acceleration which equal A ft, B ft/sec, and C ft/sec² respectively. The form of the input can be represented as

$$r(t) = A + Bt + Ct^2 \tag{4-36}$$

The steady-state response of the system may be obtained by considering each component of the input separately, and then adding the results by means of superposition. The resulting steady-state error is of the following form.

$$e(t)_{ss} = \frac{A}{1 + K_p} + \frac{B}{K_v} + \frac{2C}{K_a} \tag{4-37}$$

It is interesting to see how the various types of system summarized in Table 4-1 would respond to this input.

a.   Type 0 System

$$e(t)_{ss} = \frac{A}{1 + K_p} + \infty + \infty \tag{4-38}$$

Equation 4-38 indicates that a type 0 system will be able to follow the position input component of A ft, but not the velocity or acceleration inputs of B ft/sec and C ft/sec² respectively. Figure 4-3 illustrates the response of this system.

b.   Type 1 System

$$e(t)_{ss} = 0 + \frac{B}{K_v} + \infty \tag{4-39}$$

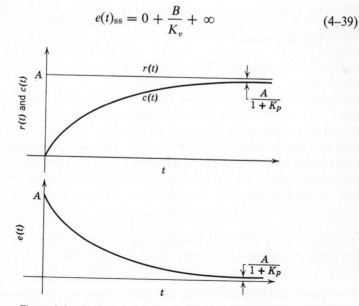

Figure 4-3.   Response of a type 0 system to a step input.

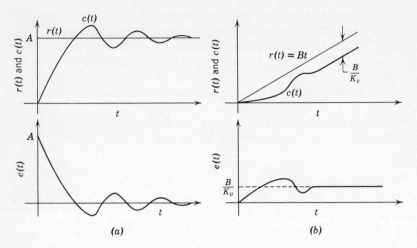

Figure 4–4.   Response of a type 1 system to (a) step and (b) ramp inputs.

The result of equation 4–39 indicates that the type 1 system will follow the position input component with zero error and the velocity input component with a finite error of B/K_v. This system will not, however, be able to follow the acceleration input component. It is interesting to note that the units of B/K_v are feet. This should be interpreted to mean that there is a fixed positional error due to the constant velocity input component. Figure 4–4 illustrates the response of this system.

c.   Type 2 System

$$e(t)_{ss} = 0 + 0 + \frac{2C}{K_a} \tag{4–40}$$

The result of equation 4–40 indicates that the type 2 system will follow the position and velocity input components with zero error and the acceleration input component with a finite error of $2C/K_a$. It is interesting to note that the units of $2C/K_a$ are feet. This should be interpreted to mean that there is a fixed positional error due to the constant acceleration input component. Figure 4–5 illustrates the response of this system.

d.   Type 3 System

$$e(t)_{ss} = 0 + 0 + 0 \tag{4–41}$$

The result of equation 4–41 indicates that the type 3 system can follow all the input components of equation 4–36 with zero error.

A set of useful and generalized error coefficients may be obtained for any system by substituting the unfactored form of equation 4–13 into equation 4–8. This technique, which is valid only when $H(s) = 1$, can be used to obtain errors during both the transient and the steady-state phases. These error coefficients relate the steady-state system error to the input function and its successive derivatives. In addition, the relation between the error coefficients and the steady-state constants during the steady-state phase will also be illustrated.

The unfactored form of equation 4–13 is

$$G(s)H(s) = \frac{K(1 + X_1s + X_2s^2 + X_3s^3 + \cdots + X_Ps^P)}{s^n(1 + Y_1s + Y_2s^2 + Y_3s^3 + \cdots + Y_Qs^Q)} \quad (4\text{–}42)$$

The result of substituting equation 4–42 into equation 4–8 and setting $H(s) = 1$ is

$$\frac{E(s)}{R(s)} = \left[1 + \frac{K(1 + X_1s + X_2s^2 + X_3s^3 + \cdots + X_Ps^P)}{s^n(1 + Y_1s + Y_2s^2 + Y_3s^3 + \cdots + Y_Qs^Q)}\right]^{-1} \quad (4\text{–}43)$$

which can be rewritten as

$$\frac{E(s)}{R(s)} = \frac{s^n(1 + Y_1s + Y_2s^2 + Y_3s^3 + \cdots + Y_Qs^Q)}{\begin{array}{c} s^n(1 + Y_1s + Y_2s^2 + Y_3s^3 + \cdots + Y_Qs^Q) \\ + K(1 + X_1s + X_2s^2 + X_3s^3 + \cdots + X_Ps^P) \end{array}} \quad (4\text{–}44)$$

By collecting like powers together in the numerator and denominator of equation 4–44, the following equation results:

$$\frac{E(s)}{R(s)} = \frac{L_0 + L_1s + L_2s^2 + L_3s^3 + \cdots}{M_0 + M_1s + M_2s^2 + M_3s^3 + \cdots} \quad (4\text{–}45)$$

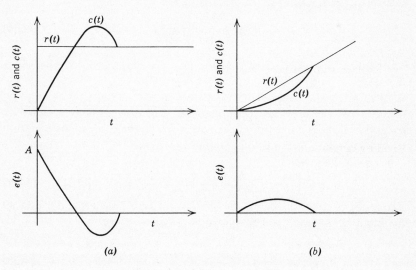

Figure 4–5. Response of a type 2 system to (a) step and (b) ramp inputs.

By dividing the denominator into the numerator, a series expansion results in ascending powers of s.

$$\frac{E(s)}{R(s)} = C_0 + C_1 s + C_2 s^2 + C_3 s^3 + C_4 s^4 + \cdots \quad (4\text{-}46)$$

or

$$e(t) = C_0 r(t) + C_1 \dot{r}(t) + C_2 \ddot{r}(t) + C_3 \dddot{r}(t) + C_4 \ddddot{r}(t) + \cdots \quad (4\text{-}47)$$

The coefficients C_0, C_1, C_2, C_3, C_4, and so on, are defined as the error coefficients. During the steady-state phase ($s \to 0$) they are related to the steady-state constants previously described as follows:

$$C_0 = \frac{1}{1 + K_p} \quad (4\text{-}48)$$

$$C_1 = \frac{1}{K_v} \quad (4\text{-}49)$$

$$C_2 = \frac{1}{K_a} \quad (4\text{-}50)$$

$$C_n = \frac{1}{\lim_{s \to 0} s^n G(s)} \quad (4\text{-}51)$$

To illustrate the use of the error coefficients, let us consider a unity feedback system where

$$G(s) = \frac{600(1 + s)}{s(1 + 50s)} \quad (4\text{-}52)$$

The Laplace transform of the error is

$$E(s) = \frac{R(s)}{1 + G(s)} = \frac{s(1 + 50s)}{s(1 + 50s) + 600(1 + s)} R(s) \quad (4\text{-}53)$$

Dividing denominator into numerator, we obtain

$$E(s) = \left(\frac{s}{600} + \frac{s^2}{12.24} - \frac{s^3}{12.24} + \frac{s^4}{13.35} + \cdots \right) R(s) \quad (4\text{-}54)$$

The error in the time domain can be expressed as

$$e(t)_{ss} = \frac{\dot{r}(t)}{600} + \frac{\ddot{r}(t)}{12.24} - \frac{\dddot{r}(t)}{12.24} + \frac{\ddddot{r}(t)}{13.35} + \cdots \quad (4\text{-}55)$$

Therefore the error coefficients are

$$C_0 = 0, \qquad C_1 = \frac{1}{600}$$

$$C_2 = \frac{1}{12.24}, \qquad C_3 = -\frac{1}{12.24}$$

$$C_4 = \frac{1}{13.35}$$

If the input $r(t)$ is of the form

$$r(t) = A + B(t) \tag{4-56}$$

then $\dot{r}(t) = B$ and $\ddot{r}(t) = \dddot{r}(t) = \ddddot{r}(t) = 0$. By substituting these values into equation 4–55 and letting $t \to \infty$, the steady-state error is obtained:

$$e(t)_{ss} = 0 \times A + \frac{B}{600} + \frac{0}{12.24} - \frac{0}{12.24} + \frac{0}{13.35} + \cdots \tag{4-57}$$

$$\therefore \quad e(t)_{ss} = \frac{B}{600} \quad \text{(units of position)} \tag{4-58}$$

The same result could have been obtained for the steady-state phase by applying the results derived previously for the steady-state constants that are summarized in Table 4–1.

Equations 4–46 and 4–47 can also be used in order to determine system errors during a transient. For this application, the coefficients C_0, C_1, C_2, C_3, C_4, and so on, would be defined as dynamic error coefficients. For a given input, the error at any time can be obtained by appropriate substitution into equation 4–47. As the transient approaches the steady state, the coefficients tend to become constants, and may be evaluated by the relation given previously in equation 4–51.

4–5. TRANSIENT RESPONSE

In addition to stability, sensitivity, and accuracy, control engineers are always quite concerned with the transient response of a feedback system. Transient response characteristics are usually defined on the basis of a step input. The response of a type 1, second-order system to a step input is quite useful for purposes of defining the various transient parameters. Should a problem arise where the system is higher than second order, a reasonably good approximation can be made by assuming that the system is second order if one pair of complex conjugate roots dominate. This point is amplified during the discussion of the pole-zero root locus in a

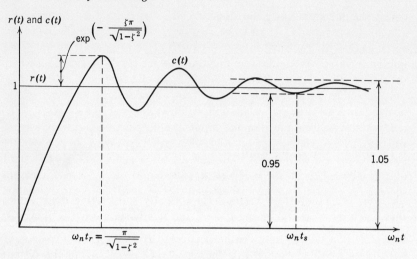

Figure 4–6.   Response of a type 1, second-order system to a unit step.

later chapter. For purposes of illustration, let us consider the type 1, second-order system analyzed in Section 3–7. There we had a unity feedback system whose closed-loop transfer function $C(s)/R(s)$ was given by

$$\frac{C(s)}{R(s)} = \frac{\omega_n^{\,2}}{s^2 + 2\zeta\omega_n s + \omega_n^{\,2}} \qquad (4\text{–}59)$$

Its response to a unit step input was given by

$$e(t) = 1 + \frac{e^{-\zeta\omega_n t}}{\sqrt{1 - \zeta^2}} \sin\left(\omega_n t\sqrt{1 - \zeta^2} - \alpha\right) \qquad (4\text{–}60)$$

where

$$\alpha = \sin^{-1}\sqrt{1 - \zeta^2}$$
$$\zeta < 1$$

The input and output responses are illustrated in Figure 4–6.

The time for the feedback system to reach its first overshoot is commonly referred to as the rise time, t_r. As was derived in Section 3–7 (see equation 3–116) and is illustrated in Figure 4–6,

$$\omega_n t_r = \frac{\pi}{\sqrt{1 - \zeta^2}} \qquad (4\text{–}61)$$

or,   Rise time $= t_r = \dfrac{\pi}{\omega_n\sqrt{1 - \zeta^2}} \qquad (4\text{–}62)$

The time required for the system to damp out all transients is commonly called the solution time, t_0. Theoretically, for a type 1, second-order system this is infinity. In practice, however, the control engineer usually specifies that the transient is over when the error is reduced below some minimum value. When the minimum level is set at 5% of the initial error, the term settling time, t_S, is used to define this characteristic. The settling time, which is approximately equal to four time constants of the envelope of the damped sinusoidal oscillation, is illustrated in Figure 4–6.

Upon the application of a step input, the output of a feedback system will usually exceed the input. As is illustrated in Figure 4–6, a type 1, second-order system may oscillate several times around the steady-state output, depending on the value of the damping ratio ζ. The first over-shoot is of particular interest to the designer of feedback control systems. The ratio of this overshoot's peak value to the steady-state settling value of the system is usually expressed as a percentage. The amount of overshoot allowable depends entirely on the particular problem. An overshoot of 10% is reasonable. Notice that the percentage overshoot of the system illustrated in Figure 4–6 is $\exp(-\zeta\pi/\sqrt{1 - \zeta^2}) \times 100\%$. A 10% overshoot corresponds to a damping ratio of approximately 0.6 for this system.

Even though the control-system engineer has chosen suitable and reasonable values for rise time, settling time, and the peak overshoot, he really does not know whether he has designed the optimum system. For example, if he designs the rise time to be very small, invariably the peak value of the overshoot increases and so does the settling time. On the other hand, if he decides to design for minimum overshoot, the rise time increases. It is true that the engineer can compromise in the design and have a system with reasonable performance. However, since the characteristics of rise time and peak overshoot have conflicting requirements on ζ, the control engineer does not know whether he has designed a system with an optimum transient response. If we consider rise time and peak overshoot alone, we conclude that an optimum value for the damping ratio is approximately 0.4. If, however, we consider settling time alone as the criterion of performance, an optimum damping ratio of approximately 0.7 is desirable.

In order to resolve the conflict that exists between rise time, peak overshot, and settling time, several authors have attempted to develop criteria for synthesizing the optimum transient performance. Most of these techniques have considered the magnitude of the error and the time at which the error has occurred during the transient as important. A very useful criterion which penalizes long-duration transients is known as the integral of time multiplied by the absolute value of error (ITAE).[2] It is studied next. This criterion is quite selective and very useful when optimizing the transient response of any order system.

Table 4–2.   The minimum ITAE standard forms for a zero-error-displacement system[2]

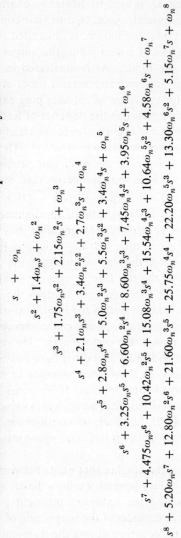

$$s + \omega_n$$

$$s^2 + 1.4\omega_n s + \omega_n^2$$

$$s^3 + 1.75\omega_n s^2 + 2.15\omega_n^2 s + \omega_n^3$$

$$s^4 + 2.1\omega_n s^3 + 3.4\omega_n^2 s^2 + 2.7\omega_n^3 s + \omega_n^4$$

$$s^5 + 2.8\omega_n s^4 + 5.0\omega_n^2 s^3 + 5.5\omega_n^3 s^2 + 3.4\omega_n^4 s + \omega_n^5$$

$$s^6 + 3.25\omega_n s^5 + 6.60\omega_n^2 s^4 + 8.60\omega_n^3 s^3 + 7.45\omega_n^4 s^2 + 3.95\omega_n^5 s + \omega_n^6$$

$$s^7 + 4.475\omega_n s^6 + 10.42\omega_n^2 s^5 + 15.08\omega_n^3 s^4 + 15.54\omega_n^4 s^3 + 10.64\omega_n^5 s^2 + 4.58\omega_n^6 s + \omega_n^7$$

$$s^8 + 5.20\omega_n s^7 + 12.80\omega_n^2 s^6 + 21.60\omega_n^3 s^5 + 25.75\omega_n^4 s^4 + 22.20\omega_n^5 s^3 + 13.30\omega_n^6 s^2 + 5.15\omega_n^7 s + \omega_n^8$$

4–6. THE ITAE CRITERION FOR OPTIMIZING THE TRANSIENT RESPONSE[2]

The mathematical expression for the integral of time multiplied by the absolute value of error is given by

$$I = \int_0^\infty t \, |e| \, dt \tag{4–63}$$

An advantage of the use of time in this integral is that large initial errors do not give rise to a large value of the integral, and, at the same time, that it places emphasis on long-duration transients. The result of using a time-weighting function is very desirable since the initial error of a general feedback system is quite unavoidable. Therefore, a criterion which is insensitive to the initial error is very useful.

If this criterion is applied to the type 1, second-order system described by equation 4–59, the optimum damping ratio is approximately 0.7. A table of transfer functions, for systems whose transfer functions have unity in the numerator, has been prepared by Graham and Lathrop.[2] They show the optimum form of the denominator which will minimize the integral of equation 4–63. For example, the optimum form for a type 1, second-order system is given by

$$\frac{C(s)}{R(s)} = \frac{1}{s^2 + 1.4\omega_n s + \omega_n^2} \tag{4–64}$$

where $\zeta = 1.4/2 = 0.7$. A second-order system having the form given by equation 4–64 would have a transient response which would minimize the integral of equation 4–63. The optimum form for a third-order system would be given by

$$\frac{C(s)}{R(s)} = \frac{1}{s^3 + 1.75\omega_n s^2 + 2.15\omega_n^2 s + \omega_n^3} \tag{4–65}$$

A third-order system having the form given by equation 4–65 would have a transient response which would minimize the integral of equation 4–63.

Table 4–2, which has been obtained from Ref. 2, shows the optimum denominator transfer function for systems through the eighth order which will minimize the integral of equation 4–63. These standard forms provide a quick and simple method for synthesizing an optimum dynamic response. The application of the ITAE criterion to a practical problem will now be illustrated.

Figure 4–7 shows a fourth-order feedback system containing five feedback paths. Its transfer function is obtained by means of signal flow graphs, which were discussed in Chapter 2. In order that this system

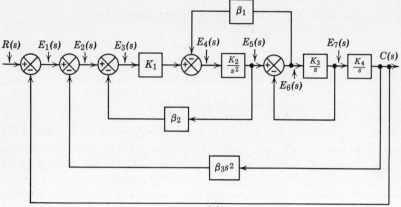

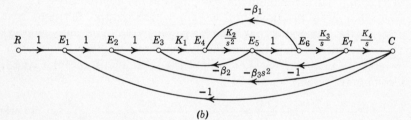

$$\Delta = 1 - \left[-\frac{K_1K_2K_3K_4}{s^4}(1 + \beta_3 s^2) - \frac{1K_2K\beta_2}{s^2} - \frac{K_3}{s} - \frac{K_2\beta_1}{s^2} \right] + \left(\frac{K_1K_2\beta_2}{s^2} \times \frac{K_3}{s} \right)$$

$$G_1 = \frac{K_1K_2K_3K_4}{s^4}$$

$$\Delta_1 = 1$$

$$\frac{C(s)}{R(s)} = G = \frac{K_1K_2K_3K_4/s^4}{1 + \dfrac{K_1K_2K_3K_4}{s^4}(1 + \beta_3 s^2) + \dfrac{K_1K_2\beta_2}{s^2} + \dfrac{K_3}{s} + \dfrac{K_2\beta_1}{s^2} + \dfrac{K_1K_2K_3\beta_2}{s^3}}$$

$$\therefore \quad \frac{C(s)}{R(s)} = \frac{K_1K_2K_3K_4}{s^4 + K_3 s^3 + (K_1K_2\beta_2 + K_2\beta_1 + K_1K_2K_3K_4\beta_3)s^2 + K_1K_2K_3\beta_2 s + K_1K_2K_3K_4}$$

Figure 4–7. System transfer function of a fourth-order system.

satisfy the ITAE criterion for optimizing the transient response, the denominator of the system transfer function must equal the fourth-order equation given in Table 4–2, and the numerator of the system transfer function must equal unity. This requires that we normalize the system transfer function which is basically equivalent to a time scale change in the time domain.

From Figure 4–7, the system transfer function is

$$\frac{C(s)}{R(s)} = \frac{K_1K_2K_3K_4}{s^4 + K_3s^3 + (K_1K_2\beta_2 + K_2\beta_1 + K_1K_2K_3K_4\beta_3)s^2 + K_1K_2K_3\beta_2s + K_1K_2K_3K_4} \tag{4-66}$$

Dividing numerator and denominator by $K_1K_2K_3K_4$, we obtain

$$\frac{C(s)}{R(s)} = \left[\frac{1}{K_1K_2K_3K_4} s^4 + \frac{1}{K_1K_2K_4} s^3 \right.$$
$$\left. + \left(\frac{\beta_3}{K_3K_4} + \frac{\beta_1}{K_1K_3K_4} + \beta_3 \right)s^2 + \frac{\beta_2}{K_4} s + 1 \right]^{-1} \tag{4-67}$$

In order to normalize equation 4–67, the substitution

$$[(K_1K_2K_3K_4)^{-1}]^{1/4}s = s' \tag{4-68}$$

is made. Therefore, we obtain a normalized system transfer function equal to

$$\frac{C(s)}{R(s)} = \left[s'^4 + \frac{(K_1K_2K_3K_4)^{3/4}}{K_1K_2K_4} s'^3 + \left(\frac{\beta_3}{K_3K_4} + \frac{\beta_1}{K_1K_3K_4} + \beta_3 \right) \right.$$
$$\left. \times (K_1K_2K_3K_4)^{1/2}s'^2 + \left(\frac{\beta_2}{K_4} \right)(K_1K_2K_3K_4)^{1/4}s' + 1 \right]^{-1} \tag{4-69}$$

$$\frac{C(s)}{R(s)} = \left\{ s'^4 + \frac{K_3^{3/4}}{(K_1K_2K_4)^{1/4}} s'^3 \right.$$
$$+ \left[\frac{(K_1K_2)^{1/2}\beta_3}{(K_3K_4)^{1/2}} + \frac{K_2^{1/2}\beta_1}{(K_1K_3K_4)^{1/2}} + (K_1K_2K_3K_4)^{1/2}\beta_3 \right]s'^2$$
$$\left. + \frac{(K_1K_2K_3)^{1/4}}{K_4^{3/4}} \beta_2s' + 1 \right\}^{-1} \tag{4-70}$$

Comparing the denominator of equation 4–70 with the fourth-order system shown in Table 4–2, we see that the following equalities must be met in order to satisfy the ITAE criterion:

$$\frac{K_3^{3/4}}{(K_1K_2K_4)^{1/4}} = 2.1\omega_n \tag{4-71}$$

$$\frac{(K_1K_2)^{1/2}\beta_3}{(K_3K_4)^{1/2}} + \frac{K_2^{1/2}\beta_1}{(K_1K_3K_4)^{1/2}} + (K_1K_2K_3K_4)^{1/4}\beta_3 = 3.4\omega_n^2 \tag{4-72}$$

$$\frac{(K_1K_2K_3)^{1/4}}{K_4^{3/4}} \beta_2 = 2.7\omega_n^3 \tag{4-73}$$

$$\omega_n^4 = 1 \tag{4-74}$$

The system parameters can therefore be determined easily.

In a typical practical problem, the control engineer may know the values of

$$K_1 = 2K_a \qquad \beta_1 = 5$$
$$K_2 = 80$$
$$K_3 = 40$$
$$K_4 = 1$$

and desire to obtain the values of K_a, β_2, and β_3 using the ITAE criterion. From equations 4–71 through 4–74, he can easily determine that

$$K_a = 20.5$$
$$\beta_2 = 0.14$$
and $$\beta_3 = 2.76 \times 10^{-3}$$

in order that the ITAE criterion be satisfied.

An analog computer can be a very useful tool for examining the transient response of such a system, as certain parameters are varied from their ITAE criterion condition values. Successive steps in simulating the system, whose block diagram is shown in Figure 4–7a, on an analog computer are shown in Figure 4–8. A normalized time scale is used, in accordance with equation 4–68, to aid in the monitoring of any point within the system. Substituting the values of

$$K_1 = 41 \qquad K_3 = 40$$
$$K_2 = 80 \qquad K_4 = 1$$

into equation 4–68, we obtain
$$s = 19s'$$

Therefore, the corresponding values of K_2/s^2, K_3/s, K_4/s, and $\beta_3 s^2$ for computer simulation are given by

$$\frac{K_2}{s^2} = \frac{K_2}{(19s')^2} = \frac{80}{(19)^2(s')^2} = \frac{0.22}{(s')^2} \qquad \text{(see } R_A \text{ in Figure 4–8a)}$$

$$\frac{K_3}{s} = \frac{K_3}{(19s')} = \frac{40}{19s'} = \frac{2.1}{s'}$$

$$\frac{K_4}{s} = \frac{K_4}{(19s')} = \frac{1}{19s'} = \frac{0.053}{s'} \qquad \text{(see } R_B \text{ in Figure 4–8a)}$$

$$(\beta_3)s^2 = \beta_3(19s')^2 = 2.76 \times 10^{-3}(19)^2(s')^2 = 0.99(s')^2$$

It is recommended that the reader check the corresponding values and structure of Figure 4–7a and Figure 4–8a.

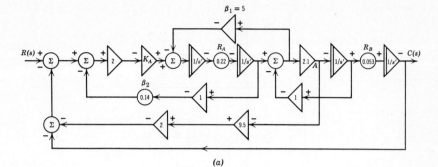

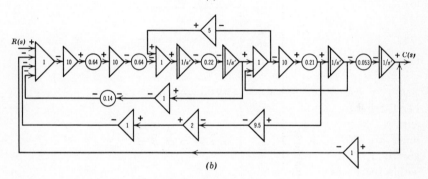

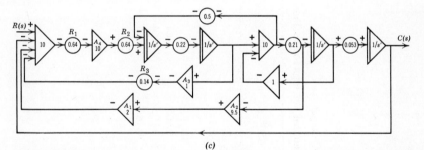

Figure 4–8.   Successive steps in simulating the system shown in Figure 4–7a on an analog computer.

In accordance with standard practice, the term $(\beta_3)s^2$ is obtained by taking the output from point A in Figure 4–8a, and manipulating it appropriately, in order to avoid differentiators with their wide bandwidths and associated noise problems. In addition, observe from Figure 4–8 that two amplifiers are required to obtain K_1 and $(\beta_3)s^2$ in order to maintain proper phase relationships within the simulated feedback loops. To emphasize the importance of phase relationships, the phase of each

Table 4–3. Amplifier and attenuator settings for various conditions

Component	ITAE Values	$+50\%K_1$	$+100\%\beta_2$	$+100\%\beta_3$	$-100\%K_1$	$-100\%\beta_2$	$-100\%\beta_3$
A_1	2	2	2	4	2	2	0
A_2	9.5	9.5	9.5	9.5	9.5	9.5	9.5
A_3	1	1	1	1	1	1	1
A_4	10	10	10	10	10	10	10
R_1	0.64	0.905	0.64	0.64	0	0.64	0.64
R_2	0.64	0.905	0.64	0.64	0.64	0.64	0.64
R_3	0.14	0.14	0.28	0.14	0.14	0	0.14

point in the simulated system is shown based on the assumption of a positive input signal. Observe from Figure 4–8c that the final system simulation reduces to four integrators, six single-input amplifiers, one multiple input amplifier, and seven attenuators.

In order to illustrate the effect of parameter variations on the transient response, an analog computer was actually programmed. Specifically, K_1, β_2, and β_3 were each varied in the following manner:

$$K_1: \quad +50\%, \; -100\%$$

$$\beta_2: \quad \pm 100\%$$

$$\beta_3: \quad \pm 100\%$$

Table 4–3 illustrates the settings of the various attenuators R_n and amplifiers A_n for each of these conditions. Notice that amplifier gain settings

Table 4–4. Resulting overshoot and rise time for various conditions

Condition	% Overshoot	Rise Time (seconds)
ITAE	7.3	0.25
$+50\% \, K_1$	10.9	0.21
$+100\% \, \beta_2$	overdamped	0.35
$+100\% \, \beta_3$	1.0	0.30
$-100\% \, K_1$	unstable	
$-100\% \, \beta_2$	unstable	
$-100\% \, \beta_3$	76.0	0.12

were limited to ten in order to minimize drift problems. Table 4–4 indicates the resultant actual overshoots and rise times for each of these conditions. The rise time indicated corresponds to true time after the scale change, given by equation 4–68, was accounted for.

The results indicated by Table 4–4 are quite reasonable and indicate that the ITAE criterion values appears to result in an optimum condition. *Increasing K_1 by 50%* results in an increase in the net forward gain of the system which causes a greater overshoot and a slight decrease in the rise time. *Decreasing K_1 by 100%* basically opens up the position feedback loop and the system is unstable. *Increasing β_2 by 100%* results in increased feedback of a minor loop which causes an overdamped response in this case. By *decreasing β_2 by 100%*, or opening up this minor feedback loop, the system becomes unstable. *Increasing β_3 by 100%* results in greater feedback that is proportional to acceleration. This causes increased damping in the system with a resultant decrease in overshoot and increase in rise time. *Decreasing β_3 by 100%*, or opening up this minor feedback loop, removes much of the damping in the system. This causes an extremely large overshoot that is usually undesirable.

This procedure enables us to determine the system's characteristics quite easily. The ITAE criterion appears to be a straightforward method for optimizing the transient response of a system when the transfer function is known. Generally, it produces smaller overshoots and oscillations than other criteria appearing in the literature.

4–7. THE ROOT-MEAN-SQUARE ERROR CRITERION FOR MINIMIZING THE EFFECTS OF NOISE

Many inputs to a feedback control system are random. Should the control engineer decide to design a system having random inputs based on the preceding ITAE criterion, it is quite likely that the performance of the system will be poor. What he would be forced to do is to apply, successively, the ITAE criterion to the various random inputs $r_1, r_2, \ldots, r_n$ and to average the results, which must be weighted appropriately by the probability of occurrence of each input. This very tedious task is quite complex and is not performed in practice. Instead, random inputs, such as noise, are usually characterized by their statistical properties.

Statistical design theory is concerned only with random processes. The performance criterion used in statistical design, which is fully discussed by James, Nichols, and Phillips,[3] is called the root-mean-square (rms) error. It can be easily defined by considering the system in Figure 4–9. The random input is represented by $r_r(t)$ and the random output by $c_a(t)$. The rms error, $\overline{e^2}$, is defined as the average value of the square of the difference between the actual system output, $c_a(t)$, and the desired system output, $c_d(t)$. It is expressed as

$$\overline{e^2} = \lim_{T \to \infty} \frac{1}{2T} \int_{-T}^{T} [c_a(t) - c_d(t)]^2 \, dt \qquad (4\text{–}75)$$

From a statistical viewpoint, a feedback control system should be designed to minimize the rms error $\overline{e^2}$.

To say that a system is designed to minimize the rms error basically means that emphasis is placed on reducing the errors according to the square of the error magnitude. Therefore, such a system attempts to

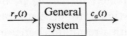

Figure 4–9.   Statistical system terminology.

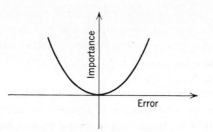

Figure 4–10. Truxal's error weighting of rms error criterion. From Automatic Feedback Control System Synthesis, J. G. Truxal, McGraw-Hill Book Company, New York, 1955. Used by permission.

reduce the large errors at the cost of many small errors. To aid in visualizing this concept, Truxal[4] suggests the use of an "error versus importance" curve. A plot of error versus relative importance of error results in the curve shown in Figure 4–10.

It is important to emphasize at this point that the rms error does not characterize the system error completely. Other very important considerations must also be examined. For example, the rms error is completely independent of the frequency spectrum distribution of the error. The control engineer should therefore not expect this criterion to characterize a complex system completely. However, the rms error is the most useful statistical performance criterion applied to random-type inputs. Its application is fully explored in Chapter 8.

4-8. OTHER PRACTICAL CONSIDERATIONS

The control engineer must concern himself with several other practical aspects before becoming able to state intelligently and completely the expected system performance. The concluding section of this chapter qualitatively discusses considerations of feedback system bandwidth, resonances, nonlinearities, size, weight, power, and economics. Hopefully, this will aid in giving the reader a complete bird's-eye view of the problem.

Feedback system bandwidth is usually defined as the point where the open-loop gain equals unity. The bandwidth of a system is dictated by its particular application. Usually, the control engineer is interested in designing the system to respond to a certain spectrum of input signal frequencies and to suppress all inputs above a certain frequency. It is important to emphasize that we should not arbitrarily design for a large bandwidth. Although large bandwidths usually result in large error constants, with a small resulting system error, they also result in a system that responds to extraneous noise inputs and has considerable jitter. The desirable approach is to design the feedback system bandwidth to be just large enough to pass the desired input signal frequency spectrum and then attenuate all larger frequency signals.

All underdamped feedback systems exhibit at least one resonant frequency when excited with sinusoidal signals. In complex systems containing several minor feedback loops, several system resonant frequencies are present.[5] The control engineer should design the resonant frequencies to be as far away in frequency from the external resonances which may be coupled into the system and act as forcing functions. Should the load resonances contain frequencies near the resonant frequencies of the feedback system, the system performance will be seriously affected.

Nonlinearities are other factors which affect the performance of a control system. The control engineer is primarily concerned with backlash, stiction, and coulomb friction. Backlash, which was illustrated in Section 4–3, is the amount of free motion of one gear while its mating gear is held fast. Stiction is the frictional force which prevents motion until the driving force exceeds some minimum value. Coulomb friction is a constant frictional drag which opposes motion, but has a magnitude that is independent of velocity. Each of these nonlinearities has an effect on the performance of feedback systems. More will be said regarding nonlinearities in Chapter 7.

Other factors which the practicing control engineer must be concerned with are size, weight, power consumption, and economics. The system must conform to certain specifications of size and weight. These are very important factors which usually dictate the design of the system. For example, these specifications may decide the type of power drive to be used. Power is another very important consideration. The system must usually perform within a certain allowable power consumption. This may decide whether the electronics should be designed with vacuum tubes or transistors. Size, weight, and power consumption are usually very critical items for airborne applications. Last, but not least, is the question of economics. A basic fact of life is that most practicing control engineers work for organizations whose primary purpose is to make a profit. They must, therefore, design the feedback system as inexpensively as possible within the framework of good system performance.

REFERENCES

1. Control System Performance Measures: Past, Present, and Future, W. C. Schultz and V. C. Rideout, *IRE Trans. Auto. Control*, **AC–6**, No. 1, 22 (Feb. 1961).

2. The Synthesis of Optimum Transient Response: Criteria and Standard Forms, Dunstan Graham and R. C. Lathrop, *AIEE Trans.*, **72, Pt. 2,** *Appl. Ind.*, 273 (1953).
3. *Theory of Servomechanisms*, H. M. James, N. B. Nichols, and R. S. Phillips, McGraw-Hill Book Co., New York, 1947.
4. *Automatic Feedback Control System Synthesis*, J. G. Truxal, McGraw-Hill Book Co., New York, 1955.
5. Minimizing Servo Load Resonance Error with Frequency Selective Feedback, S. M. Shinners, *Control Eng.*, 51 (Jan. 1962).

STABILITY CRITERIA

5–1. INTRODUCTION

For proper controlling action, a feedback system must be stable. Previous chapters have indicated that feedback systems have the serious disadvantage that they may inadvertently act as oscillators. A feedback control system must maintain stability when the system is subjected to: commands at its input, extraneous inputs anywhere within the feedback loop, power supply variations, and changes in the parameters of the elements comprising the feedback loop.

A *stable system* is defined as one whose transients decay to zero in the steady state, and an *unstable system* as one whose response increases without bound for a bounded input command. The stability analysis of this chapter is limited to linear systems. We consider a *linear system* to be one for which the principle of superposition is valid and which may be described by an ordinary linear differential equation. The analysis and study of nonlinear systems are performed in Chapter 7.

This chapter focuses attention on the stability of the general feedback system which was illustrated in Figure 2–5. The closed-loop transfer function of this system, given by equation 2–53, is repeated below:

$$\frac{C(s)}{R(s)} = \frac{G(s)}{1 + G(s)H(s)} \tag{5–1}$$

The characteristic equation for this generalized system can be obtained by setting the denominator of the system transfer function equal to zero.

$$1 + G(s)H(s) = 0 \tag{5–2}$$

This is the equation that determines system stability. All the methods of stability analysis investigate this equation in some manner.

In general, the following two general approaches exist for determining stability.

1. Calculating the exact roots of equation 5–2

2. Determination of the bounded region where the roots of equation 5–2 exist

Using the first approach, the control engineer has at his disposal the following two tools.

    a. Classical approach
    b. Root locus method

Using the second approach, the control engineer has at his disposal the following six major tools.

    a. Routh-Hurwitz criterion
    b. Nyquist diagram
    c. Bode plot
    d. Loci of constant M and α
    e. Nichols chart
    f. Loci of constant $1/M$ and $-\alpha$

This chapter presents each of these methods together with their relative merits. The application of these methods to the design of linear feedback control systems is presented in Chapter 6.

5–2. CLASSICAL APPROACH

It has been shown in Section 3–7 that it is possible to relate the output of a feedback control system to its input by means of a differential equation. Essentially, this was an application of the classical approach to a linear, second-order system. This approach can easily be extended for determining system stability based on our definition of a stable system: one whose transients decay to zero in the steady state. Although this technique does have the advantage of being theoretically exact, it has the disadvantage of being too laborious for systems higher than the third order. In addition, this method does not indicate the direction that the control engineer should travel in case redesign is necessary. We illustrate the classical approach in this section and indicate its usefulness.

Let us expand the system transfer function, given previously by equation 5–1, in the following manner:

$$\frac{C(s)}{R(s)} = \frac{G(s)}{1 + G(s)H(s)} = \frac{A_1 s^l + A_2 s^{l-1} + A_3 s^{l-2} + \cdots + A_l}{B_1 s^m + B_2 s^{m-1} + B_3 s^{m-2} + \cdots + B_m}$$

$$(5\text{-}3)$$

Equation 5–3 can be rewritten as

$$(B_1 s^m + B_2 s^{m-1} + B_3 s^{m-2} + \cdots + B_m)C(s)$$
$$= (A_1 s^l + A_2 s^{l-1} + A_3 s^{l-2} + \cdots + A_l)R(s) \quad (5\text{-}4)$$

The right-hand side of equation 5–4 depends on the magnitude and characteristics of the input, $R(s)$, and determines the steady-state response of the differential equation. The left-hand side of equation 5–4 determines the transient characteristics of the system on the application of the input signal. The steady-state solution will have the same characteristics as that of the input. Therefore, for a bounded input, it is only necessary to analyze the transient solution for purposes of determining stability.

Setting the left-hand side of equation 5–4 equal to zero, we can focus our attention on the transient response.

$$(B_1 s^m + B_2 s^{m-1} + B_3 s^{m-2} + \cdots + B_m)C(s) = 0 \qquad (5–5)$$

The transient solution to equation 5–5 has the form

$$c(t) = K_1 e^{s_1 t} + K_2 e^{s_2 t} + K_3 e^{s_3 t} + \cdots + K_m e^{s_m t} \qquad (5–6)$$

When multiple roots occur ($s_1 = s_2$), the transient solution has the form

$$c(t) = K_1 e^{s_1 t} + K_2 t\, e^{s_2 t} + K_3 e^{s_3 t} + \cdots + K_m e^{s_m t} \qquad (5–7)$$

The coefficients $K_1, K_2, K_3, \ldots, K_m$ depend on the initial conditions of the system. The exponents $s_1, s_2, s_3, \ldots, s_m$ represent the roots of equation 5–5.

We have defined instability earlier in this chapter as what occurs when the output of a system increases without bound for a bounded input command. Equations 5–6 and 5–7 indicate that this can occur when any of the roots $s_1, s_2, s_3, \ldots, s_m$ have positive real parts. This would cause

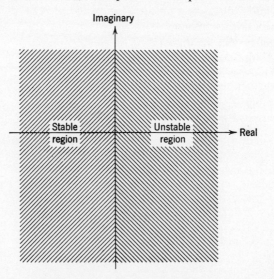

Figure 5–1.   Stable and unstable regions of the complex plane.

$c(t)$ to approach infinity as t became infinite. Since the coefficients K_1, K_2, K_3, ..., K_m have finite values, we can conclude that system stability is determined by the characteristics of the exponential terms in the transient response for inputs which are bounded.

The imaginary axis is the dividing line between stable and unstable systems. This is illustrated in Figure 5–1. Should any poles lie on the imaginary axis, the system will oscillate at a constant amplitude. If multiple roots occur along the imaginary axis, the output increases without bound for a bounded input command. Except for the case where a single pole occurs at the origin of the complex plane, we assume any system that has poles existing along the imaginary axis to be unstable.

The use of the classical approach for determining system stability is theoretically exact. It is, however, very difficult to use for systems higher than the third order because of the great amount of labor involved in factoring the characteristic equation.

5–3. ROUTH-HURWITZ STABILITY CRITERION

The Routh-Hurwitz stability criterion is an algebraic procedure for determining whether a system is stable or unstable. It is performed by examining the signs and magnitudes of the characteristic equation's coefficients without actually having to factor its roots. Although this method overcomes one of the disadvantages of the classical approach, it still does not indicate the relative degree of stability or instability.

Routh[1] and Hurwitz[2] determined the necessary and sufficient conditions for stability from the signs and magnitudes of the characteristic equation's coefficients independently. Although their respective criteria differ somewhat, both furnish essentially the same information. A useful form of their criterion will be described in this section.

Let us represent the general form of a system's characteristic equation by

$$B_1 s^m + B_2 s^{m-1} + B_3 s^{m-2} + \cdots + B_m = 0 \qquad (5\text{–}8)$$

The coefficients of this equation are arranged in two rows as follows:

$$
\begin{array}{cccccc}
B_1 & B_3 & B_5 & B_7 & \cdots \\
B_2 & B_4 & B_6 & B_8 & \cdots
\end{array}
\qquad (5\text{–}9)
$$

All the coefficients of this equation are assumed to be real and, in addition, B_1 is assumed to be positive. Additional rows of coefficients are derived from these two in the following manner:

$$
\begin{array}{cccc}
B_1 & B_3 & B_5 & B_7 & \cdots \\
B_2 & B_4 & B_6 & B_8 & \cdots \\
U_1 & U_3 & U_5 & U_7 & \cdots \\
U_2 & U_4 & U_6 & U_8 & \cdots \\
V_1 & V_3 & V_5 & V_7 & \cdots \\
V_2 & V_4 & V_6 & V_8 & \cdots
\end{array}
\qquad (5\text{--}10)
$$

where

$$
U_1 = \frac{B_2 B_3 - B_1 B_4}{B_2} ; \qquad U_3 = \frac{B_2 B_5 - B_1 B_6}{B_2}
$$

$$
U_2 = \frac{U_1 B_4 - B_2 U_3}{U_1} ; \qquad U_4 = \frac{U_1 B_6 - B_2 U_5}{U_1} \qquad (5\text{--}11)
$$

$$
V_1 = \frac{U_2 U_3 - U_1 U_4}{U_2} ; \qquad V_3 = \frac{U_2 U_5 - U_1 U_6}{U_2}
$$

This pattern will continue until all the terms in a row are zero. The number of rows obtained will correspond to $m + 1$ where m is the order of the characteristic equation. The criterion of stability is to check that all the terms in the left-hand column ($B_1, B_2, U_1, U_2, V_1, V_2, \ldots$) have the same sign. If all these coefficients have the same sign, there are no roots in the right half plane. If there are X changes of sign, then X roots exist in the right half plane. Let us illustrate this with a simple example. Consider the following characteristic equation of a feedback control system:

$$
1 + G(s)H(s) = s^3 + 4s^2 + 100s + 500 = 0 \qquad (5\text{--}12)
$$

Using the procedure described, the resulting array is

$$
\begin{array}{rr}
. \quad 1 & 100 \\
4 & 500 \\
-25 & \\
500 &
\end{array}
\qquad (5\text{--}13)
$$

There are two changes of sign in the first column: 4 to -25 and -25 to 500. Therefore, there are two roots in the right half plane.

If the first term in any row is zero, and the other terms of the row are not zero, the array of equation 5–10 may be continued by replacing the first column zero by an arbitrary small constant ϵ, which is usually chosen to be positive. The process is then continued in the usual manner. Let us illustrate the procedure for this particular case with a simple example.

Consider the following characteristic equation of a feedback control system:

$$1 + G(s)H(s) = s^5 + s^4 + 4s^3 + 4s^2 + 2s + 1 = 0 \qquad (5\text{--}14)$$

Using the procedure described, the resulting array is

$$
\begin{array}{ccc}
1 & 4 & 2 \\
1 & 4 & 1 \\
\text{Replace this row} \rightarrow \quad (0 & 1 &) \\
\text{with} \rightarrow \quad \epsilon & 1 & \\
\dfrac{4\epsilon - 1}{\epsilon} & 1 & \\
\dfrac{-\epsilon^2 + 4\epsilon - 1}{4\epsilon - 1} & & \\
1 & &
\end{array}
\qquad (5\text{--}15)
$$

The limiting value of the term in the left-hand column, fourth row, is negative. The limiting value of the term in the left-hand column, fifth row, is positive. Therefore there are two changes of sign, and two roots must lie in the right half plane.

A very important practical case occurs when all the terms in a row are zero. Physically, this means that a pair of roots exist which are the negatives of each other. They may be complex conjugate, or one may lie on the positive real axis and the other on the negative real axis. For this special case, the array of equation 5–10 can be completed by obtaining a subsidiary equation from the preceding row. This equation is then differentiated and the resulting coefficients are used to complete the array. The roots of the subsidiary equation are the actual roots of the characteristic equation. This procedure is illustrated with a simple example. Consider the following characteristic equation of a feedback control system:

$$1 + G(s)H(s) = s^3 + 10s^2 + 16s + 160 = 0 \qquad (5\text{--}16)$$

Using the procedure described, the resulting array is

$$
\begin{array}{cc}
1 & 16 \\
10 & 160 \\
0 & 0
\end{array}
\qquad (5\text{--}17)
$$

The presence of zeros in the third row indicates that there are roots which are negatives of each other. Using the coefficients of the second row for the subsidiary equation, we obtain

$$10s^2 + 160 = 0 \qquad (5\text{--}18)$$

In order to complete the array, equation 5–18 is differentiated and the resulting coefficients are then inserted into the array as follows:

$$20s = 0 \tag{5-19}$$

The resulting new array is given by

$$
\begin{array}{cc}
1 & 16 \\
10 & 160 \\
20 & \quad \cdot \\
160 &
\end{array}
\tag{5-20}
$$

No roots lie in the right half plane since there are no changes of sign in the left-hand column. The roots which are negatives of each other can be obtained from equation 5–18 as $\pm j4$, indicating a pair of complex conjugate poles.

Although the Routh-Hurwitz criterion gives the control engineer a relatively quick determination of absolute stability, it does not provide an indication of the direction that the control engineer ought to travel in order to improve his design. In addition, it does not give an indication of relative system performance. Its main attribute is to serve as a check of other design criteria.

5–4. NYQUIST STABILITY CRITERION[3]

The Nyquist stability criterion is a very valuable tool which determines the degree of stability, or instability, of a feedback control system. In addition, it aids in determining the direction that the control engineer should go in order to improve both the steady-state and the transient response of a feedback control system. The Nyquist stability criterion can be applied by means of a polar plot of the open-loop transfer function, $G(j\omega)H(j\omega)$; a polar plot of the inverse open-loop transfer function, $[G(j\omega)H(j\omega)]^{-1}$; a log magnitude–phase angle plot of $G(j\omega)H(j\omega)$ versus frequency plot (Bode diagram). This section presents the first case only: a polar plot of the open-loop transfer function $G(j\omega)H(j\omega)$, which is usually referred to as the Nyquist diagram. Following sections present the other two methods.

The Nyquist diagram and the associated stability criterion determine the number of roots of the characteristic equation which have positive real parts from a polar plot of the open-loop transfer function, $G(j\omega)H(j\omega)$ in the complex plane. Let us consider the characteristic equation, given previously by equation 5–2, which is repeated next.

$$1 + G(s)H(s) = 0 \tag{5-21}$$

System stability can be determined from equation 5–21 by locating its roots in the complex plane. Assuming that $G(s)$ and $H(s)$, in their general form, are functions of s which are given by

$$G(s) = \frac{N_A(s)}{D_A(s)} \tag{5–22}$$

and

$$H(s) = \frac{N_B(s)}{D_B(s)} \tag{5–23}$$

then we can say that

$$G(s)H(s) = \frac{N_A(s)N_B(s)}{D_A(s)D_B(s)} \tag{5–24}$$

Substituting equation 5–24 into equation 5–21, we obtain the following equivalent expression for the characteristic equation:

$$1 + G(s)H(s) = 1 + \frac{N_A(s)N_B(s)}{D_A(s)D_B(s)} = \frac{D_A(s)D_B(s) + N_A(s)N_B(s)}{D_A(s)D_B(s)}$$

$$\tag{5–25}$$

In terms of factored roots, we may rewrite equation 5–25 as

$$1 + G(s)H(s) = \frac{D_A(s)D_B(s) + N_A(s)N_B(s)}{D_A(s)D_B(s)}$$

$$= \frac{(s + s_1)(s + s_2)(s + s_3)\cdots}{(s + s_A)(s + s_B)(s + s_C)\cdots} \tag{5–26}$$

The factors $s + s_1, s + s_2, \ldots$ are conventionally referred to as the *zeros* of the characteristic equation. This terminology is probably due to the fact that the characteristic equation equals zero when $s = -s_1, -s_2$, and so on. The factors $s + s_A, s + s_B, \ldots$ are conventionally referred to as the *poles* of the characteristic equation. This terminology is probably due to the fact that the characteristic equation goes to infinity when $s = -s_A, -s_B$, and so on. The rise to infinity is termed a pole.

Since the characteristic equation is the denominator of the closed-loop system transfer function given by equation 5–1, we see that the zeros of equation 5–26 are the poles of equation 5–1. Therefore, for a stable system, it is necessary that the roots $s_1, s_2, s_3, \ldots$ have positive real parts. The roots s_A, s_B, s_C, have no real restrictions on them. As we shall shortly see, however, if we try to determine stability based on $G(s)H(s)$ above, then a knowledge of the roots $s_A, s_B, s_C, \ldots$ is also required. The only limitations of the Nyquist criterion are that the system be describable by a linear differential equation having constant coefficients and that the limit of the open-loop transfer function $G(s)H(s)$ approach a constant or zero as s approaches infinity.

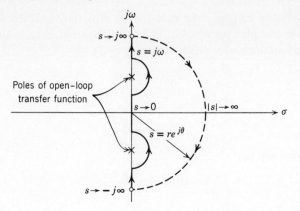

Figure 5–2. Locus of s in the complex plane for determining the Nyquist diagram.

The Nyquist diagram is a polar plot in the complex plane of $1 + G(s)$ $H(s)$ as the magnitude of s approaches infinity in the manner indicated in Figure 5–2. Notice that the locus of s avoids poles of $G(s)H(s)$ which lie anywhere on the imaginary axis by small semicircular paths passing to the right. These semicircular paths are assumed to have radii of infinitesimal magnitude. Any roots of the characteristic equation having positive real parts will lie within the area of the locus in the complex plane illustrated by Figure 5–2.

Use is made of Cauchy's[4] theorem in order to determine the number of encirclements around the origin as $1 + G(s)H(s)$ traverses the contour depicted in Figure 5–2. This theorem states that if a function $F(s)$ is analytic within a closed contour, except for some poles and zeros, then the number of times the origin of $F(s)$ is encircled in traversing the closed contour is equal to the number of zeros minus the number of poles of $F(s)$, with the multiplicity of order properly accounted for. In our particular case, the function $F(s)$ equals $1 + G(s)H(s)$. Observe that for this case the origin of $1 + G(s)H(s)$ is given by

$$G(s)H(s) = -1 \qquad (5\text{--}27)$$

Therefore, if $G(s)H(s)$ is sketched for the contour defined by Figure 5–2, the number of times that $G(s)H(s)$ encircles the point $-1 + j0$ equals the number of zeros minus the number of poles of $1 + G(s)H(s)$ for s in the right half plane.

Figure 5–3 illustrates a polar plot, corresponding to the contour defined by Figure 5–2, for a typical control system whose characteristic equation is

$$1 + G(s)H(s) = 1 + \frac{K}{s(1 + T_1 s)(1 + T_2 s)} \qquad (5\text{--}28)$$

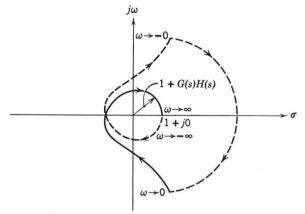

Figure 5–3. Polar plot of $1 + G(s)H(s)$.

The dotted portion of the curve denotes the negative-frequency portion. Notice that the polar plot for negative frequencies is the conjugate of the positive portion. Figure 5–4 illustrates the same polar plot with the origin shifted to the point $-1 + j0$. This simplifies the drawing of the polar plot of $1 + G(s)H(s)$, since we need now only sketch $G(s)H(s)$. The resulting curve will correspond to $1 + G(s)H(s)$ as is indicated on the new set of coordinates. In practice, this is very advantageous since $G(s)H(s)$ is a function which is much more readily available to the control engineer than $1 + G(s)H(s)$.

With the Nyquist diagram's polar plot sketched on a set of axes where the origin is shifted to the $-1 + j0$ point, the Nyquist stability criterion can be stated algebraically as

$$N = P - Z \tag{5–29}$$

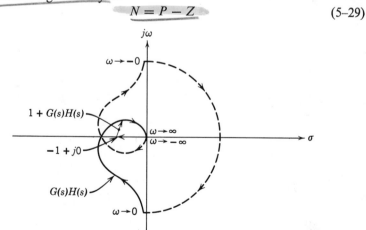

Figure 5–4. Polar plot of $1 + G(s)H(s)$ *with change of origin.*

starts at -180   2 poles at origin,
         -90   1 pole "   "   jω 5

½ turn the close for each
pole at
origin

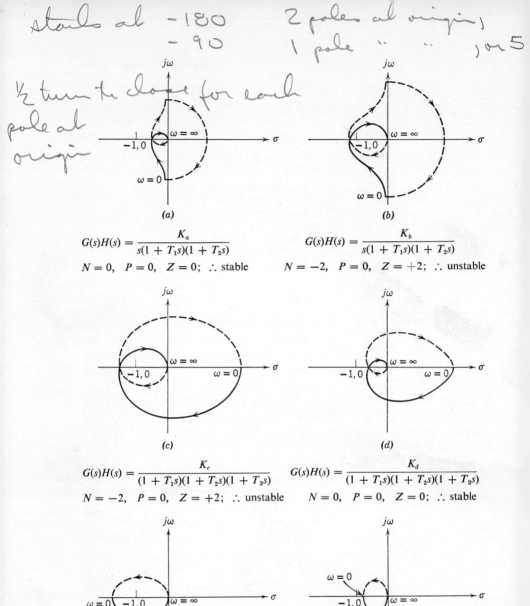

$$G(s)H(s) = \frac{K_a}{s(1 + T_1s)(1 + T_2s)}$$

$N = 0, \quad P = 0, \quad Z = 0; \quad \therefore \text{ stable}$

$$G(s)H(s) = \frac{K_b}{s(1 + T_1s)(1 + T_2s)}$$

$N = -2, \quad P = 0, \quad Z = +2; \quad \therefore \text{ unstable}$

$$G(s)H(s) = \frac{K_c}{(1 + T_1s)(1 + T_2s)(1 + T_3s)}$$

$N = -2, \quad P = 0, \quad Z = +2; \quad \therefore \text{ unstable}$

$$G(s)H(s) = \frac{K_d}{(1 + T_1s)(1 + T_2s)(1 + T_3s)}$$

$N = 0, \quad P = 0, \quad Z = 0; \quad \therefore \text{ stable}$

$$G(s)H(s) = \frac{K_e}{(-1 + Ts)}$$

$N = 1, \quad P = 1, \quad Z = 0; \quad \therefore \text{ stable}$

$$G(s)H(s) = \frac{K_f}{(-1 + Ts)}$$

$N = 0, \quad P = 1, \quad Z = 1; \quad \therefore \text{ unstable}$

Figure 5–5.   Examples of typical Nyquist diagrams.

where N is the number of counterclockwise rotations of the Nyquist diagram about the $-1 + j0$ point of the complex plane, P is the number of poles of the open-loop transfer function $G(s)H(s)$ having positive real parts, and Z is the number of roots of the characteristic equation having positive real parts (Z must equal zero for stability). In most practical cases, the open-loop transfer function is in itself stable and P would equal zero. Since Z must equal zero for stability, N must equal zero for these practical systems.

Figure 5–5 illustrates several examples of application of the Nyquist stability criterion using the relationship given by equation 5–29. In all cases, the values of the open-loop transfer function $G(s)H(s)$ are shown together with the values of N, P, and Z. Notice that those systems, whose Nyquist diagrams are illustrated in parts (a) through (d), are stable on an open-loop basis while those in parts (e) and (f) are unstable on an open-loop basis. The systems illustrated in parts (a), (d), and (e) are stable on a closed-loop basis, while the systems illustrated in parts (b), (c), and (f) are unstable on a closed-loop basis.

It is quite clear that the control engineer can get a good picture of a system's margin of stability from the Nyquist diagram. The proximity of the $G(s)H(s)$ locus to the $-1 + j0$ point is an indication of relative stability: The farther away the locus is from this point, the greater the margin of stability; the closer the locus is to this point, the smaller the margin of stability. The relative degree of stability is conventionally measured by the distance two points on the $G(s)H(s)$ locus are from the point $-1 + j0$. This is illustrated in Figure 5–6 by the points A and B.

The point A is defined by the intersection of the $G(s)H(s)$ locus and a circle having its center at the origin and a radius of unity. Obviously, the magnitude of $G(s)H(s)$ at point A is unity and is denoted by $[G(j\omega)H(j\omega)]_1$ in Figure 5–6. The phase of $[G(j\omega)H(j\omega)]_1$ with respect to the positive real axis is defined as being positive in the counterclockwise sense and is designated as θ. The *phase margin* γ is defined as the phase angle which $[G(j\omega)H(j\omega)]_1$ makes with respect to the negative real axis. It is related to θ by the expression

$$\gamma = 180° + \theta \tag{5–30}$$

A positive value of phase margin indicates stability, a negative value of phase margin indicates instability. A zero value of phase margin indicates that the $G(s)H(s)$ locus passes through the $-1 + j0$ point. The magnitude of $+\gamma$ indicates the relative degree of stability. A qualitative desirable design value of phase margin is 60°.

The point B is defined by the intersection of the $G(s)H(s)$ locus and the negative real axis. The *gain margin* is defined as the reciprocal of the

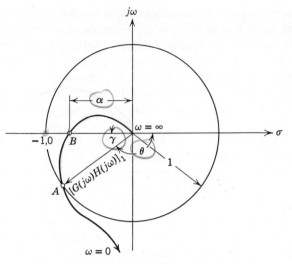

Figure 5-6.   Definition of phase and gain margin.

$$G(s)H(s) = \frac{K}{s(1 + T_1s)(1 + T_2s)} \cdot$$

Phase margin $= 180° + \theta$
Gain margin $= 20 \log_{10} 1/\alpha$

magnitude of the $G(s)H(s)$ locus at point B. For the configuration illustrated in Figure 5–6, the gain margin equals $1/\alpha$. The significance of the gain margin is that the system gain could be increased by a factor of $1/\alpha$ before the $G(s)H(s)$ locus would intersect the $-1 + j0$ point. A positive value of gain margin indicates stability; a negative value of gain margin indicates instability. The magnitude of the gain margin indicates the relative degree of stability. Gain margin is usually expressed in decibels as follows:

$$\text{Gain margin in db} = 20 \log_{10} \frac{1}{\alpha} \qquad (5\text{--}31)$$

A qualitative desirable design value of gain margin is 12 db.

5–5. CLOSED-LOOP FREQUENCY RESPONSE FROM CONSTANT-MAGNITUDE AND PHASE ANGLE CIRCLES SUPERIMPOSED ON THE NYQUIST DIAGRAM

In addition to determining system stability, the Nyquist diagram can also be used to determine the closed-loop frequency response. The reader has been exposed to the closed-loop frequency response of a feedback

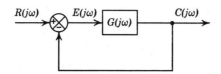

Figure 5–7.   General block diagram of a simple feedback control system.

control system previously, in Section 3–7. We observed in that section the closed-loop transient response of a type 1, second-order system to a step input. The results of this analysis are summarized in Figures 3–37 and 3–38. The dependence of the closed-loop's maximum peaking and the radian frequency at which this peaking occurs have been clearly illustrated to be a function of the damping factor ζ in Section 3–7. It is also a fact that the maximum peaking, and the radian frequency at which the peaking occurs, is a function of the damping factor ζ for higher-order systems. This section demonstrates the method of obtaining the closed-loop frequency response from the Nyquist diagram by utilizing constant-magnitude and phase angle circles superimposed on the complex plane.

Let us use the simple feedback control system illustrated in Figure 5–7 in order to define the nomenclature and terminology to be used in this section. The closed-loop transfer function is given by

$$\frac{C(j\omega)}{R(j\omega)} = \frac{G(j\omega)}{1 + G(j\omega)} \tag{5–32}$$

Dividing denominator into numerator, we may also say that the closed-loop transfer function is given by

$$\frac{C(j\omega)}{R(j\omega)} = M(\omega)\, e^{j\alpha(\omega)} \tag{5–33}$$

where $M(\omega)$ represents the amplitude component of the transfer function and $\alpha(\omega)$ represents the phase component of the transfer function. The radian frequency at which the maximum value of $C(j\omega)/R(j\omega)$ occurs is conventionally referred to as the resonant frequency of the system, ω_p. The maximum value of $C(j\omega)/R(j\omega)$ is conventionally labeled M_p. For the system illustrated in Figure 5–7, we would expect a typical closed-loop frequency response to have the general form shown in Figure 5–8.

From Section 3–7 we know that a small margin of stability would mean a relatively small value for ζ and a relatively large value for M_p. This can be further clarified if we examine the Nyquist diagrams illustrated in Figure 5–9. Notice that $M(\omega)$ is much less than unity for the case of a system having a large degree of stability, as shown in part (*a*) of the figure. This situation would correspond to a relatively large value of ζ. In contrast, $M(\omega)$ is much greater than unity for the case of a system having a

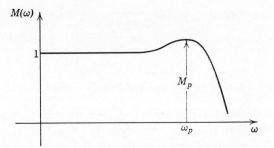

Figure 5–8. A typical closed-loop frequency response curve for the system shown in Figure 5–7.

very small degree of stability, as shown in part (*b*) of the figure. This situation would correspond to a relatively small value of ζ. We next develop the loci of constant-magnitude and phase angle circles in the complex plane in order to be able to determine M_p and ω_p quantitatively for a feedback control system.

The magnitude component of equation 5–32 can be written as

$$M(\omega) = \left| \frac{G(j\omega)}{1 + G(j\omega)} \right| \qquad (5\text{--}34)$$

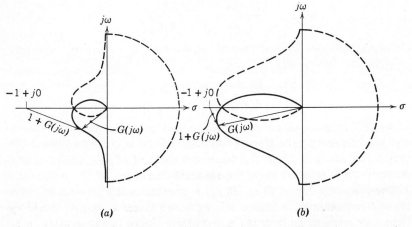

Figure 5–9. Qualitative stability comparison of two systems illustrating corresponding values of $M(\omega)$. (a) Stable system having a large degree of stability;

$$\frac{C(j\omega)}{R(j\omega)} = \left| \frac{G(j\omega)}{1 + G(j\omega)} \right| = M(\omega) \ll 1$$

(b) Stable system having a very small degree of stability;

$$\left| \frac{C(j\omega)}{R(j\omega)} \right| = \left| \frac{G(j\omega)}{1 + G(j\omega)} \right| = M(\omega) \gg 1.$$

$G(j\omega)$, a complex quantity, may be represented in rectangular coordinates as

$$G(j\omega) = x + jy \tag{5-35}$$

Substituting equation 5–35 into equation 5–34, we obtain the following expression:

$$M(\omega) = \left| \frac{x + jy}{1 + x + jy} \right| = \left[\frac{x^2 + y^2}{(1 + x)^2 + y^2} \right]^{1/2} \tag{5-36}$$

Squaring equation 5–36, and rearranging some terms, results in

$$M^2 = \frac{x^2 + y^2}{(1 + x)^2 + y^2} \tag{5-37}$$

$$\left(x - \frac{M^2}{1 - M^2} \right)^2 + y^2 = \left(\frac{M}{1 - M^2} \right)^2 \tag{5-38}$$

From analytic geometry, the equation of a circle is given by

$$(x - h)^2 + y^2 = R^2 \tag{5-39}$$

where h = center of circle
R = radius of circle

Comparing equations 5–38 and 5–39, we see that equation 5–38 is the equation of a circle whose center is on the real axis at

$$h = \frac{M}{1 - M^2} \tag{5-40}$$

and whose radius is given by

$$R = \left| \frac{M}{1 - M^2} \right| \tag{5-41}$$

Therefore the loci of constant-magnitude circles, in the complex plane, is a family of circles, with M as a parameter, as is illustrated in Figure 5–10.

Observe from Figure 5–10 that as M approaches infinity, which represents a condition of violent oscillation, the center of the M circle approaches $-1 + j0$ and the radius approaches zero. This certainly agrees with the qualitative analysis of Figure 5–9. As M approaches zero, the center of the M circle approaches the origin and the radius approaches zero. Figure 5–10 also illustrates that the centers for all M circles greater than unity lie to the left of the $-1 + j0$ point and all the centers for all M circles less than unity lie to the right of the $-1 + j0$ point. The dividing case, $M = 1$, has a loci of infinite radius and is represented by a straight line perpendicular to the real axis and crossing at $x = -\frac{1}{2}$.

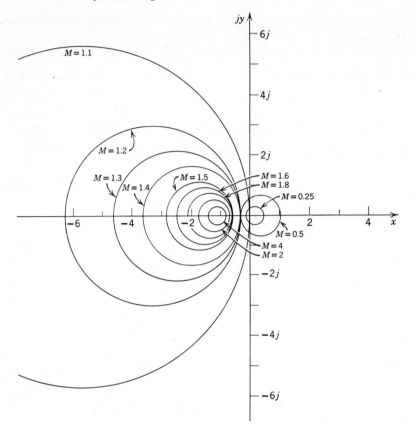

Figure 5–10.   Loci of constant-magnitude circles in the complex plane.

The constant-phase angle loci of the complex plane can be developed in a manner similar to that used for the constant-magnitude loci. Representing $G(j\omega)$ by its rectangular coordinates, $x + jy$, we may represent the phase angle component of equation 5–32 as

$$\frac{C(j\omega)}{R(j\omega)} = \frac{x + jy}{1 + x + jy} = M(\omega)\, e^{j\alpha(\omega)} \qquad (5\text{--}42)$$

where

$$\alpha = \tan^{-1}\frac{y}{x} - \tan^{-1}\frac{y}{1 + x} \qquad (5\text{--}43)$$

This expression can be simplified to

$$\tan \alpha = \frac{y}{x^2 + x + y^2} \qquad (5\text{--}44)$$

For a constant-phase angle α, the value of tan α is constant. Representing tan α by a constant P, we can simplify equation 5–44 to

$$(x + \tfrac{1}{2})^2 + \left(y - \frac{1}{2P}\right)^2 = \frac{1}{4}\frac{P^2 + 1}{P^2} \tag{5–45}$$

Comparing equations 5–39 and 5–45, we see that equation 5–45 is the equation of a circle whose center lies at

$$x = -\tfrac{1}{2}, \qquad y = \frac{1}{2P} \tag{5–46}$$

and whose radius is given by

$$R = \frac{1}{2}\left(\frac{P^2 + 1}{P^2}\right)^{1/2} \tag{5–47}$$

Therefore, the loci of constant phase angles in the complex plane are a family of circles, with P as a parameter, as is illustrated in Figure 5–11.

The constant-magnitude and phase angle loci can be used for the analysis and/or synthesis of a feedback control system. From an analysis viewpoint, we can use the M and α loci to obtain the closed-loop frequency response from the Nyquist diagram and determine the maximum value of peaking, M_p and the frequency at which it occurs, ω_p. From a synthesis viewpoint, we can use the M and α loci to meet certain requirements as to the values of M_p and ω_p. We demonstrate the use of this method as a tool for analysis in this section. Its value as a tool for synthesis is illustrated in Chapter 6.

Let us determine the closed-loop frequency response for the type 1, third-order feedback control system illustrated in Figure 5–12. Specifically, we are interested in obtaining the values of M_p and ω_p. This can be obtained by superimposing a set of M loci onto the complex plane containing the Nyquist diagram corresponding to $G(s)H(s)$, as is illustrated in Figure 5–13. The intersections of the M loci and the Nyquist diagram result in the magnitude of the closed-loop frequency response, as shown in Figure 5–14. The process of drawing this response is basically one of replotting the data on a new set of coordinates. The resulting response indicates a value of $M_p = 2.2$ and an $\omega_p = 10$ radians/second. Notice that a set of α loci was not required for the solution to this problem.

In practice, a value of $M_p = 2.2$ does not represent a good design. Usually, M_p is chosen somewhere between 1.1 and 1.5. Therefore some compensation is required. The technique of compensation is illustrated in Chapter 6. Let us here, however, indicate how the constant loci may be used to limit M_p to some maximum value, say 1.3. Since the interior of the $M = 1.3$ circle consists entirely of constant-magnitude circles which represent M loci greater than 1.3, we must confine the Nyquist diagram to

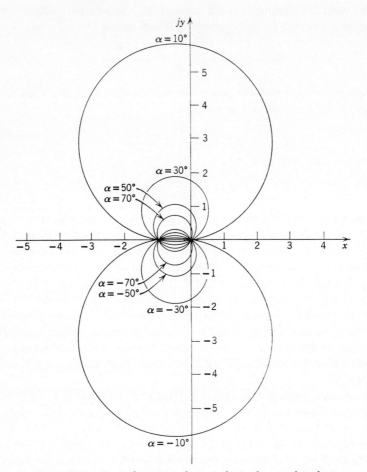

Figure 5–11.   Loci of constant-phase circles in the complex plane.

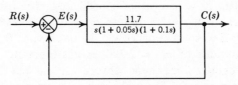

Figure 5–12.   A type 1, third-order feedback control system.

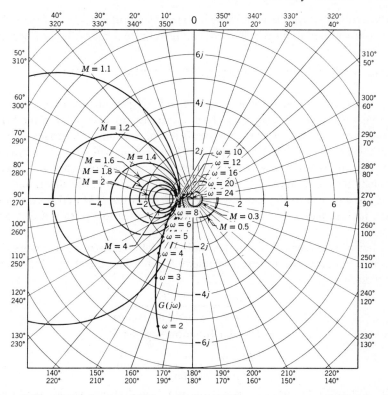

Figure 5–13. *Determination of M from the Nyquist diagram and constant M loci for the system shown in Figure 5–12.*

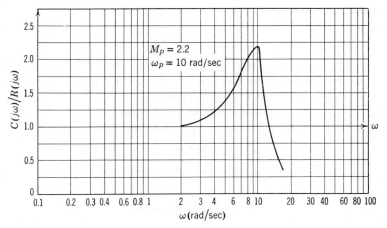

Figure 5–14. *Closed-loop frequency response for the system shown in Figure 5–12.*

the exterior of the $M = 1.3$ circle. The system illustrated in Figure 5–12 is compensated to meet certain maximum requirements of M_p in Chapter 6.

5–6. INVERSE POLAR PLOT AND STABILITY CRITERION

The inverse polar plot is usually much simpler to use than the direct polar plot (Nyquist diagram). In addition, the inverse polar plane brings out more of the salient characteristics of nonunity feedback control systems than the direct polar plane. This section will develop the inverse polar plot and stability criterion. In addition, the corresponding inverse constant-magnitude, $1/M$, and phase angle, $-\alpha$, loci are illustrated. As we shall demonstrate, it is much easier to draft the $1/M$ and $-\alpha$ loci onto the inverse plane than it is to draft the M and α loci onto a direct polar plane.

Let us consider the nonunity feedback system illustrated in Figure 5–15 which contains the feedback element $H(j\omega)$. The direct system transfer function is given by

$$\frac{C(j\omega)}{R(j\omega)} = \frac{G(j\omega)}{1 + G(j\omega)H(j\omega)} \tag{5–48}$$

and the inverse system transfer function is given by

$$\frac{R(j\omega)}{C(j\omega)} = \frac{1}{G(j\omega)} + H(j\omega) \tag{5–49}$$

It is interesting to observe from equation 5–49 that the individual effects of $G(j\omega)$ and $H(j\omega)$ on the inverse transfer function may be easily determined since they appear as two separate components. Therefore, we can conclude that the effect of changes in $H(j\omega)$ are more evident when using the inverse polar plane than when using the direct polar plane.

The stability criterion for an inverse polar plane can be specified in an algebraic manner similar to that used for the Nyquist diagram.

Let $N =$ number of counterclockwise rotations of the inverse diagram about the origin as s takes on the values illustrated in Figure 5–2

$G_Z =$ zeros of $G(j\omega)$ having positive real parts

$H_P =$ poles of $H(j\omega)$ having positive real parts

$Z =$ roots of the characteristic equation having positive real parts

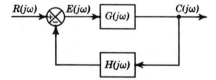

Figure 5–15.   A nonunity feedback control system.

The stability criterion for the inverse polar plane can be stated algebraically as

$$N = G_Z + H_P - Z \qquad (5\text{--}50)$$

Since Z must be zero for stability, we can restate the stability criterion as

$$N = G_Z + H_P \qquad (5\text{--}51)$$

It is important to point out here that as s approaches $\pm j\infty$ in accordance with Figure 5–2, the inverse diagram has an infinite value. Conventionally, we take a circular path having infinite radius in order to close the contour and be able to determine the value of N. The number of revolutions R of this circular path is given by

$$R = \tfrac{1}{2}(s_Z - s_P) \qquad (5\text{--}52)$$

where s_Z = number of zeros of the system transfer function $C(s)/R(s)$
s_P = number of poles of the system transfer function $C(s)/R(s)$.

When $H(j\omega)$ equals unity, equation 5–49 reduces to

$$\frac{R(j\omega)}{C(j\omega)} = \frac{1}{G(j\omega)} + 1 \qquad (5\text{--}53)$$

The corresponding inverse polar plot can be drawn by sketching only $1/G(j\omega)$ and considering the origin at $-1 + j0$. This technique is similar to the procedure used for the Nyquist diagram. Figure 5–16 illustrates several typical inverse polar plots for systems having unity feedback. In all cases, the values of $G(s)$, N, G_Z, H_P, and Z are shown. Notice that the systems shown in parts (a) and (b) are stable on an open-loop basis while those in parts (c) and (d) are unstable on an open-loop basis. The systems illustrated in parts (b) and (c) are stable on a closed-loop basis; those in parts (a) and (d) are unstable on a closed-loop basis.

The expression of equation 5–49 can be written, in a manner similar to that given by equation 5–33, as

$$\frac{R(j\omega)}{C(j\omega)} = \frac{1}{M(\omega)} e^{-j\alpha(\omega)} \qquad (5\text{--}54)$$

M and α have the same definition here as in equation 5–33. The loci of constant $1/M$ are circles since $R(j\omega)/C(j\omega)$ is merely the distance from any point of the inverse polar plot to the $-1 + j0$ point. The radii of the circles equal $1/M$. The loci of points having a constant angle, $-\alpha$, are straight lines which radiate from the $-1 + j0$ point. Figure 5–17 illustrates a family of $1/M$ circles and straight lines of constant $-\alpha$. Since the control engineer is usually interested in M, and not $1/M$, the corresponding values of M are illustrated on Figure 5–17, in parentheses.

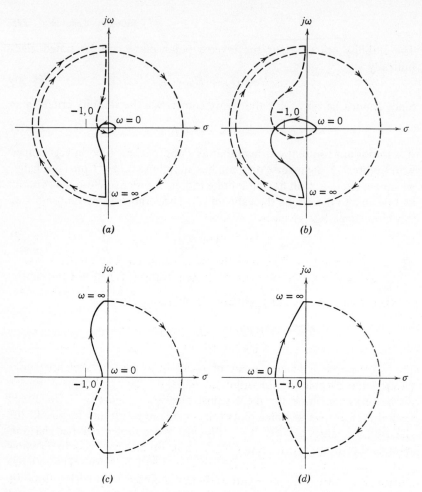

Figure 5–16. Examples of typical inverse polar plots for systems having unity feedback.
For (a),

$$G(s) = \frac{K_a}{(1 + T_1s)(1 + T_2s)(1 + T_3s)}$$

$$N = -2, \quad G_Z = 0, \quad H_P = 0, \quad Z = 2; \quad \therefore \text{ unstable}$$

For (b),

$$G(s) = \frac{K_b}{(1 + T_1s)(1 + T_2s)(1 + T_3s)}$$

$$N = 0, \quad G_Z = 0, \quad H_P = 0, \quad Z = 0; \quad \therefore \text{ stable}$$

For (c),

$$G(s) = \frac{K_c}{(-1 + Ts)}$$

$$N = 0, \quad G_Z = 0, \quad H_P = 0, \quad Z = 0; \quad \therefore \text{ stable}$$

For (d),

$$G(s) = \frac{K_d}{(-1 + Ts)}$$

$$N = -1, \quad G_Z = 0, \quad H_P = 0, \quad Z = 1; \quad \therefore \text{ unstable}$$

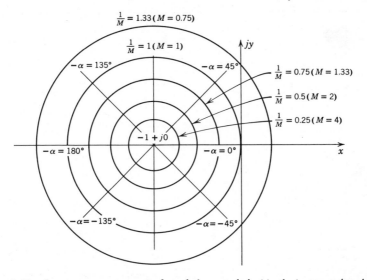

Figure 5–17. Inverse constant-magnitude and phase angle loci in the inverse polar plane.

The great advantage of the inverse plane is its use for designing feedback control systems which have nonunity feedback. For this case, the curves of $1/G(j\omega)$ and $H(j\omega)$ are drawn separately and then added in accordance with equation 5–49 in order to obtain $R(j\omega)/C(j\omega)$. The inverse system transfer function $R(j\omega)/C(j\omega)$ equals the distance from the origin to the resulting curve. In addition, the $1/M$ circles and $-\alpha$ radial lines are drawn from the origin for this case instead of from the point $-1 + j0$ as was done in the case of unity feedback. We next demonstrate the use of this tool for analysis by an example. The tool's value for synthesis is illustrated in Chapter 6.

Let us determine the value of M_p for the type 1, third-order feedback control system illustrated in Figure 5–18. This can be obtained by measuring the shortest distance between the $-1 + j0$ point and the inverse polar plot as is illustrated in Figure 5–19. This distance equals 0.35 and represents the radius of a $1/M$ circle whose M value is 2.86. Notice that all other distances from the $-1 + j0$ point to the inverse polar plot represent M values less than 2.86; therefore, the value of M_p for this system is 2.86.

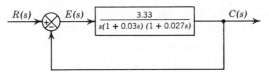

Figure 5–18. A type 1, third-order feedback control system.

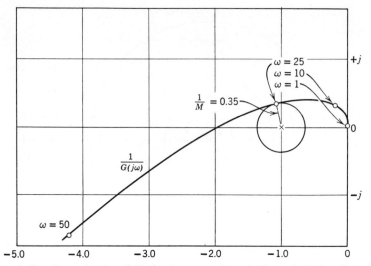

Figure 5–19.   Determination of M_p for the system shown in Figure 5–18 from the inverse polar loci.

Since a value of $M_p = 2.86$ does not represent a good design, we wish to modify this system in some manner in order to lower the value of M_p to an acceptable level. We demonstrate in Chapter 6 the use of tachometric feedback in order to accomplish this. Let us here, however, indicate how the constant $1/M$ loci may be used to limit M_p to some maximum value, say 1.1. The $1/M$ locus corresponding to an $M_p = 1.1$ is $1/1.1 = 0.91$. Since the interior of the $1/M = 0.91$ circle consists entirely of constant-magnitude circles which represent M loci greater than 1.1, we must confine the inverse polar plot to the exterior of the $1/M = 0.91$ circle. The system illustrated in Figure 5–18 is compensated, to meet certain maximum requirements of M_p, in Chapter 6.

5–7. BODE DIAGRAM APPROACH[6]

The Bode diagram approach is the most commonly used method for the analysis and synthesis of linear feedback control systems. This method, which is basically an extension of the Nyquist stability criterion, has the same limitations and uses as the Nyquist diagram. The presentation of information in the Bode diagram approach, however, is modified to permit relatively quick determinations of the effects of changes in system response without the laborious calculations associated with the Nyquist diagram.

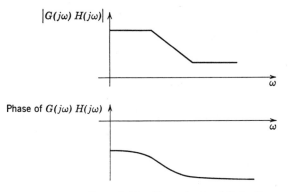

Figure 5-20.   Typical pair of Bode diagrams.

The Nyquist diagram contains information as to the path that the complex variable s traverses, and the amplitude and phase of the open-loop transfer function $G(s)H(s)$. As s traverses the imaginary axis, it has the value of real frequency ω, and the plot corresponds to $G(j\omega)H(j\omega)$. We can illustrate the same amount of information by means of two diagrams which have ω as a common axis. These two diagrams, illustrated in Figure 5-20, are usually referred to as Bode diagrams. It is important to emphasize that the Bode diagrams provide information only of s corresponding to the imaginary axis and therefore representing a realistic set of frequency response curves.

In order to gain some insight for drawing the Bode diagrams, let us consider the simple feedback control system illustrated in Figure 5-21. Let us assume that the input into the system, $r(t)$, is a sinusoidal waveform of frequency ω and unity amplitude. It may be represented by the expression

$$r(t) = \sin \omega t \tag{5-55}$$

Assuming a linear system, the output would have the general form

$$c(t) = a \sin (\omega t - \phi) \tag{5-56}$$

where a = gain of system
ϕ = phase shift of the system

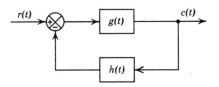

Figure 5-21.   Representative feedback control system.

Let us represent the system transfer function as

$$T(j\omega) = \frac{C(j\omega)}{R(j\omega)} = a(j\omega)\, e^{-j\phi(j\omega)} \tag{5-57}$$

Here $T(j\omega)$ is a complex function which can be represented by an amplitude $a(j\omega)$ and a phase shift of $\phi(j\omega)$. In the Bode diagram approach, the amplitude is expressed in decibels and is plotted versus frequency on semilogarithmic graph paper. The amplitude, in decibels, is expressed by

$$\text{Amplitude in db} = 20\log_{10} a(j\omega) \tag{5-58}$$

The phase shift $\phi(j\omega)$ is conventionally expressed in degrees.

By introducing the logarithm concept, the tedious process of multiplying two complex numbers is simplified to one of addition. For example, let us consider two complex numbers: $G_a(j\omega)$ and $G_b(j\omega)$. The logarithm of the product of two complex quantities

$$G_a(j\omega) = a_a(j\omega)\, e^{-j\phi_a(j\omega)} \tag{5-59}$$

and

$$G_b(j\omega) = a_b(j\omega)\, e^{-j\phi_b(j\omega)} \tag{5-60}$$

is given by

$$\log_{10} G_a(j\omega)G_b(j\omega) = \log_{10} a_a(j\omega) + \log_{10} a_b(j\omega)$$
$$+ j[\phi_a(j\omega) + \phi_b(j\omega)] \tag{5-61}$$

Equation 5-61 illustrates the fact that the logarithm of two complex numbers is the sum of the logarithms of the magnitude components plus j times the sum of the phase angle components. In addition, equation 5-61 shows that the logarithm of the magnitude and phase components, respectively, are separate functions of the common parameter ω and can be sketched separately as was shown in Figure 5-20.

Bode's theorems are presented in Chapter 6 when we discuss the Bode diagram approach for the design of feedback control systems in order to meet certain specifications. In this chapter, however, it is important to emphasize the fact that the Bode diagram approach applies only to linear "minimum-phase" networks. The basic definition of a "minimum-phase" network[5] is a network having a minimum phase shift possible for the number of energy storage elements in the network. This definition, restricts the poles and zeros of "minimum-phase" networks to the left half of the complex plane. A little thought indicates that when we specify either the amplitude or phase of a "minimum-phase" network, we have also automatically specified the other. This concept is the basis of one of Bode's theorems.

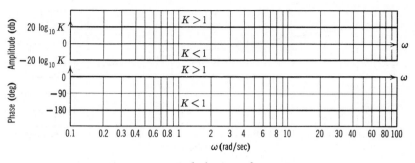

Figure 5-22. Bode diagram of a constant.

Understanding the basic concepts of the Bode diagram, let us now gain the facility for constructing them. The laborious procedure of plotting the amplitude and phase of $G(j\omega)H(j\omega)$ by means of substituting several values of $j\omega$, is not necessary when drawing the Bode diagram, because we can use several "short-cuts." These "short-cuts" are based on simplifying approximations which permit the control engineer to represent the exact, smooth plots with straight asymptotic lines. The difference between actual amplitude characteristics and the asymptotic approximations is only a few decibels. Now we shall demonstrate the application of this approximating technique to six common, representative transfer functions: a constant, a pure integration, a pure differentiation, a simple phase-lag network, a simple phase-lead network, and a quadratic phase-lag network. The basic concepts illustrated are then used to draw the Bode diagram of the transfer function for a representative system.

a. Bode Diagram of a Constant. Using the definition of equation 5–58, the logarithm of a constant K, or $1/K$, is given by

$$(K)_{db} = 20 \log_{10} K \qquad (5\text{--}62)$$

$$\left(\frac{1}{K}\right)_{db} = -20 \log_{10} K \qquad (5\text{--}63)$$

The corresponding phase angle of a constant is either zero or 180°, depending on whether it is positive or negative, respectively. Figure 5–22 illustrates the Bode diagram of a constant.

b. Bode Diagram of a Pure Integration. The Bode diagram of a pure integration

$$G(j\omega) = \frac{1}{j\omega} \qquad (5\text{--}64)$$

can be obtained by taking the logarithm equation 5–64 as

$$20 \log_{10} \frac{1}{j\omega} = -20 \log_{10} \omega - j\frac{\pi}{2} \qquad (5\text{--}65)$$

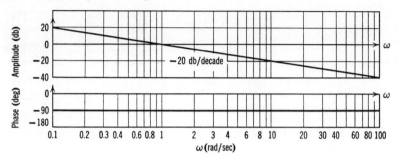

Figure 5–23.   Bode diagram of a pure integration, $G(j\omega) = 1/j\omega$.

Figure 5–23 illustrates the Bode diagram of a pure integration. Notice that the resulting amplitude curve is linear when the amplitude is plotted on a linear scale and the frequency is plotted on a logarithmic scale. The slope of the amplitude characteristic is a constant and equals −20 db/decade. A slope of −20 db/decade also corresponds to a slope of −6 db/octave. The phase characteristic for the pure integration is constant and equals −90°.

c. **Bode Diagram of a Pure Differentiation.**   The Bode diagram of a pure differentiation

$$G(j\omega) = j\omega \qquad (5\text{–}66)$$

can be obtained in a manner similar to that used for the pure integration. The major differences are that the amplitude characteristics now have a positive slope and the phase characteristic is positive. Figure 5–24 illustrates the Bode diagram of a pure differentiation.

d. **Bode Diagram of a Simple Phase-Lag Network.**   A phase-lag network produces a phase lag which is a function of frequency. The transfer function of such a network is given by

$$G(j\omega) = \frac{a}{j\omega + a} = \left(j\frac{\omega}{a} + 1 \right)^{-1} \qquad (5\text{–}67)$$

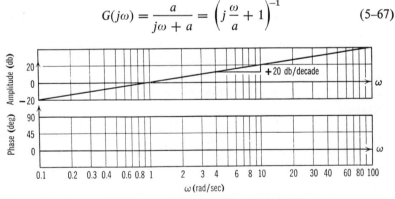

Figure 5–24.   Bode diagram of a pure differentiation, $G(j\omega) = j\omega$.

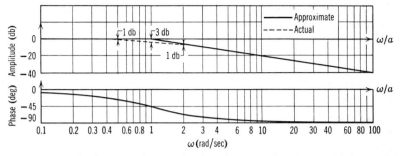

Figure 5–25. Bode diagram of a simple phase-lag network, $G(j\omega) = [j(\omega/a) + 1]^{-1}$.

This transfer function can be obtained using one resistor and one capacitor, with the output being taken from the capacitor. The Bode diagram for this transfer function can be obtained as follows:

$$20 \log_{10} \left(j\frac{\omega}{a} + 1 \right)^{-1} = -20 \log_{10} \left(\frac{\omega^2}{a^2} + 1 \right)^{\frac{1}{2}} - j \tan^{-1} \frac{\omega}{a} \quad (5\text{–}68)$$

Figure 5–25 illustrates the Bode diagram of a simple phase-lag network. The dotted portion of the amplitude characteristics represents the exact plot, and the heavy-line segments represent the straight-line asymptotic approximation. They differ by a maximum of 3 db at ω/a equal to unity.

The asymptotic approximations can be drawn quite easily. For example, when ω/a is much less than unity, the imaginary component is very much smaller than the real component (unity), and the imaginary component can be neglected. Therefore,

$$20 \log_{10} 1 = 0 \text{ db/decade} \quad \text{for} \quad \frac{\omega}{a} \ll 1 \quad (5\text{–}69)$$

When ω/a is much greater than unity, the imaginary component is much greater than the real component (unity) and the real component may be neglected. Therefore,

$$20 \log_{10} \left(j\frac{\omega}{a} \right)^{-1} = -20 \log_{10} \frac{\omega}{a} \text{ db} \quad \text{for} \quad \frac{\omega}{a} \gg 1 \quad (5\text{–}70)$$

Equation 5–70 is very similar to the amplitude characteristics for a pure integrator, given by equation 5–65, and has a slope of -20 db/decade. At $\omega/a = 1$, the two asymptotes join each other. This frequency ($\omega = a$) is conventionally referred to as a break frequency. Ordinarily, the straight-line asymptotic approximation is accurate for most applications. If further correction is needed, the exact curve can be obtained from the approximate curve by using the following corrections: -1 db at $\omega/a = 0.5$ and 2; -3 db at $\omega/a = 1$.

The phase shift produced by the simple phase-lag network can be obtained from the expression

$$\text{Phase lag} = -\tan^{-1}\frac{\omega}{a} \tag{5-71}$$

The phase shift at the break frequency corresponds to $-45°$; at $\omega = 0$ it corresponds to $0°$; at $\omega = \infty$ it corresponds to $-90°$. Notice that this phase-lag network is a "minimum-phase" network since it has the minimum phase shift possible for the number of energy storage elements in the network (one).

e. Bode Diagram of a Simple Phase-Lead Network. The Bode diagram of a simple phase-lead network

$$G(j\omega) = j\frac{\omega}{a} + 1 \tag{5-72}$$

can be obtained in a manner similar to that used for the simple phase-lag network. The major differences are that the amplitude characteristic has a positive slope, and the phase characteristic has a positive (phase lead) value. Figure 5–26 illustrates the Bode diagram of a simple phase-lead network.

f. Bode Diagram of a Quadratic Phase-Lag Network. Let us reconsider the closed-loop transfer function of the type 1, second-order system

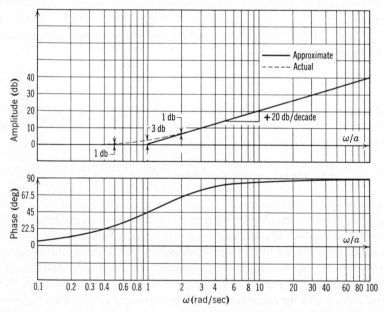

Figure 5–26. Bode diagram of a simple phase-lead network, $G(j\omega) = j(\omega/a) + 1$.

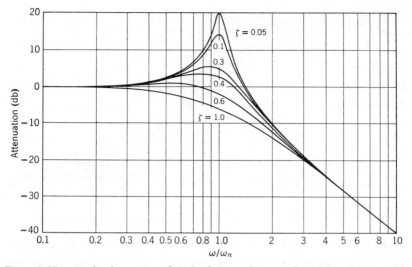

Figure 5–27. Amplitude portion of Bode diagram for a quadratic phase-lag network.

considered in Section 3–7. Repeating equation 3–90, and replacing s with $j\omega$, we have the closed-loop system transfer function as

$$\frac{C(j\omega)}{R(j\omega)} = \frac{\omega_n^{\,2}}{(j\omega)^2 + 2\zeta\omega_n(j\omega) + \omega_n^{\,2}} \tag{5–73}$$

Normalizing this equation, we obtain

$$\frac{C(j\omega)}{R(j\omega)} = \left[\left(j\,\frac{\omega}{\omega_n}\right)^2 + 2\zeta\omega_n\left(j\,\frac{\omega}{\omega_n^{\,2}}\right) + 1\right]^{-1} \tag{5–74}$$

The Bode diagram for this transfer function can be obtained as follows:

$$20\log_{10}\left[\left(j\,\frac{\omega}{\omega_n}\right)^2 + 2\zeta\left(j\,\frac{\omega}{\omega_n}\right) + 1\right]^{-1}$$

$$= -20\log_{10}\left[\left(\frac{2\zeta\omega}{\omega_n}\right)^2 + \left(1 - \frac{\omega^2}{\omega_n^{\,2}}\right)^2\right]^{1/2} - j\tan^{-1}\frac{2\zeta\omega_n\omega}{\omega_n^{\,2} - \omega^2} \tag{5–75}$$

Figures 5–27 and 5–28 illustrate the Bode diagram of the quadratic phase-lag network for various values of damping factor, ζ. The dotted portion of the amplitude characteristics represents the straight-line asymptotic approximation and the heavy-line portions represent the exact plot. For a $\zeta = 1$, the two curves differ by a maximum of 6.2 db at ω/ω_n equal to unity.

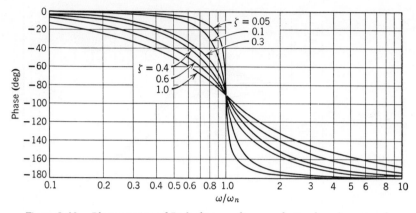

Figure 5–28.   Phase portion of Bode diagram for a quadratic phase-lag network.

The asymptotic approximations can be drawn quite simply. For example, when ω/ω_n is much less than unity, the imaginary component is very much smaller than the real component, and the imaginary component can be neglected. Therefore,

$$20 \log_{10} \sqrt{1} = 0 \text{ db/decade} \quad \text{for} \quad \frac{\omega}{\omega_n} \ll 1 \qquad (5\text{–}76)$$

When ω/ω_n is much greater than unity, the dominant term is

$$20 \log_{10}\left[\left(j\frac{\omega}{\omega_n}\right)^2\right]^{-1} = -20 \log_{10}\left[\left(-\frac{\omega^2}{\omega_n^2}\right)^2\right]^{\frac{1}{2}}$$

$$= -40 \log_{10}\frac{\omega}{\omega_n} \quad \text{for} \quad \frac{\omega}{\omega_n} \gg 1 \qquad (5\text{–}77)$$

This indicates that the slope of the straight-line asymptotic approximation for $\omega/\omega_n \gg 1$ is twice that of a double phase-lag network. The difference between the approximate curve and the exact curve depends on the damping factor, ζ. Similar analysis indicates the phase shift possible is twice that of the simple phase-lag network.

Let us next apply the basic concepts and tools developed in this section for the transfer function of a representative feedback control system. Consider a unity feedback system whose open-loop transfer function is given by

$$G(j\omega) = \frac{775}{j\omega} \frac{0.1j\omega + 1}{0.5j\omega + 1} \frac{0.2j\omega + 1}{j\omega + 1}$$

$$\times \left[0.655 \times 10^{-4}(j\omega)^2 + 6.55 \times 10^{-3}j\omega + 1\right]^{-1} \quad (5\text{–}78)$$

This transfer function contains a pure integration, two phase lags, two

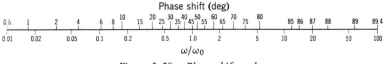

Phase shift (deg)

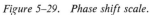

Figure 5–29. Phase shift scale.

phase leads, and a quadratic phase-lag network. Each of these character-istics have previously been considered individually. The simplest proce-dure for plotting the amplitude characteristics for the entire transfer function is to start by locating one point, say $j\omega = 1$. Using the straight-line asymptotic approximation technique, the assumption is made that the real or imaginary components which are larger at $\omega = 1$ predominate. (If they are both equal, either component may be used.) At the same time, the slope at $\omega = 1$ is determined. For the problem at hand, at $\omega = 1$

$$[G(j\omega)]_{\omega=1} = \frac{775}{j1} \frac{1}{1} \frac{1}{j1 \text{ or } 1} \frac{1}{1} \tag{5–79}$$

Equation 5–79 indicates that the gain is 775 (57.5 db) and the slope is changing from -20 db/decade to -40 db/decade at $\omega = 1$. The next step is to locate all the break frequencies (frequencies at which the slopes change because a real or imaginary component starts or stops to predom-inate). The break frequencies for this transfer function are at $\omega = 1$ (-20 db/decade to -40 db/decade); $\omega = 2$ (-40 db/decade to -60 db/decade); $\omega = 5$ (-60 db/decade to -40 db/decade); $\omega = 10$ (-40 db/decade to -20 db/decade); 123.8 (-20 db/decade to -60 db/decade). The corresponding phase characteristics can most easily be determined using superposition of the individual phase characteristics of each com-ponent and utilizing the scale shown in Figure 5–29. This scale, which can be easily derived from the tangent relationship of equation 5–71, gives the effect of a break frequency occurring at $\omega = \omega_0$ to the resultant phase shift occurring at frequency ω. For example, at $\omega/\omega_0 = 5$, the phase shift contributed by the break occurring at $\omega/\omega_0 = 1$ is 78.7°, while at $\omega/\omega_0 = 0.2$ the phase shift contributed by this break is only 11.3°.

Figure 5–30 illustrates the composite Bode diagram for the transfer function given by equation 5–78. Notice that the peaking due to the quadratic phase-lag component, which corresponds to a ζ of 0.405, is indicated in addition to its asymptotic approximation.

At this point in the development of the Bode diagram, it seems appro-priate to relate the Nyquist stability criterion to the Bode amplitude and phase frequency response diagrams. When we discussed the Nyquist diagram, the degree of stability was defined in terms of the phase and gain margins present (see Figure 5–6). This can easily be related to the

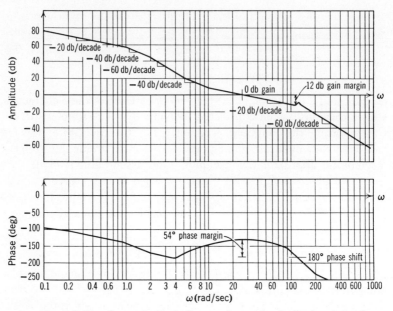

Figure 5–30. Composite Bode diagram for a unity feedback system where

$$G(j\omega) = \frac{775}{j\omega}\frac{0.1j\omega + 1}{0.5j\omega + 1}\frac{0.2j\omega + 1}{j\omega + 1}$$

$$\times\,[0.655 \times 10^{-4}(j\omega)^2 + 6.55 \times 10^{-3}j\omega + 1]^{-1}.$$

Bode frequency response diagrams by making use of the following two facts.

1. The unit circle of the Nyquist diagram transforms into the unity or 0-db line of the amplitude plot for all frequencies.
2. The negative real axis of the Nyquist diagram transforms into a negative 180° phase shift line for all frequencies.

Therefore, the phase margin can be determined on the Bode diagram by determining the phase shift present when $G(j\omega)H(j\omega)$ crosses the 0-db line (this is commonly referred to as the crossover frequency). For the example illustrated in Figure 5–30, the phase shift is 126° (this corresponds to the θ of Figure 5–6) and the resulting phase margin, γ, is 54°. The gain margin can be obtained on the Bode diagram by determining the gain present when $G(j\omega)H(j\omega)$ crosses the $-180°$ line. For the example illustrated in Figure 5–30, the gain is -12.5 db when the phase shift is $-180°$ (this corresponds to $20 \log_{10} \alpha$ of Figure 5–6) and the resulting gain margin, $20 \log_{10}(1/\alpha)$, is approximately 12 db.

The Bode diagram method has the very practical virtue that the amplitude and phase frequency responses can easily be measured in the laboratory. The relative ease of synthesizing feedback control systems with the Bode diagram approach is further demonstrated in Chapter 6.

5-8. THE NICHOLS CHART[6]

The amplitude and phase information presented by the M and α circles in the complex plane can also be presented by plotting amplitude versus phase directly. Usually amplitude is plotted in decibels as the ordinate and phase in degrees as the abscissa. These graphs, or charts, are usually referred to as Nichols charts in honor of their originator.[7]

The defining equations of the Nichols charts can be derived in a manner very similar to that used for the M and α circles. Reconsidering the basic relationships of the unity feedback control system illustrated in Figure 5-9, let us represent the complex vector $G(j\omega)$ by an amplitude and phase as follows:

$$G(j\omega) = |G(j\omega)|\, e^{j(\pi+\gamma)} \tag{5-80}$$

where γ = phase margin (see Figure 5-6). Substituting equation 5-80 into the system transfer function, as given by equation 5-32, we obtain

$$\frac{C(j\omega)}{R(j\omega)} = \frac{G(j\omega)}{1 + G(j\omega)} = \frac{|G(j\omega)|\, e^{j(\pi+\gamma)}}{1 + |G(j\omega)|\, e^{j(\pi+\gamma)}} \tag{5-81}$$

This equation may be simplified to

$$\frac{C(j\omega)}{R(j\omega)} = \frac{|G(j\omega)|\, e^{j\gamma}}{|G(j\omega)|\, e^{j\gamma} - 1} \tag{5-82}$$

Dividing through by $|G(j\omega)|\, e^{j\gamma}$, we obtain

$$\frac{C(j\omega)}{R(j\omega)} = \left[1 - \frac{e^{-j\gamma}}{|G(j\omega)|}\right]^{-1} \tag{5-83}$$

Using the trigonometric relationship for the exponential term, we obtain the expression

$$\frac{C(j\omega)}{R(j\omega)} = \left[1 - \frac{\cos\gamma}{|G(j\omega)|} + \frac{j\sin\gamma}{|G(j\omega)|}\right]^{-1} \tag{5-84}$$

The expression of equation 5-84 has a magnitude M and phase angle α which are given by

$$M(\omega) = \left\{\left[1 + \frac{1}{|G(j\omega)|^2} - \frac{2\cos\gamma}{|G(j\omega)|}\right]^{\frac{1}{2}}\right\}^{-1} \tag{5-85}$$

and

$$\alpha(\omega) = \tan^{-1}\frac{\sin\gamma}{\cos\gamma - |G(j\omega)|} \tag{5-86}$$

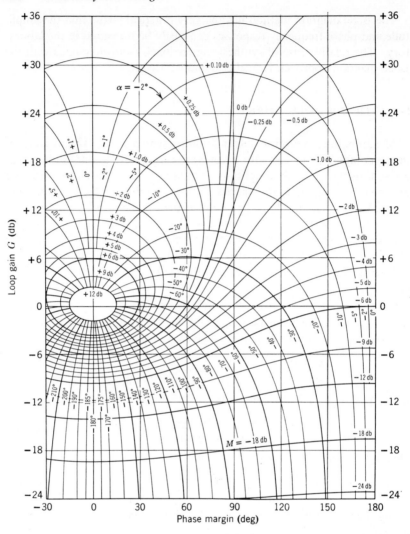

Figure 5–31.   Nichols chart.

M and α have the same definition in this section as they did in Sections 5–5 and 5–6. A detailed plot of $|G|$ in decibels versus γ, with M and α as parameters, is illustrated in Figure 5–31. Notice the symmetry of these curves about the 0° phase margin ordinate.

The stability criterion for the Nichols chart is quite simple since the $-1 + j0$ point of the complex plane corresponds to the 0-db, 0° phase margin point of Figure 5–31. Therefore, for minimum phase systems, the feedback control system is stable if a plot of $G(j\omega)H(j\omega)$ on the Nichols chart lies to the right of the $0°$ phase margin ordinate when crossing the 0-db abscissa line.

The Nichols chart can be used for the analysis and/or synthesis of a feedback control system. For analysis, we can use the Nichols chart to obtain the closed-loop frequency response from the Bode diagram and determine the maximum value of peaking M_p and the frequency at which it occurs, ω_p. From a synthesis viewpoint, we can use the Nichols chart to meet certain requirements as to the values of M_p and ω_p. We demonstrate the use of this method as a tool for analysis in this section. Its value as a tool for synthesis is illustrated in Chapter 6.

Let us determine the closed-loop frequency response for the type 1, third-order feedback control system which was illustrated in Figure 5–12 and previously analyzed by means of the M- and α-circle method. Specifically, we are now interested in obtaining the values of M_p and ω_p using the Nichols chart. They can be obtained by first drawing the Bode diagram as shown in Figure 5–32. Then, for each value of ω, the magnitude (actual or corrected values) and phase of $G(j\omega)$ are then plotted onto a Nichols chart as shown in Figure 5–33. The intersections of $G(j\omega)$ with

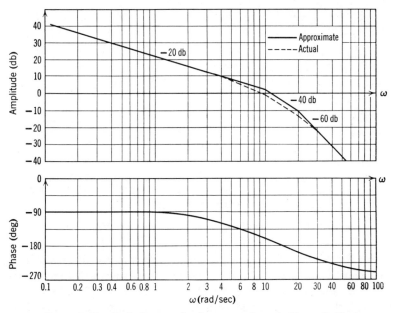

Figure 5–32. Bode diagram for the system shown in Figure 5–12 where

$$G(s)H(s) = \frac{11.7}{s(1 + 0.05s)(1 + 0.1s)}$$

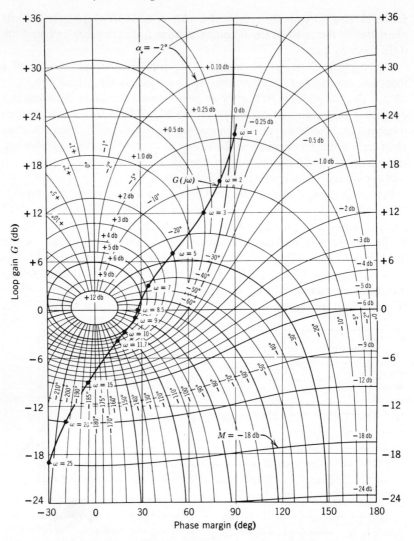

Figure 5–33. Nichols chart for the system shown in Figure 5–12.

$M(\omega)$ on the Nichols chart give the closed-loop response from which M_p and ω_p can be obtained. The resulting response, shown in Figure 5–34, indicates a value of $M_p = 6.8$ db (2.2) and an $\omega_p = 10$ rad/sec. This agrees with the values obtained using the M-circle method. Notice that a set of α loci was not required for the solution to this problem.

The comments in Section 5–5 regarding an $M_p = 2.2$ are also true here. The technique of compensation of this system utilizing the Nichols chart

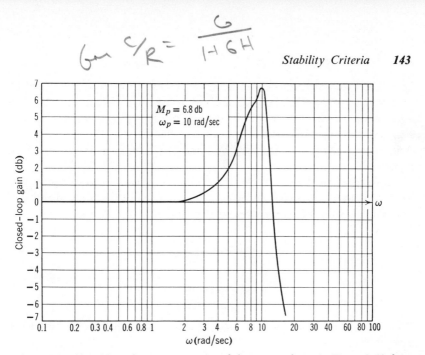

$$\left(\text{for } C/R = \frac{G}{1 + GH}\right)$$

Figure 5-34. *Closed-loop frequency response of the system shown in Figure 5-12 from the Nichols chart of Figure 5-33.*

is illustrated in Chapter 6. Let us here, however, indicate how the constant M loci on the Nichols chart may be used to limit M_p to some maximum value, say 2.2 db (1.3). Since the interior of the $M = 2.2$ db locus consists entirely of constant-magnitude loci which represent M greater than 2.2 db, we must confine the Nichols locus to the exterior of the $M = 2.2$ db locus. The system illustrated in Figure 5-12 is compensated, to meet certain maximum requirements of M_p, in Chapter 6 utilizing the Nichols chart.

5-9. THE ROOT LOCUS METHOD

The root locus method is a graphical technique for determining the roots of a system's closed-loop characteristic equation as a function of gain. The basic principle of this method is the relationship which exists between the poles of the closed loop's transfer function to the poles and zeros of the open-loop transfer function and its gain. The root locus method, which was conceived by Evans,[8-10] has several distinct advantages. A complete, detailed, and very accurate transient and steady-state solution can be obtained since the closed loop's poles can be obtained directly from the root loci. In addition, approximate solutions may be obtained, with a considerable reduction of labor, if very accurate solutions are not required.

The root locus method has found an ever-increasing use in the field of modern control over the last decade, and its use appears to have increasing application in the future. This section presents the methods of constructing the root locus and of interpreting the results. The technique for synthesizing a system utilizing the root locus method is discussed in Chapter 6.

Let us consider the general feedback control system illustrated in Figure 5–15. Assuming that $G(s)$ and $H(s)$ are composed of fractions of rational polynomials in s, we may represent $G(s)$ and $H(s)$ as follows:

$$G(s) = \frac{N_G(s)}{D_G(s)} \qquad (5\text{–}87)$$

$$H(s) = \frac{N_H(s)}{D_H(s)} \qquad (5\text{–}88)$$

Therefore, the closed-loop transfer function of this general system is given by

$$\frac{C(s)}{R(s)} = \frac{G(s)}{1 + G(s)H(s)} = \frac{N_G(s)D_H(s)}{D_G(s)D_H(s) + N_G(s)N_H(s)} \qquad (5\text{–}89)$$

The root locus method plots the roots of the denominator of equation 5–89: $1 + G(s)H(s) = D_G(s)D_H(s) + N_G(s)N_H(s)$.

In order to find the poles of the closed-loop transfer function,

$$1 + G(s)H(s) = 0 \qquad (5\text{–}90)$$

or, $$G(s)H(s) = -1 = 1\underline{/\pm n\pi} \qquad (5\text{–}91)$$

where $n = 1, 3, 5, 7, \ldots$. Equation 5–91 specifies two conditions which must be satisfied for the existence of a closed-loop pole.

1. The angle of $G(s)H(s)$ must lie along the negative real axis of the s plane:

$$\text{Angle of } G(s)H(s) = \pm n\pi \qquad (5\text{–}92)$$

where $n = 1, 3, 5, 7, \ldots$.
2. The magnitude of $G(s)H(s)$ must be unity:

$$|G(s)H(s)| = 1 \qquad (5\text{–}93)$$

The construction of the root locus for a particular system can start by locating the open-loop poles and zeros in the complex plane. Other points on the locus can be obtained by choosing various test points and determining whether they satisfy the relationship of equation 5–92. The angle of $G(s)H(s)$ can be easily determined at any test point in the complex plane by measuring the angles contributed to it by the various poles and zeros. For example, consider a feedback control system where

$$G(s)H(s) = \frac{K(s + s_A)(s + s_C)}{s(s + s_B)(s + s_D)} \qquad (5\text{-}94)$$

At some exploratory point s_E, $G(s)H(s)$ has the value

$$G(s_E)H(s_E) = \frac{K(s_E + s_A)(s_E + s_C)}{s_E(s_E + s_B)(s_E + s_D)} \qquad (5\text{-}95)$$

Pictorially, equation 5–95 can be represented by Figure 5–35, where the vectors

$$\alpha = s_E + s_A$$
$$\beta = s_E + s_B$$
$$\gamma = s_E + s_C$$
$$\delta = s_E + s_D$$
$$\epsilon = s_E$$

The angle of $G(s_E)H(s_E)$ is the sum of the angles determined by the vectors α, β, γ, δ, and ϵ:

Angle $G(s_E)H(s_E) = \Sigma$ angles of vectors α, β, γ, δ, and ϵ to point s_E

$$(5\text{-}96)$$

If the sum of the angles equals $\pm n\pi$, then the point s_E lies on the root locus. If it does not, the point s_E does not lie on the locus and a new point must be tried. When a point is found which does satisfy equation

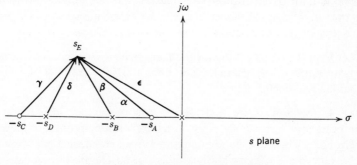

Figure 5–35.   *Vector representation of*

at the exploratory point s_E.

5–92, the vector magnitudes are determined and are substituted into equation 5–93 in order to find the value of the gain constant K at the exploratory point s_E:

$$|G(s_E)H(s_E)| = \frac{K\ |(s_E + s_A)|\ |(s_E + s_C)|}{|s_E|\ |(s_E + s_B)|\ |(s_E + s_D)|} = 1 \qquad (5\text{–}97)$$

Fortunately, the actual construction of a root locus does not entail an infinite search through the complex plane. Since the zeros of the characteristic equation are continuous functions of the coefficients, the root locus is a continuous curve. Therefore, the root locus must have certain general patterns which are governed by the location and number of open-loop zeros and poles. Once these governing rules are established, the drawing of a root locus is not a tedious and lengthy trial and error. We next present nine basic rules which aid in determining the approximate location of the root locus.

RULE 1.   The number of separate loci equals the order of the characteristic equation. This is true since there are as many roots (and branches) of the root locus as the order of the characteristic equation. Each segment, or branch, of the root locus describes the variation of a particular pole of the closed-loop system as the gain is varied.

RULE 2.   The open-loop poles define the start of the root locus ($K = 0$), and the open-loop zeros define the termination of the root locus ($K = \infty$). This can easily be shown by considering equation 5–97. At open-loop zeros, K must equal infinity since there is a zero in the expression due to either s_A or s_C. However, K must equal zero when open-loop poles occur since there is a zero in the expression due to s_B or s_D. When the order of the denominator of equation 5–94 is greater than the numerator, the root locus *ends at infinity*. However, if the order of the numerator of equation 5–94 is greater than the denominator, the root locus *starts at infinity*.

RULE 3.   Complex portions of the root locus always occur as complex conjugate pairs if the characteristic equation is a rational polynomial in s having real coefficients.

RULE 4.   Sections of the real axis are part of the root locus if the sum of the poles and zeros to the right of an exploratory point along the real axis are odd. This is easily demonstrated from equation 5–96. Since the angular contribution along the real axis due to complex conjugate poles cancels, the total angle of $G(s)H(s)$ is due only to the contributions of the real poles and zeros. Therefore, at any exploratory point along the real axis, the angular contribution due to a pole or zero to its right is 180°, while that due to a pole or zero to its left is zero.

RULE 5. Angles of asymptotes to the root locus α_n are given by

$$\alpha_n = \pm \frac{n\pi}{p - z} \qquad (5\text{-}98)$$

where
$$p = \text{number of open-loop poles}$$
$$z = \text{number of open-loop zeros}$$
$$n = \text{an odd integer}$$

This can be shown by considering the root locus as it is mapped far away from the group of open-loop poles and zeros. In this area, all the poles and zeros contribute about the same angular component. Since the total angular component must add up to ±180 degrees or some odd multiple, equation 5-98 exists. Figure 5-36 illustrates the asymptotes of a third-order system where

$$G(s)H(s) = \frac{K}{s(s + 4)(s + 5)} \qquad (5\text{-}99)$$

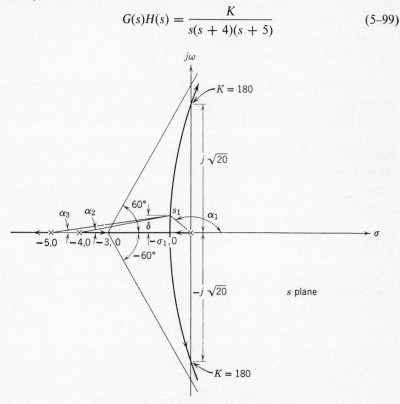

Figure 5-36. Root locus of a system where

$$G(s)H(s) = \frac{K}{s(s + 4)(s + 5)}$$

The asymptotic angles for the roots locus illustrated in Figure 5–36 are

$$\alpha_1 = \pm \frac{\pi}{3} = \pm 60°$$

$$\alpha_3 = \pm \frac{3\pi}{3} = \pm \pi°$$

RULE 6. The intersection of the asymptotic lines and the real axis occurs along the real axis at s_r, where

$$s_r = \frac{\sum_{\text{poles}} - \sum_{\text{zeros}}}{\text{No. of finite poles} - \text{No. of finite zeros}} \qquad (5\text{–}100)$$

The value of s_r is basically the centroid of the open-loop pole and zero configuration. The intersection of the asymptotes for the root locus illustrated in Figure 5–36 is given by

$$s_r = \frac{(-4 - 5) - 0}{3 - 0} = -3$$

RULE 7. The point of breakaway of the root locus from the real axis can be obtained by considering the transition from the real axis to a point s_1 which is a small distance δ off the axis. The basis of this method is that the transition from the real axis to s_1 must result in a zero net change of the angle of $G(s)H(s)$. This is illustrated for the root locus considered in Figure 5–36. For this example,

$$-(\alpha_1 + \alpha_2 + \alpha_3) = -180° \qquad (5\text{–}101)$$

The very small angles we are considering are equal to their tangents, in radians, as follows:

$$-\left(\pi - \frac{\delta}{\sigma_1}\right) - \frac{\delta}{4 - \sigma_1} - \frac{\delta}{5 - \sigma_1} = -\pi \qquad (5\text{–}102)$$

This can be rewritten as

$$-\frac{\delta}{\sigma_1} + \frac{\delta}{4 - \sigma_1} + \frac{\delta}{5 - \sigma_1} = 0 \qquad (5\text{–}103)$$

Canceling δ, and simplifying, results in the equation

$$-\frac{1}{\sigma_1} + \frac{1}{4 - \sigma_1} + \frac{1}{5 - \sigma_1} = 0 \qquad (5\text{–}104)$$

Solution of equation 5–104 results in $\sigma_1 = 1.47$. This is indicated in Figure 5–36.

RULE 8. The intersection of the root locus and the imaginary axis can be determined by applying the Routh-Hurwitz stability criterion to the denominator of equation 5–89. Assuming unity feedback, the characteristic equation for the system illustrated in Figure 5–36 is given by

$$s^3 + 9s^2 + 20s + K = 0 \qquad (5\text{--}105)$$

The resulting Routh-Hurwitz array is given by

$$
\begin{array}{cc}
1 & 20 \\
9 & K \\
\dfrac{180 - K}{9} & \\
K &
\end{array}
\qquad (5\text{--}106)
$$

For this simple array, a zero in the third row indicates a pair of complex conjugate poles crossing the imaginary axis. The corresponding value of gain and the value of s at which this occurs can be obtained as follows: For the third row to equal zero,

$$\frac{180 - K}{9} = 0 \qquad (5\text{--}107)$$

or
$$K = 180$$

Therefore the root locus tells us that this system is stable for all gains up to a value of 180. The corresponding value of s occurring at the crossing of the imaginary axis can be obtained from the expression

$$9s^2 + 180 = 0 \qquad (5\text{--}108)$$

or
$$s = \pm j\sqrt{20}$$

These values are illustrated in Figure 5–36.

RULE 9. The angles made by the root locus leaving a complex pole can be evaluated by applying the principle of equation 5–92. This is illustrated by considering the system shown in Figure 5–37. Let us calculate the angle that the root locus makes with the complex pole located at $-2 + 2j$. An exploratory point s_E, will be assumed slightly displaced from this pole. The angles contributed to this point, due to various open-loop poles of the system, are given by

$$-135° - 90° - \theta = -180° \qquad (5\text{--}109)$$

or
$$\theta = -45°$$

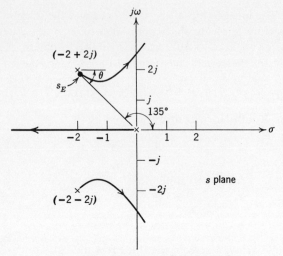

Figure 5-37.   *Root locus of a system where*

$$G(s)H(s) = \frac{K}{s(s^2 + 4s + 8)}$$

Therefore, the angle contributed by the branch of the root locus leaving the pole at $-2 + 2j$ must be sufficient to satisfy the basic relationship given by equation 5-92.

The negative sign appears before each of the angles in equation 5-109 since they are in the denominator of the expression given by equation 5-92. If zeros were present, however, they would contribute positive angles since they are in the numerator of the expression given by equation 5-92.

After the root locus has been sketched by using the nine rules presented, the graphical accuracy may be improved by determining the exact location of a few points. This can easily be performed by applying the relationship of equation 5-92. The gain K at any point can be determined by applying the relationship given by equation 5-93.

In general, constructing a detailed root locus is a very tedious, time-consuming method. Several mechanical construction aids are available. The most commonly used device is known as the Spirule, shown in Figure 5-38.[11] This clear-plastic device, which consists of a disk and arm, functions as an angle summer and locus calibrator. A logarithmic spiral curve on the arm portion enables the logarithm of a length to be calibrated as an angle. Therefore, the addition of angles reduces to a process of adding logarithms. The control engineer should develop facility in using the Spirule if he intends to use the powerful root locus tool for the design of feedback control systems.

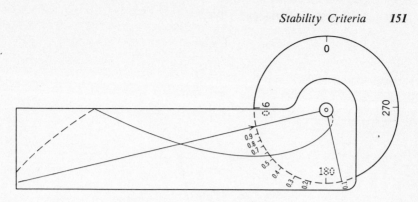

Figure 5–38. A sketch of a Spirule.

This section will conclude with an illustration of the root locus procedure. The details of each step will be clearly and concisely illustrated.
The technique of stabilizing this system, utilizing the root locus method,
is illustrated in chapter 6.

Consider a unity feedback system whose forward-loop transfer function
is given by

$$G(s) = \frac{K}{[(s + 1)(s - 1)(s + 4)^2]} \qquad (5\text{–}110)$$

This system has four poles: three on the negative real axis and one on the
positive real axis. In addition, it has four zeros at infinity. The root
locus of this system, illustrated in Figure 5–39, can be drawn on the basis
of the nine rules, as follows.

RULE 1. There are four separate loci since the characteristic equation,
$1 + G(s)H(s)$, is a fourth-order equation.

RULE 2.   The root locus starts $(K = 0)$ from the poles located at $1, -1$,
and a double pole at -4. All loci terminate $(K = \infty)$ at zeros which are
located at infinity for this problem.

RULE 3.   Complex portions of the root locus occur in complex conjugate pairs.

RULE 4.   The portions of the real axis between -1 and 1 are part of
the root locus.

RULE 5.   The four loci approach infinity as K becomes large at angles
given by

$$\alpha_1 = \pm \frac{\pi}{4} = \pm 45°$$

and

$$\alpha_3 = \pm \frac{3\pi}{4} = \pm 135°$$

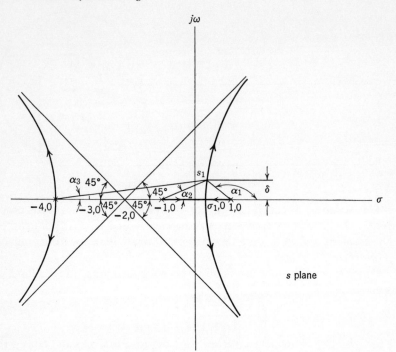

Figure 5–39. Root locus of a system where

$$G(s)H(s) = \frac{K}{(s + 1)(s - 1)(s + 4)^2}$$

RULE 6. The intersections of the asymptotic lines and the real axis occur at

$$s_r = \frac{-8 - 0}{4 - 0} = -2$$

RULE 7. The point of breakaway from the real axis occurring between -1 and 1 will be assumed to lie along the positive real axis at σ_1. The angles contributed from the various poles to a point s_1 that lies a small distance δ off the positive real axis is

$$-(\alpha_1 + \alpha_2 + \alpha_3) = -180°$$

$$-\left(\pi - \frac{\delta}{1 - \sigma_1}\right) - \frac{\delta}{1 + \sigma_1} - \frac{2\delta}{4 + \sigma_1} = -\pi$$

or

$$\frac{-\delta}{1 - \sigma_1} + \frac{\delta}{1 + \sigma_1} + \frac{2\delta}{4 + \sigma_1} = 0$$

Solving, we obtain

$$\sigma_1 = 0.23$$

RULE 8. This particular root locus intersects the imaginary axis only at the origin.

RULE 9. This rule does not apply to this problem.

It is interesting to observe from the root locus illustrated in Figure 5–39 that the system is always unstable since at least one root of the characteristic equation always lies in the right half plane. We illustrate in Chapter 6 the stabilization of this system by means of a lead network.

REFERENCES

1. *Advanced Dynamics of a System of Rigid Bodies*, E. Routh, Macmillan and Co., London, 1905.
2. Uber die Bedingungen, unter welchen eine Gleichung nur Wurzeln mit negativen realen Theilen besitzt, A. Hurwitz, *Math. Ann.*, **46**, 273, (1895).
3. Regeneration Theory, H. Nyquist, *Bell System Tech. J.*, **11**, 126, (Jan. 1932).
4. *Functions of a Complex Variable*, W. F. Osgood, The National University of Peking Press, Peking, 1936, p. 162.
5. Minimizing Servo Load Resonance Error with Frequency Selective Feedback, S. M. Shinners, *Control Eng.*, 51, (Jan. 1962).
6. *Servomechanisms and Regulating System Design*, H. Chestnut and R. W. Mayer, John Wiley and Sons, New York, 1959, Vol. 1, second edition.
7. *Theory of Servomechanisms*, H. M. James, N. B. Nichols, and R. S. Phillips, McGraw-Hill Book Co., New York, 1947.
8. Graphical Analysis of Control Systems, W. R. Evans, *Trans. AIEE*, **67, Pt. 1,** 547, (1948).
9. Control System Synthesis by Root Locus Method, W. R. Evans, *Trans. AIEE*, **69, Pt. 1,** 66, (1950).
10. *Control System Dynamics*, W. R. Evans, McGraw-Hill Book Co., New York, 1954.
11. The Spirule, developed by W. R. Evans, is available from the Spirule Company, Whittier, Calif.

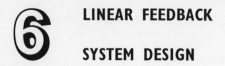

LINEAR FEEDBACK

SYSTEM DESIGN

6-1. INTRODUCTION

After having analyzed the stability of a feedback control system, using any of the tools presented in Chapter 5, the control engineer will probably want to modify the system's performance. In addition, he will need to reassure himself that the feedback control system's open-loop gain is adequate for accuracy, and that the transient response is desirable for the particular application. In order for the system to meet the requirements of stability, accuracy, and transient response, certain types of equipment must be added to the basic feedback control system. We use the term design to encompass the entire process of basic system modifications to meet the specifications of stability, accuracy, and transient response. The terms compensation and/or stabilization are used to indicate the process of achieving the requirements of stability alone.

The compensating device may be inserted into the feedback control system either in cascade with the forward portion of the loop (cascade compensation) as shown in Figure 6–1, or as part of a minor feedback loop (feedback compensation) as shown in Figure 6–2. The cascade compensation technique is usually concerned with the addition of phase-lag, phase-lead, and phase lag-lead devices. The feedback compensation technique is primarily concerned with the addition of rate (tachometer or gyro) or acceleration (accelerometer) feedback devices. The type of compensation chosen depends on the application of the particular control system under consideration.

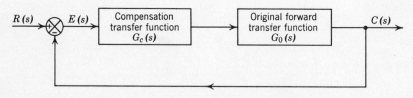

Figure 6–1.   Illustration of cascade compensation.

154

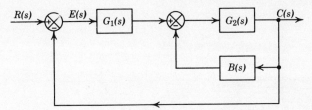

Figure 6–2. Illustration of minor-loop feedback compensation.

This chapter focuses attention on the tools presented in Chapter 5 which are of practical and useful interest to the control engineer. In addition, not all the stability criteria presented are useful with both cascade and feedback compensation. In this chapter we focus our attention only on the application of techniques to those particular design problems they are most suited to solve. Chapter 10 discusses the design of linear feedback control systems from the modern optimal control theory approach.

6–2. CASCADE COMPENSATION TECHNIQUES

Let us consider the system of Figure 6–1 as our basic starting point in order to analyze the effects of cascade compensation. The compensating transfer function, $G_c(s)$, is designed in order to provide additional phase lag, phase lead, or a combination of both, in order to achieve certain specifications regarding stability. We illustrate and derive the transfer functions for representative d-c-type compensating networks, and indicate the extension of the procedure in Section 6-4 for feedback control systems where the reference frequency is other than d-c.

A *phase-lag network* is a device which shifts the phase of the control signal in order that the phase of the output lags the phase of the input. An electrical network performing this function was illustrated in Table 2–2 (Chapter 2) as item 4. Its transfer function was as follows:

$$\frac{E_{\text{out}}(s)}{E_{\text{in}}(s)} = \frac{1 + R_2 C_2 s}{1 + (R_1 + R_2)C_2 s} \tag{6–1}$$

Defining

$$T_2 = R_2 C_2$$

and

$$T_1 = (R_1 + R_2)C_2$$

we can rewrite equation 6–1 as

$$\frac{E_{\text{out}}(s)}{E_{\text{in}}(s)} = \frac{1 + T_2 s}{1 + T_1 s} \tag{6–2}$$

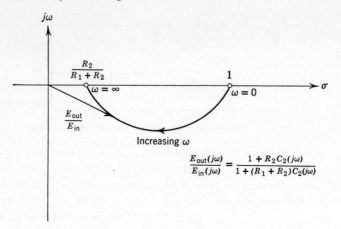

$$\frac{E_{out}(j\omega)}{E_{in}(j\omega)} = \frac{1 + R_2 C_2(j\omega)}{1 + (R_1 + R_2)C_2(j\omega)}$$

Figure 6–3.   A complex plane plot for a phase-lag network.

Observe that $T_1 > T_2$ for a phase-lag network. A complex-plane plot of this network as a function of frequency is shown in Figure 6–3. Notice that the output voltage lags the input in phase angle for all values of frequency except for $\omega = 0$ and $\omega = \infty$. In addition, observe that the magnitude of E_{out}/E_{in} decreases from unity at $\omega = 0$ to $R_2/(R_1 + R_2)$ at $\omega = \infty$. A corresponding Bode diagram for the phase-lag network is illustrated in Figure 6–4. The values for the frequency at which the maximum phase lag occurs, ω_{max}, and the value of the maximum phase lag, ϕ_{max}, can be easily derived. From the transfer function given in equation 6–2, the phase shift contribution is given by

$$\phi = \tan^{-1} \omega T_2 - \tan^{-1} \omega T_1 \tag{6-3}$$

The value of ω_{max} can be derived as follows by differentiating equation 6–3 with respect to ω, and then setting the resulting expression equal to zero.

$$\frac{d\phi}{d\omega} = \frac{T_2}{1 + \omega^2 T_2^2} - \frac{T_1}{1 + \omega^2 T_1^2} = 0$$

Simplifying, we obtain the expression

$$1 - \omega^2 T_1 T_2 = 0 \tag{6-4}$$

or,

$$\omega_{max} = \frac{1}{\sqrt{T_1 T_2}} \tag{6-5}$$

The phase shift corresponding to ω_{max}, ϕ_{max}, can be found by substituting equation 6–5 into equation 6–3 and solving for ϕ. The result is

$$\phi_{max} = \tan^{-1} \frac{T_2}{\sqrt{T_1 T_2}} - \tan^{-1} \frac{T_1}{\sqrt{T_1 T_2}} \tag{6-6}$$

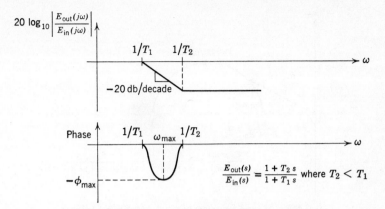

Figure 6–4. Bode diagram of a phase-lag network.

Simplifying, we obtain

$$\phi_{max} = \tan^{-1}\left(\frac{T_2}{T_1}\right)^{1/2} - \tan^{-1}\left(\frac{T_1}{T_2}\right)^{1/2} \tag{6-7}$$

Corresponding values of ϕ_{max} for certain ratios of T_1/T_2, which are useful for design purposes, are listed in Table 6–1.

Table 6–1. ϕ_{max} **as a function of** T_1/T_2

T_1/T_2	$\phi_{max}(degrees)$
1	0
2	−19.4
4	−36.9
8	−49.8
10	−55.0

A *phase-lead network* is a **device** which shifts the phase of the control signal in order that the phase of the output leads the phase of the input. An electrical network performing this function was illustrated in Table 2–2 as item 3. Its transfer function was

$$\frac{E_{out}(s)}{E_{in}(s)} = \frac{R_2}{R_1 + R_2}\frac{1 + R_1C_1s}{1 + [R_2/(R_1 + R_2)]R_1C_1s} \tag{6-8}$$

Defining

$$T_1 = R_1C_1$$

and

$$T_2 = \frac{R_2}{R_1 + R_2}R_1C_1 = \frac{R_2}{R_1 + R_2}T_1$$

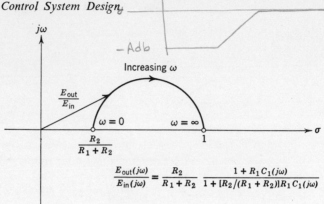

$$\frac{E_{out}(j\omega)}{E_{in}(j\omega)} = \frac{R_2}{R_1 + R_2} \cdot \frac{1 + R_1 C_1(j\omega)}{1 + [R_2/(R_1 + R_2)]R_1 C_1(j\omega)}$$

Figure 6–5.   A complex plane plot for a phase-lead network.

we can rewrite equation 6–8 as

$$\frac{E_{out}(s)}{E_{in}(s)} = \frac{T_2}{T_1} \cdot \frac{1 + T_1 s}{1 + T_2 s} \tag{6-9}$$

Observe that $T_1 > T_2$. A complex-plane plot of this network as a function of frequency is shown in Figure 6–5. Notice that the output voltage leads the input in phase angle for all values of frequency except for $\omega = 0$ and $\omega = \infty$. In addition, notice that the magnitude of E_{out}/E_{in} increases from T_2/T_1 at $\omega = 0$ to unity at $\omega = \infty$. A corresponding Bode diagram for the phase-lead network is illustrated in Figure 6–6. The corresponding

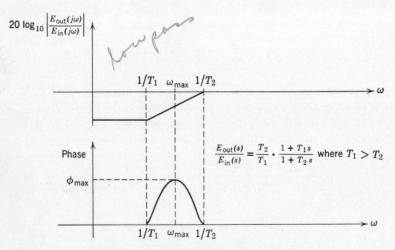

Figure 6–6.   Bode diagram of a phase-lead network.

values of ω_{max} and ϕ_{max} for the phase-lead network are

$$\omega_{max} = \frac{1}{\sqrt{T_1 T_2}} \tag{6-10}$$

$$\phi_{max} = \tan^{-1}\left(\frac{T_1}{T_2}\right)^{\frac{1}{2}} - \tan^{-1}\left(\frac{T_2}{T_1}\right)^{\frac{1}{2}} \tag{6-11}$$

The values shown in Table 6–1 are also true for the phase-lead case except that they are opposite in sign. An important practical point to emphasize is that the control engineer would never in practice use any ratio of $T_1/T_2 >$ 10 since he is paying a penalty of a 10:1 attenuation (-20 db) in accordance with equation 6–9. Therefore, this attenuation must be made up for, somewhere in the feedback control system, with an amplification whose ratio is T_1/T_2.

A phase lag-lead network is a device which shifts the phase of a control signal in order that the phase of the output lags at low frequencies and leads at high frequencies relative to the input. An electrical network performing this function was illustrated in Table 2–2 as item 5. Its transfer function was as follows:

$$\frac{E_{out}(s)}{E_{in}(s)} = \frac{(1 + R_1 C_1 s)(1 + R_2 C_2 s)}{R_1 R_2 C_1 C_2 s^2 + (R_1 C_1 + R_2 C_2 + R_1 C_2)s + 1} \tag{6-12}$$

Defining

$$T_1 = R_1 C_1$$

$$T_2 = R_2 C_2$$

and

$$T_{21} = R_1 C_2$$

we can rewrite equation 6–12 as

$$\frac{E_{out}(s)}{E_{in}(s)} = \frac{T_1 T_2 s^2 + (T_1 + T_2)s + 1}{T_1 T_2 s^2 + (T_1 + T_2 + T_{21})s + 1} \tag{6-13}$$

A complex-plane plot of this network as a function of frequency is shown in Figure 6–7. Notice that the output voltage lags the input in phase angle for low frequencies and leads in phase angle for high frequencies. In addition, notice that the magnitude of E_{out}/E_{in} decreases at an intermediate range of frequencies and increases to unity as ω approaches 0 and ∞. A corresponding Bode diagram for the phase lag-lead network is illustrated in Figure 6–8.

The stabilizing effect of cascaded, phase-shifting networks can easily be demonstrated using the classical approach. For example, let us consider the configuration illustrated in Figure 6–1, where the original forward

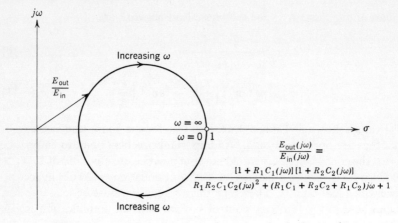

Figure 6–7.   *A complex plane plot for a phase lag-lead network.*

transfer function, $G_0(s)$, is given by

$$G_0(s) = \frac{\omega_n{}^2}{s(s + 2\zeta\omega_n)} \qquad (6\text{--}14)$$

If this system were uncompensated [$G_c(s) = 1$], then the transfer function $G_0(s)$ would result in our familiar type 1, second-order system response which was discussed at great length in Chapter 3, Section 3–7. The resulting damping factor of the system would be given by ζ and its natural resonant frequency by ω_n. Let us now assume that we add some compensation to this system in the form represented by

$$G_c(s) = \frac{1 + T_1 s}{1 + T_2 s} \qquad (6\text{--}15)$$

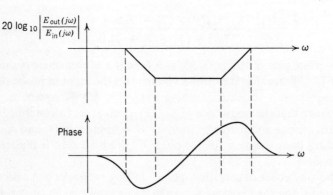

Figure 6–8.   *Bode diagram of a phase lag-lead network.*

The resulting system transfer function with compensation is given by

$$\frac{C(s)}{R(s)} = \frac{\omega_n{}^2 + T_1\omega_n{}^2 s}{T_2 s^3 + (1 + 2\zeta\omega_n T_2)s^2 + (2\zeta\omega_n + T_1\omega_n{}^2)s + \omega_n{}^2} \quad (6\text{–}16)$$

For the *phase-lead compensation case*, let us assume that T_2 is very much smaller than T_1. Therefore, for all practical purposes, we may assume that $T_2 = 0$. For this condition, equation 6–16 reduces to the form

$$\frac{C(s)}{R(s)} = \frac{\omega_n{}^2 + T_1\omega_n{}^2 s}{s^2 + (2\zeta\omega_n + T_1\omega_n{}^2)s + \omega_n{}^2} \quad (6\text{–}17)$$

Comparing the denominators of equations 6–17 and 3–90, we observe that the equivalent damping factor with compensation can be obtained as follows:

$$2\zeta\omega_n + T_1\omega_n{}^2 = 2\zeta_{eq}\omega_n \quad (6\text{–}18)$$

where ζ_{eq} = an equivalent damping factor with phase-lead compensation. Solving for ζ_{eq}, we obtain

$$\zeta_{eq} = \zeta + \frac{T_1\omega_n}{2} \quad (6\text{–}19)$$

Therefore, we can conclude that the addition of phase-lead compensation has increased the damping factor from ζ to ζ_{eq} by an amount equal to $T_1\omega_n/2$.

In a similar manner, the *effect of phase-lag compensation* can be shown to increase the equivalent damping factor. Rearranging equation 6–16 as follows

$$\frac{C(s)}{R(s)} = \frac{(1/T_2)(\omega_n{}^2 + T_1\omega_n{}^2 s)}{s^3 + (1/T_2)(1 + 2\zeta\omega_n T_2)s^2 + (1/T_2)(2\zeta\omega_n + T_1\omega_n{}^2)s + (1/T_2)\omega_n{}^2}$$

$$(6\text{–}20)$$

we observe that the denominator is in a form which can be compared with the characteristic equation of a type 1, third-order system, which is given by

$$s^3 + 2\zeta\omega_n s^2 + \omega_n{}^2 s + M\omega_n{}^3 = 0 \quad (6\text{–}21)$$

where ζ = damping factor and M = another parameter indicative of damping. We see from equation 6–21 that the coefficient of the s^2 term is directly proportional to the damping factor ζ. Therefore, the equivalent damping factor with compensation can be obtained from the coefficient of the s^2 term in the denominator of equation 6–20 as follows:

$$\frac{1}{T_2}(1 + 2\zeta\omega_n T_2) = 2\zeta_{eq}\omega_n \quad (6\text{–}22)$$

Solving for ζ_{eq}, we obtain

$$\zeta_{eq} = \frac{1}{2T_2\omega_n} + \zeta \tag{6-23}$$

Thus, we can conclude that the addition of phase-lag compensation has increased the damping factor from ζ to ζ_{eq} by an amount equal to $1/2T_2\omega_n$.

Logically, we ought to ask ourselves next, what is the steady-state error resulting from cascade compensation? To answer this question intelligently, we must find the steady-state error resulting from the application of a ramp input for the cases of no compensation and compare it with those resulting from cascade compensation. We choose a unit ramp as our input since it is the only input which results in a finite following error for a type 1 system. The transfer function relating error to input for the system shown in Figure 6–1 is given by

$$\frac{E(s)}{R(s)} = \frac{1}{1 + G_c(s)G_0(s)} \tag{6-24}$$

Assuming that

$$G_c(s) = 1 \quad \text{(no cascade compensation)}$$

$$G_0(s) = \frac{\omega_n^2}{s(s + 2\zeta\omega_n)}$$

and

$$R(s) = \frac{1}{s^2} \quad \text{(a unit ramp input)}$$

we find that

$$E(s) = \frac{1}{s} \frac{s + 2\zeta\omega_n}{s^2 + 2\zeta\omega_n s + \omega_n^2} \tag{6-25}$$

Applying the final-value theorem to equation 6–25, we find the steady-state error to be

$$e_{ss} = \lim_{s \to 0} sE(s) = \frac{2\zeta\omega_n}{\omega_n^2} = \frac{2\zeta}{\omega_n} \tag{6-26}$$

For the case with cascade compensation (either phase-lead or -lag), a similar analysis yields the following result:

$$G_c(s) = \frac{1 + T_1s}{1 + T_2s}, \quad G_0(s) = \frac{\omega_n^2}{s(s + 2\zeta\omega_n)}, \quad R(s) = \frac{1}{s^2}$$

$$\therefore \quad E(s) = \frac{1}{s} \frac{(s + 2\zeta\omega_n)(1 + T_2s)}{s(s + 2\zeta\omega_n)(1 + T_2s) + \omega_n^2(1 + T_1s)} \tag{6-27}$$

Applying the final-value theorem to equation 6–27, the steady-state error is found to be

$$e_{ss} = \lim_{s \to 0} sE(s) = \frac{2\zeta\omega_n}{\omega_n^2} = \frac{2\zeta}{\omega_n} \tag{6-28}$$

Comparing the results of equations 6–26 and 6–28, we conclude that the addition of cascade compensation does not increase or decrease the steady-state following error of the system.

6–3. MINOR-LOOP FEEDBACK COMPENSATION TECHNIQUES

Let us next consider the general system illustrated in Figure 6–2. The compensating element in this case is the transfer function $B(s)$. In order to have a basis of comparison, we follow a similar analysis for minor-loop feedback compensation as was performed for the case of cascade compensation. We assume that the minor-loop feedback element $B(s)$ is a d-c-type element. The extension of this method of stabilization to feedback control systems where the reference frequency is other than d-c is considered in Section 6–4.

The minor-loop feedback element $B(s)$ usually consists of a tachometer whose output is proportional to the rate of the output, and/or an accelerometer whose output is proportional to the acceleration of the output. In general, phase-lag-, -lead, and/or lag-lead networks may also be cascaded with the tachometer and/or accelerometer.

The stabilizing effect of minor-loop feedback compensation can easily be demonstrated using the classical approach. We assume that the system illustrated in Figure 6–2 consists of simple rate (tachometer) feedback. The specific transfer functions for the system are

$$G_1(s) = 1$$
$$G_2(s) = \frac{\omega_n^2}{s(s + 2\zeta\omega_n)}$$
$$B(s) = bs$$

Without any rate feedback, the configuration represents a simple type 1, second-order system whose damping factor is ζ and natural resonant frequency is ω_n. The resulting system transfer function with compensation is given by

$$\frac{C(s)}{R(s)} = \frac{\omega_n^2}{s^2 + (2\zeta\omega_n + \omega_n^2 b)s + \omega_n^2} \tag{6–29}$$

Comparing the denominators of equations 6–29 and 3–90, we observe that the equivalent damping factor with compensation can be obtained by setting the coefficients of the s terms equal to each other, as follows.

$$2\zeta\omega_n + \omega_n^2 b = 2\zeta_{eq}\omega_n \tag{6–30}$$

where ζ_{eq} = an equivalent damping factor with compensation. Solving for ζ_{eq}, we obtain

$$\zeta_{eq} = \zeta + \frac{\omega_n b}{2} \tag{6-31}$$

Therefore, we can conclude that the addition of minor-loop compensation using rate feedback has increased the damping factor from ζ to ζ_{eq} by an amount equal to $\omega_n b/2$.

Let us next determine the steady-state error resulting from the use of minor-loop rate feedback compensation. We assume that the input to this type 1 system is a unit ramp in order to have a finite steady-state following error and have a basis for comparison. From our discussion of cascade compensation in Section 6–2 we know from equation 6–26 that the resulting steady-state error of this system without any compensation ($b = 0$) is $2\zeta/\omega_n$. For the case of minor-loop rate feedback compensation, the resulting expression for $E(s)$ is given by

$$E(s) = \frac{1}{s} \left[\frac{(s + 2\zeta\omega_n + b\omega_n{}^2)}{s(s + 2\zeta\omega_n + b\omega_n{}^2) + \omega_n{}^2} \right] \tag{6-32}$$

Applying the final-value theorem, the steady-state error is found to be

$$E_{ss} = \lim_{s \to 0} sE(s) = \frac{2\zeta\omega_n + b\omega_n{}^2}{\omega_n{}^2} = \frac{2\zeta}{\omega_n} + b \tag{6-33}$$

Therefore, the steady-state following error of the system with minor-loop rate feedback compensation has increased by a factor of b. The interesting aspect of this result is that the steady-state following error has increased by the constant, b. This unfavorable result can easily be remedied by placing

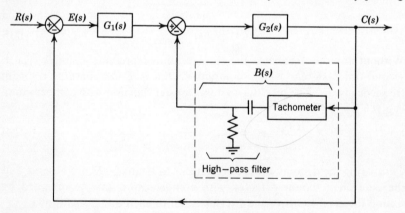

Figure 6–9. Illustration of minor-loop feedback compensation using a tachometer in cascade with a high-pass filter.

a high-pass filter in cascade with the tachometer. Such a filter would block the steady-state value of the tachometer output. This technique is illustrated in Figure 6–9.

6–4. COMPENSATION IN D-C, CARRIER, AND HYBRID FEEDBACK CONTROL SYSTEMS

We have so far concentrated our attention on *d-c feedback control systems*. The term d-c is used to characterize the form of the reference input, actuating signal, manipulated variable signal, and controlled variable output. These quantities may be electrical, mechanical, hydraulic, and/or thermal.

Carrier feedback control systems are configurations where the reference input, actuating signal, manipulated variable signal, and controlled variable output are sinusoidal quantities. Usually the frequencies of these signals are 60, 400, or 1000 cps.

Hybrid feedback control systems are configurations in which d-c and carrier signals are both present. This section illustrates and describes the operation of these three basic types of feedback control system.

Assuming that the voltage across potentiometers R_1 and R_2 is d-c, Figure 6–10 represents a good example of a *d-c feedback control system*. For this system, a constant input signal results in d-c-type signals everywhere in the system. The control engineer can compensate this system using cascade or minor-loop feedback compensation techniques using the elementary d-c type elements which have been discussed previously.

A *carrier-type feedback control system* which performs a similar function is illustrated in Figure 6–11. The synchro control transformer[1] and synchro generator[1] constitute the error-sensing detector for this type

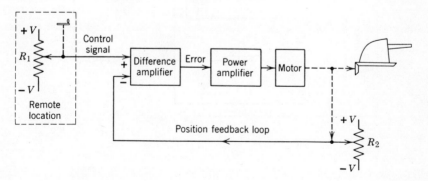

Figure 6–10.   An automatic positioning system for a gun turret.

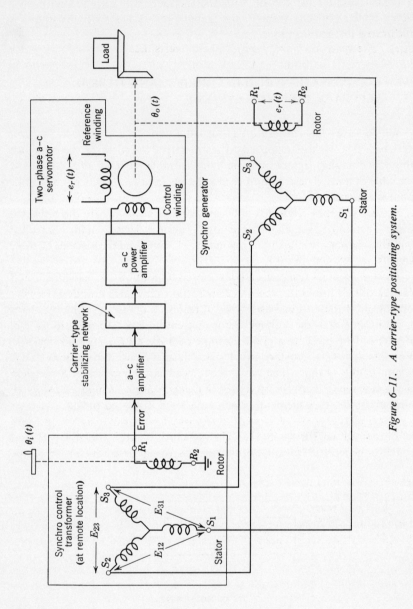

Figure 6–11.   A carrier-type positioning system.

of feedback control system. The *synchro generator* applies to its three stator leads, voltages, whose relative magnitude and polarity is indicative of the angular position of the rotor which is excited by a reference voltage $e_r(t)$. The *synchro control transformer* converts these three voltages, which are received on its stator leads, into a single voltage which is proportional to the sine of the angular difference of the two rotor shafts.

$$\text{Error} \propto \sin\left[\theta_i(t) - \theta_0(t)\right] \qquad (6\text{--}34)$$

Synchros are basically transformers in which one winding can rotate. The stator voltages of the synchro generator are all electrically in phase but displaced $120°$ in space. The reference voltage $e_r(t)$ sets up an alternating magnetic field in the synchro generator which induces the following voltages between the three stator leads:

$$E_{nm} = K_{nm} \cos\left[\theta_0(t) - 30°\right] \qquad (6\text{--}35)$$

Connecting the stator windings of the synchro generator to the synchro control transformer induces a corresponding alternating magnetic flux in the control transformer. If the input and output shaft angles are in agreement, the resulting error voltage is zero. If they are out of agreement, however, an error voltage is generated in accordance with equation 6–34.

Any resulting error voltage is amplified successively by a-c voltage and power amplifiers. The amplified error signal is applied to the two-phase a-c servomotor which positions the output shaft angle until it is in agreement with the input shaft angle and the resulting error is zero. A description of the operation of the two-phase a-c servomotor can be found in Section 3–3.

The intelligence (or error) signal in carrier-type systems is modulated with a sinusoidal carrier signal of frequency ω_c in the following manner:

$$m(t) = e(t) \cos \omega_c t \qquad (6\text{--}36)$$

where $e(t)$ = intelligence signal
$m(t)$ = resulting modulated signal

The intelligence signal $e(t)$ can be typically represented by the expression

$$e(t) = E \cos \omega_1 t \qquad (6\text{--}37)$$

Substituting equation 6–37 into equation 6–36, we obtain the expression for the total modulated signal as follows:

$$m(t) = E \cos \omega_1 t \cos \omega_c t \qquad (6\text{--}38)$$

Using the trigonometric relationship that

$$\cos A \cos B = \tfrac{1}{2}\left[\cos(A + B) + \cos(A - B)\right] \qquad (6\text{--}39)$$

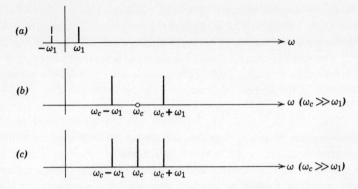

Figure 6–12. Comparison of various frequency spectra: (a) d-c control system with an intelligence bandwidth of ω_1; (b) carrier-type system with an intelligence bandwidth of ω_1; (c) conventional AM system with an intelligence bandwidth of ω_1.

equation 6–38 can be rewritten as

$$m(t) = \tfrac{1}{2}E[\cos(\omega_c + \omega_1)t + \cos(\omega_c - \omega_1)t] \qquad (6\text{–}40)$$

Observe from this result that the resulting modulated signal contains an upper and lower sideband, but not the carrier frequency. Since the carrier frequency does not appear explicitly in the resulting modulated signal, the term *carrier-suppressed modulation* is used to describe this operation.

It is important to realize the distinction between carrier-suppressed modulation and amplitude modulation (AM) which is found in communication systems. The relationship describing conventional AM is given by

$$m(t) = [1 + Ke(t)] \cos \omega_c t \qquad (6\text{–}41)$$

where K = modulation index. For the case of 100% modulation ($K = 1$) and

$$e(t) = \cos \omega_1 t \qquad (6\text{–}42)$$

the resulting expression for the modulated signal is

$$m(t) = [1 + \cos \omega_1 t] \cos \omega_c t = \cos \omega_c t + \cos \omega_1 t \cos \omega_c t \quad (6\text{–}43)$$

Using the trigonometric identity of equation 6–39, equation 6–43 reduces to

$$m(t) = \cos \omega_c t + \tfrac{1}{2}\cos(\omega_c + \omega_1)t + \tfrac{1}{2}\cos(\omega_c - \omega_1)t \qquad (6\text{–}44)$$

Therefore, in conventional AM, the carrier frequency is present in addition to the two sidebands.

Figure 6–12 compares the frequency spectrum of d-c control systems, carrier-type control systems, and conventional AM systems. Figure 6–13 illustrates the resulting waveforms for carrier-suppressed modulation and conventional AM, assuming 100% modulation for the latter.

Carrier-type control systems can be stabilized by means of cascaded carrier-type networks or by means of minor-loop feedback compensation techniques. The former stabilization is much more difficult to design than its d-c equivalent and the latter is as readily available as its d-c equivalent. We next consider the design of carrier-type networks for the cascade compensation of carrier-type systems.

The *carrier-type network* must operate directly on the envelope of the suppressed-carrier waveform shown in Figure 6–13a. We would like to define a transfer function for such a network in terms of the suppressed

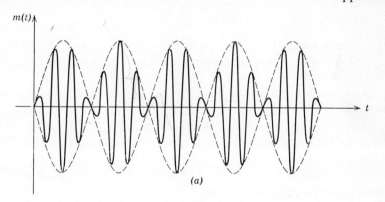

(a)

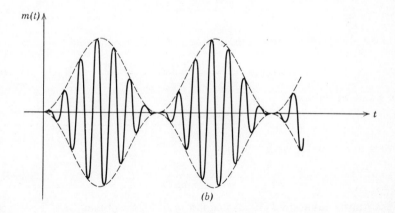

(b)

Figure 6–13. Comparison of carrier-suppressed modulation and conventional AM. (a) Carrier-suppressed modulation where $m(t) = e(t) \cos \omega_c t$. (b) Conventional AM (100% modulation) where $m(t) = [1 + e(t)] \cos \omega_c t$.

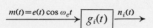

Figure 6–14.   Ideal   carrier-type network transfer function.

$$g(t) = \frac{n(t)}{m(t)}$$

Figure 6–15.   Transfer function of corresponding   d-c-type   network.

carrier input and output waveforms. For example, consider the carrier-type network shown in Figure 6–14. Ideally, we would desire to specify a transfer function

$$g_i(t) = \frac{n_i(t)}{m(t)} \tag{6–45}$$

where

$$m(t) = e(t) \cos \omega_c t$$

in a manner similar to that for the d-c-type network illustrated in Figure 6–15. Let us proceed to determine whether this is at all possible for carrier-type networks.[2]

The Laplace transform of the input can be obtained in the following manner:

$$m(t) = e(t) \cos \omega_c t \tag{6–46}$$

Since the

$$\cos \omega_c t = \frac{e^{j\omega_c t} + e^{-j\omega_c t}}{2} \tag{6–47}$$

we may rewrite equation 6–46 as

$$m(t) = \frac{e(t) \, e^{j\omega_c t} + e(t) \, e^{-j\omega_c t}}{2} \tag{6–48}$$

Taking the Laplace transform of equation 6–48, we obtain

$$M(s) = \frac{E(s - j\omega_c) + E(s + j\omega_c)}{2} \tag{6–49}$$

In a similar manner,

$$N_i(s) = \frac{N(s - j\omega_c) + N(s + j\omega_c)}{2} \tag{6–50}$$

From Figure 6–15, we know that

$$G(s) = \frac{N(s)}{M(s)} \tag{6–51}$$

Substituting equation 6–51 into equation 6–50, we obtain

$$N_i(s) = \frac{G(s - j\omega_c)M(s - j\omega_c) + G(s + j\omega_c)M(s + j\omega_c)}{2} \tag{6–52}$$

Division of equation 6–52 by equation 6–49 results in the following ideal transfer function for the carrier-type network.

$$G_i(s) = \frac{G(s - j\omega_c)M(s - j\omega_c) + G(s + j\omega_c)M(s + j\omega_c)}{E(s - j\omega_c) + E(s + j\omega_c)} \quad (6\text{–}53)$$

Unfortunately, this $G_i(s)$ is not physically reliable with passive elements since the transfer function depends on the input signal. Therefore, we cannot design a linear passive network having exact arithmetic symmetry or antisymmetry about the nonzero carrier frequency. By arithmetic antisymmetry, we mean that

$$G_i(j\omega)]_{\omega=\omega_c-\omega_1} = -G_i(j\omega)]_{\omega=\omega_c+\omega_1} \quad (6\text{–}54)$$

Thus, an approximation must be made by the control engineer. The simplest one, and one which gives very good results for $\omega_c \gg \omega_1$, is to design the carrier-type network to have geometrical symmetry or antisymmetry instead of arithmetic symmetry. By geometrical antisymmetry, we mean that

$$G_i(j\omega)]_{\omega=\omega_c-\omega_a} = -G_i(j\omega)]_{\omega=\omega_c+\omega_b} \quad (6\text{–}55)$$

where

$$\frac{\omega_a}{\omega_c} = \frac{\omega_c}{\omega_b}, \quad \text{or} \quad \omega_c{}^2 = \omega_a\omega_b \quad (6\text{–}56)$$

Two methods are available for synthesizing networks having geometrical symmetry.[3]

1. Low-pass–bandpass transformations
2. Approximation by a function having poles on the negative real axis

The *low-pass–bandpass transformation* consists of synthesizing an RLC carrier-type network from an equivalent d-c-type network. Each inductance of the d-c network L is replaced by a series resonant circuit consisting of an inductor of $L/2$ and a capacitance which results in a resonance at the carrier frequency ω_c. Each capacitance of the d-c network, C, is replaced by a parallel resonant circuit consisting of a capacitance $C/2$ and an inductor which results in a resonance at the carrier frequency ω_c. All resistors remain unchanged in the transformation. The procedure of this transformation is summarized in Figure 6–16. Several examples of low-pass–bandpass transformations[2] are illustrated in Figure 6–17. Circuits 1 and 2 represent lead networks, and circuits 3 and 4 represent lag networks. In terms of the low-pass–bandpass transformation parameters, circuit 2

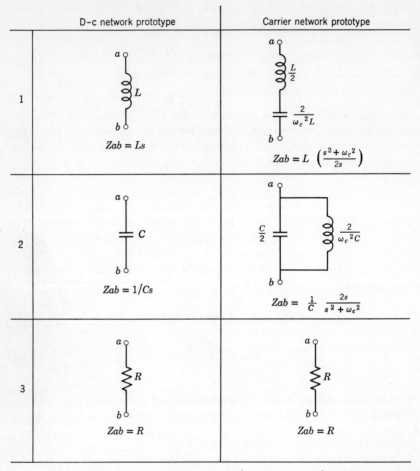

D-c network prototype	Carrier network prototype

1

$Zab = Ls$

$Zab = L\left(\dfrac{s^2 + \omega_c^2}{2s}\right)$

2

$Zab = 1/Cs$

$Zab = \dfrac{1}{C}\dfrac{2s}{s^2 + \omega_c^2}$

3

$Zab = R$

$Zab = R$

Figure 6–16.   D-C to carrier type network prototype transformations.

has a carrier transfer function, $G_c(s)$, which is given by

$$G_c(s) = \alpha\,\frac{1 + Ts}{1 + \alpha Ts} \qquad (6\text{–}57)$$

where

$$\alpha = \frac{R_2}{R_1 + R_2}$$

$$T = \frac{2L}{R_2}$$

Observe the similarity to its d-c equivalent network.

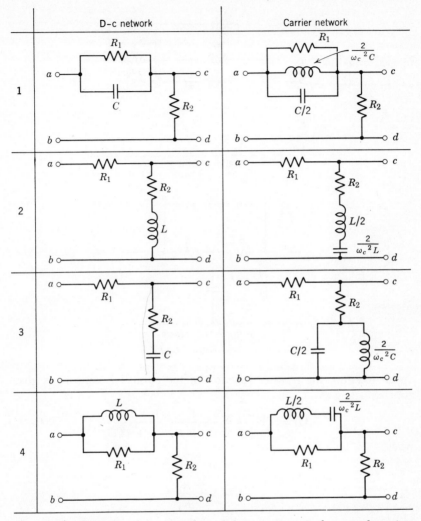

Figure 6–17. Examples of d-c networks and their carrier equivalent transformations.

The *approximation by a function having poles on the negative real axis* results in the parallel-T and bridged-T lead notch networks which consist of resistors and capacitors only. These networks are discussed extensively in the literature. For a good discussion from the control engineer's viewpoint, see Refs. 4 and 5. These circuits are shown in Figure 6–18. The parallel-T lead network is shown in an unconventional manner with a potentiometer in order to show how the time constant may be changed. This form is quite useful from an experimental viewpoint. In terms of this

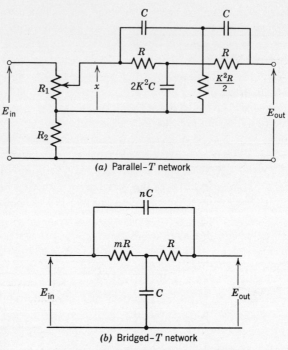

(a) Parallel-T network

(b) Bridged-T network

Figure 6–18. Carrier-type lead networks.

approximation, the transfer function of the parallel-T network is given approximately by

$$G_c(s) = \frac{E_{out}(s)}{E_{in}(s)} = \frac{R_2}{R_1 + R_2} \cdot \frac{1 + jT\alpha\omega_s}{1 + jT\omega_s} \qquad (6\text{–}58)$$

where

$$\omega_s = \omega - \omega_c$$

$$\alpha = 1 + \frac{R_1}{R_2}x$$

$$\omega_c = \frac{1}{KRC}$$

$$T = \frac{K}{K^2 + 1}\frac{1}{\omega_c}$$

Observe the similarity to its d-c equivalent network.

The low-pass–bandpass transformation has an advantage over the technique of approximating an RC network with poles on the negative real axis; resonance of the LC circuits can be achieved with one simple adjustment. The RC networks are very difficult to tune, and once they are tuned they have a tendency to become detuned with temperature changes and aging effects. However, the resulting low-pass–bandpass transformation networks have the disadvantage that they use a choke, which is usually bulky and relatively expensive.

A *hybrid feedback control system* which performs a function similar to the d-c control system of Figure 1–8, and the carrier-type control system of Figure 6–11, is shown in Figure 6–19. The primary modification to the carrier-type configuration has been the replacing of the carrier-type stabilizing network with a demodulator, d-c compensating network and modulator. The *demodulator* is a phase-sensitive detector which gives a d-c output voltage proportional to the carrier voltage impressed on it and having a polarity which is dependent on the polarity of the carrier voltage. Schematic diagrams of an electronic and mechanical demodulator are shown in Figures 6–20 and 6–21, respectively. The reader is referred to the literature[6] for extensive descriptions of these circuits and many similar versions including the use of matched transistors. The rectified output of the demodulator can then be compensated by a conventional d-c *compensating network*. In order to be able to drive the two-phase a-c servomotor, the output of the d-c compensating network must first be modulated back to the carrier frequency. The *modulator* is a phase-sensitive device which gives a carrier voltage output proportional to the d-c input voltage impressed upon it. The demodulator circuits shown in Figures 6–20 and 6–21 can serve as modulators by reversing the signal flow through them.

The hybrid system has several advantages over the d-c and carrier-type systems. By using a-c amplification in the hybrid configuration, the complexity and expense of d-c amplification is eliminated. In addition, the demodulation-modulation process has the advantage of eliminating any *quadrature voltage* (a voltage which is 90° out of phase with the reference carrier voltage). This would ordinarily saturate the a-c amplifiers of the carrier system.

An obvious disadvantage of the hybrid configuration is that it requires additional equipment. In addition, the demodulation process results in the generation of harmonics. This may be easily demonstrated for the circuits shown in Figures 6–20 and 6–21. The demodulation process is basically the modulation of the carrier frequency by the carrier frequency itself. For example, assume that the input (modulated signal) is given by

$$m(t) = e(t) \cos \omega_c t \tag{6-59}$$

Modulating this signal by the carrier frequency results in the following output from the circuit:

$$n(t) = m(t) \cos (\omega_c t + \phi) \tag{6-60}$$

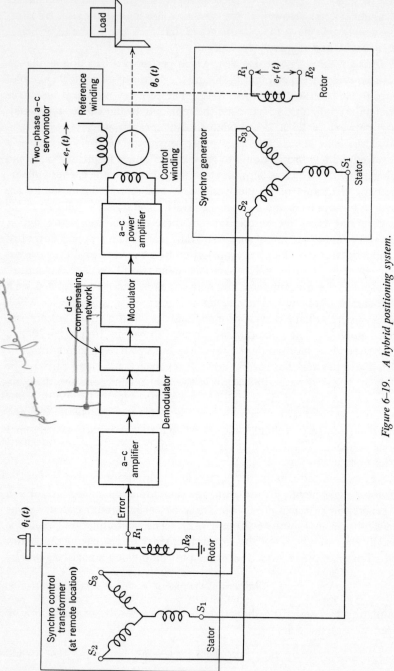

Figure 6–19. A hybrid positioning system.

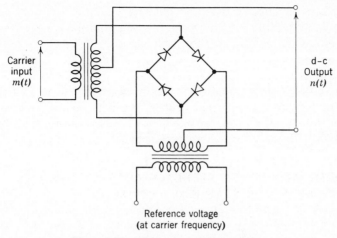

Figure 6–20.   Basic electronic demodulator.

where ϕ = some arbitrary phase shift. Substituting equation 6–59 into equation 6–60 results in the following expression for the output:

$$n(t) = e(t) \cos \omega_c t \cos (\omega_c t + \phi) \qquad (6\text{–}61)$$

Using the trigonometric relation that

$$\cos A \cos B = \tfrac{1}{2} \cos (A + B) + \tfrac{1}{2} \cos (A - B) \qquad (6\text{–}62)$$

we may rewrite equation 6–61 as

$$n(t) = \tfrac{1}{2} e(t) \cos \phi + \tfrac{1}{2} e(t) \cos (2\omega_c t + \phi) \qquad (6\text{–}63)$$

Therefore, the output of the demodulator has a d-c signal component and a second-harmonic component of the carrier frequency. For most situations this is not a serious disadvantage since the carrier frequency is

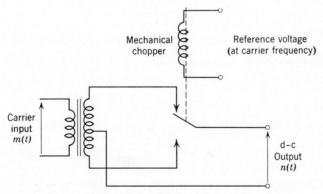

Figure 6–21.   Basic mechanical demodulator using a chopper.

usually so much greater than the bandwidth of the feedback control system. In some situations, however, it is not, and the effect of the harmonic term must be accounted for in the design.

For the remainder of this chapter, we consider only the details concerned with the design of d-c-type systems. It is quite evident from the discussion of this section that the d-c compensating network can always be implemented in carrier systems either by using a hybrid configuration (addition of a demodulator and modulator) or by transforming the d-c network into an equivalent carrier-type network.

6–5. DESIGN OF LINEAR FEEDBACK CONTROL SYSTEMS UTILIZING THE CLASSICAL APPROACH

Much insight into the design of linear systems can be obtained from the classical approach. In this section we consider the compensation and resulting performance of a type 1, second-order system by means of cascade and minor-loop rate feedback techniques. This problem is useful in unifying concepts which were introduced in Chapters 3, 4, and 5, together with the design techniques to be illustrated later in this chapter.

Let us consider the type 1, second-order system illustrated in Figure 6–22. We assume that the original forward-loop transfer function $G_0(s)$ is given by

$$G_0(s) = \frac{14.4}{s(0.1s + 1)} \tag{6–64}$$

The closed-loop transfer function of this system, $C(s)/R(s)$, is given by

$$\frac{C(s)}{R(s)} = \frac{G_0(s)}{1 + G_0(s)} = \frac{14.4}{s(0.1s + 1)} \bigg/ \left[1 + \frac{14.4}{s(0.1s + 1)}\right] \tag{6–65}$$

or

$$\frac{C(s)}{R(s)} = \frac{144}{s^2 + 10s + 144} \tag{6–66}$$

Comparing equations 3–90 and 6–66, we observe that the natural resonant frequency of the system ω_n is given by

$$\omega_n^2 = 144 \tag{6–67}$$

or

$$\omega_n = 12 \text{ radians/second} \tag{6–68}$$

and that the damping factor of the system, ζ, is given by

$$2\zeta\omega_n = 10 \tag{6–69}$$

or

$$\zeta = 0.413 \tag{6–70}$$

If the system is subjected to a unit step input, the transient response will have the form shown in Figure 3–37 (interpolate between $\zeta = 0.4$ and

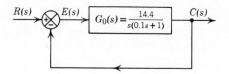

Figure 6–22.   A type 1, second-order feedback control system.

$\zeta = 0.6$).   The maximum per cent overshoot can be obtained from equation 3–119 as follows:

$$\text{Maximum per cent overshoot} = \exp\left(-\frac{\zeta\pi}{\sqrt{1 + \zeta^2}}\right) \times 100\%$$

For $\zeta = 0.413$, $\qquad\qquad$ (6–71)

$$\text{Maximum per cent overshoot} = 23.5\%$$

Let us assume, for this application, that the optimum control-system performance is obtained when the transient response reaches its final steady-state value in minimum time without having any overshoots. From the discussion of Section 3–7, we know that a critically damped system ($\zeta = 1$) meets these requirements. We demonstrate how this can be achieved using cascaded compensation and minor-loop rate feedback compensation.

Figure 6–23 illustrates the form that the system illustrated in Figure 6–22 would have if cascaded compensation were used. We attempt to achieve a damping factor equal to 1 using a lead network where

$$G_c(s) = \frac{1 + T_1 s}{1 + T_2 s} \qquad\qquad (6–72)$$

As was assumed previously, in Section 6–2, we consider that T_2 equals zero since it is so very much smaller than T_1. Therefore, $G_c(s)$ reduces to

$$G_c(s) = 1 + T_1 s \qquad\qquad (6–73)$$

The closed-loop system transfer function for this case was derived in Section 6–2 (see equation 6–17) as

$$\frac{C(s)}{R(s)} = \frac{\omega_n^2 + T_1\omega_n^2 s}{s^2 + (2\zeta\omega_n + T_1\omega_n^2)s + \omega_n^2} \qquad (6–74)$$

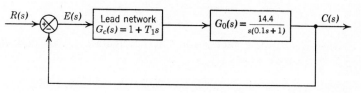

Figure 6–23.   Cascade compensation of the system shown in Figure 6–22.

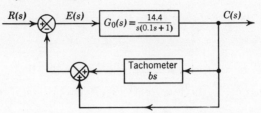

Figure 6-24. Minor-loop feedback compensation of the system shown in Figure 6-22.

The equivalent damping factor for this situation was derived in Section 6-2 (see equation 6-19) as

$$\zeta_{eq} = \zeta + \frac{T_1 \omega_n}{2} \tag{6-75}$$

The object in this problem is to design $\zeta_{eq} = 1$ for the case where

$$\zeta = 0.413 \quad \text{and} \quad \omega_n = 12$$

Substituting these values into equation 6-75, we find that

$$T_1 = 0.0978$$

From our development of the subject matter, we know that the resulting system will be stable, will be critically damped, and will have a steady-state following error to a unit step input of zero. The steady-state following error of the system to a unit ramp input was derived (see equation 6-26) as

$$e_{ss}]_{\text{ramp input}} = \frac{2\zeta}{\omega_n} = \frac{2(0.413)}{12} = 0.0695 \text{ units} \tag{6-76}$$

Let us next attempt to achieve the same type of optimum control system using minor-loop rate feedback compensation. Figure 6-24 illustrates the form that the system illustrated in Figure 6-22 would have if minor-loop feedback compensation were used. We shall attempt to achieve a damping factor equal to 1 using tachometer feedback. The closed-loop system transfer function for this case was derived, previously, in Section 6-2 (see equation 6-29) as

$$\frac{C(s)}{R(s)} = \frac{\omega_n^2}{s^2 + (2\zeta\omega_n + \omega_n^2 b)s + \omega_n^2} \tag{6-77}$$

The equivalent damping factor for this configuration was derived in Section 6-2 (see equation 6-31) as

$$\zeta_{eq} = \zeta + \frac{\omega_n b}{2} \tag{6-78}$$

The object in this problem is to design $\zeta_{eq} = 1$ for the case where

$$\zeta = 0.413 \quad \text{and} \quad \omega_n = 12$$

Substituting these values into equation 6–78, we find that

$$b = 0.0978$$

The reason that b equals the same value as T_1 for the lead case is that rate feedback acts effectively as a pure lead term (no lag component) and we had assumed that T_2 of the lead network was zero. This is illustrated further when we discuss design using the Bode plot, in Section 6–8.

From our development of the subject matter, we know that the resulting system will be stable, will be critically damped, and will have a steady-state following error to a unit step input of zero. The steady-state following error of the system to a unit ramp input was derived (see equation 6–33) as

$$e_{ss}]_{\text{ramp input}} = \frac{2\zeta}{\omega_n} + b = 0.0695 + 0.0978 = 0.1673 \text{ units} \quad (6\text{–}79)$$

This increase has been accounted for in Section 6–3, together with methods for reducing it back to a value of 0.0695.

6–6. DESIGN UTILIZING CONSTANT-MAGNITUDE AND PHASE ANGLE CIRCLES SUPERIMPOSED ON THE NYQUIST DIAGRAM

Constant-magnitude and phase angle circles were developed in Section 5–5. We demonstrated in that section how the control engineer could obtain the closed-loop frequency response of a feedback control system by superimposing these loci onto the Nyquist diagram. Specifically, we obtained the closed-loop frequency response of the system shown in Figure 5–12. The intersections of the constant-magnitude loci and the corresponding Nyquist diagram were shown in Figure 5–13. The resulting closed-loop frequency response was illustrated in Figure 5–14. It indicated a maximum value of peaking M_p of 2.2, and the frequency at which it occurred, ω_p, to be 10 radians/second. This result was checked in Section 5–8 using the Nichols chart approach. We indicated in Section 5–5 that a value of $M_p = 2.2$ does not represent a good design; usually, a value of M_p between 1.1 and 1.5 represents an optimum one. This section demonstrates how the control engineer may use the constant-magnitude and phase angle circles superimposed on the Nyquist diagram in order to achieve a specified design.

Let us assume for this problem that an acceptable value of M_p is 1.3. This may be achieved by adding a phase-lag or phase-lead network in cascade to the forward-loop transfer function $G(s)$. A phase-lag network is used for this problem although a solution can be found as easily using a phase-lead network. The object of this exercise is to modify the compensated open-loop transfer function in order that the Nyquist diagram is tangent to the $M = 1.3$ circle. By restricting the Nyquist diagram to areas external to the $M = 1.3$ circle, we have limited M_p to 1.3 since the interior of the circle represents values of M greater than 1.3.

The procedure for finding the time constants of the lag network

$$G_c(s) = \frac{1 + T_2 s}{1 + T_1 s} \tag{6-80}$$

which will achieve an $M_p = 1.3$ is by trial and error. With a little foresight and intelligent reasoning, however, we do not have to attempt more than two solutions. With some luck, a solution on the first trial is possible. For the problem at hand, the type of reasoning necessary for achieving a possible solution on the first trial will be demonstrated.

Studying the characteristics of Figure 5–13, we see that relatively large $G(j\omega)$ vectors exist for frequencies less than $\omega = 3$. It is not desired to shift these vectors into the interior of the $M = 1.3$ circle by means of the phase-lag network. Therefore we must limit the maximum phase lag to about 30°. From Table 6–1, this corresponds to a ratio of approximately

$$\frac{T_1}{T_2} = 3 \tag{6-81}$$

In addition, studying the characteristics of Figure 5–13 we observe that it is desirable to attenuate the $G(j\omega)$ vector by at least a factor of 0.5 in the range of frequencies between $\omega = 5$ and $\omega = 12$. A phase-lag network whose ratio of T_1/T_2 is 3 will achieve this if ω_{max} is chosen at about 1. We know from equation 6–5 that

$$\omega_{max} = \frac{1}{\sqrt{T_1 T_2}} \tag{6-82}$$

Since $\omega_{max} = 1$, equations 6–81 and 6–82 can be solved, simultaneously, for the values of T_1 and T_2. The results are as follows:

$$\begin{aligned} T_2 &= 0.58 \\ T_1 &= 1.74 \end{aligned} \tag{6-83}$$

Therefore the phase-lag network we shall use for our first trial is

$$G_c(s) = \frac{1 + 0.58s}{1 + 1.74s} \tag{6-84}$$

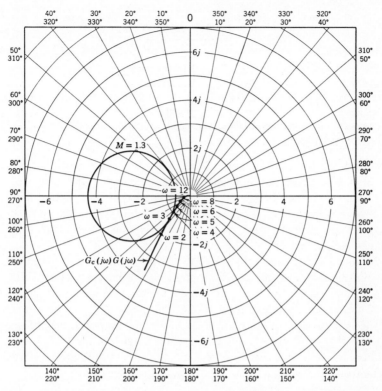

Figure 6–25. Compensation of the system shown in Figure 5–12 for $M_p = 1.3$.

Figure 6–25 illustrates the resulting compensated Nyquist diagram being tangent to the constant-magnitude loci corresponding to $M = 1.3$. Therefore a solution has been achieved on the first trial. Certainly, if the reader's thinking deviated slightly, and a solution was not obtainable on the first trial, a solution could easily have been obtained on the second trial.

6–7. DESIGN UTILIZING THE INVERSE POLAR PLOT

The inverse polar plot was developed in Section 5–6. We demonstrated there how the control engineer could obtain the closed-loop frequency response of a feedback control system by superimposing the inverse magnitude and phase-angle loci on the inverse Nyquist diagram. Specifically, we obtained the closed-loop frequency response of the system shown in Figure 5–18. The intersection of the inverse Nyquist diagram and the inverse magnitude circle was shown in Figure 5–19. It indicated a maximum value of peaking M_p of 2.86 and the frequency at which it

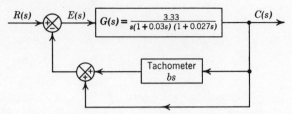

Figure 6–26. Rate feedback compensation of the system shown in Figure 5–18 in order to achieve an $M_p = 1.1$.

occurred, ω_p, to be 25 radians/second. We indicated in Section 5–6 that a value of $M_p = 2.86$ does not represent a good design. Of course, we want M_p to have a value between 1.1 to 1.5. This section demonstrates how the control engineer may use the inverse constant-magnitude and phase angle circles superimposed on the inverse Nyquist diagram in order to achieve a specified design.

As was discussed in Section 5–6, the inverse plane is a very useful tool when designing feedback control systems which have nonunity feedback. We demonstrate how we may add minor-loop rate feedback to the system shown in Figure 5–18 in order to reduce the value of M_p to 1.1. The object of this exercise is to modify the compensated open-loop transfer function in order that the inverse Nyquist diagram is tangent to the $1/M = 1/1.1 = 0.91$ circle. By restricting the inverse Nyquist diagram to areas external to this circle, we have limited M_p to 1.1 since the interior of this circle represents values of M greater than 1.1.

Figure 6–26 illustrates the resulting configuration after the addition of rate feedback to the system shown in Figure 5–18. The rate feedback constant, b, is assumed to have the unit volts/radian/second. From equation 5–49, we know that

$$\frac{R(j\omega)}{C(j\omega)} = \frac{1}{G(j\omega)} + H(j\omega) \qquad (6\text{–}85)$$

For this problem,

$$G(j\omega) = \frac{3.33}{j\omega(1 + 0.03j\omega)(1 + 0.027j\omega)} \qquad (6\text{–}86)$$

and

$$H(j\omega) = 1 + bj\omega \qquad (6\text{–}87)$$

The first step in the procedure is to plot $1/G(j\omega) + 1$ from equation 6–85 onto the inverse plane together with the inverse constant-magnitude loci corresponding to $1/M = 0.91$, as shown in Figure 6–27. A simple study of these two characteristics indicates that if point B, which corresponds to $\omega = 17$, were raised by a value of $0.45j$, then the two curves should just clear each other. However, the resulting compensated

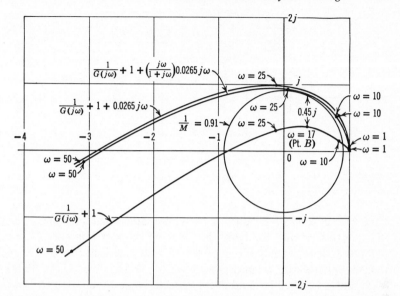

Figure 6–27. Compensation of the system shown in Figure 5–19 for $M_p = 1.1$.

characteristic curve will actually be shifted slightly in frequency with the result that some additional margin is available as shown. Therefore, the value of the rate feedback constant b necessary to achieve this is given by

$$bj\omega = 0.45j \quad \text{at} \quad \omega = 17 \tag{6–88}$$

or

$$b = 0.0265$$

From our discussion in Section 6–3, we know that minor-loop rate feedback increases the steady-state error of the system by a constant component. We indicated there that a simple method for eliminating this increase in steady-state error was to placé a high-pass filter in cascade with the tachometer which would block the steady-state value of the tachometer output. Let us, therefore, determine the time constants of a simple high-pass filter which can perform this function, but which also must not increase M beyond 1.1. Figure 6–28 illustrates the new configuration. The effect of the high-pass network on the inverse plane is to change the compensated characteristics from

$$\frac{1}{G(j\omega)} + 1 + 0.0265j\omega \tag{6–89}$$

to

$$\frac{1}{G(j\omega)} + 1 + \frac{Tj\omega}{1 + Tj\omega} 0.0265j\omega \tag{6–90}$$

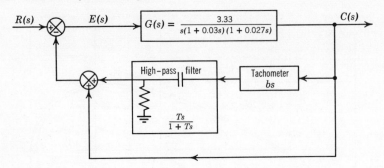

Figure 6–28.   Modification of the configuration shown in Figure 6–26 in order to minimize the steady-state error.

This will effectively modify the compensated characteristics with an effective phase lead. Studying the characteristics of Figure 6–27, we can easily see that if the vectors of the compensated system are provided sufficient phase lead, we may exceed $M = 1.1$. However, if T is chosen so that there is no effective lead at frequencies greater than about 10, we will not have the resulting compensated characteristics fall inside the $1/M = 0.91$ circle. Therefore, we choose $T = 1$. The resulting compensated inverse transfer function, with minor-loop compensation consisting of a tachometer in cascade with a high-pass filter, is given by

$$\frac{1}{G(j\omega)} + 1 + \frac{j\omega}{1 + j\omega} 0.0265 j\omega \tag{6–91}$$

and is illustrated on the inverse plane of Figure 6–27. Notice that we have not exceeded the specification of $M = 1.1$.

As a matter of interest, we next compare the steady-state error resulting from an input of a unit ramp for the uncompensated system illustrated in Figure 5–18 (case A); the compensated system using minor-loop rate feedback shown in Figure 6–26 (case B); and the compensated system using minor-loop rate feedback in cascade with a high-pass filter illustrated in Figure 6–28 (case C). We should ultimately conclude that the steady-state errors for cases A and C are equal and are less than that resulting for case B. Let us prove to ourselves that this is true.

Case A.   For the system shown in Figure 5–18,

$$G(s) = \frac{3.33}{s(1 + 0.03s)(1 + 0.027s)} \tag{6–92}$$

and

$$R(s) = \frac{1}{s^2} \tag{6–93}$$

The system error for this system can be obtained by substituting equations 6–92 and 6–93 into the expression

$$\frac{E(s)}{R(s)} = \frac{1}{1 + G(s)} \tag{6-94}$$

The resulting expression is

$$E(s) = \frac{(1 + 0.03s)(1 + 0.027s)}{s[s(1 + 0.03s)(1 + 0.027s) + 3.33]} \tag{6-95}$$

Applying the final-value theorem, we obtain the steady-state error as follows:

$$e_{ss} = \lim_{s \to 0} sE(s) = \frac{1}{3.33} = 0.3 \tag{6-96}$$

Case B.   For the system shown in Figure 6–26,

$$G(s) = \frac{3.33}{s(1 + 0.03s)(1 + 0.027s)} \tag{6-97}$$

$$R(s) = \frac{1}{s^2} \tag{6-98}$$

and

$$b = 0.0265 \tag{6-99}$$

The system error for this system can easily be obtained from the equivalent block diagram of Figure 6–29. The resulting expression for system error is

$$\frac{E(s)}{R(s)} = \frac{1}{1 + G'(s)} \tag{6-100}$$

The resulting expression is

$$E(s) = \frac{(1 + 0.03s)(1 + 0.027s) + 3.33b}{s[s(1 + 0.03s)(1 + 0.027s) + 3.3bs + 3.33]} \tag{6-101}$$

Applying the final-value theorem, we obtain the steady-state error as

$$e_{ss} = \lim_{s \to 0} sE(s) = \frac{1 + 3.33b}{3.33} = 0.3 + b \tag{6-102}$$

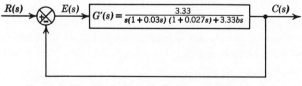

Figure 6–29.   Equivalent block diagram of Figure 6–26.

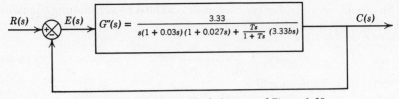

Figure 6–30.   Equivalent block diagram of Figure 6–28.

Since

$$b = 0.0265$$

$$e_{ss} = 0.3 + 0.0265 = 0.3265 \tag{6-103}$$

This result agrees with what we would expect from our discussion of Section 6–3.

Case C.   For the system shown in Figure 6–28,

$$G(s) = \frac{3.33}{s(1 + 0.03s)(1 + 0.027s)} \tag{6-104}$$

$$R(s) = \frac{1}{s^2} \tag{6-105}$$

$$T = 1 \tag{6-106}$$

and

$$b = 0.0265 \tag{6-107}$$

The system error for this system can easily be obtained from the equivalent block diagram of Figure 6–30. The resulting expression for system error is

$$\frac{E(s)}{R(s)} = \frac{1}{1 + G''(s)} \tag{6-108}$$

The resulting expression is

$$E(s) = \frac{(1 + 0.03s)(1 + 0.027s) + 3.33b[s/(1 + s)]}{s\{s(1 + 0.03s)(1 + 0.027s) + 3.3b[s/(1 + s)] + 3.33\}} \tag{6-109}$$

Applying the final-value theorem, we obtain the steady-state error as follows:

$$e_{ss} = \lim_{s \to 0} sE(s) = \frac{1}{3.33} = 0.3 \tag{6-110}$$

This result is exactly the same as the steady-state error for case A.

The results of cases A, B, and C, indicated by equations 6–96, 6–103, and 6–110, respectively, vividly demonstrate the fact that the steady-state error is increased by the addition of minor-loop rate feedback compensation. However, the increase in steady-state error can be eliminated by means of a high-pass network placed in cascade with the tachometer.

6–8. DESIGN UTILIZING THE BODE DIAGRAM APPROACH

The elements necessary to construct and analyze the open-loop frequency response of a feedback control system utilizing the Bode diagram approach were presented in Section 5–7. This section illustrates how the Bode diagram can be used for designing a feedback control system in order to meet certain specifications regarding relative stability, transient response, and accuracy. It is important to emphasize, at this point of the discussion, that the Bode diagram approach is used very frequently by the practicing control engineer. Its use is due to the fact that the theoretically anticipated results may be relatively simply checked with actual performance in the laboratory just by opening the feedback loop and obtaining an open-loop frequency response of the system.

Bode's primary contribution to the control art is summarized in two theorems, known, naturally enough, as Bode's theorems.[7] These are mathematical and a little difficult to comprehend at first glance. Therefore we introduce their concepts first in a qualitative manner, and then present the mathematical statements. Once having been exposed to these mathematical statements, the control engineer should attempt to store the gist of these theorems somewhere in his memory and thereafter use them only as tools to guide him in the proper direction for designing feedback control systems. Fortunately, it is not necessary to utilize the mathematical statements of Bode's theorems every time we attempt to design a system.

Bode's first theorem basically states that the slopes of the asymptotic amplitude-log frequency curve implies a certain corresponding phase shift. For example, in Section 5–7 it was shown that a slope of 0 db/decade (or 0 db/octave) resulted in a phase shift of $0°$; a slope of 20 db/decade (or 6 db/octave) resulted in a phase shift of $90°$; a slope of 40 db/decade (or 12 db/octave) resulted in a phase shift of $180°$; a slope of -20 db/decade (or -6 db/octave) resulted in a phase shift of $-90°$; a slope of -40 db/decade (or -12 db/octave) resulted in a phase shift of $-180°$, etc. Furthermore, this theorem states that the slope at crossover (where the attenuation-log frequency curve crosses the 0-db line) is weighted more heavily towards determining system stability than a slope further removed from this frequency. In addition, a slope an octave away from crossover is weighted more heavily towards determining system stability than a slope 2 octaves away. This concept basically results in a rather complex weighting factor which is a measure of relative importance towards determining system stability.

From the material presented so far, this theorem certainly makes sense. The crossover frequency is one of the two points that the control engineer checks to determine the degree of stability when using the Bode diagram. Specifically, he measures the phase shift at this particular frequency in order to determine his phase margin. A feedback control system whose slope at crossover is −20 db/decade, and whose other slope sections are relatively far away from crossover in accordance with the relative weighting function, implies a phase shift of approximately 90° and a corresponding phase margin of about 90°. This value of phase margin certainly implies a stable system. A system, however, whose slope at crossover is −40 db/decade, and whose other slope sections are relatively far away from crossover in accordance with the relative weighting function, implies a phase shift of approximately 180° and a corresponding phase margin of about 0°. This value of phase margin implies a system which is on the verge of being unstable and would probably be so when actually tested. More steeper slopes would indicate negative phase margins and definitely unstable systems. Therefore the control engineer strives to maintain the slope of the amplitude-log frequency curve, in the vicinity of crossover, at a slope of −20 db/decade. Notice that the system, illustrated in Figure 5–30, has slopes of −60 db/decade that are relatively far removed from the crossover frequency. Therefore this system has a fairly respectable phase margin of 54° by maintaining the −20-db/decade slope for about an octave below, and about 2 octaves above, crossover.

Bode's second theorem basically states that the amplitude and phase characteristics of linear, minimum-phase shift systems are uniquely related. When we specify the slope of the amplitude-log frequency curve over a certain frequency interval, we have also specified the corresponding phase shift characteristics over that frequency interval. Conversely, if we specify the phase shift over a certain frequency interval, we have also specified the corresponding amplitude-log frequency characteristics over that frequency interval. The theorem emphasizes the fact that we can specify the amplitude-log frequency characteristic over a certain interval of frequencies together with the phase shift-log frequency characteristics over the remaining frequencies.

The second theorem may appear quite trivial at first glance. Its implications, however, are quite important. The material presented so far has not violated this theorem. We make further use of this theorem when designing feedback control systems using the Bode diagram approach.

To emphasize Bode's theorems, we present them in mathematical form. As stated previously, it is not necessary to use the mathematical form of Bode's theorems every time we use the Bode diagram technique. However, it is good to go through the mathematical form at least once and gain a solid foundation for and facility in understanding their meaning.

The formal *mathematical statement of Bode's first theorem* is given by the following expression.

$$\phi(\omega_d) = \frac{\pi}{2} \left| \frac{dG}{dn} \right|_d + \frac{1}{\pi} \int_{-\infty}^{\infty} \left(\left| \frac{dG}{dn} \right| - \left| \frac{dG}{dn} \right|_d \right) \ln \coth \left| \frac{n}{2} \right| dn$$

(6–111)

where $\phi(\omega_d)$ represents the phase shift of the system in radians at the desired frequency ω_d

G represents the gain in nepers (1 neper $= \ln |e|$)

$$N = \ln \frac{\omega}{\omega_d}$$

$\left| \dfrac{dG}{dn} \right|$ represents the slope of the amplitude-log frequency curve in nepers per unit change of n (note that 1 neper/unit change of n is equivalent to 20 db/decade)

$\left| \dfrac{dG}{dn} \right|_d$ represents the slope of the amplitude-log frequency curve at the reference frequency ω_d

$\ln \coth \left| \dfrac{n}{2} \right|$ represents the weighting function plotted in Figure 6–31

The first term of equation 6–111 represents the phase shift contributed by the slope of the amplitude-log frequency curve at the reference frequency ω_d. For example, it results in a phase shift of 90° for every neper per unit

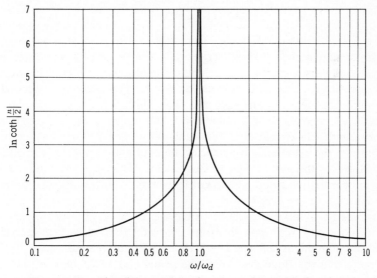

Figure 6–31. Plot of the weighting function used in Bode's first theorem.

of n (20 db/decade). The second term of equation 6–111 is proportional to the integral of the product of the weighting function and the difference in slope of the amplitude-log frequency curve at a frequency ω as compared to its value at the reference frequency, ω_d. Attention is drawn to the fact that it is the weighting function that determines the phase shift contribution at ω_d due to the amplitude-log frequency curve which exists at some frequency ω. Since the second term of equation 6–111 is zero for large values of n and where $n = 0$, the value of the integral will be relatively small compared to the first term if the slope of dG/dn is constant over a relatively wide range of frequencies about ω_d. Therefore, under these conditions, the phase shift would be determined primarily by the first term of equation 6–111. Following this line of reasoning, the slope of the amplitude-log frequency curve should be less than -2 nepers per unit of n (-40 db/decade) over a relatively wide range of frequencies at crossover.

The formal *mathematical statement of Bode's second theorem* is given by the following expression:

$$\int_0^{\omega_s} \frac{G \, d\omega}{\sqrt{\omega_s^2 - \omega^2}(\omega^2 - \omega_d^2)} + \int_{\omega_s}^{\infty} \frac{\phi \, d\omega}{\sqrt{\omega^2 - \omega_s^2}(\omega^2 - \omega_d^2)}$$

$$= \frac{\pi}{2} \frac{\phi(\omega_d)}{\omega_d \sqrt{\omega_s^2 - \omega_d^2}} \qquad \text{(for } \omega_d < \omega_s\text{)} \quad \text{(6–112)}$$

$$= -\frac{\pi}{2} \frac{G(\omega_d)}{\omega_d \sqrt{\omega_d^2 - \omega_s^2}} \qquad \text{(for } \omega_d > \omega_s\text{)}$$

where ω_s represents the frequency in radians per second below which the amplitude-log frequency characteristic is specified and above which the phase characteristic is specified. All other nomenclatures used in equation 6–112 are the same as used for equation 6–111. This theorem emphasizes the interdependence of amplitude and phase shift over the entire range of positive frequencies. In addition, notice that although it is possible to specify amplitude or phase in one range of frequencies, and the other quantity in the remaining frequencies, these quantities reflect their presence back into the other range of frequencies. Therefore the integration with respect to frequency is performed over the entire range of positive frequencies.

The design of several systems using the Bode diagram approach is considered next. We shall illustrate a method that as well as meeting certain requirements of relative stability also determines steady-state accuracy from the Bode diagram. The reader should attempt to capture the procedures followed and gain a feeling for some of the numbers involved.

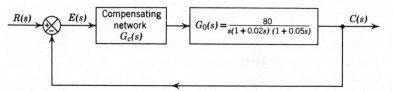

Figure 6–32. A type 1, *third-order system which is to be compensated.*

Let us first consider the type 1, third-order system illustrated in Figure 6–32. Its open-loop transfer function $G_0(s)$ is given by

$$G_0(s) = \frac{80}{s(1 + 0.02s)(1 + 0.05s)} \tag{6–113}$$

The Bode diagram for the uncompensated system $[G_c(s) = 1]$ is illustrated in Figure 6–33. It indicates a crossover frequency ω_c of 38 radians/second; a phase margin γ of $-17°$; and a gain margin of -6 db. These results indicate that the uncompensated system is definitely unstable. Let us next attempt to compensate this system with a simple lag and then a

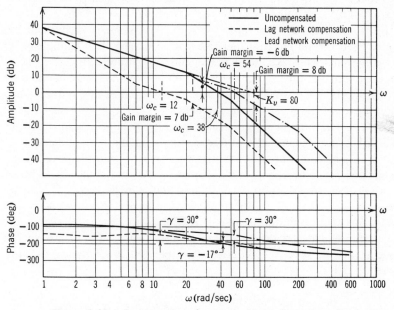

Figure 6–33. Compensation of a type 1, *third-order system where*

$$G_0(s) = \frac{80}{s(1 + 0.02s)(1 + 0.05s)}$$

Compensation networks:

$$\text{Lag case: } G_c(s) = \frac{1 + 0.143s}{1 + s} \qquad \text{Lead case: } G_c(s) = \frac{1 + 0.04s}{1 + 0.005s}$$

lead network. To achieve an optimum transient response for the specific application of this system, the phase margin should be approximately 30° and the gain margin about 6 db. In addition, a maximum open-loop gain of 38 db at 1 radian/second is required by accuracy considerations.

Let us first consider the lag network compensation case. Applying Bode's theorems in order to achieve the specified phase and gain margins, we would expect that the −20-db/decade slope in the vicinity of the new crossover frequency should not extend over too wide a range of frequencies since the relative stability that is desired is rather moderate. Let us assume that the lag network is of the form

$$G_c(s) = \frac{1 + T_2 s}{1 + T_1 s} \qquad (6\text{-}114)$$

where

$$T_1 > T_2$$

In Section 6–2 we studied the characteristics of the phase-lag network. In particular, Figure 6–4 illustrated the Bode diagram of a general phase-lag network. Notice that this type of network is of such a nature that it attenuated all high-frequency components above $\omega = 1/T_2$ by a factor of T_2/T_1. From the Bode diagram viewpoint, this attenuating characteristic can be used for stabilization purposes by reshaping the uncompensated amplitude characteristics, so that the initial −20 db/decade is made to cross over the 0-db line rather than the −40 db/decade segment. In other words, the control engineer would attempt to stabilize this system with a phase-lag network by placing the frequencies $1/T_1$ and $1/T_2$ in the range of frequencies below about 10 radians/second. It would be desirable that the −20-db/decade segment start at least around 10 radians/second and cross over the 0-db line before 20 radians/second where the amplitude-log frequency characteristic changes to a slope of −40 db/decade. In addition, we would not want $1/T_1$ to occur at less than 1 radian/second, since an open-loop gain of 38 db has been specified at $\omega = 1$ radian/second. The final phase of the solution is by means of trial and error. However, the procedure converges quite rapidly. Usually, two or three trials should prove sufficient. For the requirements specified, a phase-lag network where

$$G_c(s) = \frac{1 + 0.143s}{1 + s} \qquad (6\text{-}115)$$

results in a phase margin of 30° and a gain margin of 7 db. This is close enough to the desired result for all practical purposes.

Let us next consider the lead-network compensation case. Applying Bode's theorems in order to achieve the specified phase and gain margins, we would expect that the −20-db/decade slopes in the vicinity of the new crossover frequency should not extend over too wide a range of frequencies since the relative stability desired is rather moderate. Let us assume that the lead network has the form

$$G_c(s) = \frac{T_2}{T_1} \cdot \frac{1 + T_1 s}{1 + T_2 s} \qquad (6\text{--}116)$$

where

$$T_1 > T_2$$

In Section 6–2 we studied the characteristics of the phase-lead network. We assume that any low-frequency attenuation, which is due to the ratio of T_2 to T_1, is made up for by increasing the gain of the feedback control system by a like amount. The Bode diagram of a general phase-lead network was shown in Figure 6–6. From the Bode diagram viewpoint, this type of characteristic can be used for stabilization purposes by reshaping the uncompensated amplitude characteristics so that a -40-db/decade slope is made to cross over the 0-db line along a synthesized -20-db/decade slope rather than the -40-db/decade segment. The range of frequencies where the control engineer can place the frequencies $1/T_1$ and $1/T_2$ is quite limited in this particular problem. $1/T_1$ can be placed between 20 and 38 radians/second. The closer it is to 20 radians/second, the greater will be its stabilizing effect. The break frequency $1/T_2$ should not be made any lower than 50 radians/second. The further away this break is from 38 radians/second, the greater will be the stabilizing effect of the lead network. It can be seen that this particular solution does not modify the open-loop characteristics in the vicinity of 1 radian/second and the accuracy specification of 38 db at 1 radian/second will easily be achieved. The final phase of the solution is one of trial and error. However, the procedure converges very rapidly. For the requirements specified, a phase-lead network where

$$G_c(s) = \frac{1 + 0.04s}{1 + 0.005s} \qquad (6\text{--}117)$$

results in a phase margin of 30° and a gain margin of 8 db. This is close enough to the desired result for all practical purposes. Observe the fact that although we are actually crossing the 0-db line at an asymptotic slope of -40 db/decade, the system is still stable. This can clearly be understood from Bode's first theorem and the weighting diagram shown in Figure 6–31. Notice that the resulting lead network has a low-frequency attenuation of 0.005/0.04 which must be made up by increasing the gain by a factor of 0.04/0.005.

If we have a choice of using the phase-lag or phase-lead network, the phase-lag network solution would be preferable since it meets the required specifications with a narrower bandwidth than the lead network case

($\omega_c = 12$ for the former; $\omega_c = 54$ for the latter). A feedback control system having a narrower bandwidth will reject a greater amount of noise than one having a wider bandwidth. This is discussed further in Chapter 8 when we consider the statistical design of feedback control systems. In addition, the phase-lead network has the disadvantage of requiring a greater amount of amplification within the control system than the lag network.

The steady-state error coefficients can be determined from the Bode diagram. The definition and importance of these error coefficients have been discussed in Section 4–4. For type 1 systems, the velocity constant K_v can be obtained by extending the initial -20-db/decade slope until it intersects the 0-db line. The frequency at which it intersects this line is equal to the velocity constant. We recall from our discussion in Section 4–4 that K_v was obtained by letting s approach zero when utilizing the final-value theorem (see equation 4–22). Therefore, the time constant factor terms having the form $1 + Ts$ or $(Ts)^2 + 2\zeta Ts + 1$ all approach unity. This permits the control engineer to obtain K_v directly by considering only the initial slope of the Bode diagram. For the Bode diagram shown in Figure 6–33, the value K_v obtained graphically is 80. Using the definition given by equation 4–22, we obtain

$$K_v = \lim_{s \to 0} sG(s)H(s) \tag{6–118}$$

Since

$$G(s) = \frac{80}{s(1 + 0.02s)(1 + 0.05s)}$$

and

$$H(s) = 1$$

then

$$K_v = \lim_{s \to 0} \frac{s(80)}{s(1 + 0.02s)(1 + 0.05s)} = 80 \tag{6–119}$$

Therefore the analytic and graphical methods agree. It is also interesting to note that the velocity constant is the same for the uncompensated and compensated systems.

For a type 2 system, which contains an s^2 term in the denominator, the acceleration constant K_a can be obtained in a similar manner. The initial -40-db/decade slope is extended until it intersects the 0-db line. The frequency at which it intersects this line is equal to the acceleration constant. The reasoning is very similar to that presented for type 1 systems and their corresponding velocity constants.

The next system we consider is illustrated in Figure 6–34. This consists of a type 0, third-order system which has an unwanted external input $U(s)$.

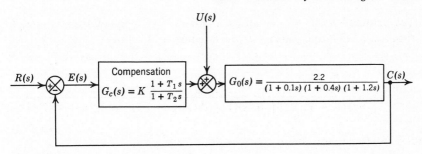

Figure 6–34. A type 0, third-order system having an unwanted external input.

The open-loop transfer function for the uncompensated system, $G_0(s)$, is given by

$$G_0(s) = \frac{2.2}{(1 + 0.1s)(1 + 0.4s)(1 + 1.2s)} \qquad (6\text{–}120)$$

It is desired that the steady-state error, resulting from an unwanted external step input signal at $U(s)$, not exceed 0.1 unit. The compensation device $G_c(s)$ is to contain amplification which will meet this accuracy requirement together with a phase-lead or phase-lag network which will provide a phase margin of about 30° and a gain margin of 5 db. These phase and gain margins appear to be optimum for this system from the viewpoints of transient response and relative stability, considering the system's particular application.

The value of gain required for $G_c(s)$ will be computed first. For this calculation, $U(s)$ is assumed to be the input and $E(s)$ is assumed to be the output. The transfer function between these two points is given by

$$\frac{E(s)}{U(s)} = \frac{\dfrac{2.2}{(1 + 0.1s)(1 + 0.4s)(1 + 1.2s)}}{1 + K\dfrac{(1 + T_1s)}{(1 + T_2s)}\left[\dfrac{2.2}{(1 + 0.1s)(1 + 0.4s)(1 + 1.2s)}\right]} \qquad (6\text{–}121)$$

This equation can be simplified to the expression

$$\frac{E(s)}{U(s)} = \frac{2.2(1 + T_2s)}{(1 + T_2s)(1 + 0.1s)(1 + 0.4s)(1 + 1.2s) + 2.2K(1 + T_1s)} \qquad (6\text{–}122)$$

Setting $U(s) = 1/s$, we obtain the expression for the Laplace transform of the error, $E(s)$, as

$$E(s) = \frac{2.2(1 + T_2s)}{s[(1 + T_2s)(1 + 0.1s)(1 + 0.4s)(1 + 1.2s) + 2.2K(1 + T_1s)]} \qquad (6\text{–}123)$$

The required value of K can be obtained by applying the final-value theorem to $E(s)$ and setting the result equal to 0.1 unit.

$$\lim_{s\to 0} sE(s) = 0.1$$

$$= \lim_{s\to 0} \frac{s[2.2(1 + T_2 s)]}{s[(1 + T_2 s)(1 + 0.1s)(1 + 0.4s)(1 + 1.2s) + 2.2K(1 + T_1 s)]}$$

(6–124)

Solving for K, we obtain

$$K = 9.55 \qquad (6–125)$$

Let us next determine the compensating network required to achieve a phase margin of 30° and a gain margin of 5 db. The transfer function of the uncompensated system, with $K = 9.55$, is given by

$$KG_0(s) = \frac{21}{(1 + 0.1s)(1 + 0.4s)(1 + 1.2s)} \qquad (6–126)$$

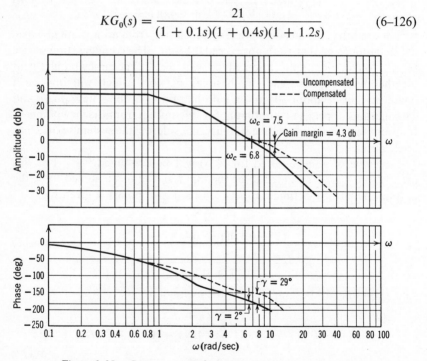

Figure 6–35. Compensation of a type 0, third-order system where

$$KG_0(s) = \frac{21}{(1 + 0.1s)(1 + 0.4s)(1 + 1.2s)}$$

and

$$G_c(s) = \frac{1 + 0.167s}{1 + 0.05s}$$

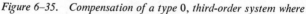

Its Bode diagram, which is drawn in Figure 6–35, indicates a phase margin of 2° and a gain margin of 1.7 db. We wish to increase the phase margin by about 30°. From Table 6–1, it can be seen that a time constant ratio of 4 will result in a phase shift of approximately 37° at a frequency which was given by equation 6–5:

$$\omega_{max} = \frac{1}{\sqrt{T_1 T_2}} \tag{6-127}$$

We must be careful when using this approach, since we actually desire to have this phase shift occur close to the crossover frequency in order to achieve the specified phase margin. Therefore a trial-and-error procedure results. A phase-lead network corresponding to

$$\frac{1 + 0.167s}{1 + 0.05s} \tag{6-128}$$

results in a phase margin of 29° and a gain margin of 4.3 db. This is close enough to the desired result for all practical purposes. It is interesting to note that this lead network gives its maximum phase lead, of about 37°, at a frequency of 5.2 radians/second. This accounts for the fact that we only achieved a phase margin of 29° at a crossover frequency of 7.5 radians/second.

The concluding problem we consider using the Bode diagram approach consists of designing the feedback control system illustrated in Figure 6–36. For this particular system, we desire that the steady-state error resulting from an input of 110 radians/second be equal to 0.25 radians. The uncompensated open-loop transfer function $G_0(s)$ is given by

$$G_0(s) = \frac{K_v}{s(1 + T_m s)} \tag{6-129}$$

where K_v = velocity constant
T_m = motor time constant = 0.025 seconds

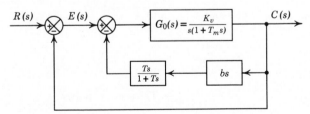

Figure 6–36. Use of rate feedback in cascade with a high-pass filter in order to compensate a feedback control system.

This transfer function consists of an amplifier, positioning motor, gear train, and load. In order to achieve the required accuracy, K_v must equal

$$K_v = \frac{\omega}{\text{Error}} = \frac{110 \text{ radians/sec.}}{0.25 \text{ radians}} = 440/\text{sec.} \qquad (6\text{--}130)$$

We want a phase margin of approximately 55° for this system. This will be achieved by means of minor-loop rate feedback compensation which is cascaded with a simple RC high-pass filter (lead network) in order not to increase the steady-state following error to velocity inputs. The phase margin of 55° is optimum for the system from the viewpoint of relative stability and transient response.

The open-loop frequency response we are interested in plotting on the Bode diagram is that obtained with the minor rate loop closed and the outer position loop opened. Therefore, we are interested in obtaining the equivalent transfer function between $E(s)$ and $C(s)$. This can easily be obtained as follows:

$$\frac{C(s)}{E(s)} = \frac{K_v/s(1 + T_m s)}{1 + \left[\dfrac{K_v}{s(1 + T_m s)}\right] bs\left(\dfrac{Ts}{1 + Ts}\right)} \qquad (6\text{--}131)$$

This equation can be simplified to the form

$$\frac{C(s)}{E(s)} = \frac{K_v(1 + Ts)}{s[(1 + T_m s)(1 + Ts) + K_v bTs]} \qquad (6\text{--}132)$$

Expanding the denominator of equation 6–132, we obtain the expression

$$s[T_m Ts^2 + (T_m + T + K_v bT)s + 1] \qquad (6\text{--}133)$$

This expression can be put into the following form:

$$s[(1 + T_m's)(1 + T_1 s)] \qquad (6\text{--}134)$$

by defining the time constants T_m' and T_1 as

$$T_m' = \frac{T_m}{T_1} T \qquad (6\text{--}135)$$

and

$$T_1 = -T_m' + T_m + (1 + K_v b)T \qquad (6\text{--}136)$$

Therefore, we may redraw Figure 6–36 as shown in Figure 6–37. For any set of values for T_m, T, K_v, and b, we can derive T_m' and T_1 by solving

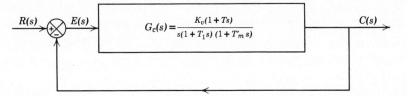

Figure 6-37. *Equivalent block diagram for the system shown in Figure 6-36.*

the simultaneous equations 6-135 and 6-136. Another approach is to choose T and T_1 from the Bode diagram which meets the specified phase margin and solve for the required rate feedback constant b.

The procedure we follow when compensating this system is to draw the Bode diagram for the uncompensated system in accordance with equation 6-129 and then fit the characteristics of the compensated system in accordance with

$$G_c(s) = \frac{C(s)}{E(s)} = \frac{K_v(1 + Ts)}{s(1 + T_m's)(1 + T_1s)} \tag{6-137}$$

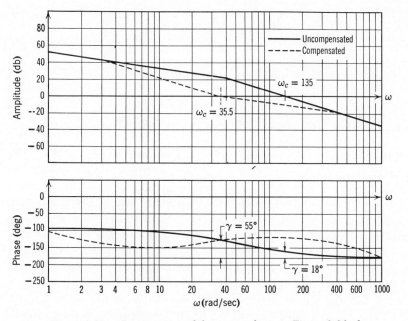

Figure 6-38. *Compensation of the system shown in Figure 6-36 where*

$$G_0(s) = \frac{440}{s(1 + 0.025s)} \quad and \quad G_c(s) = \frac{440(1 + 0.033s)}{s(1 + 0.33s)(1 + 0.0025s)}$$

until a phase margin of 55° is achieved. The compensated characteristics will then determine T and T_1, from which T_m' and the rate feedback constant b can be determined. Figure 6–38 illustrates the Bode diagram of the uncompensated and compensated systems. Values of

$$T_1 = 0.33$$

$$T = 0.033$$

and $\qquad T_m' = \frac{T_m}{T_1} T = 0.0025 \qquad$ (from equation 6–135)

results in a phase margin of 55°. From equation 6–136, the corresponding value of rate feedback constant b is 0.0186 volts/radian/second.

The type of compensation just illustrated is used quite frequently in practice. In order to really understand what is actually happening, it is important to examine the Bode diagram of Figure 6–38 closely. The net effect of the minor-loop rate feedback has been to move the motor break frequency physically from $1/T_m$ to $1/T_m'$ by the ratio given in equation 6–135. This technique is used quite frequently to compensate power servos. The net effect of the phase-lead network, in the minor-loop feedback path, is to appear as a phase lag, for the equivalent open-loop characteristics of Figure 6–37. This can be easily understood since we effectively see the reciprocal of the feedback element when looking into a closed-loop system which has an open-loop gain much greater than unity.

6–9. DESIGN UTILIZING THE NICHOLS CHART

The Nichols chart method has been developed in Section 5–8. We demonstrated in that section how the control engineer could obtain the closed-loop frequency response of a feedback control system by super-imposing the open-loop gain-phase characteristics onto the Nichols chart. Specifically, we obtained the closed-loop frequency response of the system shown in Figure 5–12. The intersections of the open-loop gain-phase characteristics and the Nichols closed-loop gain characteristics were shown in Figure 5–33. The resulting closed-loop frequency response was illustrated in Figure 5–34. It indicated a maximum value of peaking, M_p, of 6.8 db (2.2) and the frequency at which it occurred, ω_p, to be 10 radians/second. This result agreed with the results obtained using the constant-magnitude and phase angle circle method of Section 5–5. We indicated in Sections 5–5 and 5–8 that a value of $M_p = 6.8$ db (2.2), as the reader must remember, does not represent a good design. This section demonstrates

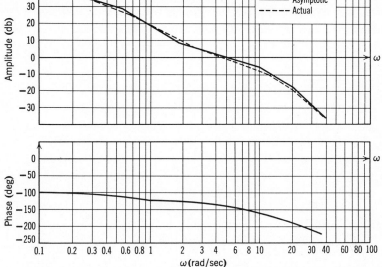

Figure 6–39. Bode diagram for the compensated system of Figure 5–12 where

$$G(s)G_c(s)H(s) = \frac{11.7(1 + 0.58s)}{s(1 + 0.05s)(1 + 0.1s)(1 + 1.74s)}$$

how the control engineer may use the Nichols chart to achieve a specified design.

As was assumed in Section 6–6, a value of M_p equal to 1.3 (2.3 db) is considered acceptable. Section 6–6 illustrated how the phase-lag network

$$G_c(s) = \frac{1 + 0.58s}{1 + 1.74s} \tag{6–138}$$

in cascade with the original forward-loop transfer function $G(s)$ achieved an M_p of 1.3 (2.3 db). Although we know the answer in advance for this problem, it is interesting to go through the mechanics. We shall demonstrate that for an M_p of 2.3 db the object is to modify the gain-phase characteristics on the Nichols chart so that it is just tangent to the 2.3-db locus and does not enter it. By restricting the gain-phase characteristics to areas external to the $M = 2.3$-db locus, we shall have limited M_p to 2.3 db since the interior of this locus represents values of M greater than 2.3 db.

In order to obtain the gain-phase characteristics of the open-loop system, the Bode diagram is first drawn as indicated in Figure 6–39. Then for each

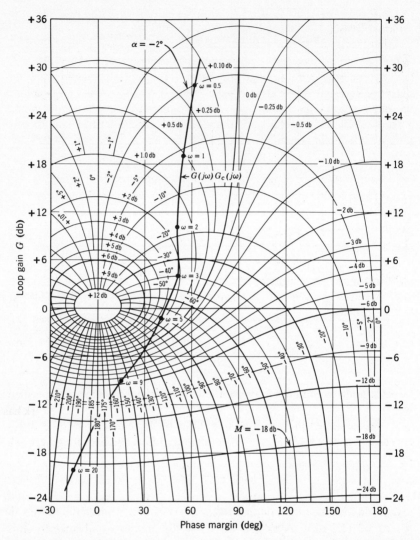

Figure 6–40.   Compensation of the system shown in Figure 5–12 for M = 2.3 db (1.3).

value of ω the magnitude (actual or corrected values) and phase of the open-loop compensated characteristics are plotted onto a Nichols chart as shown in Figure 6–40. Since the open-loop gain-phase characteristics are just tangent to the constant-magnitude locus corresponding to $M = 2.3$ db (1.3), we have achieved our goal. This is in agreement with the solution obtained using the M-circle method of Section 6–6.

6-10. DESIGN UTILIZING THE ROOT LOCUS

The root locus technique has been developed previously in Section 5-9. It is a very helpful tool which the control engineer can use in order to study the variation of gain, system parameters, and effect of compensation. We demonstrated in Section 5-9 the migration of poles in the complex plane as the gain of the system was varied from zero to infinity. Specifically, we obtained the root locus of a system where

$$G(s)H(s) = \frac{K}{(s + 1)(s - 1)(s + 4)^2} \qquad (6\text{--}139)$$

This was illustrated in Figure 5-39. An analysis of the root locus for this system indicated that it was always unstable since at least one of the roots of the characteristic equation always occurred in the right half plane. This section demonstrates how this system may be compensated by means of a lead network. This problem is followed by considering lag compensation for the system illustrated in Figure 5-36. In addition, we shall demonstrate how the control engineer may determine the transient response of the compensated systems in order to meet certain specifications.

Let us attempt to stabilize the system of Figure 5-39 by means of a phase-lead network in cascade with the forward-loop transfer function. The form of its transfer function is given by

$$G_c(s) = \frac{s + \alpha}{s + \beta} \qquad (6\text{--}140)$$

We assume that the effect of the pole caused by the phase-lead network has a negligible effect as compared to its zero. Therefore, we assume that the transfer function of the cascaded phase-lead network can be represented by the simple expression

$$G_c(s) = s + \alpha$$

The resulting value of $G_c(s)G(s)H(s)$, which is to be examined on the root locus, is given by

$$G_c(s)G(s)H(s) = \frac{K(s + \alpha)}{(s + 1)(s - 1)(s + 4)^2}$$

We wish to investigate the effect on stability of a variation in α as follows:

Case A: $\alpha = 0.5$

Case B: $\alpha = 1$

Case C: $\alpha = 2$

Case D: $\alpha = 4$

Case E: $\alpha = 6$

The resulting root loci for all these cases are presented next. It is important to emphasize at this point that although we make use of most of the analytic tools developed in Section 5–9, we do not use all of them. This omission is due to the fact that some of the analytic techniques developed are too complex to use for higher-order systems. For example, it is very tedious to determine the value of the gain K along the root loci utilizing the relationship given by equation 5–97. Fortunately, this can be obtained much more easily with the Spirule. The approach we take in presenting the resulting root loci for this problem is to outline the results of the nine rules developed in Section 5–9 and use the Spirule wherever it is helpful. In addition, the values of gain obtained using the Spirule which are pertinent for an intelligent evaluation of the problem will be indicated. It is our feeling that this dual approach is the optimum procedure when using the root locus method.

Case A. $\alpha = 0.5$. See Figure 6–41 for the root locus sketch.

RULE 1.   There are four separate loci since the characteristic equation, $1 + G_c(s)G(s)H(s)$, is a fourth-order equation.

RULE 2.   The root locus starts $(K = 0)$ from the poles located at $1, -1$, and a double pole at -4. One locus terminates $(K = \infty)$ at the zero located at $-\alpha$ and three loci terminate at zeros located at infinity.

RULE 3.   Complex portions of the root locus occur in complex conjugate pairs.

RULE 4.   The portions of the real axis between 1 to $-\alpha$; -1 to -4; and -4 to infinity are part of the root locus.

RULE 5.   The loci approach infinity as K becomes large at angles given by

$$\alpha_1 = \pm \frac{\pi}{3} = \pm 60°$$

and

$$\alpha_3 = \pm \frac{3\pi}{3} = \pm 180°$$

RULE 6.   The intersection of the asymptotic lines and the real axis occur at

$$s_r = \frac{-8 - (-0.5)}{4 - 1} = -2.5$$

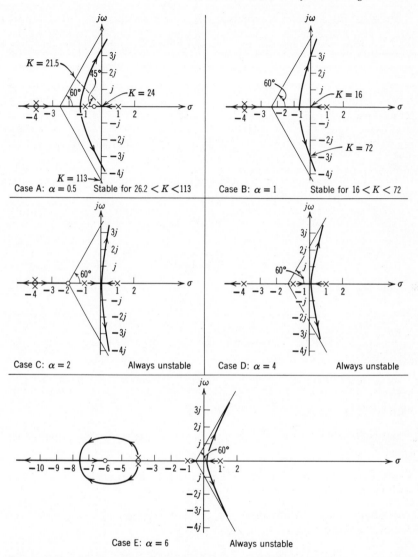

Figure 6–41. Compensation of the root locus shown in Figure 5–39 using a cascaded phase-lead network where $G_c(s) = (s + \alpha)$.

RULE 7. Using the Spirule, we found the point of breakaway from the real axis to occur at approximately -1.3.

RULE 8. Using the Spirule, we found the intersection of the root locus and the imaginary axis to occur at approximately $s = \pm j3.3$, where the gain is 113, and at the origin, where the gain is 24.

RULE 9. This rule does not apply here.

The resulting root locus sketch indicates that this system is stable when $24 < K < 113$.

Case B. $\alpha = 1$. See Figure 6–41 for the root locus sketch. A zero at $\alpha = -1$ cancels the pole at -1. Only rules with results that are different from those outlined for case A are discussed.

RULE 1. These are three separate loci, since the characteristic equation, $1 + G_c(s)G(s)H(s)$, is now a third-order equation.

RULE 2. The root locus starts from the pole located at 1 and the double pole located at -4. All loci terminate at zeros located at infinity.

RULE 4. The portions of the real axis between 1 and negative infinity are part of the root locus.

RULE 6. The intersection of the asymptotic lines and the real axis occur at

$$s_r = \frac{-7}{3} = -2.33.$$

RULE 7. Using the Spirule, we found the point of breakaway from the real axis to occur at approximately -0.67.

RULE 8. Using the Spirule, we found the intersection of the root locus and the imaginary axis to occur at approximately $s = \pm j2.8$, where the gain is 72, and at the origin, where the gain is 16.

The resulting root locus sketch indicates that this system is stable when $16 < K < 72$.

Case C. $\alpha = 2$. See Figure 6–41 for the root locus sketch. Only rules with results different from those outlined for case A are discussed.

RULE 4. The portions of the real axis between 1 to -1 and -2 to negative infinity are part of the root locus.

RULE 6. The intersection of the asymptotic lines and the real axis occurs at

$$s_r = \frac{-8 - (-2)}{4 - 1} = -2$$

RULE 7. Using the Spirule, we found the point of breakaway from the real axis to occur at approximately 0.

RULE 8. This rule does not apply here.

The resulting root locus sketch indicates that the system is always unstable since at least one of the roots of the characteristic equation always occurs in the right half plane, except for the condition where two poles exist at the origin.

Case D. $\alpha = 4$. See Figure 6–41 for the root locus sketch. A zero at $\alpha = 4$ cancels one of the poles located at -4. Only rules with results different from those outlined for case A are discussed.

RULE 4. The portions of the real axis between 1 to -1 and -4 to negative infinity are part of the root locus.

RULE 6. The intersection of the asymptotic lines and the real axis occurs at

$$s_r = \frac{-4}{+3} = -1.33$$

RULE 7. Using the Spirule, we found the point of breakaway from the real axis to occur at approximately $+0.12$.

RULE 8. This rule does not apply here.

The resulting root locus sketch indicates that the system is always unstable since at least one of the roots of the characteristic equation always occurs in the right half plane.

Case E. $\alpha = 6$. See Figure 6–41 for the root locus sketch. Only rules with results different from those outlined for case A are discussed.

RULE 4. The portions of the real axis between 1 to -1, and -6 to negative infinity, are part of the root locus.

RULE 6. The intersection of the asymptotic lines and the negative real axis occurs at

$$s_r = \frac{-8 - (-6)}{4 - 1} = -\frac{2}{3}$$

RULE 7. Using the Spirule, we found the point of breakaway from the real axis to occur at approximately $+0.14$.

RULE 8. This rule does not apply here.

The resulting root locus sketch indicates that the system is always unstable since at least one of the roots of the characteristic equation always occurs in the right half plane.

The interpretation of Figure 6–41 is quite interesting and revealing. It indicates that the exact location of the zero is very important from a stability viewpoint. Cases A and B were the only configurations which had regions of stability. The dynamic range of gain for stability had a ratio of approximately 4.8 for case A and approximately 4.5 for case B. Therefore case A is preferable. As a matter of fact, the closer the zero is to the imaginary axis, the greater the stabilizing effect it will have. This point is very important.

The transient response of the system can also be obtained by reasoning along these lines: The transient performance is often dominated by the pair of complex conjugate poles located closest to the imaginary axis. These are conventionally referred to as the dominant poles. From the discussion of Section 3–7, the dominant quadratic associated with these complex poles can be given by the following expression (see equation 3–90).

$$\frac{C(s)}{R(s)} = \frac{\omega_n{}^2}{s^2 + 2\zeta\omega_n s + \omega_n{}^2} \qquad (6\text{–}141)$$

where ζ = damping factor

ω_n = natural resonant frequency

We found in Section 3–7 that the transient response to a unit step input for $\zeta < 1$, is given by the following expression (see equation 3–111).

$$c(t) = \frac{1 + e^{-\zeta\omega_n t}}{\sqrt{1 - \zeta^2}} \sin(\omega_n\sqrt{1 - \zeta^2}\, t - \alpha) \qquad (6\text{–}142)$$

where $\alpha = \cos^{-1}(-\zeta)$. Figure 3–36 illustrated the complex-plane location of these dominant poles. The values derived for the rise time t_r (see equation 3–115) and maximum percent overshoot (see equation 3–119) are specifically for a system whose closed-loop transfer function is given by equation 6–141. These quantities change slightly if other closed-loop poles and zeros exist in addition to the dominant complex pair. However, if the other poles and zeros are at least twice as far from the imaginary axis as the dominant pair, the modified exact expressions for rise time and percent overshoot are given by[6]

$$[t_r]_{\text{mod}} = (\sqrt{1 - \zeta^2}\,\omega_n)^{-1}(\pi - \Sigma\,\phi_Z + \Sigma\,\phi_P) \qquad (6\text{–}143)$$

where $\Sigma\phi_Z$ = sum of the angles from the zeros to one of the complex poles

$\Sigma\phi_P$ = sum of the angles from the poles to one of the complex poles

and

Maximum percent overshoot

$$= \left[\left(\frac{P_1}{|P_1 - P_c|}\right)\left(\frac{P_2}{|P_2 - P_c|}\right)\left(\frac{P_3}{|P_3 - P_c|}\right)(\cdots)\right]$$

$$\times \left[\left(\frac{|Z_1 - P_c|}{Z_1}\right)\left(\frac{|Z_2 - P_c|}{Z_2}\right)\left(\frac{|Z_3 - P_c|}{Z_3}\right)(\cdots)\right]100$$

where the first set of brackets represents the product of the ratios of the poles to the absolute distances between the poles and the complex pole. The second set of brackets represents the product of the ratios of the distances between the zeros and the complex pole and the values of the zeros. These exact expressions are rarely used in practice.

Returning to the problem analyzed in Figure 6–41, let us use the information just presented to determine the value of gain for case A that will result in an optimum transient response. Let us assume that a damping factor of 0.707 results in an optimum transient response for this system from the viewpoint of rise time, maximum percent overshoot, and settling time. From the following relationship (derived from Figure 3–36), which is only approximate for case A of Figure 6–41,

$$\cos \alpha = -\zeta$$

α must equal $135°$ in order to meet this specification. This is indicated in Figure 6–41 for case A. A Spirule indicates that the value of gain corresponding to this damping factor is 21.5. Actual simulation of this system indicates that the approximations made are very good since an actual system gain of 22 resulted in a damping factor of 0.71.

The concluding design problem we consider using the root locus consists of employing cascaded phase-lag compensation in order to improve the steady-state performance of a feedback control system. The object is to increase its gain while maintaining an optimum dynamic response. Specifically, we consider the system whose root locus was illustrated in Figure 5–36. For this system

$$G(s)H(s) = \frac{K}{s(s + 4)(s + 5)} \tag{6-144}$$

The root locus of Figure 5–36 indicated that the system was stable when $0 < K < 180$. Let us assume that a damping factor of 0.707 achieves an optimum dynamic response for this system. In addition, we must maintain a velocity constant K_v of 30 in order to meet specified accuracy requirements. Exploring just the surface of this problem, we see that the root locus will yield the value of K which will give the required damping factor. For example, the enlarged version of Figure 5–36 in Figure 6–42 indicates that a $K = 26.6$ will result in a damping factor of 0.707. This value of gain, obtained using the Spirule, does not maintain the required velocity constant 30. The actual value of K_v resulting from $K = 26.6$ is

$$K_v = \lim_{s \to 0} sG(s)H(s) = \lim_{s \to 0} \frac{s(26.6)}{s(s + 4)(s + 5)} = 1.33 \tag{6-145}$$

Therefore it is clear that we cannot just increase the gain K to a value providing the required velocity constant, since this would decrease the

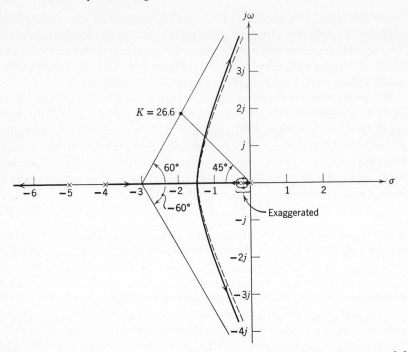

Figure 6–42. Compensation of the root locus shown in Figure 5–36 using a cascaded phase-lag network.

damping factor and adversely affect the transient response. Using the root locus for a solution, we show how these two conflicting factors can be resolved.

Let us assume that the phase-lag compensator is of the form

$$G_c(s) \frac{s + n\alpha}{s + \alpha} \tag{6–146}$$

where n = ratio of the break frequencies. Equation 6–146 indicates that this compensator provides a low-frequency gain in addition to the phase lag. The open-loop transfer function of the compensated system is given by

$$G_c(s)G(s)H(s) = \frac{K}{s(s + 4)(s + 5)} \frac{s + n\alpha}{s + \alpha} \tag{6–147}$$

In general, the distances of $n\alpha$ and α from the origin in the s plane are chosen small compared to the distances of the other zeros and poles of the uncompensated open-loop transfer function, so that the added pole and zero of the compensator will not contribute significant phase lag in the vicinity of the closed-loop bandwidth (crossover frequency). This result is quite clear from study of the Bode diagram. Certainly we do not wish to add the phase-lag contribution in the vicinity of the crossover frequency. Therefore the combination of pole and zero will appear quite close together on the root locus and very close to the origin. This combination is often called a dipole.

In order to complete the design, α will be chosen as 0.01 and n will be chosen using the following derivation, which will achieve a $K_v = 30$.

$$K_v = 30 = \lim_{s \to 0} s G_c(s) G(s) H(s) \tag{6-148}$$

Substituting equation 6–147 into equation 6–148, we obtain

$$30 = \lim_{s \to 0} s \left[\frac{K}{s(s + 4)(s + 5)} \right] \frac{s + n\alpha}{s + \alpha} \tag{6-149}$$

or

$$30 = \frac{Kn}{(4)(5)} \tag{6-150}$$

Since we desire that $K = 26.6$ from a transient viewpoint, we must have

$$n = \frac{30(4)(5)}{26.6} = 22.6 \tag{6-151}$$

The completed root locus for the compensated system whose open-loop transfer function is given by

$$G_c(s) G(s) H(s) = \frac{K}{s(s + 4)(s + 5)} \frac{s + 0.226}{s + 0.01} \tag{6-152}$$

is shown dotted, and slightly exaggerated, in Figure 6–42. Observe that because the dipole is added near the origin, the original root locus is not changed significantly, since the two poles and zero near the origin tend to merge into a single pole.

6–11. THE "BEST" METHOD FOR LINEAR SYSTEM DESIGN?

Any control system engineer who claims that a particular method is the "best" method to use for all problems is not making full use of the tools at his disposal. To claim that any one method is "best" is similar to claiming that the carpenter's "best" tool is his screwdriver. Certainly this is not true. His screwdriver is important, but his hammer, pliers, drill, and saw also play a very important role in his work.

The analogy holds true for the control system engineer. He should regard the methods presented in Chapters 5 and 6 as tools for his trade.

Each tool (or method) complements the other; none is "best". Certainly, for particular applications, one method may be better than others. In general, however, the control engineer should not restrict himself to only one method.

After several years of experience in this field, I wish to present the following guide lines in attempting to choose a method, or methods, for designing a feedback control system. For systems of the second order or less, all the methods presented reveal about the same amount of information and are of about the same complexity. For systems from the third to about the seventh order, there are two primary approaches, each of which complements the other. One of these approaches is the use of the Bode diagram method in conjunction with the Nichols chart and using the Routh-Hurwitz criterion as a check. The other approach is the root locus method, with the Routh-Hurwitz criterion again used as a check. For systems greater than about the seventh order, I find the root locus more complex than the Bode diagram–Nichols chart approach. This statement, however, is general, and like all general statements is not true all the time. For example, no matter what order the system is, we would not use the Bode diagram–Nichols chart approach if the system had nonminimum-phase shift characteristics. Here we would have to use the root locus method. Therefore we wish to leave the reader with the understanding that he should consider all methods first before deciding what tool, or tools, he will use for his final design.

REFERENCES

1. *Servomechanism Practice*, W. R. Ahrendt, McGraw-Hill Book Co., New York, 1954.
2. *Automatic Feedback Control System Synthesis*, J. G. Truxal, McGraw-Hill Book Co., New York, 1955.
3. A-C Stabilizing Networks, A. D. Groner, *Control Eng.*, 55 (Sept. 1954).
4. *Vacuum Tube Amplifiers*, G. E. Valley, Jr., and H. Wallman, McGraw-Hill Book Co., New York, 1948.
5. *Servomechanism Fundamentals*, H. Lauer, R. N. Lesnick, and L. E. Matson, McGraw-Hill Book Co., New York, 1960.
6. *Control Engineer's Handbook*, edited by J. G. Truxal, McGraw-Hill Book Co., New York, 1955.
7. *Network Analysis and Feedback Amplifier Design*, H. W. Bode, D. Van Nostrand Co., New York, 1945.

7 NONLINEAR FEEDBACK CONTROL SYSTEM DESIGN

7-1. INTRODUCTION

The theory and application of feedback control system design presented in previous chapters were restricted to linear systems, that is, systems that can be presented by a linear differential equation. In practice, linear systems possess the property of linearity only over a certain range of operation; all physical systems are nonlinear to some degree. Therefore it is extremely important that the control engineer acquire a facility for analyzing feedback control systems of varying degrees of non-linearity.

Any attempt by the control engineer to restrict his thinking rigorously to linear systems can only result in severe complications in the feedback control system's design. To operate in a linear manner over a wide range of variation of signal amplitude and frequency would require components of an extremely high quality; such a system would probably be impractical from the viewpoints of cost, space, and weight. In addition, the restriction of linearity severely limits the realizable feedback control system's charac-teristics and its resultant attainable functions.

In practice, linear operation is required only for small deviations about the quiescent operating point. The saturation of amplifying devices having large deviations about the quiescent operating point is usually acceptable. The presence of nonlinearities in the form of dead zones, for small devi-ations about the quiescent operating point, is also usually acceptable. In both cases the control engineer attempts to limit the effects of non-linearities to acceptable tolerances, since it is impractical to eliminate the problem entirely.

It is interesting to note that nonlinearities may be intentionally intro-duced into a system in order to compensate for the effects of other undesirable nonlinearities, or to obtain better performance than would be achieved using linear elements. A simple example of an intentional non-linearity is the use of a nonlinear damped system to optimize a system's response in accordance with the magnitude of the error.[1] The on-off

215

contactor (relay) servo, where the feedback control system applies full torque as soon as the error exceeds a specified value, is another case of an intentional nonlinear system. As is illustrated in Chapter 11, many systems utilize nonlinear devices to achieve adaptivity.

The purpose of this chapter is to examine the broad aspects of nonlinear systems. We first study the characteristics of nonlinearities and then present several methods for analyzing unintentional nonlinear feedback control systems. We follow with several illustrations of synthesizing nonlinear systems having intentional nonlinearities. Since many techniques for designing nonlinear systems are also applicable to time-variable systems, a discussion of time-variable systems is included and concludes the presentation of this chapter.

We should emphasize here that methods of analyzing nonlinear systems have not progressed as rapidly as have techniques for analyzing linear systems. Comparatively speaking, at the present time we are still in the developmental stage. However, the various methods presented in this chapter will enable the control engineer to analyze and synthesize nonlinear feedback control systems quantitatively. Nonlinear systems and time-variable systems are considered from the viewpoint of modern optimal control theory in Chapter 10.

7-2. LINEAR AND NONLINEAR DIFFERENTIAL EQUATIONS

A linear differential equation of the nth order, having constant coefficients, can be represented as

$$A_n \frac{d^n y}{dt^n} + A_{n-1} \frac{d^{n-1} y}{dt^{n-1}} + \cdots + A_0 y = x(t) \qquad (7-1)$$

where $\qquad$ $x(t)$ represents the input to the system
$\qquad$ t represents time and is the independent variable
$\qquad$ $y(t)$ represents the dependent variable, or the output of a
$\qquad\qquad$ system, and
$A_n, A_{n-1}, \ldots, A_0$ are constants

This equation is of the form derived for several representative mechanical and electrical systems in Chapter 3. For example, equation 3-9, which is repeated next, gave the differential equation of motion for a mechanical system which had a force $f(t)$ applied to a mass, damper, and spring.

$$M \frac{d^2 y}{dt^2} + B \frac{dy}{dt} + Ky(t) = f(t) \qquad (7-2)$$

The mass of the system is represented by the constant M, the damping factor by the constant B, and the spring constant by K.

Detailed solutions for the class of differential equations having the form shown in equation 7–1 are available. They have been studied in great detail, and several powerful techniques, such as the Laplace transformation, exist for their solution. All the analytical methods discussed in Chapters 5 and 6 are based on systems which can be represented by simple differential equations having this general form.

If any of the coefficients A_n, $A_{n-1}, \ldots, A_0$ are functions of the independent variable time, then the linear differential equation is said to have variable coefficients. This condition can be represented by the following general linear differential equation:

$$A_n(t)\frac{d^n y}{dt^n} + A_{n-1}(t)\frac{d^{n-1}y}{dt^{n-1}} + \cdots + A_0(t)y = x(t) \qquad (7\text{–}3)$$

where A_n, $A_{n-1}, \ldots, A_0$ are all functions of time. The solution to linear differential equations having variable coefficients is considered in the last section of this chapter.

If the coefficients of the differential equation are functions of the dependent variable y, then a nonlinear differential equation results. Its general form can be written

$$A_n\frac{d^n y}{dt^n} + A_{n-1}\frac{d^{n-1}y}{dt^{n-1}} + \cdots + A_1\frac{dy}{dt} + A_0 y$$

$$+ \epsilon f\left(y, \frac{dy}{dt}, \ldots, \frac{d^{n-1}y}{dt^{n-1}}\right) = x(t) \quad (7\text{–}4)$$

where $x(t)$ represents the input to the system
         t represents time and is the independent variable
         $y(t)$ represents the dependent variable, or the output of
         a system
   A_n, $A_{n-1}, \ldots, A_0$ are constants
         ϵ is a constant indicating the degree of nonlinearity
         present, and
$f\left(y, \dfrac{dy}{dt}, \ldots, \dfrac{d^{n-1}y}{dt^{n-1}}\right)$ is a nonlinear function of its variables.

Notice that if $\epsilon = 0$, equation 7–4 reduces to equation 7–1, which represents a linear differential equation having constant coefficients. This leads us to reason, further, that a small amount of nonlinearity in a system means that ϵ is small in comparison with the coefficients A_n, $A_{n-1}, \ldots, A_0$. In addition, a large amount of nonlinearity means that ϵ is large compared to A_n, $A_{n-1}, \ldots, A_0$.

7-3. PROPERTIES OF LINEAR SYSTEMS THAT ARE NOT VALID FOR NONLINEAR SYSTEMS

Several inherent properties of linear systems, which greatly simplify the solution for this class of systems, are not valid for nonlinear systems. The failure of these characteristics to apply to nonlinear systems further complicates the analysis of these complex systems.

Superposition is a fundamental property of linear systems. As a matter of fact, several authors consider this a definition of a linear system. The principle of superposition implies that if $c_1(t)$ is the response of a feedback control system to $r_1(t)$, $c_2(t)$ is its response to $r_2(t)$, and $c_3(t)$ is its response to $r_3(t)$, then the system's response to $r_1(t) + r_2(t) + r_3(t)$ is $c_1(t) + c_2(t) + c_3(t)$. Unfortunately, the superposition principle does not apply to nonlinear systems. Therefore several mathematical tools and processes used in the design of linear systems cannot be used for nonlinear systems.

Stability of linear systems has been shown (in Chapter 5) to depend only on the system's parameters. The stability of nonlinear systems, however, depends on the initial conditions and the nature of the input signal as well as the system parameters. The control engineer cannot expect a nonlinear system that exhibits a stable response to one type of input to have a stable response to other types of input. We shall shortly illustrate nonlinear systems that are stable for very small or very large signals, but not for both.

We normally expect the output of a linear system, excited by a sinusoidal signal, to have the same frequency as the input, although its amplitude and phase may differ. However, the output of nonlinear systems usually contains additional frequency components.

In linear continuous systems, it does not matter whether two cascaded elements G_1 and G_2 are expressed as G_1G_2 or G_2G_1. Unfortunately, in nonlinear systems G_1G_2 may not equal G_2G_1.

The question of stability is clearly defined in linear systems: A system is either stable or unstable. An unstable linear system grows without bound, either exponentially or in an oscillatory mode with the envelope of the oscillations increasing exponentially. In nonlinear systems, system instability may mean a constant-amplitude output having an arbitrary waveform.

7-4. UNUSUAL CHARACTERISTICS THAT ARE UNIQUE TO NONLINEAR SYSTEMS

This section describes in detail some of the unusual characteristics that are unique to nonlinear systems. These phenomena, which do not occur

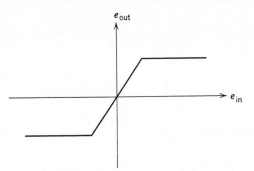

Figure 7–1.   Saturation characteristics.

in linear systems, may be desirable or undesirable depending on the application. We discuss specifically the following unusual characteristics: limit cycles, soft and hard self-excitation, hysteresis, jump resonance, and subharmonic generation.

Limit cycles are oscillations of fixed amplitude and period that occur in nonlinear systems. Depending on whether the oscillation converges or diverges from the conditions represented, limit cycles can be either stable or unstable. It is possible that conditionally stable systems may contain both a stable and an unstable limit cycle. The occurrence of limit cycles in nonlinear systems makes it necessary to define instability in terms of acceptable magnitudes of oscillation, since a very small nonlinear oscillation may not be detrimental to the performance of a system.

Self-excited oscillations occurring in systems that are unstable in the presence of very small signals are called *soft self-excitation*. Self-excited oscillations occurring in systems that are unstable in the presence of very large signals are called *hard self-excitation*. Since soft and hard types of oscillation can occur, the control engineer must specify the dynamic range of operation completely when designing a nonlinear system. A feedback control system containing an element having saturation characteristics, as illustrated in Figure 7–1, could exhibit soft self-excitation. A feedback control system containing an element having dead-zone characteristics, as illustrated in Figure 7–2, could exhibit hard self-excitation.

Hysteresis is a nonlinear phenomenon which is most usually associated with magnetization curves or backlash of gear trains. A conventional magnetization curve whose path depends on whether the magnetizing force $\mathscr{H}$ is increasing or decreasing is shown in Figure 7–3.

Jump resonance,[2] another form of hysteresis, is of considerable interest. It exhibits itself in the closed-loop frequency response of certain nonlinear systems, as illustrated in Figure 7–4. As the frequency ω is increased and the input amplitude R is held constant, the response follows the curve

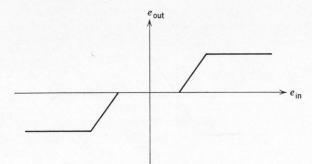

Figure 7–2.   Dead-zone characteristics.

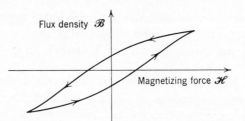

Figure 7–3.   Conventional hysteresis loop.

AFB. At point *B*, a small change in frequency results in a discontinuous jump to point *C*. The response then follows the curve to point *D* upon further increase in frequency. As the frequency is decreased from point *D*, the response follows the curve to points *C* and *E*. At point *E*, a small change in frequency results in a discontinuous jump to point *F*. The response follows the curve to point *A* for further decreases in frequency. Observe from this analysis that the response never actually follows the

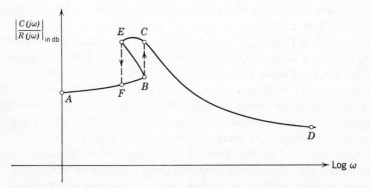

Figure 7–4.   Closed-loop response of a system with jump resonance.

curve segment *BE*. This portion of the curve represents a condition of unstable equilibrium. It is interesting to note that the feedback control system must be of the second order, or higher, for the phenomenon of jump resonance to occur.

Subharmonic generation[3] refers to nonlinear systems whose output contains subharmonics of the input's sinusoidal excitation frequency. The transition from normal harmonic operation to subharmonic operation is usually quite sudden. Once the subharmonic operation is established, however, it is usually quite stable. In general, if sinusoidal signals f_1 and f_2 are added and their sum is applied to a nonlinear device, the output contains frequency components $af_1 \pm bf_2$, where a and b assume all possible integers including zero.

7-5. METHODS AVAILABLE FOR ANALYZING NONLINEAR SYSTEMS

The control engineer has several tools for the analysis of nonlinear systems. All these techniques depend on the severity of the nonlinearity and/or the order of the system under consideration. We consider most of the useful and popular techniques in this chapter and illustrate their practical application.

The analysis of nonlinear systems is concerned with the existence and effects of limit cycles, soft and hard self-excitation, hysteresis, jump resonance, and subharmonic generation. In addition, the system's response to specific input functions must be determined. The major difficulty of analyzing nonlinear systems is that no single technique is generally applicable to all problems.

Quasi-linear systems, where the deviation from linearity is not too large, permit the use of certain *linearizing approximations*. The *describing-function* approach, which is limited to quasi-linear systems of any order, simplifies the problem by assuming that the input to the nonlinear system is sinusoidal and the only significant frequency component of the output is that component having the same frequency as the input. It is also possible to determine *absolute stability* for certain quasi-linear systems *from the system's characteristic polynomial* by means of a method similar to the Routh-Hurwitz criterion.

Nonlinear systems can often be approximated by several linear regions. The *piecewise linear* approach, which is a very powerful method, permits the segmented linearization of any nonlinearity for any order of system. The *phase-plane method* is a very useful technique for analyzing the response of a second-order system whose nonlinearity can be large or small. Extension of the phase-plane method to systems of higher order has resulted in a technique called the phase space. *Liapunov's stability criterion* is a very powerful method for determining the steady-state stability of nonlinear systems.

Systems of very high order having severe nonlinearities have hardly been dealt with in general analytical terms. This problem usually requires the use of *numerical methods*, such as the use of *analog or digital computers*, for a solution. It is worth emphasizing at this point that any nonlinear differential equation can be solved by these techniques provided many small increments are used. However, the resulting solution is valid only for the specific problem being considered. It is very difficult to extend the result and obtain a general solution which can be used for other problems.

7-6. LINEARIZING APPROXIMATIONS

In quasi-linear systems, where the deviation from linearity is not too great, approximations of linearity may permit the extension of ordinary linear concepts. This approach acknowledges that certain system characteristics change from operating point to operating point, but it assumes linearity in the neighborhood of a specific operating point. The technique of linearizing approximations is universally used by the engineer and may be more familiar to the reader under the names "small-signal theory" and/or "theory of small perturbations."

Linearizing approximations were utilized when we discussed the two-phase a-c servomotor in Section 3-3. For this device, Figure 3-24 illustrated the quasi-linear characteristics existing between developed torque and speed. However, by approximating the torque-speed curves with straight lines, the linear differential equation 3-60 was formulated. We then obtained the transfer function of the two-phase, a-c servomotor, assuming that it was a linear device. It is left as an exercise to the reader in Problem 7-1 to determine the effect of various linearizing approximations.

The effects of a small amount of nonlinearity can be studied analytically by considering the general nonlinear differential equation 7-4:

$$A_n \frac{d^n y}{dt^n} + A_{n-1} \frac{d^{n-1} y}{dt^n} + \cdots + A_1 \frac{dy}{dt} + A_0 y$$
$$+ \epsilon f\left(y, \frac{dy}{dt}, \ldots, \frac{d^{n-1} y}{dt^{n-1}}\right) = x(t)$$

An expansion of the solution to this differential equation, for small nonlinearities, can be written in a power series of ϵ as

$$y(t) = y_{(0)}(t) + \epsilon y_{(1)}(t) + \epsilon^2 y_{(2)}(t) + \epsilon^3 y_{(3)}(t) + \cdots \qquad (7-5)$$

From equation 7–5, $y(t)$ may be interpreted as composed of a linear component $y_{(0)}(t)$ and several linear deviation factors: $\epsilon y_{(1)}(t) + \epsilon^2 y_{(2)}(t) + \cdots$. Assuming that ϵ is very small, the nonlinear components will not seriously affect the system's behavior if a linear approximation is assumed. Therefore, within the realm of reasonable engineering approximations, the control engineer may be able to extend linear theory for certain feedback control systems which exhibit a small amount of nonlinearity. It is very interesting that this is just the reason why linear theory has had such good results even though practical systems are never purely linear.

7–7. THE DESCRIBING-FUNCTION CONCEPT[4,5]

Describing functions attempt to extend the very powerful transfer function approach of linear systems to quasi-linear systems. They are defined as the ratio of the fundamental component of the output response from a nonlinear device to that of a sinusoidal input signal. In general, the describing function depends on the input signal's amplitude and frequency. It is usually a complex number that indicates the amplitude and phase relationships existing between the input and the fundamental component of the output from a nonlinear element. We study the basic limitations of the describing-function method of analysis and compare it with the transfer function concept for linear systems. The philosophy and technique for utilizing the describing function will be formulated.

If the input to a nonlinear element is a sinusoidal signal, the describing-function analysis assumes that the output is a periodic signal having the same fundamental period as that of the input signal. In addition, the analysis is only concerned with the fundamental component of the output waveform. All harmonics, subharmonics, and any d-c component are neglected. This assumption is reasonable since the harmonic terms are small compared to the fundamental term. In addition, a feedback control system usually provides additional attenuation of the harmonic terms because of its inherent filtering action. Most nonlinear elements do not generate a d-c term since they are symmetrical, nor do they generate any subharmonic terms. Therefore, in practice the fundamental term is the only significant component of the output of a nonlinear element. In addition, the describing-function analysis assumes that there is only one nonlinear element in the feedback control system and that it is not time-varying. If a system contains more than one nonlinearity, we must lump all the nonlinearities together and obtain an overall describing function.

An analysis of these limitations indicates that the describing function is based on a rather poor mathematical foundation. The technique gives

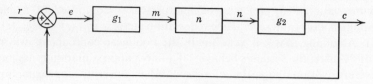

Figure 7–5.   General nonlinear system.

reasonable results only for quasi-linear systems and is practically invalid for systems containing extreme nonlinearities. The describing function does have the advantage, however, that it can be used for systems of any order and is fairly simple to apply.

It is important to emphasize that the describing-function technique is a very powerful tool for analyzing and designing quasi-linear systems. The describing function should be thought of as a generalized transfer function for nonlinear systems. Linear criteria of stability, for example, the Nyquist diagram, the Nichols chart, and the root locus, can be easily applied to determine system stability, with the added constraint that stability must be analyzed as a function of signal level and frequency of the input signal.

In order to derive a mathematical expression for the describing function, let us consider the nonlinear system illustrated in Figure 7–5. In accordance with the definition of the describing function, let us assume that the input into the nonlinear element n is given by

$$m = M \sin \omega t \tag{7-6}$$

In general, the steady-state output of the nonlinear device can be represented by the series

$$n = N_1 \sin (\omega t + \phi_1) + N_2 \sin (2\omega t + \phi_2) + N_3 \sin (3\omega t + \phi_3) + \cdots \tag{7-7}$$

By definition, the describing function is

$$N(M, \omega) = \frac{N_1}{M} e^{j\phi_1} \tag{7-8}$$

Notice that the generalized describing function depends on the amplitude of the input signal, the amplitude of the fundamental frequency component of the output, and the phase shift of the fundamental frequency component with respect to the input. When analyzing a nonlinear system by the describing-function method, the control engineer determines the describing function as a function of the amplitude and frequency of the input. The nonlinear element is then considered to have a gain and phase shift varying with the amplitude and frequency of the input signal.

When we attempt to compare the describing-function and transfer function concepts, we must consider all the characteristics discussed in Section 7–3. In addition, we must recognize that all the peculiar characteristics discussed in Section 7–4 are also present. Therefore, when utilizing the describing-function analysis for quasi-linear systems, we must recognize the basic limitations of the describing function: the fact that the superposition principle is not valid; the fact that stability depends on the characteristics of the input signal and the order of the elements in the system; and the occurrence of limit cycles, self-excitation, hysteresis effects, and jump resonances.

7–8. DERIVATION OF DESCRIBING FUNCTIONS FOR COMMON NONLINEARITIES[5,6]

The describing functions for several common nonlinearities are derived in this section. The procedure most commonly used is to derive the Fourier series of the output waveshape from the nonlinear device and consider only the fundamental component. Let us consider the nonlinear element n in an overall feedback control system, as shown in Figure 7–5. Assuming that the input m is given by a sinusoidal signal where

$$m = M \sin \omega t \qquad (7\text{–}9)$$

we can represent the output waveshape by a Fourier series given by the expression

$$n(\omega t) = \frac{A_0}{2} + \sum_{K=1}^{K=\infty} A_K \cos K\omega t + \sum_{K=1}^{K=\infty} B_K \sin K\omega t \qquad (7\text{–}10)$$

where

$$A_K = \frac{2}{T} \int_{-T/2}^{T/2} n(\omega t) \cos q\omega t \, d(\omega t) \qquad (7\text{–}11)$$

where $q = 2, 4, 6, \ldots$ and

$$B_K = \frac{2}{T} \int_{-T/2}^{T/2} n(\omega t) \sin l\omega t \, d(\omega t) \qquad (7\text{–}12)$$

where $l = 1, 3, 5, \cdots$. In general, if $n(\omega t) = -n(-\omega t)$, then the function is odd and $A_K = 0$. In addition, if $n(\omega t) = n(-\omega t)$, then the function is even and $B_K = 0$.

Since the describing function is only concerned with the fundamental component of the output, it is necessary that we obtain only A_1 and B_1 where

$$A_1 = \frac{2}{T} \int_{-T/2}^{T/2} n(\omega t) \cos \omega t \, d(\omega t) \qquad (7\text{–}13)$$

$$B_1 = \frac{2}{T} \int_{-T/2}^{T/2} n(\omega t) \sin \omega t \, d(\omega t) \qquad (7\text{–}14)$$

For $m = M \sin \omega t$, the describing function can then be obtained from the expression

$$N(M, \omega) = \frac{B_1}{M} + j\frac{A_1}{M} = \left[\left(\frac{B_1}{M}\right)^2 + \left(\frac{A_1}{M}\right)^2 \right]^{\frac{1}{2}} \bigg/ \tan^{-1}\frac{A_1}{B_1} \quad (7\text{-}15)$$

The control engineer is usually concerned with the nonlinearities due to dead zones, saturation, backlash, on-off relay control systems, coulomb friction, and stiction. We specifically derive and catalog the describing functions for them, so that the reader will have a handy reference for some common describing functions. In addition, the procedure should enable the control engineer to develop the facility for calculating the describing function of any nonlinearity he may encounter.

1. Describing Function of a Dead Zone

Figure 7–6 illustrates the nonlinear characteristics of a dead zone. The relationships between input and output of this nonlinearity can be expressed by the equations

$$n = 0 \quad \text{for} \quad -D < m < D \tag{7-16}$$

$$n = K_1 M(\sin \omega t - \sin \omega t_1) \quad \text{for} \quad m > D \tag{7-17}$$

$$n = K_1 M(\sin \omega t + \sin \omega t_1) \quad \text{for} \quad m < -D \tag{7-18}$$

Figure 7–7 illustrates typical input and output waveshapes. Notice that the output is an odd function, and therefore $A_K = 0$. The symmetry over the four quarters of the period allows us to evaluate the expression

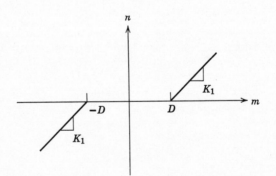

Figure 7–6. Nonlinear characteristics of a dead zone.

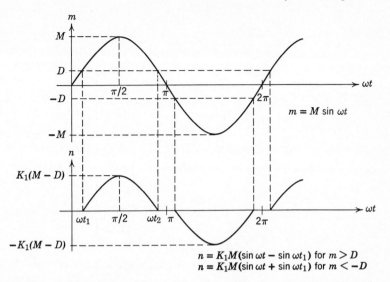

$m = M \sin \omega t$

$n = K_1 M(\sin \omega t - \sin \omega t_1)$ for $m > D$
$n = K_1 M(\sin \omega t + \sin \omega t_1)$ for $m < -D$

Figure 7–7. Input and general form of the output wave shape from a nonlinear device having dead-zone characteristics.

for the Fourier coefficient, B_1, by taking four times the integral over one-quarter of a cycle, as follows:

$$B_1 = \frac{4}{\pi} \int_0^{\pi/2} n(\omega t) \sin \omega t \, d(\omega t) \qquad (7\text{--}19)$$

Substituting equations 7–16 and 7–17 into equation 7–19, we obtain

$$B_1 = \frac{4}{\pi} \left[\int_0^{\omega t_1} (0) \sin \omega t \, d(\omega t) + \int_{\omega t_1}^{\pi/2} K_1 M(\sin \omega t - \sin \omega t_1) \sin \omega t \, d(\omega t) \right] \qquad (7\text{--}20)$$

This can be simplified to

$$B_1 = \frac{4 K_1 M}{\pi} \int_{\omega t_1}^{\pi/2} (\sin \omega t - \sin \omega t_1) \sin \omega t \, d(\omega t) \qquad (7\text{--}21)$$

Since $\omega t_1 = \sin^{-1}(D/M)$, equation 7–21 can be written as

$$B_1 = \frac{4 K_1 M}{\pi} \int_{\sin^{-1}(D/M)}^{\pi/2} \left(\sin^2 \omega t - \frac{D}{M} \sin \omega t \right) d(\omega t) \qquad (7\text{--}22)$$

Integrating, we obtain the expression

$$B_1 = \frac{4 K_1 M}{\pi} \left[-\frac{1}{2} \cos \omega t \sin \omega t + \frac{1}{2} \omega t + \frac{D}{M} \cos \omega t \right]_{\sin^{-1}(D/M)}^{\pi/2} \qquad (7\text{--}23)$$

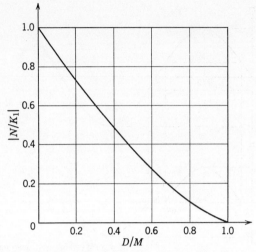

Figure 7–8.   Normalized describing function for a dead zone.

Simplification of equation 7–23 results in the expression

$$B_1 = \frac{2K_1 M}{\pi}\left(\frac{\pi}{2} - \frac{D}{M}\cos\sin^{-1}\frac{D}{M} - \sin^{-1}\frac{D}{M}\right) \qquad (7\text{–}24)$$

From equation 7–24, since the describing function is the ratio of the amplitude of the fundamental component of the output B_1 to M, it can be expressed as

$$N_{dz}(M) = \frac{B_1}{M} = \frac{2K_1}{\pi}\left(\frac{\pi}{2} - \frac{D}{M}\cos\sin^{-1}\frac{D}{M} - \sin^{-1}\frac{D}{M}\right) \qquad (7\text{–}25)$$

Notice that the describing function for a dead zone is only a function of the amplitude of the input and not of frequency. Figure 7–8, obtained from equation 7–25, is a sketch of the normalized value of the describing function N/K_1 as a function of the ratio D/M. For very small values of D/M the normalized describing function approaches unity. For values of $D/M \geqslant 1$ it equals zero, which basically implies that the input must be greater than the dead-zone magnitude in order to obtain an output. Notice that the describing function for dead zones does not introduce any phase shift since it is an odd function.

2.   Describing Function of Saturation

Figure 7–9 illustrates the nonlinear characteristics of saturation. The relationships between input and output of this nonlinearity can be

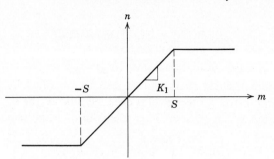

Figure 7–9. Nonlinear characteristics of saturation.

expressed by the following equations.

$$n = K_1 M \sin \omega t \quad \text{for} \quad m < S \qquad (7\text{–}26)$$

$$n = \pm K_1 S \qquad \text{for} \quad m > \pm S \qquad (7\text{–}27)$$

Figure 7–10 illustrates typical input and output waveshapes.

Notice that the output waveshape is an odd function for the case of saturation just as it was for the case of a dead zone. Therefore, the expression for the Fourier coefficient B_1 of the output waveshape is

$$n(\omega t) = B_1 \sin K\omega t \qquad (7\text{–}28)$$

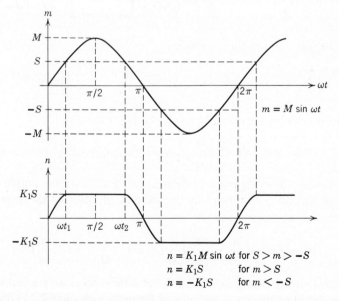

Figure 7–10. Input and general form of the output wave shape from a nonlinear device having saturation characteristics.

where

$$B_1 = \frac{2}{T} \int_{-T/2}^{T/2} n(\omega t) \sin \omega t \, d(\omega t) \qquad (7\text{-}29)$$

As was true for the previous case of dead-zone nonlinearities, the expression for the Fourier coefficient B_1 can be obtained by taking four times the integral over a quarter of a cycle because of the symmetry over the four quarters of the period. This results in the expression

$$B_1 = \frac{4}{\pi} \int_0^{\pi/2} n(\omega t) \sin \omega t \, d(\omega t) \qquad (7\text{-}30)$$

Substituting equations 7–26 and 7–27 into equation 7–30, we obtain

$$B_1 = \frac{4}{\pi} \left[\int_0^{\omega t_1} K_1 M \sin \omega t \sin \omega t \, d(\omega t) + \int_{\omega t_1}^{\pi/2} K_1 M \sin \omega t_1 \sin \omega t \, d(\omega t) \right]$$
$$(7\text{-}31)$$

This can be simplified to

$$B_1 = \frac{4K_1 M}{\pi} \left[\int_0^{\omega t_1} \sin^2 \omega t \, d(\omega t) + \int_{\omega t_1}^{\pi/2} \sin \omega t_1 \sin \omega t \, d(\omega t) \right] \qquad (7\text{-}32)$$

Since $\omega t_1 = \sin^{-1}(S/M)$, equation 7–32 can be written as

$$B_1 = \frac{4K_1 M}{\pi} \left[\int_0^{\sin^{-1}(S/M)} \sin^2 \omega t \, d(\omega t) + \int_{\sin^{-1}(S/M)}^{\pi/2} \frac{S}{M} \sin \omega t \, d(\omega t) \right]$$
$$(7\text{-}33)$$

Integrating, we obtain the expression

$$B_1 = \frac{4K_1 M}{\pi} \left[\left[-\tfrac{1}{2} \cos \omega t \sin \omega t + \tfrac{1}{2}\omega t \right]_0^{\sin^{-1}(S/M)} - \frac{S}{M} \left[\cos \omega t \right]_{\sin^{-1}(S/M)}^{\pi/2} \right]$$
$$(7\text{-}34)$$

Simplification of equation 7–34 results in the expression

$$B_1 = \frac{2K_1 M}{\pi} \left(\frac{S}{M} \cos \sin^{-1} \frac{S}{M} + \sin^{-1} \frac{S}{M} \right) \qquad (7\text{-}35)$$

Since the describing function is defined as the ratio of the amplitude of the fundamental component of the output, B_1, to M, the describing function can be expressed as

$$N_{\text{sat}}(M) = \frac{B_1}{M} = \frac{2K_1}{\pi} \left(\frac{S}{M} \cos \sin^{-1} \frac{S}{M} + \sin^{-1} \frac{S}{M} \right) \qquad (7\text{-}36)$$

Notice that the describing function for saturation is only a function of the amplitude of the input and not of frequency. Figure 7–11, obtained from equation 7–36, is a sketch of the normalized value of the describing

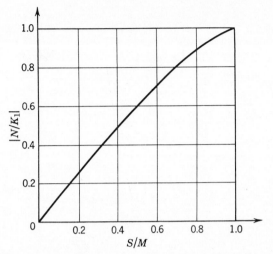

Figure 7–11. Normalized describing function for saturation.

function N/K_1 as a function of the ratio S/M. For very small values of S/M, the normalized describing function approaches zero. For values of $S/M \geqslant 1$ it equals unity, which basically implies that the output is un-affected by the saturation level if $S > M$. Notice that the describing function for saturation does not introduce any phase shift since it is an odd function.

3. Describing Function of Backlash

Backlash, or mechanical hysteresis, is defined as the difference in motion between an increasing and a decreasing output. Figure 7–12 illustrates a representative physical model of backlash, and Figure 7–13 illustrates its characteristics. The source of backlash that usually receives the most attention is the "looseness" inherent in mechanical gearing. Although attempts have been made to design gears and other mechanical trans-mission techniques so as to fit their mating members very tightly, it is practically impossible to eliminate backlash entirely.

The describing function for backlash can be derived for either of the following cases:

$$D < M \leqslant 2D \tag{7-37}$$

or

$$M > 2D \tag{7-38}$$

The describing function for the trivial case where $M < D$ is zero. Figure 7–14 illustrates typical input and output waveshapes for the first case, and Figure 7–15 illustrates the situation for the second case. Obviously, the

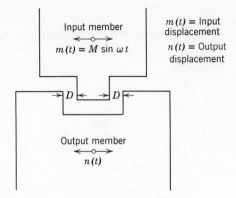

Figure 7–12.   *Physical model of backlash.*

describing function for either case has the same form. Our derivation specifically considers the model of the first case.

From Figure 7–14, the relationships between input and output for this nonlinearity can be expressed by the following equations.

$$n(\omega t) = -(M - D) \qquad \text{for} \quad 0 < \omega t < \omega t_1 \qquad (7\text{–}39)$$

$$n(\omega t) = M \sin \omega t - D \quad \text{for} \quad \omega t_1 < \omega t < \frac{\pi}{2} \qquad (7\text{–}40)$$

$$n(\omega t) = M - D \qquad \text{for} \quad \frac{\pi}{2} < \omega t < \omega t_2 \qquad (7\text{–}41)$$

$$n(\omega t) = M \sin \omega t + D \quad \text{for} \quad \omega t_2 < \omega t < \frac{3\pi}{2} \qquad (7\text{–}42)$$

$$n(\omega t) = -(M - D) \qquad \text{for} \quad \frac{3\pi}{2} < \omega t < 2\pi \qquad (7\text{–}43)$$

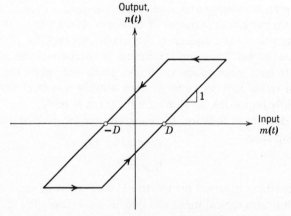

Figure 7–13.   *Characteristics of backlash.*

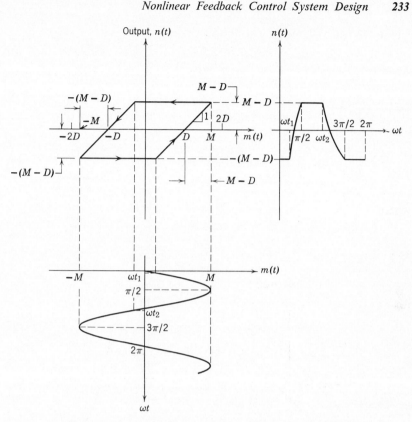

Figure 7–14. Backlash characteristics where $D < M \leqslant 2D$.

Notice that the output waveshape is neither an odd nor an even function. This means that the Fourier series of the output waveshape is

$$n(\omega t) = \sum_{K=1}^{K=\infty} A_K \cos K\omega t + \sum_{K=1}^{K=\infty} B_K \sin K\omega t \qquad (7\text{--}44)$$

where

$$A_K = \frac{2}{T} \int_{-T/2}^{T/2} n(\omega t) \cos q\omega t \, d(\omega t) \qquad (7\text{--}45)$$

and

$$B_K = \frac{2}{T} \int_{-T/2}^{T/2} n(\omega t) \sin l\omega t \, d(\omega t) \qquad (7\text{--}46)$$

Since the describing function is concerned only with the fundamental component of the output, we are only interested in A_1 and B_1. From equations 7–39 through 7–45, we can express A_1 as

$$A_1 = \frac{2}{2\pi}\left[\int_0^{\omega t_1} -(M - D)\cos \omega t\, d(\omega t) + \int_{\omega t_1}^{\pi/2} (M \sin \omega t - D)\cos \omega t\, d(\omega t)\right.$$

$$+ \int_{\pi/2}^{\omega t_2} (M - D)\cos \omega t\, d(\omega t) + \int_{\omega t_2}^{3\pi/2} (M \sin \omega t + D)\cos \omega t\, d(\omega t)$$

$$\left. + \int_{3\pi/2}^{2\pi} -(M - D)\cos \omega t\, d(\omega t)\right] \qquad (7\text{–}47)$$

where $$\omega t_1 = \sin^{-1}\left(\frac{2D}{M} - 1\right)$$

and $$\omega t_2 = \omega t_1 + \pi$$

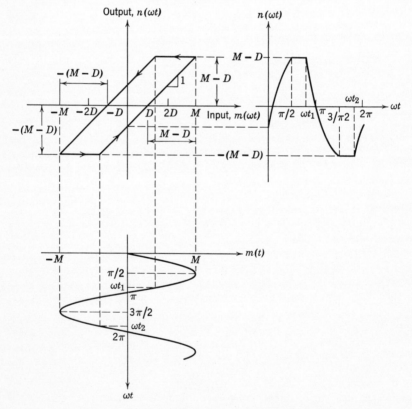

Figure 7–15. *Backlash characteristics where* $M > 2D$.

From equations 7–39 through 7–44 and equation 7–46, we can express B_1 as

$$B_1 = \frac{2}{2\pi}\left[\int_0^{\omega t_1} -(M - D)\sin \omega t\, d(\omega t) + \int_{\omega t_1}^{\pi/2} (M \sin \omega t - D)\sin \omega t\, d(\omega t)\right.$$

$$+ \int_{\pi/2}^{\omega t_2}(M - D)\sin \omega t\, d(\omega t) + \int_{\omega t_2}^{3\pi/2}(M \sin \omega t + D)\sin \omega t\, d(\omega t)$$

$$\left.+ \int_{3\pi/2}^{2\pi} -(M - D)\sin \omega t\, d(\omega t)\right] \tag{7-48}$$

Integrating equations 7–47 and 7–48, we obtain the following:

$$A_1 = \frac{2D}{\pi M}\left(\frac{2D}{M} - 2\right)M \tag{7-49}$$

and

$$B_1 = \frac{1}{\pi}\left[\frac{\pi}{2} - \sin^{-1}\left(\frac{2D}{M} - 1\right) + \left(\frac{2D}{M} - 1\right)\cos \sin^{-1}\left(\frac{2D}{M} - 1\right)\right]M \tag{7-50}$$

Therefore, the describing function for backlash is given by

$$N_{\text{backl}}(M) = \frac{1}{M}\sqrt{A_1^2 + B_1^2}\left/\tan^{-1}\frac{A_1}{B_1}\right. \tag{7-51}$$

This expression is valid only when the positive slope of the backlash characteristic, as shown in Figures 7–14 and 7–15, is unity. If it is any other value, such as K_1, then equation 7–51 is multiplied by K_1.

Notice that the describing function for backlash is only a function of the amplitude of the input and not of the frequency. Figures 7–16 and 7–17, which have been obtained from equations 7–49 through 7–51, are sketches of the amplitude and phase characteristics of the describing function as a function of the ratio D/M, respectively. Notice that a phase lag occurs at low amplitudes. This phase lag introduces problems of stability in feedback control systems.

4. Describing Function of an On-Off Element Having Hysteresis

A class of systems of great practical importance to the control engineer is that of "on-off" control systems. In these systems, as soon as the error signal exceeds a certain level, a relay switches on full corrective torque having proper polarity to the control system. When the error falls below a certain level, all the corrective torque is removed. On-off control systems are characterized by slow speed and poor accuracy. However, these simple and relatively inexpensive devices find many practical uses, in

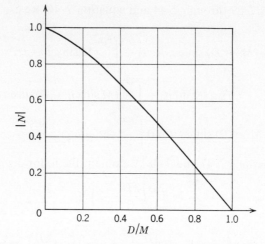

Figure 7–16.   Amplitude characteristics for the describing function of backlash.

thermostatic control of heat, in automobile voltage regulators, in aircraft control applications where space and weight limitations are very critical, and so on.

The basis of on-off control systems, the relay or contactor, has a variety of characteristics.   For the purpose of deriving a describing function, we consider a three-position contactor exhibiting hysteresis characteristics. We choose a three-position rather than two-position contactor because we are interested in the phase of the corrective signal for control systems. Figure 7–18 illustrates the control signal–correction signal characteristics and waveshapes for such a device.   The hysteresis effect occurs because

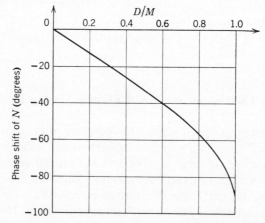

Figure 7–17.   Phase characteristics for the describing function of backlash.

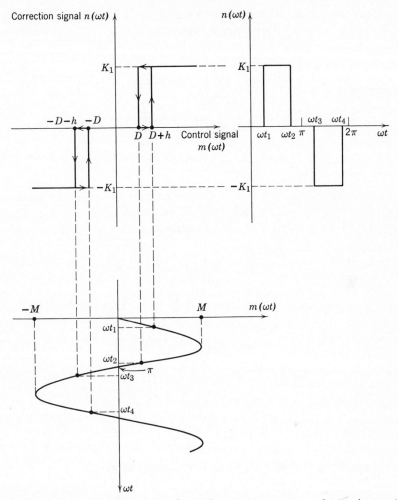

Figure 7–18. On-off characteristics for a three-position contactor having hysteresis.

of the different values of control signal for corrective torque application and its removal. Torque is applied when the control signal reaches $\pm(D + h)$, but it is not removed until the control signal equals $\pm D$. The relationships between input and output for this nonlinearity can be expressed by the following equations.

$$
\begin{aligned}
n(\omega t) &= 0 & \text{for} \quad 0 < \omega t < \omega t_1 \\
n(\omega t) &= K_1 & \text{for} \quad \omega t_1 < \omega t < \omega t_2 \\
n(\omega t) &= -K_1 & \text{for} \quad \omega t_3 < \omega t < \omega t_4 \\
n(\omega t) &= 0 & \text{for} \quad \omega t_4 < \omega t < 2\pi
\end{aligned}
\qquad (7\text{–}52)
$$

Notice that the output waveshape is neither an odd nor an even function. The Fourier series of the output waveshape is

$$n(\omega t) = \sum_{K=1}^{K=\infty} A_K \cos K\omega t + \sum_{K=1}^{K=\infty} B_K \sin K\omega t \qquad (7\text{--}53)$$

where

$$A_K = \frac{2}{T} \int_{-T/2}^{T/2} n(\omega t) \cos q\omega t \, d(\omega t) \qquad (7\text{--}54)$$

$$B_K = \frac{2}{T} \int_{-T/2}^{T/2} n(\omega t) \sin l\omega t \, d(\omega t) \qquad (7\text{--}55)$$

Since the describing function is concerned only with the fundamental component of the output, we are only interested in A_1 and B_1. From equations 7–52 through 7–54, we can express A_1 as

$$A_1 = \frac{2}{2\pi} \Bigg[\int_0^{\omega t_1} (0) \cos \omega t \, d(\omega t) + \int_{\omega t_1}^{\omega t_2} (K_1) \cos \omega t \, d(\omega t)$$

$$+ \int_{\omega t_2}^{\omega t_3} (0) \cos \omega t \, d(\omega t) + \int_{\omega t_3}^{\omega t_4} (-K_1) \cos \omega t \, d(\omega t) \Bigg] \qquad (7\text{--}56)$$

where

$$\omega t_1 = \sin^{-1} \frac{D+h}{M}$$

$$\omega t_2 = \pi - \sin^{-1} \frac{D}{M}$$

$$\omega t_3 = \omega t_1 + \pi$$

$$\omega t_4 = \omega t_2 + \pi$$

From equations 7–52 and equation 7–55, we can express B_1 as

$$B_1 = \frac{2}{2\pi} \Bigg[\int_0^{\omega t_1} (0) \sin \omega t \, d(\omega t) + \int_{\omega t_1}^{\omega t_2} (K_1) \sin \omega t \, d(\omega t)$$

$$+ \int_{\omega t_2}^{\omega t_3} (0) \cos \omega t \, d(\omega t) + \int_{\omega t_3}^{\omega t_4} (-K_1) \sin \omega t \, d(\omega t) \Bigg] \qquad (7\text{--}57)$$

Integrating equations 7–56 and 7–57, we obtain the expressions

$$A_1 = - \frac{2K_1}{\pi} \left(\frac{h}{M} \right) \qquad (7\text{--}58)$$

$$B_1 = \frac{2K_1}{\pi} \left[\cos \sin^{-1} \frac{D+h}{M} - \cos \left(\pi - \sin^{-1} \frac{D}{M} \right) \right] \qquad (7\text{--}59)$$

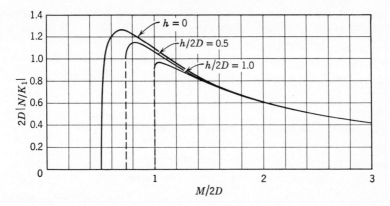

Figure 7–19a. Amplitude characteristics for the describing function of an on-off device having hysteresis.

The describing function for a three-position contactor on-off element having hysteresis is given by the expression

$$2\,D\,N_{\text{on-off}}(M) = \frac{2D}{M}\sqrt{A_1{}^2 + B_1{}^2}\,\bigg/\!\tan^{-1}\frac{A_1}{B_1} \tag{7–60}$$

Notice that the describing function for this device is only a function of the amplitude of the input and not of frequency. Figures 7–19a and 7–19b,

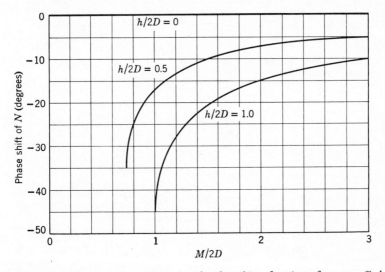

Figure 7–19b. Phase characteristics for the describing function of an on-off device having hysteresis.

which have been obtained from equations 7–58 and 7–59, are sketches of the normalized amplitude and phase characteristics of the describing function as a function of the ratio M/D, respectively. Notice that the phase lag is zero when hysteresis is not present and grows progressively worse as the hysteresis increases.

5. Describing Functions of Coulomb Friction and Stiction

In Chapter 3 we considered the effect of damping in linear systems. Damping, a form of friction, is known as "viscous friction." It has the characteristic that its magnitude is always proportional to velocity, as is illustrated in Figure 7–20a. The damping factor B is the slope of this characteristic. Another type of frictional force commonly found in control systems is known as "coulomb friction." Unlike viscous friction, it is not proportional to velocity but is a constant force that always opposes the velocity. This nonlinear phenomenon is illustrated in Figure 7–20b, where the coulomb friction force is denoted by $\pm F_c$. Another nonlinear form of frictional force, known as static friction or "stiction," is the value of

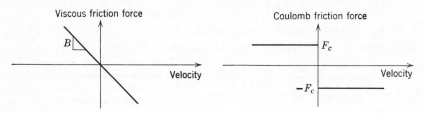

Figure 7–20a.   Viscous friction characteristics.

Figure 7–20b.   Coulomb friction characteristics.

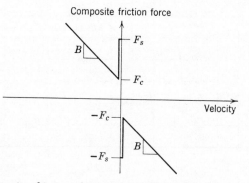

Figure 7–20c.   Composite friction characteristics illustrating viscous, coulomb, and stiction friction.

the frictional force at zero velocity. It is usually denoted by $\pm F_s$. Figure 7–20c illustrates the composite frictional-force characteristics generally encountered when controlling some load.

To determine the describing function of coulomb friction, we can express the relationship between the input and output as

$$n(\omega t) = m(\omega t) \pm F_c$$

where $m(\omega t) =$ applied force
$F_c =$ force necessary to overcome coulomb friction
$n(\omega t) =$ output force

The corresponding steady-state waveforms are given by

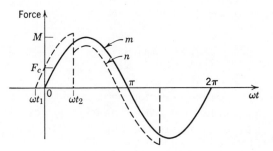

It should be noted that the discontinuities of the output waveform correspond to zero velocity since the force required to overcome coulomb friction changes sign at those instants. The relationship between the input and output forces is

$$n(\omega t) = M \sin \omega t + F_c \quad \text{for} \quad -\omega t_1 < \omega t < \omega t_2$$
$$n(\omega t) = M \sin \omega t - F_c \quad \text{for} \quad \omega t_2 < \omega t < \pi \tag{7-61}$$

where $\omega t_1 = \sin^{-1} \gamma$
$\omega t_2 = \cos^{-1}(\pi\gamma/2)$
$\gamma = F_c/M$

The fundamental components of the output A_1 and B_1 are

$$A_1 = \frac{2}{\pi} \int_{-\omega t_1}^{\omega t_2} M(\sin \omega t + \gamma) \cos \omega t \, d(\omega t)$$

$$+ \frac{2}{\pi} \int_{\omega t_2}^{\pi - \omega t_1} M(\sin \omega t - \gamma) \cos \omega t \, d(\omega t) \tag{7-62}$$

$$B_1 = \frac{2}{\pi} \int_{-\omega t_1}^{\omega t_2} M(\sin \omega t + \gamma) \sin \omega t \, d(\omega t)$$

$$+ \frac{2}{\pi} \int_{\omega t_2}^{\pi - \omega t_1} M(\sin \omega t - \gamma) \sin \omega t \, d(\omega t) \quad (7\text{–}63)$$

Integrating equations 7–62 and 7–63, we obtain the following expressions:

$$A_1 = 2M\gamma \left[\frac{4}{\pi^2} - \gamma^2 \right]^{1/2} \quad (7\text{–}64)$$

$$B_1 = M[1 - 2\gamma^2] \quad (7\text{–}65)$$

The resulting expression for coulomb friction is

$$N(\gamma) = \left[1 - 4 \left(1 - \frac{4}{\pi^2} \right) \gamma^2 \right]^{1/2} \bigg/ \tan^{-1} \frac{2\gamma(4/\pi^2 - \gamma^2)^{1/2}}{1 - 2\gamma^2} \quad (7\text{–}66)$$

Observe that the describing function for coulomb friction depends only on the amplitude of the input and not on its frequency. The gain-phase relationship of the describing function for coulomb friction is illustrated in Figure 7–31a, as part of an example.

The describing function for the simultaneous occurrence of both coulomb friction and stiction is considered next. Waveform relationships between the applied force $m(\omega t)$, the output force $n(\omega t)$, and the forces necessary to overcome coulomb friction and stiction F_c and F_s are given by

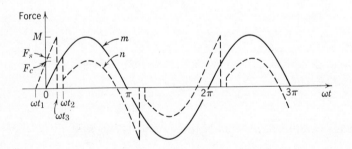

The expressions for the fundamental components of the Fourier coefficients are

$$A_1 = \frac{2}{\pi} \int_{\omega t_2}^{\pi + \omega t_3} M(\sin \omega t - \gamma) \cos \omega t \, d(\omega t) \quad (7\text{–}67)$$

$$B_1 = \frac{2}{\pi} \int_{\omega t_2}^{\pi + \omega t_3} M(\sin \omega t - \gamma) \sin \omega t \, d(\omega t) \tag{7-68}$$

where $\omega t_1 = \sin^{-1} \gamma$

$\omega t_2 = \sin^{-1}(F_s/M)$

$\omega t_3 = \cos^{-1}(\pi\gamma/2)$

$\gamma = F_c/M$

The describing function for the combined case of coulomb friction and stiction is obtained by integrating equations 7-67 and 7-68. The resultant expression is

$$N(\gamma) = \frac{1}{\pi} \{[\pi - (\omega t_2 - \omega t_3) - \cos \omega t_2 (2 \sin \omega t_1 - \sin \omega t_2) - \cos \omega t_3 (2 \sin \omega t_1 + \sin \omega t_3)]^2$$

$$+ [\sin \omega t_3 (2 \sin \omega t_1 + \sin \omega t_3) + \sin \omega t_2 (2 \sin \omega t_1 - \sin \omega t_2)]^2\}^{1/2}$$

$$\Big/ \tan^{-1} \frac{\sin \omega t_3 (2 \sin \omega t_1 + \sin \omega t_3) + \sin \omega t_2 (2 \sin \omega t_1 - \sin \omega t_2)}{\pi - (\omega t_2 - \omega t_3) - \cos \omega t_2 (2 \sin \omega t_1 - \sin \omega t_2) - \cos \omega t_3 (2 \sin \omega t_1 + \sin \omega t_3)}$$

$$\tag{7-69}$$

Observe from this expression that the describing function for the combined case of coulomb friction and stiction is a function of the amplitude of the input and the relative magnitudes of friction but not of frequency. Figure 7-31*b* illustrates the gain-phase relationship of the describing function for the combined case of coulomb friction and stiction, as part of an example.

7–9. USE OF THE DESCRIBING FUNCTION TO DETERMINE SYSTEM STABILITY[7]

The describing function of a nonlinear element can be utilized to determine the stability of a nonlinear feedback control system. Let us consider the system illustrated in Figure 7–5. Assuming that the describing function of the nonlinearity is $N(M, \omega)$, the transfer function of the feedback control system illustrated is

$$\frac{C(j\omega)}{R(j\omega)} = \frac{N(M, \omega)G(j\omega)}{1 + N(M, \omega)G(j\omega)} \tag{7-70}$$

Stability can be determined from the zeros of the characteristic equation

$$1 + N(M, \omega)G(j\omega) = 0 \tag{7-71}$$

Therefore any combination of values of input amplitude M and frequency ω which satisfy the equation

$$G(j\omega) = -\frac{1}{N(M, \omega)} \tag{7-72}$$

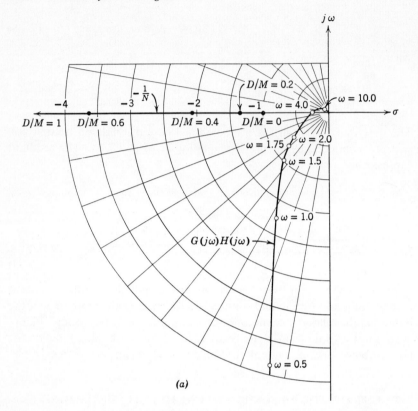

Figure 7–21. Nyquist diagram stability analysis of nonlinear system containing a dead zone. (a) Stable system where

$$G(j\omega)H(j\omega) = \frac{2}{j\omega(1 + 0.5j\omega)(1 + 0.1j\omega)}$$

(b) Unstable system where

$$G(j\omega)H(j\omega) = \frac{17}{j\omega(1 + 0.5j\omega)(1 + 0.1j\omega)}$$

are capable of sustaining an oscillation. If a combination of amplitude and frequency can be found which satisfies equation 7–72, the feedback control system can have a sustained oscillation and is unstable.

Methods for determining system stability from the describing function are the Nyquist diagram, the Nichols chart (gain-phase plots), and/or the root locus analysis. The latter method is only useful when $N(M, \omega)$ is of a special form where the approximation $s = j\omega$ can be made in order to obtain $N(M, s)$. Even if this substitution can be made, however, the root locus method is hardly ever used since it is very difficult to obtain when the describing function is a complex number. In addition, even if the

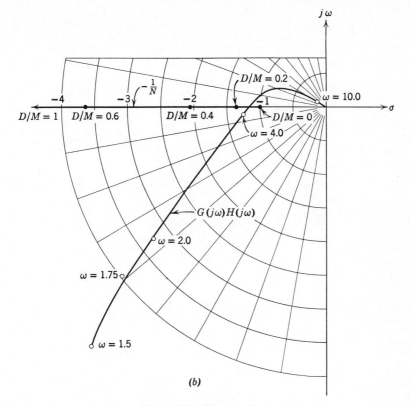

Figure 7–21 (Continued)

describing function is real, the root locus does not yield any more useful information than the first two methods.

From experience, I have found the Nyquist diagram and the gain-phase plot to be the most revealing techniques for stability analysis when utilizing the describing-function method. Two separate sets of loci, corresponding to $G(j\omega)$ and $-1/N(M, \omega)$ of equation 7–72, are sketched on the same graph for either of these methods. Generally, the sketch of $-1/N(M, \omega)$ will be a family of curves for different input magnitudes M and frequencies ω. Intersections of the two loci indicate solutions to equation 7–72 and yield information as to the magnitude M and frequency ω of sustained oscillation. If no intersections result, the system is stable. The relative distance to a possible intersection is a criterion of relative stability. This is next illustrated on the Nyquist and gain-phase diagram for several representative systems.

Figure 7–21 illustrates a comparative analysis on the Nyquist diagram

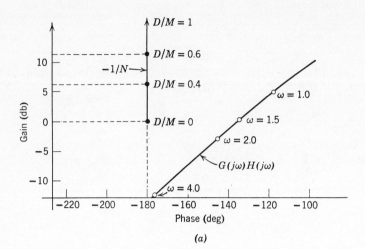

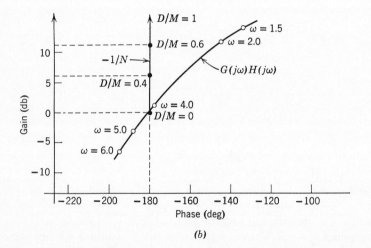

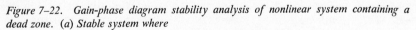

Figure 7–22. Gain-phase diagram stability analysis of nonlinear system containing a dead zone. (a) Stable system where

$$G(j\omega)H(j\omega) = \frac{2}{j\omega(1 + 0.5j\omega)(1 + 0.1j\omega)}$$

(b) Unstable system where

$$G(j\omega)H(j\omega) = \frac{17}{j\omega(1 + 0.5j\omega)(1 + 0.1j\omega)}$$

for a nonlinear system containing a dead zone. Part (*a*) of the figure illustrates a stable system where a dead zone is present and

$$G(j\omega)H(j\omega) = \frac{2}{j\omega(1 + 0.5j\omega)(1 + 0.1j\omega)} \qquad (7\text{--}73)$$

Part (*b*) of the figure illustrates an unstable system when dead zone is present and

$$G(j\omega)H(j\omega) = \frac{17}{j\omega(1 + 0.5j\omega)(1 + 0.1j\omega)} \qquad (7\text{--}74)$$

An intersection occurs at an ω of approximately 4.5 and a D/M of 0.09. This is to be interpreted as the frequency and amplitude which satisfy equation 7–72 and result in a limit cycle.

Figure 7–22 illustrates a comparative stability analysis on the gain

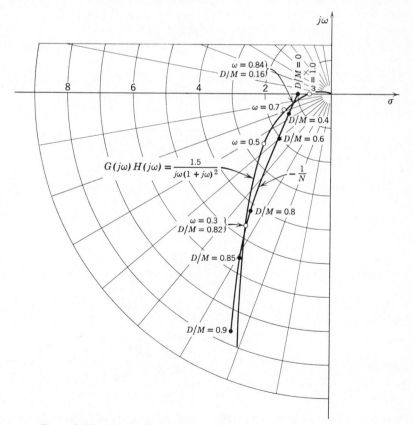

Figure 7–23. Nyquist diagram of nonlinear system containing backlash.

phase diagram for the corresponding situation that was illustrated in Figure 7–21 on the Nyquist diagram. Part (*a*) of Figure 7–22 illustrates a stable system, and part (*b*) illustrates an unstable system having a limit cycle at a frequency of approximately 4.5 radians/second and a D/M of 0.09.

Figure 7–23 illustrates the Nyquist diagram stability analysis for a nonlinear system containing backlash where

$$G(j\omega)H(j\omega) = \frac{1.5}{j\omega(1 + j\omega)^2} \qquad (7\text{–}75)$$

Notice that the system has two points of intersection corresponding to a pair of limit cycles. The system is unstable for all points of operation between the two points of intersection corresponding to $\omega = 0.84$, $D/M = 0.16$ and $\omega = 0.3$, $D/M = 0.82$. Whenever a describing function is enclosed, however, as in Figure 7–23, a stable limit cycle occurs only at the intersection having the largest amplitude of oscillation. Therefore, the intersection corresponding to $\omega = 0.84$ and $D/M = 0.16$ is a stable limit cycle and all other resulting unstable limit cycles increase in amplitude until they reach this limit cycle.

Figure 7–24 illustrates a comparative stability analysis on the gain-phase diagram for the corresponding situation illustrated in Figure 7–23

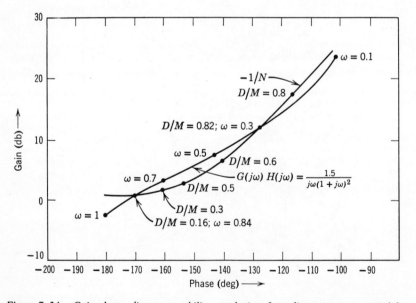

Figure 7–24. *Gain-phase diagram stability analysis of nonlinear system containing backlash.*

on the Nyquist diagram. Notice the agreement between the two graphs. We next use the gain-phase plot illustrated in Figure 7–24 to demonstrate how the control engineer may design a nonlinear feedback control system using describing functions.

7–10. DESIGN OF NONLINEAR FEEDBACK CONTROL SYSTEMS USING DESCRIBING FUNCTIONS[8]

The function of this section is to illustrate to the reader the procedure of compensating for undesirable nonlinearities in a system. We draw on the analytic tools developed in previous sections in order to demonstrate the procedure to be followed by the control engineer. Specifically, we consider the nonlinearity to be backlash. The gain-phase plot will be used for analysis, although we could use the Nyquist diagram equally as well.

Oscillating input signals, having frequencies very much greater in magnitude than the system bandwidth, can be used to maintain the output of a system containing backlash at its correct average value. This practical technique is known as "dither." It is effective in eliminating very small amplitude nonlinearities. However, the resultant increased wear on the system is a serious disadvantage of this very simple approach to the problem. For systems which are to operate continuously for long periods of time, it is mandatory to utilize different approaches which will eliminate backlash. Reducing the system gain, addition of phase-lead networks, and introducing rate feedback are all relatively simple electrical methods which can be used to eliminate the effects of backlash. We next demonstrate the theoretical effects of these techniques on backlash.

Let us reconsider the nonlinear system analyzed in Figures 7–23 and 7–24. These sketches illustrated that a nonlinear system having the form shown in Figure 7–5, where

$$G(j\omega) = G_1(j\omega)G_2(j\omega) = \frac{1.5}{j\omega(1 + j\omega)^2} \qquad (7\text{–}76)$$

and having a nonlinearity corresponding to backlash, was indeed unstable. We demonstrate how this system can be stabilized by each of the following electrical methods:

a. Reducing the system gain
b. Adding a phase-lead network
c. Introducing rate feedback

1. Reducing the System Gain

In order to consider the effects of gain changes on a nonlinear system containing backlash, let us rewrite $G(j\omega)$ of equation 7–70 as

$$G(j\omega) = KG'(j\omega) \qquad (7\text{–}77)$$

where K represents the system gain and $G'(j\omega)$ represents only the system's poles and zeros. Therefore, equation 7–72 can be rewritten as

$$G'(j\omega) = -\frac{1}{KN(M, \omega)} \qquad (7\text{–}78)$$

By reducing the gain K, the limit cycle is eliminated by moving the curve of $-1/KN(M, \omega)$ upward. Figure 7–25 illustrates how the nonlinear system can be stabilized by reducing the system's gain from 1.5 to unity. At a gain setting of approximately 1.3, the curves of $G'(j\omega)$ and $-1/KN$ just clear each other. A gain setting of unity was chosen in order to maintain some margin of stability.

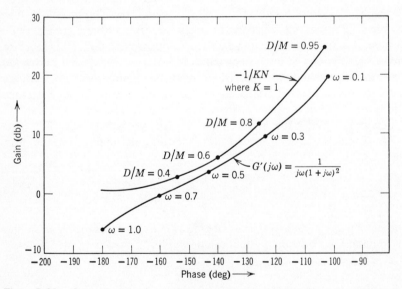

Figure 7–25. Compensation of a nonlinear system containing backlash by reducing the system gain.

2. Addition of a Phase-Lead Network

A passive phase-lead network can also be used to stabilize a nonlinear system containing backlash. The transfer function of this network is given by

$$G(j\omega)_{\text{lead}} = \frac{1 + j\omega T_1}{1 + j\omega T_2} \tag{7-79}$$

where $T_1 > T_2$. The compensated value of $G(j\omega)$, $G(j\omega)_{\text{comp}}$, is given by

$$G(j\omega)_{\text{comp}} = \frac{1.5}{j\omega(1 + j\omega)^2} \times \frac{1 + j\omega T_1}{1 + j\omega T_2} \tag{7-80}$$

For the system under consideration, a value of $T_1 = 0.8$ and $T_2 = 0.4$ will eliminate the limit cycle, as is illustrated in Figure 7–26. This is not the only lead network which could be used for compensation; it is one of many possible solutions, as can be noted from studying the gain-phase diagram.

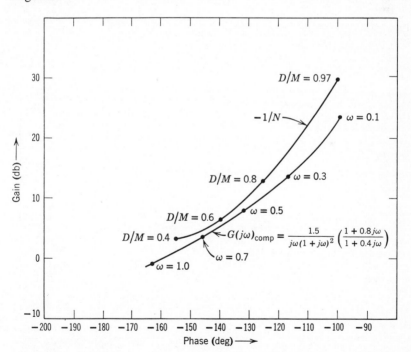

Figure 7–26. Compensation of a nonlinear system containing backlash by addition of a phase-lead network.

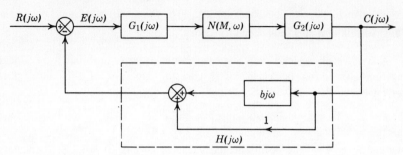

Figure 7–27. Nonlinear system containing rate and position feedback.

3. Introduction of Rate Feedback

Addition of rate feedback to the position feedback of a nonlinear system can also be a very effective method for eliminating instability due to backlash. For this configuration, which is illustrated in Figure 7–27, the value of the system feedback element $H(j\omega)$ is $1 + bj\omega$. Therefore, the stability criterion for this configuration must be modified from that given by equation 7–72 to the following expression:

$$G(j\omega)H(j\omega) = -\frac{1}{N(M, \omega)} \tag{7–81}$$

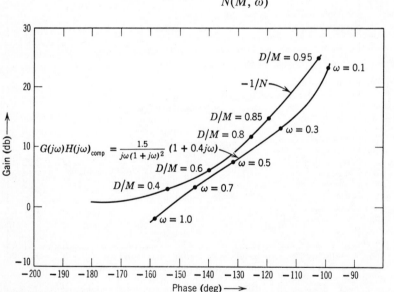

Figure 7–28. Compensation of a nonlinear system containing backlash by the introduction of rate feedback.

With rate feedback, the value of $G(j\omega)H(j\omega)$ for the system being considered is given by

$$G(j\omega)H(j\omega) = \frac{1.5}{j\omega(1 + j\omega)^2} \times (1 + bj\omega) \qquad (7\text{--}82)$$

A value of $b = 0.4$ will eliminate the limit cycle, as is illustrated in Figure 7–28, and has a relatively safe margin of stability. At a value of b approximately equal to 0.25, the curves of $G(j\omega)H(j\omega)$ and $-1/N$ just clear each other.

Since the describing-function analysis is an amplitude-sensitive method applicable to nonlinear systems, and since superposition of signals is not valid for these systems, we cannot extend this solution and obtain data on low-amplitude transient responses. Our primary attempt has only been the elimination of limit cycles. In general, however, we can say that greater margins of relative stability between the curves of $G(j\omega)H(j\omega)$ and $-1/N$ will result in low-amplitude responses having better characteristics.

7–11. DESIGN OF NONLINEAR MULTIPLE FEEDBACK CONTROL SYSTEMS USING DESCRIBING FUNCTIONS[8]

This section extends the describing-function concepts developed for nonlinear control systems to those configurations having multiple feedback paths. It will be shown that the use of the signal flow diagram and analog computer are powerful approaches to this problem. The specific system that will be considered is a positioning system containing three minor feedback paths and a nonlinearity which may correspond to backlash or nonlinear friction.

Figure 7–29 represents the block diagram of this system. The nonlinear element, which may correspond to a variety of nonlinearities, such as backlash or coulomb friction, is represented by N. The signal flow diagram approach is considered first as a method for determining stability of this system.

Figure 7–30 represents the signal flow diagram for the system whose block diagram was shown in Figure 7–29. By inspection, the overall system transfer function is given by

$$\frac{C(s)}{R(s)} = \frac{\sum\limits_{K} G_K \Delta_K}{\Delta}$$

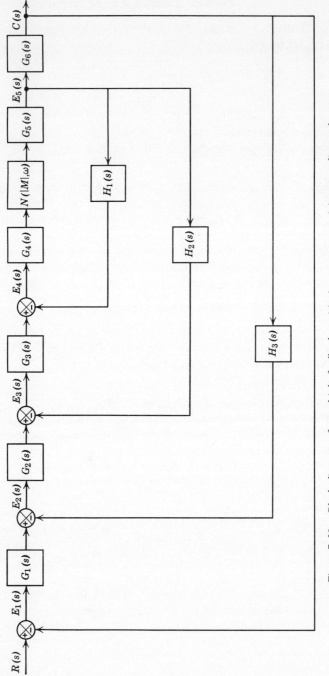

Figure 7–29. Block diagram of a multiple feedback positioning system containing a nonlinear element.

where

$$\Delta = 1 + G_4(s)G_5(s)N(|M|, \omega)H_1(s) + G_3(s)G_4(s)G_5(s)N(|M|, \omega)H_2(s)$$
$$+ G_2(s)G_3(s)G_4(s)N(|M|, \omega)G_5(s)G_6(s)H_3(s)$$
$$+ G_1(s)G_2(s)G_3(s)G_4(s)N(|M|, \omega)G_5(s)G_6(s)$$

$$G_1 = G_1(s)G_2(s)G_3(s)G_4(s)N(|M|, \omega)G_5(s)G_6(s)$$

$$\Delta_1 = 1$$

$$\frac{C(s)}{R(s)} = \frac{G_1(s)G_2(s)G_3(s)G_4(s)N(|M|, \omega)G_5(s)G_6(s)}{1 + G_4(s)G_5(s)N(|M|, \omega)H_1(s) + G_3(s)G_4(s)G_5(s)N(|M|, \omega)H_2(s)}$$
$$+ G_2(s)G_3(s)G_4(s)N(|M|, \omega)G_5(s)G_6(s)H_3(s)$$
$$+ G_1(s)G_2(s)G_3(s)G_4(s)N(M, \omega)G_5(s)G_6(s)$$

$$(7\text{–}83)$$

Equation 7–83 can be reduced to the following form:

$$\frac{C(s)}{R(s)} = \frac{G_1(s)G_2(s)G_3(s)G_4(s)N(|M|, \omega)G_5(s)G_6(s)}{1 + [G_4(s)G_5(s)H_1(s) + G_3(s)G_4(s)G_5(s)H_2(s)}$$
$$+ G_2(s)G_3(s)G_4(s)G_5(s)G_6(s)H_3(s)$$
$$+ G_1(s)G_2(s)G_3(s)G_4(s)G_5(s)G_6(s)]N(|M|, \omega)$$

Stability for this system can be determined from the zeros of the characteristic equation

$$1 + [G_4(s)G_5(s)H_1(s) + G_3(s)G_4(s)G_5(s)H_2(s)$$
$$+ G_2(s)G_3(s)G_4(s)G_5(s)G_6(s)H_3(s)$$
$$+ G_1(s)G_2(s)G_3(s)G_4(s)G_5(s)G_6(s)]N(|M|, \omega) = 0 \quad (7\text{–}84)$$

similarly to the way the stability of the nonlinear feedback control system shown in Figure 7–5 was determined by examining equation 7–71. We recommend that the reader gain some practice utilizing this approach by solving Problems 7–10 and 7–11.

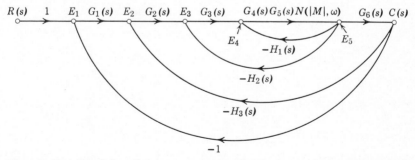

Figure 7–30. Signal flow diagram representation for the system shown in Figure 7–29.

Table 7–1. Simulation of common nonlinearities

Type of Nonlinearity	Characteristics	Simulation circuit

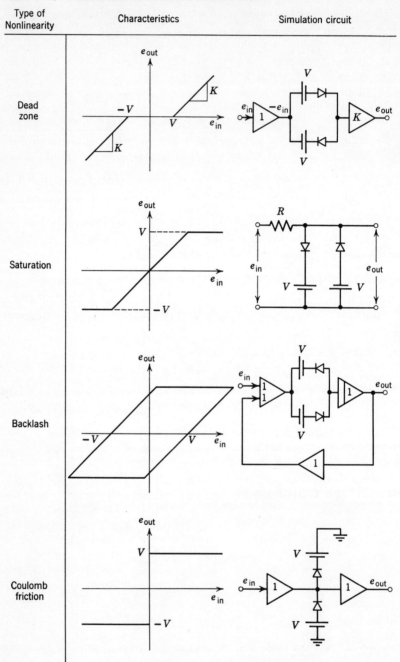

Dead zone

Saturation

Backlash

Coulomb friction

An analog computer is another extremely useful device for checking the stability of nonlinear systems having multiple feedback paths. The analog computer simulation of the system shown in Figure 7–29 is quite conventional, except for the simulation of the nonlinearity. Table 7–1 illustrates the analog representation for several nonlinearities which should prove useful to the control engineer. We recommend that the reader actually simulate the system shown in Figure 7–29 on an analog computer and determine whether any limit cycles exist for nonlinearities corresponding to backlash and coulomb friction (see Problem 7–12).

A practical example of this describing function-analog computer dual approach is presented next. A precision satellite tracking radar system containing multiple feedback loops and nonlinear friction can be represented by the equivalent block diagram of Figure 7–29. In addition to the unity position feedback loop, it contains three equivalent minor paths which feedback velocity and acceleration. The transfer functions of the linear elements for an actual system designed by the Sperry Gyroscope Company are

$$G_1(s) = \frac{1.25(1 + 4s)^2}{s^2(1 + 0.0625s)^2} \qquad G_6(s) = \frac{1}{1500s}$$

$$G_2(s) = 5.4 \qquad\qquad\qquad H_1(s) = 1.2$$

$$G_3(s) = \frac{734(1 + 0.018s)}{s(1 + 0.01s)} \qquad H_2(s) = 0.0282s$$

$$G_4(s) = \frac{1.635}{(1 + 0.01s)} \qquad\qquad H_3(s) = 10s$$

$$G_5(s) = \frac{1}{0.231s}$$

The nonlinear element, whose describing function is $N(|M|, \omega)$, represents the equivalent coulomb friction and stiction of the system.

A control system of this complexity has a ninth-order characteristic equation. This immediately limits the available techniques for analyzing system stability. The most practical technique for designing such a system is to use the describing-function method for stability analysis and an analog computer for checking the resulting transient response and accuracy.

Satellite tracking radars must contend with a wide range of dynamics, including extremely low angular velocities. This is a difficult problem for high-performance power-servo systems when nonlinear characteristics of coulomb friction and stiction are also present. This complex problem is made more difficult by high-inertia loads which limit the closed-loop bandwidth and resulting accuracy by their structural resonances.

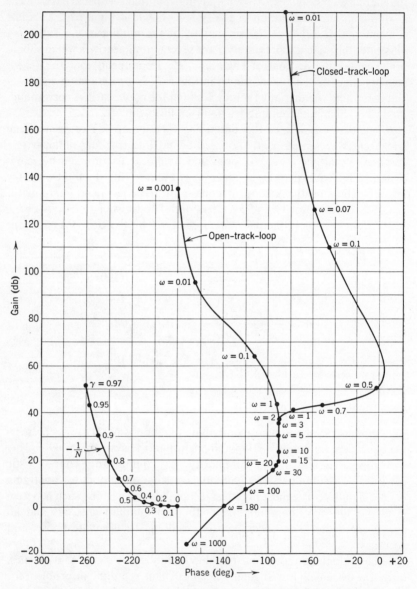

Figure 7–31a.   Example of describing-function analysis for coulomb friction.

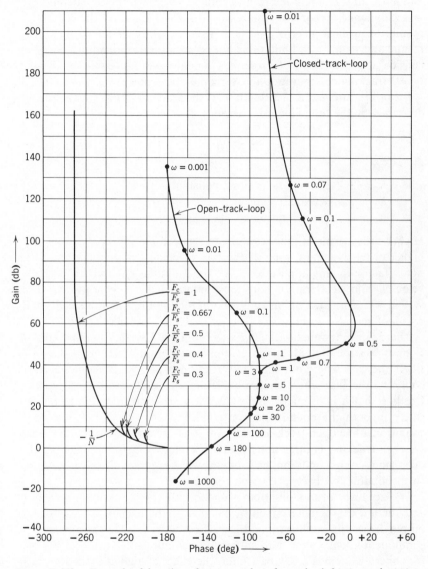

Figure 7–31b. Example of describing-function analysis for coulomb friction and stiction.

The servo-tracking loop is the most critical link in the accurate and smooth tracking of a satellite. It is therefore necessary to keep its errors and noise jitter to a minimum. In a satellite tracking radar, relatively high target dynamics occur near the zenith. In order to satisfy the conflicting requirements of large error constants with their large bandwidth requirements, and bandwidth limitations due to structural resonances and noise consideration, the Sperry Gyroscope Company synthesized this equivalent type-3 tracking configuration to overcome this problem.

From the discussion in Section 4–4, the tracking radar's error can be described by the following infinite series:

$$E(s) = R(s)\left(\sum_{n=0}^{\infty} \frac{1}{K_n} s^n \right) \tag{7-85}$$

where $K_0 = 1 + K_P = 1 +$ position constant
$\quad K_1 = K_V =$ velocity constant
$\quad K_2 = K_A =$ acceleration constant

Higher-order terms of the series can be ignored for this application since higher-order dynamics, such as the rate of change of acceleration, were not a factor in this application. A type-3 system has infinite position, velocity, and acceleration constants independent of bandwidth. This system was simulated on an analog computer and resulted in steady-state errors of zero due to inputs of position, velocity, and acceleration.

The describing-function analysis of this type-3 system is illustrated in Figures 7–31a and 7–31b. The gain-phase diagram of Figure 7–31a considers the case where only coulomb friction is present, and Figure 7–31b considers the case where coulomb friction and stiction are both present. Observe that it is of major importance for the control system to remain stable in both the open-track-loop condition and the closed-track-loop condition. The open-track-loop condition is encountered when the radar system's tracking is interrupted. From a block diagram viewpoint, the open-track-loop condition can be shown by removing $G_1(s)$ and its corresponding feedback path from Figure 7–29.

The accuracy of this describing-function analysis for coulomb friction and stiction can be determined by calculating the harmonic terms of the output from this nonlinearity. In practice, however, the third-harmonic component is usually the dominating error component. In addition, since the control system is a low-pass filter, the effect of higher-order harmonic terms is negligible. A plot of the ratio of the third harmonic to the fundamental output from the nonlinear element is illustrated in Figures 7–32a and 7–32b. For the regions of practical interest, the maximum inaccuracy of this stability analysis is less than 25 per cent.

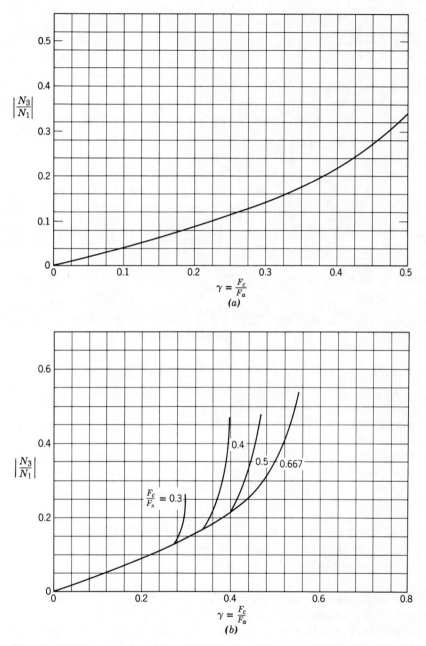

Figure 7–32. (a) Accuracy of describing-function analysis for coulomb friction. (b) Accuracy of describing-function analysis for coulomb friction and stiction.

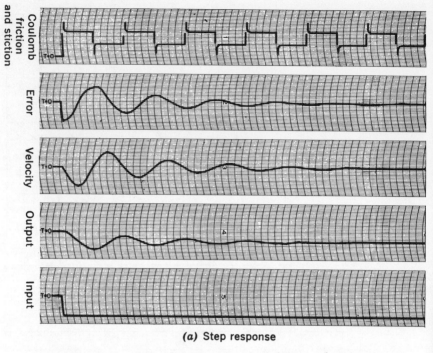

(a) Step response

Figure 7–33.   System response with coulomb friction and stiction present.

Analog computer test results are shown in Figure 7–33. Recordings of input, error, output, output velocity, and nonlinear friction for inputs corresponding to position, velocity, and acceleration are shown. Observe that the steady-state error for this synthesized type-3 system with non-linearities of coulomb friction and stiction present goes to zero for all these inputs. The reader is referred to Ref. 8 for further details of this system.

7–12.   DETERMINATION OF ABSOLUTE STABILITY OF NONLINEAR SYSTEMS FROM THE CHARACTERISTIC EQUATION

It is possible to determine absolute stability of certain quasi-linear systems from the system's characteristic equation. This method is similar to the Routh-Hurwitz criterion, which was discussed for linear systems in Chapter 5. We analyze the class of nonlinear systems to which this technique is applicable and illustrate its application.

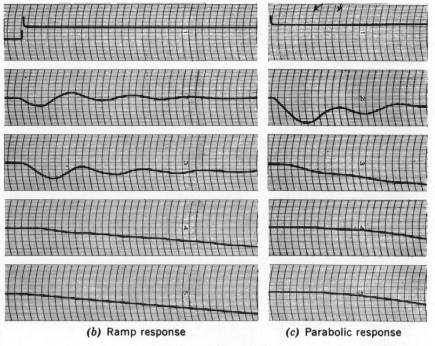

(b) Ramp response   **(c)** Parabolic response

Figure 7–33 (Continued)

Let us consider the feedback control system illustrated in Figure 7–5, which contains a nonlinear element n and two linear elements g_1 and g_2. In general, the nonlinear element's describing function depends on frequency and the amplitudes of the input signal. If the describing function is independent of frequency, we can determine absolute stability from the system's characteristic equation. If the nonlinear element's describing function depends on amplitude and frequency, the application of this modified Routh-Hurwitz criterion is considerably complicated and limited.

Let us assume that the describing function of the nonlinear element is given by $M(|M|, \omega)$, where the describing function depends on the absolute amplitude $|M|$ and frequency ω. The closed-loop transfer function of the system, shown in Figure 7–5, is given by equation 7–70 as follows:

$$\frac{C(j\omega)}{R(j\omega)} = \frac{N(|M|, \omega)G(j\omega)}{1 + N(|M|, \omega)G(j\omega)}$$

The characteristic equation of this system is given by equation 7–71:

$$1 + N(|M|, \omega)G(j\omega) = 0$$

Notice that a different characteristic equation is obtained for each absolute value of amplitude, $|M|$. The modified Routh-Hurwitz criterion can be extended to quasi-linear systems if the nonlinear element's transfer function is a real number. However, if it is a complex number, then this criterion cannot be applied. A simple example will illustrate the application of this criterion for the case where the nonlinear element's transfer function is a real number.

Let us assume that the transfer function of the linear elements is given by the expression

$$G(j\omega) = \frac{K}{j\omega(1 + Tj\omega)^2} \tag{7–86}$$

The describing function of the nonlinear element is assumed to be a real number and only a function of a particular amplitude M_1, as follows.

$$N(|M|, \omega) = N(|M_1|) \tag{7–87}$$

Substituting equations 7–86 and 7–87 into equation 7–71, we obtain the characteristic equation

$$T^2(j\omega)^3 + 2T(j\omega)^2 + j\omega + KN(|M_1|) = 0 \tag{7–88}$$

From the discussion and definitions of the Routh-Hurwitz criterion in Chapter 5, the following array results.

$$
\begin{array}{cc}
T^2 & 1 \\
2T & KN(|M_1|) \\
1 - 0.5TKN(|M_1|) & \\
KN(|M_1|) &
\end{array}
\tag{7–89}
$$

Since it is necessary that all terms in the left-hand column of 7–89 have the same sign for stability, it is necessary that

$$1 - 0.5TKN(|M_1|) > 0 \tag{7–90}$$

or

$$N(|M_1|) < \frac{2}{TK} \tag{7–91}$$

If equation 7–91 is satisfied, then all the nonlinear system's poles will be in the left half plane and the system will be stable.

As for linear systems, the application of the Routh-Hurwitz criterion to this class of problems only indicates absolute stability and gives no indication of relative stability or instability. If the transfer function of the nonlinear element has a real and imaginary component, the coefficients of the characteristic equation are complex and the Routh-Hurwitz criterion cannot be applied. In this situation, the control engineer has to resort to a more exotic method, known as Frank's theorem,[9,10] which is beyond the scope of this book.

7-13. PIECEWISE-LINEAR APPROXIMATIONS

Approximating any nonlinearity by means of piecewise-linear seg- mentation is a very powerful tool for analysis. Each linear segmented interval is represented by a relatively simple linear differential equation which can be solved by conventional linear techniques. This method, which is not limited to quasi-linear systems, has the advantage of yielding an exact solution for nonlinearities of any order. We illustrate its appli- cation by means of an example.

Let us consider the very common nonlinear characteristic of saturation. Figure 7–34 illustrates a simple feedback control system containing an integrator and an amplifier which saturates. The amplifier's gain is 5 over an input voltage range of ± 1 volt. For input voltages greater than this, the amplifier saturates. It is quite evident that two distinct linear operating regions for the amplifier exist. The control engineer can consider each of these linear regions separately, in a piecewise-linear manner, in order to obtain the composite response of the system.

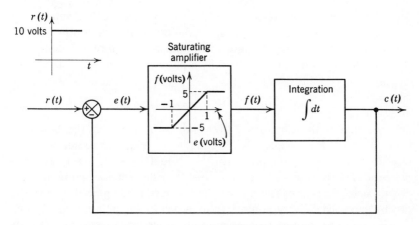

Figure 7–34. Feedback control system containing the nonlinear properties of satu- ration.

For the region of operation before the amplifier saturates, the relationships depicting the system's operation are

$$e(t) = r(t) - c(t) \tag{7-92}$$

$$f(t) = 5e(t) \tag{7-93}$$

$$c(t) = \int f(t)\, dt \tag{7-94}$$

After saturation, equations 7–92 and 7–94 are still valid. However, 7–93 changes as follows:

$$f(t) = 5 \quad \text{for} \quad e(t) > 1 \tag{7-95}$$

and $\qquad f(t) = -5 \quad \text{for} \quad e(t) < -1 \tag{7-96}$

Assuming zero initial conditions and a step input of 10 volts, the expression for the output during the unsaturated region of operation $c_{us}(t)$ is given by

$$c_{us}(t) = \int_0^t 5\, dt = 5t \tag{7-97}$$

The expression for the output during the saturated region of amplifier operation is given by

$$c_{sat}(t) = \int_{t_1}^t (10 - c)\, dt, \quad \text{or} \quad \frac{dc_{sat}}{dt} + c = 10 \tag{7-98}$$

The time t_1 represents the time at which the amplifier saturates. When $c = 9$, $e = 1$, and t_1 is 1.8 seconds. Using conventional techniques, the solution to equation 7–98 is

$$c_{sat}(t) = 10 - e^{-(t-1.8)} \tag{7-99}$$

The initial value for this region, $c_{sat}(0)$, is the same as the final value of the unsaturated region, $c_{us}(1.8) = 9$, since the boundary conditions between the linear segmented regions are continuous. Therefore, the composite solution for this problem, obtained by a piecewise-linear analysis, is

$$c_{us}(t) = 5t \qquad\qquad \text{for} \quad 0 \leqslant t \leqslant 1.8 \tag{7-100}$$

$$c_{sat}(t) = 10 - e^{-(t-1.8)} \quad \text{for} \quad t > 1.8 \tag{7-101}$$

Observe that both equations 7–100 and 7–101 agree at the boundary value of $t = 1.8$ seconds. From equation 7–100, c_{us} equals 9 at 1.8 seconds, and from equation 7–101, c_{sat} equals 9 at 1.8 seconds. The response of this system to a step input of 10 volts is sketched in Figure 7–35.

The basic piecewise-linear approach illustrated in the preceding problem can be extended to very complex nonlinearities. It is important to emphasize that the boundary conditions between linear regions are continuous. For example, in the preceding problem the final value of the

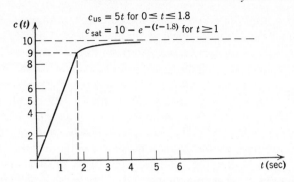

Figure 7–35. Step response of saturating system obtained from piecewise-linear analysis.

unsaturated region was the same as the initial value for the saturated region. The resulting differential equation for each segmented region is linear and can be easily solved by conventional linear techniques.

7–14. INTRODUCTION TO THE PHASE-PLANE METHOD

The phase-plane method is a technique for analyzing the transient response of a nonlinear feedback control system to a step input. The variation of the system's displacement is plotted against the system's velocity on a graph known as a "phase plane." A curve for a specific step input is known as a "phase trajectory." Curves of displacement versus velocity of a specific system, which are repeated for several step amplitudes and are plotted on the same phase plane, are called a "phase portrait."

The starting point of a phase trajectory is located at the system's initial conditions of displacement, $x(0)$, and velocity, $dx(0)/dt$. The future path of the phase trajectory after it leaves its initial starting point is an indication of the system's behavior for some step input excitation. If the phase trajectory approaches infinity on the phase plane, the system is unstable. If the phase trajectory approaches the vicinity of the origin, however, the system is stable. If the phase trajectory circles the origin continuously in a closed curve after excitation, a sustained oscillation known as a "limit cycle" exists.

The phase-plane method is specifically concerned with the solution of second-order, nonlinear, differential equations having the following general form:

$$\frac{d^2x}{dt^2} + A_1\left(x, \frac{dx}{dt}\right)\frac{dx}{dt} + A_2\left(x, \frac{dx}{dt}\right)x = 0 \qquad (7\text{--}102)$$

Equation 102 immediately emphasizes some serious limitations of the phase-plane method. It is only useful for analyzing second-order systems. In addition, the coefficients A_1 and A_2 are limited in being variables of x and/or dx/dt, but not of higher-order derivatives of dx/dt or of time. Since the right-hand side of equation 7–102 is zero, the analysis is further limited to the transient response for some initial set of conditions, or to step inputs where appropriate substitutions can be made to have the right-hand side of the differential equation equal zero. It is interesting to compare the limitations of the phase-plane method with those of the describing-function analysis, where the response of systems having any order to sinusoidal inputs could be determined. The phase-plane method can be extended to higher-order systems by means of the phase-space concept. We discuss this method later in the chapter.

The following section discusses the techniques which the control engineer can use for constructing the phase plane from the differential equation of a system. Then we examine the properties and interpretation of the phase plane. The procedure to be followed for applying the phase plane to some representative design problems then concludes our discussion of the phase-plane method.

7–15. CONSTRUCTION OF THE PHASE PORTRAIT

Three general procedures may be used by the control engineer for deriving the phase portrait of a system. They are popularly referred to as follows: (1) direct solution of the differential equation method, (2) transformation of the second-order differential equation to a first-order equation method, and (3) the method of isoclines. The first two methods are analytical techniques; the last is graphical. We shall describe these three methods next, together with some simple illustrative examples.

1. Direct Solution of the Differential Equation Method

This is the most straightforward method of obtaining the phase portrait of a system. It is usually the most useless method from a practical viewpoint since we do not have to resort to the phase-plane analysis for a solution if the differential equation is integrable. However, the phase plane does give a physical "feel" for the situation.

The procedure of this method is to solve the system's second-order differential equation for the dependent variable x. The solution for x is then differentiated in order to obtain the derivative of the dependent variable, dx/dt. The independent variable, time, is then eliminated between the two resulting equations. A single equation that relates x and dx/dt results, and can be used to plot the phase portrait directly. However, this method has the very important disadvantage that it requires the solution of a nonlinear, second-order, differential equation.

Let us illustrate the procedure in detail by first considering the simple linear system illustrated in Figure 3–14. That configuration illustrated a system where a torque $T(t)$ was applied to a body having a moment of inertia J, a twisting shaft having a stiffness factor K, and a damper having a damping factor B. Applying Newton's law of motion to this system resulted in the following relationship:

$$J \frac{d^2\theta(t)}{dt^2} + B \frac{d\theta(t)}{dt} + K\theta(t) = T(t) \qquad (7\text{–}103)$$

where $\theta(t)$ is the system's displacement. The resulting differential equation for this linear system is second order, and the phase-plane method is certainly applicable. Assuming that the system is unexcited, the resulting differential equation is given by

$$\frac{d^2\theta(t)}{dt^2} + \frac{B}{J} \frac{d\theta(t)}{dt} + \frac{K\theta(t)}{J} = 0 \qquad (7\text{–}104)$$

Equation 7–104 can be written in the more familiar form in terms of damping factor ζ and natural resonant frequency ω_n, as follows.

$$\frac{d^2\theta(t)}{dt^2} + 2\zeta\omega_n \frac{d\theta(t)}{dt} + \omega_n{}^2\theta(t) = 0 \qquad (7\text{–}105)$$

where
$$\frac{B}{J} = 2\zeta\omega_n$$

$$\frac{K}{J} = \omega_n{}^2$$

Before sketching the phase portrait for this system, let us consider the simpler case of an undamped, linear, second-order system where $\zeta = 0$. For this situation, equation 7–105 reduces to

$$\frac{d^2\theta(t)}{dt^2} + \omega_n{}^2\theta(t) = 0 \qquad (7\text{–}106)$$

From elementary calculus, the solution to equation 7–106 is that of simple harmonic motion:

$$\theta(t) = R \sin(\omega_n t + \phi) \qquad (7\text{–}107)$$

In order to obtain a relationship between $\theta(t)$ and $d\theta(t)/dt$, we differentiate

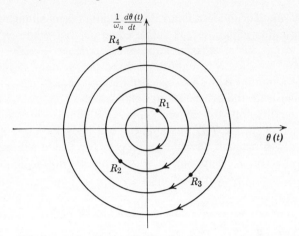

Figure 7-36. Phase portrait for a second-order linear system having no damping.

equation 7-107 and then eliminate time between the resulting equations, as follows:

$$\frac{d\theta(t)}{dt} = R\omega_n \cos(\omega_n t + \phi) \tag{7-108}$$

Eliminating time between equations 7-107 and 7-108, we obtain the expression

$$\left[\frac{1}{\omega_n}\frac{d\theta(t)}{dt}\right]^2 + [\theta(t)]^2 = R^2 \tag{7-109}$$

The phase portrait for this system can be drawn directly from equation 7-109. Observe that equation 7-109 describes a family of concentric circles in the $(1/\omega_n)(d\theta(t)/dt)$ versus $\theta(t)$ plane having a radius of R. Therefore, the phase portrait for this system (shown in Figure 7-36) is a family of concentric circles if a normalized ordinate axis is used. If the ordinate axis is not normalized, a family of ellipses results. Any set of initial conditions, such as points R_1, R_2, R_3, and R_4, specifies a particular circle. After $t = 0$, these points move around their respective circles continuously.

Let us next sketch the describing function for the case where the damping factor of this system is finite. The solution for equation 7-105 was derived in Chapter 3. The form of the solution for this system is the same as that given by equation 3-111. Setting $c(t) = \theta(t)$, we obtain the solution to equation 7-105:

$$\theta(t) = 1 + \frac{e^{-\zeta\omega_n t}}{\sqrt{1 - \zeta^2}} \sin\left(\omega_n\sqrt{1 - \zeta^2}\, t - \alpha\right) \tag{7-110}$$

Proceeding as in the previous example, the derivative of equation 7–110 is

$$\frac{d\theta(t)}{dt} = \omega_n e^{-\zeta\omega_n t} \cos(\omega_n \sqrt{1 - \zeta^2}\, t - \alpha)$$

$$- \zeta\omega_n \frac{e^{-\zeta\omega_n t}}{\sqrt{1 - \zeta^2}} \sin(\omega_n \sqrt{1 - \zeta^2}\, t - \alpha) \quad (7\text{–}111)$$

The complexity of equations 7–110 and 7–111 makes it quite difficult to eliminate time between them. Therefore we use an alternative approach. Equations 7–110 and 7–111 will be evaluated for several values of time to obtain the corresponding coordinates in a normalized phase plane. The result is plotted in Figure 7–37 for a damping factor of 0.5. Notice that the phase portrait for this linear system is a collection of noncrossing paths describing system behavior for all possible initial conditions. Since all the phase trajectories approach the origin, the system is stable as we would expect it to be.

The projection of a specific phase trajectory onto the abscissa gives the variation of $\theta(t)$ with time, and its projection onto the ordinate gives the variation of $d\theta(t)/dt$ with time. It is important to emphasize that time appears in the phase portrait implicitly as a parameter along all phase trajectories. We discuss its computation later in the chapter.

Let us next illustrate the application of this method to a nonlinear system which is described by a relatively simple nonlinear differential equation. We consider the problem of nonlinear friction which was discussed previously in Section 7–8.

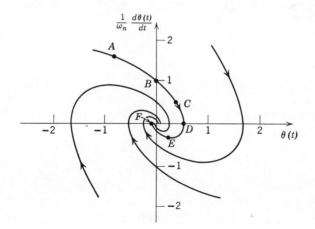

Figure 7–37. Phase portrait for a second-order linear system having a damping factor of 0.5.

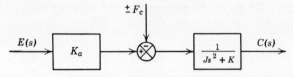

Figure 7–38.   *Block diagram of a system containing coulomb friction.*

From our understanding of the phenomenon of friction, let us determine the phase portrait for coulomb friction and extend it to the case of stiction. Figure 7–38 illustrates the block diagram of a system containing coulomb friction. The moment of inertia of the system is represented by J, the spring constant of the system by K, and the gain of the system by K_a. The equation relating $C(s)$ and $E(s)$ is given by

$$(K_a E(s) \pm F_c) \frac{1}{Js^2 + K} = C(s) \tag{7–112}$$

Assuming that the input to the system $E(s)$ is zero, we can simplify equation 7–112 to

$$Js^2 C(s) + KC(s) \pm F_c = 0 \tag{7–113}$$

The differential equation corresponding to equation 7–113 is

$$J \frac{d^2 c(t)}{dt^2} + Kc(t) \pm F_c = 0 \tag{7–114}$$

By defining the following quantities, we can normalize equation 7–114.

$$\omega = \left(\frac{K}{J}\right)^{\frac{1}{2}} \tag{7–115}$$

$$\gamma = \frac{F_c}{J\omega^2} \tag{7–116}$$

$$\alpha = \begin{cases} c - \gamma & \text{when} \quad \dot{c} < 0 \\ c + \gamma & \text{when} \quad \dot{c} > 0 \end{cases} \tag{7–117}$$

Substituting equations 7–115, 7–116, and 7–117 into equation 7–114, we obtain the relationship

$$\ddot{\alpha} + \omega^2 \alpha = 0 \tag{7–118}$$

The phase portrait for equation 7–118 in the α versus $\dot{\alpha}$ plane is the same as that for the linear, second-order system considered previously; it is shown in Figure 7–36. However, in the $\dot{c}/\omega$ versus c plane, the phase portrait for equation 7–118 is quite different. It can easily be obtained in the $\dot{c}/\omega$ versus c plane by considering equation 7–118 in two parts: one for the upper half plane where $\dot{c}/\omega > 0$, and the other for the lower half plane where $\dot{c}/\omega < 0$. A little thought shows that the phase portrait in the upper half plane is a family of semicircles, centered about $c = -\gamma$, since c is related to α merely by a simple translation. In a similar manner, the phase portrait for the lower half plane is a family of semicircles centered about $c = \gamma$. Figure 7–39 illustrates the phase portrait for this nonlinear system.

It is interesting to observe from Figure 7–39 that as soon as the response has a value within the interval on the $c(t)$ axis given by

$$-\gamma \leqslant c \leqslant \gamma \tag{7-119}$$

all motion stops. This gives rise to the possibility of large, steady-state errors resulting. For example, if the initial conditions are at point 1, the trajectory will be 1-2-3-4 and the system will not have any steady-state error. If the initial conditions are at point 5, however, the trajectory followed will be 5-6-7-8 and the system will have a steady-state error equal to γ.

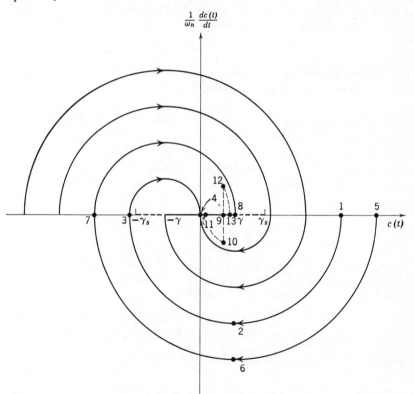

Figure 7–39. *Phase portrait for a system containing coulomb friction.*

Dither, discussed previously when we considered the describing-function analysis for backlash, is also useful for eliminating the steady-state error due to coulomb friction. Its physical effect on the steady-state error can easily be understood by studying the phase plane. For example, let us assume that a finite steady-state error exists corresponding to point 9 on Figure 7–39. By utilizing dither, which is a collection of induced oscillations of the system at a high frequency and small amplitude, point 9 will tend toward the origin. This occurs because the effect of a negative disturbance, segment 9-10, results in the system returning to point 11 on the $c(t)$ axis, while a positive disturbance, segment 9-12, results in the system returning to point 13 on the $c(t)$ axis. Since the projection 11-9 is greater than the projection 9-13, the system will tend to drive towards the origin.

Before leaving this system, let us consider the required modification to the phase portrait in Figure 7–39 for stiction. Since stiction occurs only for zero velocity and is greater than coulomb friction, its net effect is to extend the termination line on which all trajectories terminate: $-\gamma_s$ to $+\gamma_s$. These extended terminations are illustrated in Figure 7–39.

2. Transformation of the Second-Order Differential Equation to a First-Order Equation Method

If the differential equation of the system cannot be easily integrated, a new differential equation in terms of the variables of the phase plane may be formed from which the phase portrait can be obtained directly. This method can best be illustrated by considering the linear, second-order, undamped system discussed previously, whose system differential equation is

$$\frac{d^2\theta(t)}{dt^2} + \omega_n^2\theta(t) = 0 \tag{7-120}$$

In order to transform this equation into an equivalent, first-order, differential equation, let us divide through by $d\theta(t)/dt$. This results in the equation

$$\frac{d^2\theta(t)/dt^2}{d\theta(t)/dt} + \omega_n^2 \frac{\theta(t)}{d\theta(t)/dt} = 0 \tag{7-121}$$

Equation 7–121 can be simplified to

$$\frac{d[d\theta(t)/dt]}{d\theta(t)} + \omega_n^2 \frac{\theta(t)}{d\theta(t)/dt} = 0 \tag{7-122}$$

In order to simplify the notation of equation 7–122, the dot notation for derivatives will be used:

$$\frac{d\dot{\theta}(t)}{d\theta(t)} + \omega_n{}^2 \frac{\theta(t)}{\dot{\theta}(t)} = 0 \qquad (7\text{–}123)$$

Let us consider $\dot{\theta}(t)$ as the new dependent variable and $\theta(t)$ as the independent variable. The resulting equation is a first-order differential equation which is relatively simple to solve for $\dot{\theta}(t)$ as a function of $\theta(t)$. The phase trajectory of this system can therefore be sketched directly from equation 7–123. Proceeding in accordance with this method, let us operate on equation 7–123 as follows.

$$\frac{d\dot{\theta}(t)}{d\theta(t)} = -\omega_n{}^2 \frac{\theta(t)}{\dot{\theta}(t)} \qquad (7\text{–}124)$$

From elementary calculus, this equation has a solution of the form

$$\dot{\theta}(t) = \pm[C - \omega_n{}^2\theta^2(t)]^{\frac{1}{2}} \qquad (7\text{–}125)$$

where C is an arbitrary constant easily determined from the initial conditions. The result of sketching various phase trajectories from equation 7–125 will be the phase portrait illustrated in Figure 7–36, where a normalized ordinate axis is used. The initial conditions of the system determine the particular trajectory followed.

This technique can be easily extended to the systems whose phase portraits are illustrated in Figures 7–37 and 7–39. Within the bounds and limitations of the phase-plane method, this method is by far the most useful analytic technique for obtaining the phase portrait of a system.

3. Method of Isoclines

The method of isoclines is a graphical procedure for determining the phase portrait of a system. It can be used even if the system's differential equation cannot be solved by the first two analytic methods. In practice, it is usually the simplest method to use.

Isoclines are lines in the phase plane corresponding to constant slopes of the phase portrait. This technique is based on writing the differential equation of the system in the form shown by equation 7–124. It is important to emphasize that $d\dot{\theta}(t)/dt$ corresponds to the slope of the trajectories that form the phase portrait. Numerical values are assigned for the slopes $d\dot{\theta}(t)/dt$, and equation 7–124 is used to find the corresponding points in the phase plane having those slopes. Once a set of isoclines is drafted onto the phase plane, a phase trajectory may be drawn by starting at some point on an isocline and then proceeding to the next isocline along a straight line whose slope is the average of the slopes corresponding to the two isoclines. Since this procedure is basically a numerical approximation, closer spacing of the isoclines increases the accuracy of the resulting phase trajectory.

Let us illustrate the application of the isocline method to the linear, second-order, undamped and damped systems whose portraits are given in Figures 7–36 and 7–37, respectively. For the undamped case, the family of isoclines can be drawn from equation 7–124. However, in order to plot the phase portrait on a normalized plane $[(1/\omega_n)\dot{\theta}(t)$ versus $\theta(t)]$, equation 7–124 is written as follows:

$$\frac{d[\dot{\theta}(t)/\omega_n]}{d\theta(t)} = -\frac{\theta(t)}{\dot{\theta}(t)/\omega_n} \tag{7–126}$$

To simplify this expression, let

$$\dot{\Theta}(t) = \frac{\dot{\theta}(t)}{\omega_n} \tag{7–127}$$

Therefore, equation 7–126 can be rewritten as

$$\frac{d\dot{\Theta}(t)}{d\theta(t)} = -\frac{\theta(t)}{\dot{\Theta}(t)} \tag{7–128}$$

Observe from equation 7–128 that the slope of the isoclines, in the $\dot{\Theta}(t)$ versus $\theta(t)$ plane, is given by the relationship

$$\text{isocline slope} = -\frac{\theta(t)}{\dot{\Theta}(t)} \tag{7–129}$$

Isoclines having slopes corresponding to equation 7–129 constitute a family of straight lines passing through the origin in the phase plane. This is illustrated in Figure 7–40. It shows the construction of the phase trajectory starting with a point that lies on the isocline corresponding to a slope of −1.5. The motion of the phase trajectory away from point A is then downward and to the right. The segment of the phase trajectory drawn from the isocline whose slope is −1.5 to that whose slope is −2, would be a straight line whose slope is the average of −1.5 and −2, or −1.75. This is indicated on Figure 7–40 as line segment AB. In addition, the following line segment, BC, whose slope is −2.5, is illustrated. The total phase trajectory, corresponding to a set of initial conditions, is shown dotted. It is obvious from this simple example that the accuracy of the isocline method depends on the number of isoclines drawn.

Let us next construct the phase portrait for the linear, second-order,

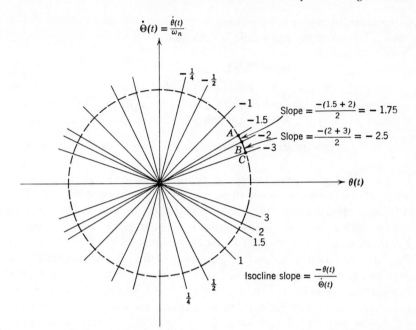

Figure 7–40. Construction of a phase trajectory for a linear, second-order, undamped system using the method of isoclines.

damped system considered previously, by means of the isocline method. From equation 7–105, the differential equation of the system is

$$\frac{d^2\theta(t)}{dt^2} + 2\zeta\omega_n\frac{d\theta(t)}{dt} + \omega_n^2\theta(t) = 0 \qquad (7\text{–}130)$$

Dividing through the expression by $1/\omega_n$ and letting $\zeta = 0.5$, we can write

$$\frac{1}{\omega_n}\frac{d^2\theta(t)}{dt^2} + \frac{d\theta(t)}{dt} + \omega_n\theta(t) = 0 \qquad (7\text{–}131)$$

Proceeding as before, this equation is divided through by $d\theta(t)/dt$ and the following expression is obtained:

$$\frac{d\{(1/\omega_n)[d\theta(t)/dt]\}}{d\theta(t)} + 1 + \frac{\theta(t)}{(1/\omega_n)[d\theta(t)/dt]} = 0 \qquad (7\text{–}132)$$

Using the dot notation, equation 7–132 can be expressed as

$$\frac{d\dot\theta(t)/\omega_n}{d\theta(t)} + 1 + \frac{\theta(t)}{\dot\theta(t)/\omega_n} = 0 \qquad (7\text{–}133)$$

Using the relation given by equation 7–127, and simplifying equation 7–133 further, the following expression is obtained:

$$\frac{d\dot{\Theta}(t)}{d\theta(t)} = -1 - \frac{\theta(t)}{\dot{\Theta}(t)} \qquad (7\text{–}134)$$

From equation 7–134, the slope of the isoclines, in the $\dot{\Theta}(t)$ versus $\theta(t)$ plane, is given by the following relationship:

$$\text{isocline slope} = -1 - \frac{\theta(t)}{\dot{\Theta}(t)} \qquad (7\text{–}135)$$

Isoclines having slopes corresponding to equation 7–135 constitute a family of straight lines passing through the origin in the phase plane. This is illustrated in Figure 7–41. The construction of the phase trajectory starting with a point which lies on the isocline corresponding to a slope of 2 is illustrated. The motion of the phase trajectory away from point A is then upward and to the right. The segment of the phase trajectory drawn from the isocline whose slope is 2 to that whose slope is 1 would be a straight line whose slope is the average of 2 and 1, or 1.5. This is indicated in Figure 7–41 as line segment AB. In addition, the following line segment BC, whose slope is 0.5, is illustrated. The total phase trajectory is shown dotted. As for the undamped system, the accuracy depends greatly on the number of isoclines drawn.

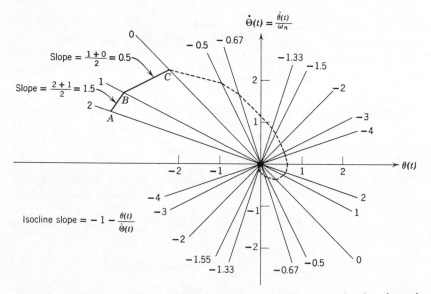

Figure 7–41. Construction of a phase trajectory for a linear, second-order, damped system using the method of isoclines.

Before leaving the discussion of constructing a phase portrait, it should be mentioned that there are several other methods available for obtaining a phase portrait. Most notable of these other methods are the method of tangents and Lienard's construction. The former technique is very similar to the method of isoclines. It consists of deriving the tangent to a trajectory at many points in the phase plane. The phase trajectory is then drawn tangent to these lines. This technique is usually a little more tedious than the method of isoclines. The reader is referred to Ref. 11 for a further discussion of the method of tangents. The latter technique, Lienard's construction, is useful if the second-order differential equation has the following special form:

$$\frac{d^2x}{dt^2} + f\left(\frac{dx}{dt}\right) + Kx = 0 \qquad (7\text{-}136)$$

where $f(dx/dt)$ represents nonlinear damping. The reader is referred to Ref. 12 for a further discussion of this specialized construction.

7–16. CHARACTERISTICS OF THE PHASE PLANE

Several characteristics are unique in the phase plane; their correct interpretation is very important for the intelligent analysis of feedback control systems. We begin by defining and illustrating several unique points called "singular points." Then we illustrate limit cycles occurring in the phase plane. The determination and location of singular points and limit cycles play a very important part in drawing the phase portrait of a system. The determination of time from the phase plane is illustrated next. This section concludes with examples of several interesting and representative phase portraits.

1. Singular Points

Singular points are points of the phase plane where the system is in a state of equilibrium. At these points both velocity and acceleration of the system are zero. Their determination is of great importance to the control engineer since they are distinguishing features of the phase portrait and greatly assist in drawing it.

Let us reconsider the general differential equation 7–102 of a second-order differential equation:

$$\frac{d^2x}{dt^2} + A_1\left(x, \frac{dx}{dt}\right)\frac{dx}{dt} + A_2\left(x, \frac{dx}{dt}\right)x = 0$$

If this equation can be described by two variables x and y and is written in the form given by equations 7–137 and 7–138, the singular points are defined as the points that make equations 7–137 and 7–138 equal zero.

$$\frac{dx}{dt} = P(x, y) \tag{7–137}$$

$$\frac{dy}{dt} = Q(x, y) \tag{7–138}$$

The characteristics of singular points may vary greatly depending on the variations of the coefficients of the first-order differential equations given by equations 7–137 and 7–138. We next proceed to determine a description of these characteristics.

The type of singular point may be found by means of a Taylor series expansion of equations 7–137 and 7–138 in the vicinity of the singular point. Assuming that the singularity occurs at $x = A$ and $y = B$, the result of expanding $P(x, y)$ and $Q(x, y)$ about these points is

$$\frac{dx}{dt} = A_1(x - A) + A_2(y - B) + A_3(x - A)^2$$
$$+ A_4(x - A)(y - B) + A_5(y - B)^2 + \cdots \tag{7–139}$$

$$\frac{dy}{dt} = B_1(x - A) + B_2(y - B) + B_3(x - A)^2$$
$$+ B_4(x - A)(y - B) + B_5(y - B)^2 + \cdots \tag{7–140}$$

We assume that the singular points are determined entirely by the coefficients of the linear terms only: A_1, A_2, B_1, and B_2. This is certainly reasonable if a sufficiently small region is chosen in the vicinity of the singularity. What we have basically done in this step is to use the technique of linearizing a quasi-linear characteristic. Therefore equations 7–139 and 7–140 reduce to

$$\frac{dx}{dt} = A_1(x - A) + A_2(y - B) \tag{7–141}$$

$$\frac{dy}{dt} = B_1(x - A) + B_2(y - B) \tag{7–142}$$

We further simplify the problem by assuming that the singularity occurs at the origin. Therefore A and B are both zero. Equations 7–141 and 7–142 reduce to the form

$$\frac{dx}{dt} = A_1 x + A_2 y \tag{7–143}$$

$$\frac{dy}{dt} = B_1 x + B_2 y \tag{7–144}$$

We have not lost any generality in using this assumption since the same result can always be obtained merely by changing the variables as follows:

$$x - A = p \tag{7-145}$$

$$y - B = q \tag{7-146}$$

The characteristics of the singular point can be determined by eliminating one of the two variables of equations 7–143 and 7–144 and studying the solution for the remaining variable. This can be easily performed by utilizing the Laplace transform of these equations, as follows:

$$sX(s) - x(0) = A_1 X(s) + A_2 Y(s) \tag{7-147}$$

$$sY(s) - y(0) = B_1 X(s) + B_2 Y(s) \tag{7-148}$$

Eliminating $Y(s)$, we obtain the solution for $X(s)$:

$$X(s) = \frac{(s - B_2)x(0) + A_2 y(0)}{s^2 - (A_1 + B_2)s + (A_1 B_2 - A_2 B_1)} \tag{7-149}$$

Assuming real coefficients, six different characteristic solutions of the denominator of equation 7–149 are possible. These solutions result in a set of singular points which can be classified as belonging to one of four types.

a. Node. A node is a point in the phase plane consisting of a family of trajectories which directly approach it (stable node) or depart from it (unstable node) without spiraling. A stable node occurs when the zeros of the denominator of equation 7–149 are both real and both in the left half of the s plane. An unstable node occurs when the zeros are both

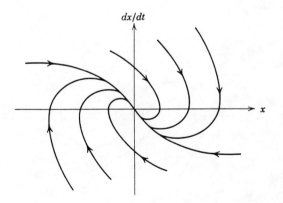

Figure 7–42. Phase portrait of a stable node.

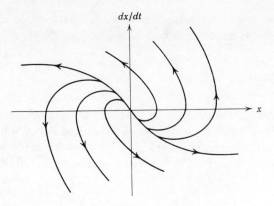

Figure 7–43. Phase portrait of an unstable node.

real and both lie in the right half of the *s* plane. Figure 7–42 illustrates a stable node and Figure 7–43 illustrates an unstable node.

b. Focus. A focus is a point in the phase plane consisting of a family of spiral trajectories which either converge on the point (stable focus) or diverge from it (unstable focus). A stable focus occurs when the zeros of the denominator of equation 7–149 are complex conjugate and lie in the left half of the *s* plane. An unstable focus occurs when the zeros are conjugate complex and lie in the right half plane. The origin of the phase portrait in Figure 7–37 is a stable focus. Figure 7–44 illustrates an unstable focus.

c. Center. A center is a point in the phase plane consisting of a family of closed curves encircling it. This occurs when the zeros of the denominator of equation 7–149 are complex conjugate and lie on the *j*ω axis. The origin of the phase portrait in Figure 7–36 is a center.

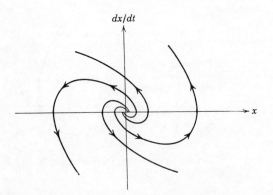

Figure 7–44. Phase portrait of an unstable focus.

dx/dt

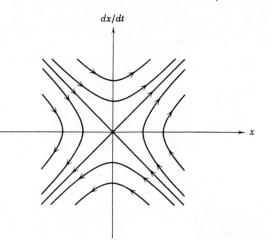

Figure 7–45.   Phase portrait of a saddle point.

d. Saddle Point.   A saddle point is a point in the phase plane that is characterized by the phase portrait illustrated in Figure 7–45. This occurs when the zeros of the denominator of equation 7–149 are real, with one existing in the right half plane and one existing in the left half plane. Except for the case where the numerator of equation 7–149 contains a zero which exactly cancels the zero of the denominator lying in the right half plane, this type of singularity always represents an unstable situation.

2.   Limit Cycles

Limit cycles are a very important characteristic of the phase plane. They are defined as isolated closed paths of the phase plane. The location and determination of the type of limit cycle, together with the singular points which exist in the phase plane, offer a complete description of the behavior of a nonlinear system.

A limit cycle can be stable or unstable depending on whether the paths in the neighborhood of the limit cycle converge toward it or away from it. They can result from either soft or hard self-excitation. These terms (defined during the discussion of the describing function) can easily be portrayed on the phase plane. Figure 7–46 illustrates a system with a soft self-excitation. Physically, this phase portrait may represent a system which has excessive gain for small signals and the output builds up in an

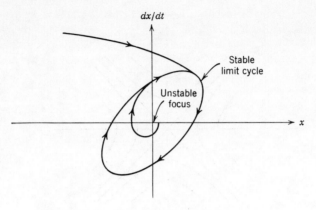

Figure 7–46. Phase portrait of soft self-excitation.

unstable manner. With large signals the output also approaches the stable limit cycle from the opposite direction as shown in Figure 7–46. A stable limit cycle exists between these two conditions where a sustained oscillation occurs. Figure 7–47 illustrates a system where a hard self-excitation exists. The generation of an oscillation depends on the initial conditions. For example, let us assume that the system is quiescently situated at the stable focus. In order for hard self-excitation to occur, a very large disturbance is required to change the state of the system to a region outside the unstable

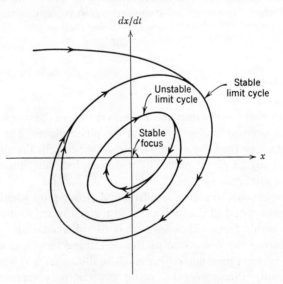

Figure 7–47. Phase portrait of hard self-excitation.

limit cycle. If this disturbance is sufficient for the operating point of the system to reach the stable limit cycle, a steady oscillation occurs.

3. Determination of Time from the Phase Plane

Although the general characteristic, second-order equation analyzed by the phase-plane method cannot be solved for x and dx/dt as functions of time directly, it is possible to obtain time from the phase-plane plot. The variation of time along a phase portrait can be found from the simple relation of the ordinate axis of the phase plane:

$$y = \frac{dx}{dt} \qquad (7\text{-}150)$$

Solving for t, we obtain the relationship

$$t = \int_A^B \frac{1}{y}\, dx \qquad (7\text{-}151)$$

Equation 7–151 shows that if the phase portrait is replotted with $1/y$, or $(dx/dt)^{-1}$, as the ordinate and x as the abscissa, the area under the resulting curve represents time. The area under the curve can be evaluated with a planimeter or by simple approximations of the areas with a series of rectangles. Let us use the phase trajectory labeled $ABCDEF$ on the phase portrait of Figure 7–37 to illustrate the determination of time. We assume that $\omega_n = 1$. Our first problem is to determine the time it takes for the function to go from A to C. Figure 7–48 represents a plot of $[d\theta(t)/dt]^{-1}$ versus $\theta(t)$ for the interval ABC. Using a series of rectangles for area summation, we find that the time is approximately equal to

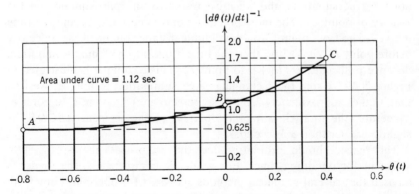

Figure 7–48. Finding time from a reciprocal phase-plane plot.

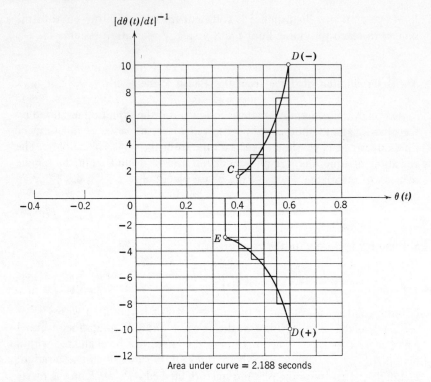

Figure 7–49. Approximating time from a reciprocal phase-plane plot when velocity passes through zero.

1.12 seconds. If we attempt to find the time it takes for the trajectory to pass from C to E, we run into a problem since $d\theta(t)/dt$ equals zero at point D and the reciprocal phase-plane plot goes to infinity. This certainly is not the true situation, and we must resort to an approximation in the vicinity of point D. The most practical approximation is to find the time it takes to go from point C to a small finite distance on the phase trajectory before point D, $D(-)$, and then the time it takes to go from a small finite distance past point D, $D(+)$, to point E. This technique is illustrated in Figure 7–49. Using the rectangular area summation technique, we find that it takes approximately 2.188+ seconds to go from point C to point E. Therefore, the total time it takes to traverse the segment $ABCDE$ is slightly greater than 3.3 seconds.

The reader should ordinarily find the reciprocal phase-plane plot sufficient for obtaining time. For academic completeness, the reader is advised that several graphical methods also exist for obtaining time from the phase plane. References 7 and 12 treat this approach thoroughly.

4. Representative Phase Portraits

In order to develop a greater facility for intelligently interpreting phase portraits, we next present additional representative phase portraits. These, with the portraits already discussed, should give the reader a good facility for interpreting phase portraits. Specifically, we consider the phase portraits of undamped and damped, second-order systems that have the nonlinear characteristics of rate and position limiting. We compare the results with the phase trajectories illustrated in Figures 7–40 and 7–41.

a. Rate Limiting of an Undamped, Second-Order System. Let us reconsider the linear, undamped, second-order system whose phase trajectory was illustrated in Figure 7–40. We shall change this linear system to a nonlinear one by adding a governor to the servo motor driving the load so that the maximum rate is limited. The resulting phase portrait is illustrated in Figure 7–50. If the initial conditions are such that the resulting phase trajectory lies anywhere within the dashed trajectory, the system will oscillate in the same manner that the undamped linear system did, as shown in Figure 7–40. However, if the initial conditions are such that they lie outside the dashed trajectory, the system's output rate increases to the maximum value allowed by the governor, and then the output's position decreases to zero, as shown in Figure 7–50. Thereafter the system will oscillate indefinitely following the dotted trajectory.

b. Position Limiting of an Undamped, Second-Order System. Let us next consider the linear, undamped, second-order system that is made nonlinear by adding limit stops to the system's output shaft, so that the maximum and minimum positions are limited. The resulting phase portrait is given in Figure 7–51. The interpretation of this phase portrait is analogous to that of Figure 7–50, except that it is shifted by 90°.

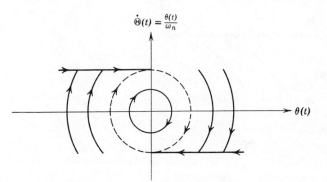

$$\dot{\Theta}(t) = \frac{\theta(t)}{\omega_n}$$

$\theta(t)$

Figure 7–50. Phase portrait of a second-order, undamped system having rate limiting.

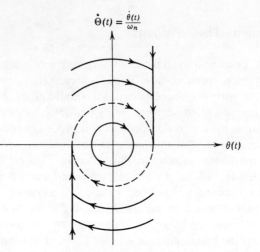

Figure 7–51. Phase portrait of a second-order, undamped system having position limiting.

c. Rate Limiting of a Damped, Second-Order System.   Let us reconsider the linear, damped, second-order system whose phase trajectory was shown in Figure 7–41. We shall change this linear system to a nonlinear one by adding a governor to the servo motor driving the load so that the maximum rate is limited. The resulting phase portrait is given in Figure 7–52. If the initial conditions are such that the resulting phase trajectory lies anywhere within the dashed trajectories, the system will follow a spiral which approaches the origin in the same manner as was shown in Figure 7–41. However, if the initial conditions are such that they lie outside the

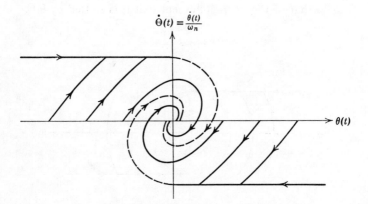

Figure 7–52. Phase portrait of a second-order, damped system having rate limiting.

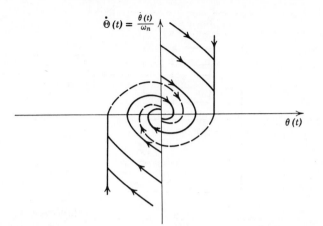

Figure 7–53.   Phase portrait of a second-order, damped system having position limiting.

dashed trajectories, the output control's rate increases to the maximum value allowed by the governor, and then the output's position decreases to zero, as shown in Figure 7–52. Thereafter the system will follow one of the dashed trajectories and will finally approach the origin.

d. Position Limiting of a Damped, Second-Order System.   Let us next consider the linear, damped, second-order system that is made nonlinear by adding limit stops to the system's output shaft, so that the maximum and minimum positions are limited. The resulting phase portrait is presented in Figure 7–53. The interpretation of this phase portrait is analogous to that of Figure 7–52, except that it is shifted by 90°.

7–17.   DESIGN OF NONLINEAR FEEDBACK CONTROL SYSTEMS USING THE PHASE-PLANE METHOD[13]

This section illustrates the design of a nonlinear feedback control system with the phase-plane method. We use the analytic tools developed in Sections 7–14 to 7–16 to demonstrate the procedure the control engineer should follow when designing a nonlinear system. Specifically, we consider an "on-off" control system. The primary function of this example is to use the transient response of the system as a guide for choosing the system's parameters. One of our main objectives will be to determine the existence of limit cycles as the system's parameters are varied. We will not, however, be able to obtain the margin of stability for the system from the phase plane. The following analysis should be compared with that obtained from the describing function in Sections 7–10 and 7–11.

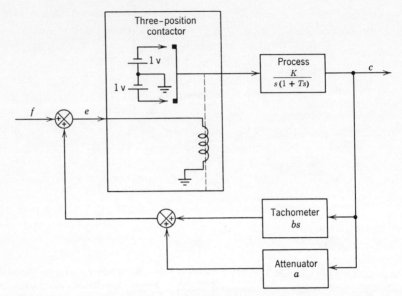

Figure 7–54. On-off control system having variable position and velocity feedback.

Let us consider the on-off control system illustrated in Figure 7–54. It has a three-position contactor which applies a corrective signal having the proper phase for corrective control action. The problem is to determine the optimum combination of variable position feedback constant, a, and variable velocity feedback constant, b, for the system's transient performance. We assume that the input r is zero and that the forcing function generated by the contactor is unity; therefore the general form of the differential equation for this system is given by

$$\frac{d^2c}{dt^2} + 2\zeta\frac{dc}{dt} + c = \text{sgn}\left(ac + b\frac{dc}{dt}\right) \tag{7-152}$$

where $0 < \zeta < 1$. The sign of the unit forcing function is given by the sign of $ac + b(dc/dt)$. Assuming that $\zeta = 0.5$, we can simplify this equation to the following:

$$\frac{d^2c}{dt^2} + \frac{dc}{dt} + c = \text{sgn}\left(ac + b\frac{dc}{dt}\right) \tag{7-153}$$

Specifically, we shall determine the transient response of this system for the following polarity combinations of a and b:

$$
\begin{array}{lll}
\text{(A)} & a > 0, & b > 0 \\
\text{(B)} & a > 0, & b < 0 \\
\text{(C)} & a < 0, & b > 0 \\
\text{(D)} & a < 0, & b < 0 \\
\end{array}
$$

In general the phase portrait for any of these systems may be obtained in a similar manner. We draw heavily on the results of our studies of singular points in drawing the various phase portraits. The basic relation analyzed in our discussion of singular points was equation 7–102:

$$\frac{d^2c}{dt^2} + A_1\left(c, \frac{dc}{dt}\right)\frac{dc}{dt} + A_2\left(c, \frac{dc}{dt}\right)c = 0 \qquad (7\text{--}154)$$

Notice that the variable has been arbitrarily changed from x to c. For our derivation of singular points, we assumed that they all occurred at the origin of the phase plane. If we are considering a simple, unexcited, underdamped, second-order system, we know that the differential equation 7–154 will result in a phase portrait similar to that in Figure 7–37, where the origin acts as a stable focus. In the case of an on-off system, however, we find that it is represented by a differential equation which is given by equation 7–153. The right-hand side of this equation can be thought of as either a unit positive or a negative forcing function. The phase portrait of a system having a unit positive forcing function will have spirals that converge towards a stable focus at $c = 1$, $dc/dt = 0$. The phase portrait of a system having a unit negative forcing function will have spirals that converge towards a stable focus at $c = -1$, $dc/dt = 0$. The on-off system we are considering actually has two stable foci because of the action of the three-position contactor. A switching line, defined by

$$ac + b\frac{dc}{dt} = 0 \qquad (7\text{--}155)$$

separates the regions where the phase trajectory spirals towards $c = 1$, $dc/dt = 0$ or $c = -1$, $dc/dt = 0$. Using this general approach, which is valid for all four cases, the transient response of these systems is illustrated next.

Case A. $a > 0$, $b > 0$. The switching line is a straight line given by the following relationship:

$$\frac{dc}{dt} = -\frac{a}{b}c \qquad (7\text{--}156)$$

It passes through the origin and lies in the second and fourth quadrants. The sign of $ac + b(dc/dt)$ is positive in the region to the right of it and negative in the region to the left of it. The phase portrait for this system, which is given in Figure 7–55, can be constructed using the method of isoclines or by transforming the second-order differential equation to a first-order equation. Observe that three trajectories are possible, depending on the initial conditions. Two represent stable states where the phase

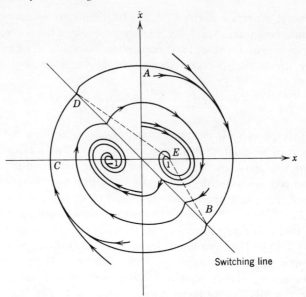

Figure 7–55.   Phase portrait for an on-off control system where $a > 0$, $b > 0$.

portrait terminates on the foci at -1 or 1, depending on the final switching input. The third possible trajectory represents a limit cycle.

Any initial condition occurring beyond the limit cycle or very close to it in the enclosed area will eventually result in the phase trajectory reaching some part of the limit cycle, $ABCDA$. For a limit cycle to occur, the distance DE from the switching line to the corresponding focus must be greater than the distance BE, which represents the distance from the subsequent crossing of the line to the focus. In addition, this must be true with respect to the other focus.

Trajectories that start sufficiently inside the limit cycle will spiral into one of the foci. However, there is no chance of these trajectories ultimately reaching the origin.

Case B. $a > 0$, $b < 0$. The switching line is a straight line given by the following relationship:

$$\frac{dc}{dt} = \frac{a}{b} c \tag{7–157}$$

It passes through the origin and lies in the first and third quadrants. In a manner similar to the first case, we can show the phase portrait to be as in Figure 7–56. Observe that any set of initial conditions which results in a trajectory intersecting the switching line outside the interval AB results in a phase trajectory spiral towards one of the two stable foci.

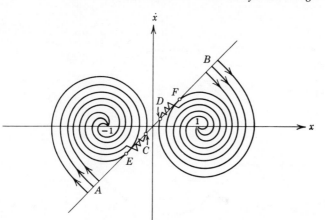

Figure 7–56.   Phase portrait for an on-off control system where $a > 0$, $b < 0$.

However, if the intersection occurs inside the interval *AB*, the trajectory theoretically ends on the switching line. Figure 7–56 indicates these points by *C* and *D*. Points *E* and *F* represent points of tangency with the switching lines for limiting trajectories. In reality, however, the system cannot just end at these points. This inconsistency is resolved by the fact that switching action of a contactor always has a certain time lag due to its dynamics. Therefore, when a solution reaches the switching line it actually proceeds for some small distance past it, before there is a change of sign in the forcing function. This results in a zigzag action along the switching line. Eventually, the trajectory spirals into one of the foci as shown in Figure 7–56. Physically, this is audible as a "chattering" of the contactor.

Case C. $a < 0$, $b > 0$. The switching line has the same form as that of case B. The phase portrait is given in Figure 7–57. For this case a stable limit cycle always prevails. Regardless of where the initial conditions occur, the final solution always winds up as a stable limit cycle.

Case D. $a < 0$, $b < 0$. The switching line has the same form as that of case A. The phase portrait, given in Figure 7–58, shows that no periodic solution exists. The solutions tend to end on the switching line. Because of the time lag of the relay, however, the trajectory zigzags towards the origin of the phase plane. The system finally oscillates at very high frequency and small amplitude around the origin. This is popularly called "chattering of the control system."

It is interesting to observe that of the four cases considered, the control-system engineer would prefer the phase portrait characteristics of case D, the only configuration which resulted in a stable equilibrium state occurring around the origin. However, we would have to tolerate some

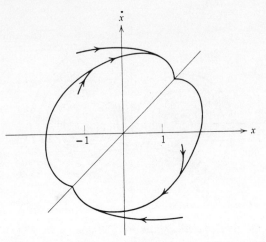

Figure 7–57. Phase portrait for an on-off control system where a $< 0, b > 0$.

chattering around the origin with this linear switching system. To eliminate the chattering the control system engineer would have to use nonlinear switching techniques.[13]

An analog computer in conjunction with an oscilloscope forms a very powerful combination that the control engineer can use to study the phase portraits of nonlinear systems as certain parameters are varied. Figure 7–59 illustrates the analog computer circuitry required for simulating the system whose block diagram was shown in Figure 7–54. Switch

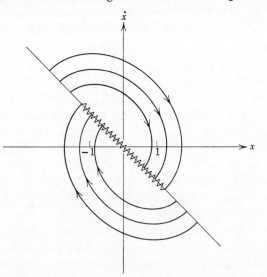

Figure 7–58. Phase portrait for an on-off control system where a $< 0, b < 0$.

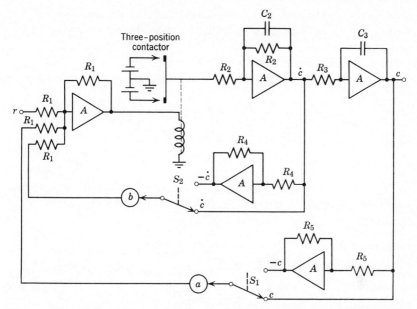

Figure 7–59. Analog computer circuit for simulating the system shown in Figure 7-54.

S_1 permits choices of $a > 0$ or $a < 0$, and switch S_2 permits choices of $b > 0$, or $b < 0$. By connecting the points $\dot{c}$ and c to the horizontal and vertical deflection plates of an oscilloscope, respectively, the phase portraits shown in Figures 7–55 through 7–58 can be obtained as switches S_1 and S_2 are varied. The reader should try this very useful exercise.

7–18. PHASE-SPACE CONCEPTS

The phase-plane method can be extended to systems of higher than the second order by means of the phase-space concept. We have demonstrated by means of the phase-plane method that a second-order, nonlinear system's transient response can be studied on a two-dimensional plot when the initial conditions of position and velocity are known. For a third-order differential equation, three initial conditions are required, and a study of the system's transient response requires a three-dimensional "phase space." The three conditions and coordinates correspond to position, velocity, and acceleration. By similar reasoning, a system described by an nth-order differential equation would require an n-dimensional phase space with a knowledge of n initial conditions. This is, indeed, an arduous task for third- and higher-order systems and is rarely used at present. I feel, however, that this method will be used to a greater extent in the future with the increasing use of computers. Therefore we use a third-order system in order to illustrate the procedure of this method.

Let us consider the phase-space solution for a third-order system whose differential equation has the following general form.

$$\frac{d^3x}{dt^3} + A_1\left(x, \frac{dx}{dt}, \frac{d^2x}{dt^2}\right)\frac{d^2x}{dt^2} + A_2\left(x, \frac{dx}{dt}, \frac{d^2x}{dt^2}\right)\frac{dx}{dt}$$
$$+ A_3\left(x, \frac{dx}{dt}, \frac{d^2x}{dt^2}\right)x = 0 \qquad (7\text{-}158)$$

Time can be eliminated from this equation by expressing this third-order differential equation in terms of the following three first-order, differential equations:

$$\frac{dx}{dt} = v \qquad (7\text{-}159)$$

$$\frac{d^2x}{dt^2} = \frac{dv}{dt} = a \qquad (7\text{-}160)$$

$$\frac{d^3x}{dt^3} = \frac{da}{dt} = -\left[A_1\left(x, \frac{dx}{dt}, \frac{d^2x}{dt^2}\right)a + A_2\left(x, \frac{dx}{dt}, \frac{d^2x}{dt^2}\right)v\right.$$
$$\left. + A_3\left(x, \frac{dx}{dt}, \frac{d^2x}{dt^2}\right)x\right] \qquad (7\text{-}161)$$

Equations 7-159, 7-160, and 7-161 can be reduced to two equations by relating x, v, and a as follows:

$$\frac{dx}{dv} = \frac{v}{a} \qquad (7\text{-}162)$$

$$\frac{da}{dv} = -\left[A_1\left(x, \frac{dx}{dt}, \frac{d^2x}{dt^2}\right) + A_2\left(x, \frac{dx}{dt}, \frac{d^2x}{dt^2}\right)\frac{v}{a}\right.$$
$$\left. + A_3\left(x, \frac{dx}{dt}, \frac{d^2x}{dt^2}\right)\frac{x}{a}\right] \qquad (7\text{-}163)$$

The solution to equations 7-162 and 7-163 involves the three variables x, v, and a, which correspond to position, velocity, and acceleration, respectively. The elimination of time has reduced by one the number of first-order differential equations necessary for specifying the phase trajectories. However, the number of phase-space dimensions required for sketching the system's transient response always equals the order of the system's differential equation.

Beginning with an initial set of conditions corresponding to x_0, v_0, and a_0, the initial slope of the x-v phase trajectory in the x-v plane can be obtained from equation 7–162. In a similar manner, the initial slope of the phase trajectory in the a-v plane can be obtained from equation 7–163. Drawing a slope from the initial point in the x-v plane determines the values of x_1 and v_1. Drawing the slope until v_1 is reached in the a-v plane determines a_1. Using equations 7–162 and 7–163 to determine the slopes of the phase trajectory between points, we can draw a complete phase trajectory.

7–19. LIAPUNOV'S STABILITY CRITERION

A. M. Liapunov[14] developed a very interesting method of determining the steady-state stability of a feedback control system based on energy considerations. He has shown that a sufficient condition for system stability is to prove that the energy stored in the system approaches zero as time approaches infinity. This section presents the first and second methods of Liapunov and illustrates their application to nonlinear feedback control systems.

Liapunov divided the general problem of analyzing the stability of nonlinear systems into two classes. The first class consists of all those methods in which the differential equation of the system can be solved. System stability or instability is determined from this solution. This approach, which is known as the "first method of Liapunov," does not say anything of particular importance concerning the solution of the nonlinear differential equations. However, Liapunov did point out in his first method that the solution may be obtained in the form of a series from which stability can be determined using his second method. In addition, he proved that approximate solutions of nonlinear differential equations often yield useful stability information.

"Liapunov's second method" concerns the determination of stability information concerning a nonlinear system without actually having to solve its differential equation. By manipulating the coefficients of the characteristic equation in a certain prescribed manner, it is possible to determine whether the poles of the system are in the right or left half plane without having to solve the equation directly. This approach for nonlinear systems is similar to the Routh-Hurwitz stability criterion for linear systems. The second method of Liapunov is a very powerful tool which has received increasing attention recently. The remainder of this section is devoted to its details and application.

Liapunov's second method, which is based on energy considerations, can best be studied from the phase plane for a simple second-order system (see Problem 7–21). It was shown in equations 7–137 and 7–138 that a second-order, nonlinear, differential equation, which can be represented by two variables x and y, can be described by the following two first-order equations:

$$\frac{dx}{dt} = P(x, y) \tag{7-164}$$

$$\frac{dy}{dt} = Q(x, y) \tag{7-165}$$

Assuming that $x = y = 0$ is a singular point, Liapunov's second method states that a system is stable if it is possible to find a function $V(x, y)$ which has the following properties: (a) $V(x, y) = 0$ only for $x = y = 0$; (b) $dV(x, y)/dt$ is never positive. In addition, this theorem states that if dV/dt is never zero, except for the possible case when $x = y = 0$, the equilibrium is defined as being asymptotically stable. It can be shown that the function V is analogous to the stored energy in the system but is not equal to it.

The proof of Liapunov's second method can best be presented by considering the phase plane of Figure 7–60. Contours of constant V are shown by the curves of C_1, C_2, and C_3. The derivative of V with respect to time, dV/dt, is given by

$$\frac{dV}{dt} = \left(\frac{\partial V}{\partial x}\right)_y \frac{dx}{dt} + \left(\frac{\partial V}{\partial y}\right)_x \frac{dy}{dt} \tag{7-166}$$

Substituting equations 7–164 and 7–165 into equation 7–166, we obtain

$$\frac{dV}{dt} = \left(\frac{\partial V}{\partial x}\right)_y P(x, y) + \left(\frac{\partial V}{\partial y}\right)_x Q(x, y) \tag{7-167}$$

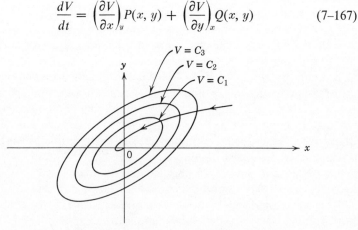

Figure 7-60.   Proof of Liapunov's stability criterion.

The partial derivatives of equation 7—167 are given by

$$\frac{\partial V}{\partial x} = \left[\left(\frac{\partial V}{\partial x} \right)_y^2 + \left(\frac{\partial V}{\partial y} \right)_x^2 \right]^{\frac{1}{2}} \cos{(0x, AB)} \qquad (7\text{--}168)$$

$$\frac{\partial V}{\partial y} = \left[\left(\frac{\partial V}{\partial x} \right)_y^2 + \left(\frac{\partial V}{\partial y} \right)_x^2 \right]^{\frac{1}{2}} \cos{(0y, AB)} \qquad (7\text{--}169)$$

where AB represents the normal to a constant V curve (or surface) with the positive direction taken from inside to outside the curve (or surface). Therefore, the derivative of V with respect to time, dV/dt, can be represented by

$$\frac{dV}{dt} = \left[\left(\frac{\partial V}{\partial x} \right)_y^2 + \left(\frac{\partial V}{\partial y} \right)_x^2 \right]^{\frac{1}{2}} V_n \qquad (7\text{--}170)$$

where V_n = the normal projection of the velocity = $P \cos{(0x, AB)}$ + $Q \cos{(0y, AB)}$. Referring to Figure 7–60, we see that a phase trajectory will cross the curve $V = C_2$ to the curve $V = C_1$ if dV/dt is never positive. From the phase plane stability criterion, this system would be stable.

To illustrate the application of Liapunov's second method, we consider the second-order, nonlinear, differential equation

$$\frac{d^2x}{dt^2} + \left[K_1 + K_2 \left(\frac{dx}{dt} \right)^2 \right] \frac{dx}{dt} + x = 0 \qquad (7\text{--}171)$$

This second-order differential equation can be written in terms of two first-order equations, which correspond to the form given by equations 7–164 and 7–165, as follows

$$\frac{dx}{dt} = y \qquad (7\text{--}172)$$

$$\frac{dy}{dt} = -K_1 y - K_2 y^3 - x \qquad (7\text{--}173)$$

Depending on the values of K_1 and K_2, stability or instability can result. For example, if $K_1 > 0$ and $K_2 > 0$, and V is given by

$$V = x^2 + y^2 \qquad (7\text{--}174)$$

this system is stable since the derivative of V with respect to time t, dV/dt, is negative, as follows.

$$\frac{dV}{dt} = 2 \left(x \frac{dx}{dt} + y \frac{dy}{dt} \right) = -2(K_1 y^2 + K_2 y^4) \qquad (7\text{--}175)$$

Equilibrium occurs at the singularity located at the origin, and the system is asymptotically stable.

It is left as an exercise for the reader to prove that the condition $K_1 < 0$ and $K_2 < 0$ corresponds to an unstable equilibrium; the condition $K_1 > 0$ and $K_2 < 0$ corresponds to a stable system only if $0 < y^2 < -K_1/K_2$, and the condition $K_1 = K_2 = 0$ represents an unstable equilibrium. The reader may find further exercises for applying this powerful technique in the problem section.

7-20. STEP-BY-STEP NUMERICAL COMPUTATION

The solution to any nonlinear differential equation can be obtained by a step-by-step numerical computation. The computation is based on the (approximating) assumption that over a short interval of time derivatives of the system's response are constant at some average value. Therefore, within each small time interval Δt we can assume a linear feedback control system and analyze its transient solution by means of conventional techniques. For a following time interval, the process is repeated with a new set of system parameters.

This method is an extension of the conventional small-signal analysis approach. The basic difference between the small-signal analysis approach for linear systems and the step-by-step numerical computation for non-linear systems is that we can permit large and rapid variations for the latter during each interval of time. However, we cannot assume that the system reaches a steady-state value within each interval of time, and hence there is greater emphasis on the initial condition, which must be recalculated at the beginning of each time interval. The length of the time interval chosen for this method depends on the rate of change of the input and the response time of the system. Obviously this technique gives more accurate results as the time intervals decrease in size.

Let us briefly illustrate the procedure of the step-by-step numerical computation method. Consider its application to the following second-order, nonlinear, differential equation.

$$\frac{d^2x}{dt^2} + A_1\left(x, \frac{dx}{dt}\right)\frac{dx}{dt} + A_2\left(x, \frac{dx}{dt}\right)x = y(t) \qquad (7\text{--}176)$$

where $y(t)$ = input to the system, $x(t)$ = output of the system. Assuming that the initial conditions x_0, and $(dx/dt)_0$ are known, we can obtain $(d^2x/dt^2)_0$ from equation 7–176 as follows:

$$\left(\frac{d^2x}{dt^2}\right)_0 = y_0 - A_1\left[x_0, \left(\frac{dx}{dt}\right)_0\right]\left(\frac{dx}{dt}\right)_0 - A_2\left[x_0, \left(\frac{dx}{dt}\right)_0\right]x_0 \quad (7\text{--}177)$$

We assume that the acceleration given by equation 7–177 is constant over the time interval Δt. Therefore, the velocity at the end of this interval is given by

$$\frac{dx}{dt}\Big]_1 = \left(\frac{dx}{dt}\right)_0 + \frac{d^2x}{dt^2}\Delta t \tag{7-178}$$

Assuming that the velocity over this interval of time is the average of $(dx/dt)_0$ and $(dx/dt)_1$, the value of x at the end of this interval is given by

$$x_1 = x_0 + \frac{1}{2}\left[\left(\frac{dx}{dt}\right)_0 + \left(\frac{dx}{dt}\right)_1\right]\Delta t \tag{7-179}$$

Since y_1, x_1, and $(dx/dt)_1$ are known, the value of $(d^2x/dt^2)_1$ can be obtained from equation 7–176 as follows:

$$\left(\frac{d^2x}{dt^2}\right)_1 = y_1 - A_1\left[x_1, \left(\frac{dx}{dt}\right)_1\right]\left(\frac{dx}{dt}\right)_1 - A_2\left[x_1, \left(\frac{dx}{dt}\right)_1\right]x_1 \tag{7-180}$$

This procedure is repeated over as many intervals of time as necessary. The resulting variation of x with time t can be obtained from the tabulated values shown in Table 7–2.

Table 7–2. Tabulation of step-by-step procedure

t	y	x	$\dfrac{dx}{dt}$	$A_1\left(x, \dfrac{dx}{dt}\right)$	$A_2\left(x, \dfrac{dx}{dt}\right)$	$\dfrac{d^2x}{dt^2}$
0	y_0	x_0	$\left(\dfrac{dx}{dt}\right)_0$	A_{1_0}	A_{2_0}	$\left(\dfrac{d^2x}{dt^2}\right)_0$
1	y_1	x_1	$\left(\dfrac{dx}{dt}\right)_1$	A_{1_1}	A_{2_1}	$\left(\dfrac{d^2x}{dt^2}\right)_1$
2	y_2	x_2	$\left(\dfrac{dx}{dt}\right)_2$	A_{1_2}	A_{2_2}	$\left(\dfrac{d^2x}{dt^2}\right)_2$
Etc.	...	...	...	...	...	...

A basic assumption of the step-by-step method is that the derivatives remain constant at some average value over a small interval of time Δt. This approximation grows more accurate as Δt grows smaller. A good rule of thumb for determining a desirable value of Δt is to try one-half of the previous value of Δt until the difference in the solutions becomes negligible.

Numerical methods for solving nonlinear differential equations are usually more accurate than the graphical methods described in this chapter. In addition, when the nonlinearity is very large, or difficult to describe graphically, it is an extremely powerful technique. Unfortunately, calculating the solution by hand is a very tedious process. The reader should become familiar with desk calculators and digital computers (if they are available). Problems 7–25 and 7–26 have been included for the reader to become familiar with the step-by-step numerical computation technique utilizing a desk calculator or a digital computer as an aid. In addition, these problems study the effects of varying Δt.

7–21. INTENTIONAL NONLINEARITIES

This chapter next presents a discussion of intentional nonlinearities, that is, nonlinearities which are deliberately introduced into a feedback control system in order to simplify the system or improve its performance. The use of simple "on-off" control systems, analyzed earlier in this chapter, are examples of an intentional nonlinearity inserted into a system in order to simplify its operation. The thermostatic heating-control systems for homes are good examples of the simplicity that can be attained. We concentrate in this section on intentional nonlinearities introduced into a system in order to improve its overall performance.

The conflict between the speed of the transient response, maximum overshoot, and settling time of an underdamped system has been discussed with great detail in Section 4-5. It was shown that systems having a large amount of damping ($\zeta \rightarrow 1$) have small overshoots and are relatively long. In contrast, systems that have a small amount of damping ($\zeta \rightarrow 0$) have large overshoots and poor relative stability. However, their rise times and response times are relatively short. The short rise time and response time of low-damped systems, together with the good relative stability and little or no overshoot of the highly damped system, can be obtained by inserting an intentional nonlinearity into the system. These devices function by adjusting the damping as a function of the magnitude of the errors and/ or the rate of error. This results in an intentional nonlinear system, which has very little damping for large errors, and a relatively large amount of damping for small errors.

Most intentional nonlinearities, whose primary function is to improve the response of a feedback control system, work on the principle of accelerating the system very rapidly for large errors and then increasing the damping factor for very small errors. The nonlinearity can be introduced in either the forward or the feedback portion of the system. In addition, some systems apply full accelerating, or decelerating, torque to the controlling motor based on a programmed optimum switching function.[15,16]

When the control engineer synthesizes an intentional nonlinear system, he must realize that all the problems inherently associated with nonlinear systems are present. The main problem that the control engineer faces when synthesizing an intentional nonlinearity is the fact that a nonlinear element may improve the system's performance with one type of input but not with another. For example, an intentional nonlinearity that improves a system's performance in response to a step input may actually produce degraded performance in response to sinusoidal signals. Therefore, because of the difficulty experienced in specifying the exact mathematical requirements, practical intentional nonlinearities are often obtained by empirical techniques.

Figure 7–61 illustrates three commonly found intentional nonlinearities. Part (*a*) shows an adjustable attenuator in the forward part of the loop which has a smaller attenuation for large errors than for small errors. Therefore, for large errors the bandwidth is increased, the relative damping is decreased, and the response time is decreased. Part (*b*) shows a technique that eliminates the time constant effect for large input signals. This method results in a reduction in low frequency gain for large errors. Part (*c*) shows a device that applies full torque to the controlling motor based on a programmed optimum switching function which reduces the system error and its derivatives in the minimum possible amount of time. With proper selection of the switching points, the feedback control system will arrive at zero position error with zero rate error. In addition, if the torque is removed, the system remains at rest with no further corrective action required. The number of switching points required to respond in the minimum amount of time to a step input has been shown[17] to be $n - 1$ where n is the order of the system. For example, the optimum response to a step input of torque for a second-order system is to accelerate the motor to its maximum rate for about half the desired distance of travel and then to switch once and decelerate at the maximum value for the remaining distance. Several useful optimum switching functions for second-order systems having torque limiting are given for a variety of damping conditions in Stout's article.[17]

7–22. ANALYSIS OF TIME-VARIABLE LINEAR SYSTEMS

The general form of a linear differential equation having variable coefficients was defined previously (see equation 7–3) as follows:

$$A_n(t)\frac{d^n y}{dt^n} + A_{n-1}(t)\frac{d^{n-1}y}{dt^{n-1}} + \cdots + A_0(t)y = x(t) \qquad (7\text{–}181)$$

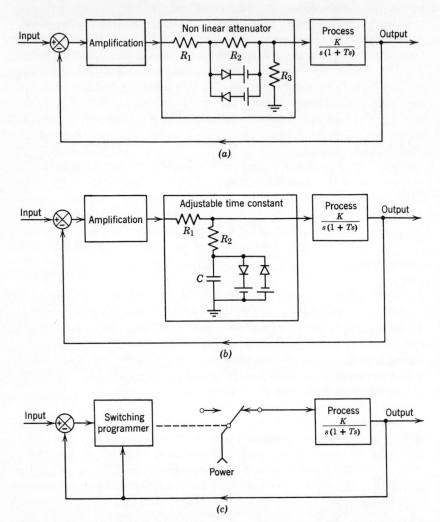

Figure 7-61. Use of intentional nonlinearities to improve system performance. (a) Variable bandwidth and damping as a function of error. For small errors, attenuation = $R_3/(R_1 + R_2 + R_3)$. For large errors, attenuation = $R_3/(R_1 + R_3)$. (b) Adjustable lag network which eliminates the capacitor's effect and reduces the low-frequency gain for large errors. (c) Programmed optimum switching to reduce the system's error and its derivatives to zero in the minimum amount of time.

This differential equation represents a class of very interesting and practical systems. Its occurrence, together with special techniques for analyzing time-variable linear systems, is discussed in this chapter since nonlinear techniques are often helpful.

In many instances it is impossible to consider certain physical parameters of a system as fixed and not variable. Ordinarily the control engineer may choose position, velocity, acceleration, and voltage as variables, while amplifier gain, tachometer constant, and resistance of a potentiometer are assumed to be fixed parameters. If the variable parameter is related to the primary signal, or dependent variable, the system is defined as being non-linear and the control engineer uses the analytic tools presented in this chapter. However, if the parameter's variation is caused by an external effect that is independent of the primary input, the variable parameter's variation is a function of time or of the independent variable. Although the law of superposition applies to this class of system, they present certain analytic difficulties. For example, the Bode diagram approach and root locus method are primarily applicable to linear differential equations having constant coefficients, and cannot be easily extended to the case of time-varying coefficients.

When the variations are slow relative to the feedback control system's response, a simple approach is to reduce the linear differential equation from one having variable coefficients to one with constant coefficients.[18] This approach is illustrated next. The reader should apply this approach to the time-variable, linear differential equations of Problem 7–27.

Representing the time-variable coefficients of equation 7–181 in series form and considering $x(t)$ as an mth-order polynomial, we obtain

$$(A_{n_0} + A_{n_1}t + \cdots)\frac{d^n y(t)}{dt^n} + \cdots + (A_{1_0} + A_{1_1}t + \cdots)\frac{dy(t)}{dt}$$

$$+ (A_{0_0} + A_{0_1}t + \cdots)y(t)$$

$$= (B_{m_0} + B_{m_1}t + \cdots)\frac{d^m x(t)}{dt^m} + \cdots + (B_{2_0} + B_{2_1}t + \cdots)\frac{d^2 x(t)}{dt^2}$$

$$+ (B_{1_0} + B_{1_1}t + \cdots)\frac{dx(t)}{dt} + (B_{0_0} + B_{0_1}t + \cdots)x(t) \quad (7\text{–}182)$$

where A_{nj} and B_{mj} represent the constants of t to the jth power in the coefficients of the derivatives. In order to determine the performance of the system at a specific instant of time t_1, the value of t_1 is substituted into the coefficients of equation 7–182. The resulting linear differential equation, which has constant coefficients, is given by

$$A_n \frac{d^n y(t)}{dt^n} + \cdots + A_1 \frac{dy(t)}{dt} + A_0 y(t)$$

$$= B_m \frac{d^m x(t)}{dt^m} + \cdots + B_1 \frac{dx(t)}{dt} + B_0 x(t) \quad (7\text{--}183)$$

This equation can be treated by the conventional linear techniques presented earlier, such as the Routh-Hurwitz criterion.

A method for determining ultimate stability of a time-variable limited system has been proposed by Kirby.[19,20] This technique basically determines the stability of equation 7–182 as $t \to \infty$. Kirby's method consists of forming a new equation from the coefficients of the highest order of t in the coefficient of each derivative as follows:

$$A_{n_j} s^n + \cdots + A_{1_j} s + A_{0_j} = 0 \quad (7\text{--}184)$$

The stability of equation 7–184 can be determined using any conventional method, for example, the Routh-Hurwitz criterion. The method is applicable only if the order of t in the coefficient of the highest derivative is as high as any order of t in the coefficients of the remaining derivatives. Another limitation of this method is that it only determines ultimate stability ($t \to \infty$).

Zadeh[21] has attempted to adapt transform methods to the solution of time-variable linear systems. The main disadvantage of his theory is that it is limited to slowly varying systems, or systems having small variations, in order that perturbation techniques may be used in the final stage of the analysis. This method, which is still in the developmental stage, appears to offer the most promise for solving time-variable linear systems.

REFERENCES

1. Considerations Pertaining to Nonlinear Techniques for Automatic Tracking of Ballistic Targets, S. Adelman and S. M. Shinners, presented at the 1962 Southwestern IRE Conference, Houston, Texas, April 1962.
2. Some Saturation Phenomena in Servomechanisms, E. Levinson, *Trans. AIEE*, **72**, **Pt. 2**, *Appl. Ind.*, 1 (March 1953).
3. The Generation and Extinction of Subharmonics, C. A. Ludeke, *Proceedings of the Symposium on Nonlinear Circuit Analysis*, Polytechnic Institute of Brooklyn, New York, April, 1953.
4. A Frequency Response Method for Analyzing and Synthesizing Contactor Servomechanisms, R. J. Kochenburger, *Trans. AIEE*, **69**, Pt. 2, *Appl. Ind.*, 270 (1950).
5. Sinusoidal Analysis of Feedback-Control Systems Containing Nonlinear Elements, E. C. Johnson, *Trans. AIEE*, **71**, Pt. 2, *Appl. Ind.*, 169 (July 1952).

6. Describing Function Method of Servomechanism Analysis Applied to Most Commonly Encountered Nonlinearities, H. D. Grief, *Trans. AIEE*, **72, Pt. 2,** *Appl. Ind.*, 243 (1953).
7. *Automatic Feedback Control System Synthesis*, J. G. Truxal, McGraw-Hill Book Co., New York, 1955.
8. Integrated Optimal Synthesis for a Radar Tracker, P. M. Lowitt and S. M. Shinners, presented at the Seventh National Military Electronics Convention, Washington, D.C., Sept. 1963.
9. Stability of Nonlinear Feedback Control Systems, J. F. Koenig, *Natl. Bur. Std. Rept. No.* 3619 (Aug. 1954).
10. Nonlinear Feedback Control Systems, E. Levinson, *Electro-Technol. (New York)*, 131 (Oct. 1962).
11. Designing Servos by the Phase-Plane Method, Ira Ritow, *Elec. Mfg.*, 98 (June 1956).
12. Phase-Plane Analysis, E. Levinson, *Electro-Technol. (New York)*, 118 (Aug. 1962).
13. *Engineering Cybernetics*, H. S. Tsien, McGraw-Hill Book Co., New York, 1954.
14. On the General Problem of Stability of Motion, A. M. Liapunov, Ph.D. Thesis, Kharkov, 1892, reprinted (in French) in *Annals of Mathematics Studies No. 17*, Princeton University Press, Princeton, N.J., 1949.
15. Nonlinear Techniques for Improving Servo Performance, D. McDonald, *Proceedings of the National Electronics Conference*, Vol. 6 (1950).
16. An Investigation of the Switching Criteria for Higher Order Contactor Servomechanisms, I. Bogner and L. F. Kazda, *Trans. AIEE*, **73, Pt. 2,** *Appl. Ind.*, 118 (1954).
17. Effects of Friction in an Optimum Relay Servomechanism, T. M. Stout, *Trans. AIEE*, **72, Pt. 2,** *Appl. Ind.*, 329 (1953).
18. *Handbook of Automation, Computation, and Control*, E. M. Grabbe, S. Ramo, and D. E. Wooldridge, John Wiley and Sons, New York, 1958, Vol. 1.
19. Stability of Servomechanisms with Linearly Varying Elements, M. J. Kirby, *Trans. AIEE*, **69, Pt. 2,** *Appl. Ind.*, 1662 (1950).
20. Stability of Varying-Element Servomechanisms with Polynomial Coefficients, M. J. Kirby and R. M. Guilianelli, *Trans. AIEE*, **70, Pt. 2,** *Appl. Ind.*, 1447 (1951).
21. Frequency Analysis of Variable Networks, L. A. Zadeh, *Proc. IRE*, **38,** 291 (1950).

STATISTICAL DESIGN

OF FEEDBACK CONTROL SYSTEMS

8-1. INTRODUCTION

In practical operation a feedback control system is subjected to inputs that are random functions of time. These signals cannot be expressed by simple analytic functions as we have expressed a step or a ramp input. A random signal can best be described as a function whose value, at any instant of time, is not completely determined by a knowledge of its past but varies in a random manner. Undesirable inputs may be due to external or internally generated noise sources. The general situation is illustrated in Figure 8–1.

Although it is difficult to obtain an accurate analytic description for random functions, they can be readily characterized by their statistical properties. The control engineer has found statistics, a science based on averages, to be a very powerful and useful tool for studying the effects of random signals. It is important to emphasize at this stage of the chapter's development that statistical design of feedback control systems is concerned specifically with the design of systems which are desirable on the average, but not for a particular type of input.

It is the purpose of this chapter to summarize the basic mathematical relationships of statistics and to apply them to the design of feedback control systems. Our emphasis is on physical reasoning and the implications of the relationships presented, rather than on the details of the

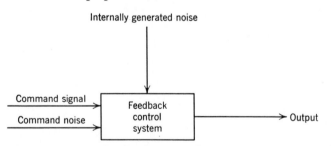

Figure 8–1. Noise sources introduced into a control system operating in a realistic environment.

mathematics. The tools of statistical design presented in this chapter will enable the control engineer to establish useful guidelines of design and to understand the practical limitations of feedback control systems operating in a realistic environment. These concepts are extended to sampled-data systems in Chapter 9 and optimal control systems in Chapter 10.

8–2. REVIEW OF PROBABILITY THEORY

The control engineer does not require a deep-rooted understanding of probability theory to be able to apply statistical design techniques intelligently to feedback control systems. He does, however, need some familiarity with the theory, since statistical design theory considers functions that are characterized by probability distributions. This section briefly considers the characteristics of probability theory that are necessary to a comprehension of statistical design techniques; they will be discussed further in this chapter. If the reader desires a more rigorous treatment of the probability theory, he should consult Refs. 1, 2, and 3.

Let us begin our discussion of probability theory by considering a *random variable*, X, which can have a value equal to any one of a finite set of real discrete numbers: $x_1, x_2, x_3, \ldots, x_n, \ldots, x_k$. This sequence of numbers is called a *random series*. The probability that X has any particular value can be described by the *probability distribution function*, $p(x_n)$, which denotes the probability that X has some value x_n. $p(x_n)$ is defined as the ratio of the number of times that X takes on the value x_n to the total number of samples. The probability $p(x_n)$ is a real number having a value varying between zero and unity. It can be expressed as

$$\sum_{n=1}^{k} p(x_n) = 1 \tag{8–1}$$

When the random variable X is a continuous function, the process is called a *random function*. The *probability distribution function*, $p(x)$, of a random variable that is continuous must be defined in a different manner. Let us define the *probability* that X takes on a value in the interval $x \leqslant X \leqslant x + dx$, as $p(x)\, dx$. The probability distribution function must satisfy the following relationship.

$$\int_{-\infty}^{\infty} p(x)\, dx = 1 \tag{8–2}$$

where $p(x) \geqslant 0$. If a certain value of X has a finite probability of occurrence, the probability distribution function $p(x)$ at that point is a delta function whose area equals the value of the probability.

If a random variable X can take on any one of a continuous set of values, then the probability that it takes on a particular value is zero. This does not mean that the event cannot occur, but that the proportion of times it does occur is zero. By similar reasoning, a probability of unity does not mean that a certain event will occur, but that the proportion of times that it does not occur is zero. If the number of possible cases is finite, however, a probability of zero does imply an impossible situation and a probability of unity implies a certainty.

The *arithmetic mean*, $\bar{x}$, is a convenient mathematical measure of the point about which the values of the random variable X are concentrated. It is defined by the expression

$$\bar{x} = \int_{-\infty}^{\infty} x p(x)\, dx \tag{8-3}$$

A measure of the scattering of the values about the arithmetic mean, known as the *dispersion of the distribution*, is usually measured in terms of the moments of $p(x)$ about the arithmetic mean $\bar{x}$. This can be expressed by the relationship

$$\overline{x^n} = \int_{-\infty}^{\infty} (x - \bar{x})^n p(x)\, dx \tag{8-4}$$

For all possible situations, $\overline{x^0}$ equals unity and $\overline{x^1}$ equals zero. The second moment, which is also called the *variance*, is the most significant higher-order moment for the analysis of random signals in linear systems. The square root of the second moment is called the standard deviation, σ. When $\bar{x}$ is zero, $\overline{x^2}$ is defined as the mean-square value of the random variable and is proportional to the average power of systems.

The probability distribution function can have a great variety of shapes. From a mathematical point of view, it is advantageous if the exact distribution curves are approximated by some relatively simple mathematical relation. In control system engineering, we are most interested in the constant and Gaussian distributions.

A *constant distribution function* refers to a random variable x whose value in an interval between x_1 and x_2 is likely to be constant. Therefore, the probability density $p(x)$ is a constant in that interval. It is also assumed that the random variable cannot exist outside this interval. The probability density can be expressed as

$$p(x) = \frac{1}{x_2 - x_1} \tag{8-5}$$

where $x_1 < x < x_2$. The arithmetic mean is expressed as

$$\bar{x} = \frac{x_2 + x_1}{2} \tag{8-6}$$

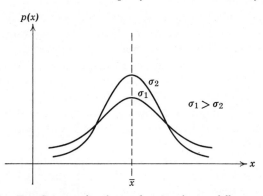

Figure 8–2. Two Gaussian distribution functions having different variances.

and the variance is given by the relation

$$\sigma^2 = \frac{(x_2 - x_1)^2}{12} \tag{8-7}$$

The *Gaussian distribution* is very important because it occurs in many practical situations. For example, the amplitude of the thermal-noise voltage appearing across a resistor, caused by the random motion of electrons, has a Gaussian distribution. Perhaps the most important property of the Gaussian distribution relates to the design of an optimum noise filter. If the input to the filter is signal and noise, both possessing Gaussian distributions, a linear filter is optimum. Improvement in filtering cannot be obtained by going to nonlinear devices. The Gaussian distribution is defined by the expression

$$p(x) = \frac{1}{\sqrt{2\pi}\,\sigma} \exp\left[-\frac{(x - \bar{x})^2}{2\sigma^2} \right] \tag{8-8}$$

where $\bar{x}$ is the mean value of the distribution and σ^2 is the variance.

Figure 8–2 illustrates the general bell-shaped curves of the Gaussian distribution function for two values of the variance. Notice that the variance is a measure of the rapidity with which the distribution drops off.

8–3. THE STATIONARY RANDOM FUNCTION

The control engineer is particularly concerned with a class of random functions possessing the property of *stationariness*. A random function is stationary when it is defined from $-\infty$ to $+\infty$, and its statistical characteristics are not changed by a shift of the function in time. For example, the statistical characteristics of the random function are the same over the time interval from T to ∞, where T can have any value over the time interval of interest. The thermal-noise voltage appearing across a resistor is a stationary random function since the statistical characteristics of noise are independent of the choice of an origin in time as long as the temperature of the resistor is constant. However, if the temperature of the resistor changes with time, then the statistical characteristics of the thermal-noise voltage change. Then the system would classify as a nonstationary random process.

We further assume that stationary random functions are members of a group of functions, or an *ensemble*, which possesses the property of *ergodicity*. The ergodic property implies that all members of the group of functions have the same statistical characteristic. Therefore, a statistical characteristic measured from one particular function has the same value as would be obtained from measurements over the entire ensemble. Basically, ergodicity implies that the initial conditions are negligible after a sufficient length of time.

8-4. STATISTICAL CHARACTERISTICS[4]

When the feedback control system under consideration is linear and the signals all possess the property of stationariness and ergodicity, the correlation function and the power-density spectrum contain all the necessary statistical information for design. We define these statistical characteristics here and apply them to practical systems in the succeeding sections. Statistical characteristics of linear sampled-data systems are discussed in Chapter 9. Continuous and sampled-data systems containing signals which do not possess the properties of stationariness and ergodicity are considered from the modern optimal control theory approach in Chapter 10.

A very useful statistical description of a stationary random function of time $x(t)$ is the *autocorrelation function*. It is defined by the expression

$$\phi_{xx}(\tau) = \lim_{T \to \infty} \frac{1}{2T} \int_{-T}^{+T} x(t)x(t + \tau)\, dt \qquad (8\text{–}9)$$

The autocorrelation function has the following properties for a stationary random function:

a. $\phi_{xx}(\tau)$ is an even function where

$$\phi_{xx}(\tau) = \phi_{xx}(-\tau) \qquad (8\text{–}10)$$

b. $\phi_{xx}(0)$ equals the mean-square value of the signal $\overline{x^2}$ and is proportional to the average power of the system, P_{avg}.

$$\phi_{xx}(0) = \overline{x^2} \propto P_{\text{avg}} \tag{8-11}$$

c. $\phi_{xx}(\tau)$ is independent of shifting the origin in time.

d. $\phi_{xx}(\tau) \leqslant \phi_{xx}(0)$ for $|\tau| > 0$

When a system contains two stationary random inputs x and y, the correlation function is expressed by the *crosscorrelation* function. It is defined by the expression

$$\phi_{xy}(\tau) = \lim_{T \to \infty} \frac{1}{2T} \int_{-T}^{T} x(t)y(t + \tau)\, dt \tag{8-12}$$

The crosscorrelation function has the following properties for stationary random functions.

a. $\phi_{xy}(\tau)$ is not an even function. However, it does satisfy the relationship given by

$$\phi_{xy}(\tau) = \phi_{xy}(-\tau) \tag{8-13}$$

b. $\phi_{xy}(\tau)$ is independent of shifting the origin in time.

Correlation functions basically describe signals in terms of characteristics in the time domain. In many cases it is convenient to describe the signals in terms of frequency domain characteristics. This may be accomplished by obtaining the Fourier transform of the autocorrelation function. This description, which is called the *power-density* spectrum, $\Phi(\omega)$, is defined by the complex integral

$$\Phi(\omega) = \int_{-\infty}^{\infty} \phi_{xx}(\tau)\, e^{-j\omega\tau}\, d\tau \tag{8-14}$$

The power-density spectrum represents a measure of the distribution of energy in the frequency spectrum. Its units are volts^2/radian/second for a voltage waveform. The power-density spectrum has the following important properties:

a. $\Phi(\omega)$ is a real, positive, number at all frequencies.

b. $\Phi(\omega)$ is an even function of frequency where

$$\Phi(\omega) = \Phi(-\omega) \tag{8-15}$$

c. $\Phi(\omega)$ measures the power-density spectrum rather than the amplitude or phase spectrum of the signal. Therefore, the relative phase of the various frequency components is lost, and a given power-density spectrum may actually correspond to a large number of different time functions.

It is interesting to note that the autocorrelation function can be obtained from the power-density spectrum by taking the inverse transform of equation 8–14 as follows:

$$\phi_{xx}(\tau) = \frac{1}{2\pi} \int_{-\infty}^{\infty} \Phi(\omega)\, e^{j\omega\tau}\, d\omega \qquad (8\text{–}16)$$

An expression for the mean-square value of the signal, which is also proportional to the average power, can be obtained by setting $\tau = 0$. The result is

$$P_{\text{avg}} \propto \text{MSV} = \overline{x^2} = \phi_{xx}(0) = \frac{1}{2\pi} \int_{-\infty}^{\infty} \Phi(\omega)\, d\omega \qquad (8\text{–}17)$$

This expression is equal to the average power if the signal is considered as the voltage across a 1-ohm resistor. The average power in any frequency band can be obtained by replacing the infinite limits of the integral of equation 8–17 by the appropriate limits corresponding to the frequency band of interest.

8–5. DETERMINATION OF THE STATISTICAL CHARACTERISTICS FOR SOME SIMPLE WAVEFORMS

Let us next apply the theory to some simple waveforms—specifically, a sine wave, white noise, and a typical random function.

A *sine wave* cannot be classified as a random function. However, most random functions contain sinusoidal signal components, and it is important to determine their effect on the overall autocorrelation function. It is important to emphasize at this point that time functions which can be expressed by analytical techniques should be handled in this manner and not by statistical methods. Therefore, when this situation occurs the sine wave should be subtracted from the original signal, and the resulting random function should be treated by statistical techniques.

The autocorrelation function for the sine wave, given by the following equation, is determined from the definition given by equation 8–9:

$$e(t) = E \sin (\omega t + \theta) \qquad (8\text{–}18)$$

Substituting equation 8–18 into equation 8–9, we obtain

$$\phi_{ee}(\tau) = \lim_{T \to \infty} \frac{1}{2T} \int_{-T}^{T} E \sin (\omega t + \theta) E \sin [\omega(t + \tau) + \theta]\, dt \qquad (8\text{–}19)$$

Since the function inside the integral is periodic in nature, the limits of integration may be considered only over one period and division need take place only over a single period. This results in the following expression:

$$\phi_{ee}(\tau) = \frac{\omega}{2\pi} E^2 \int_0^{2\pi/\omega} \sin(\omega t + \theta) \sin(\omega t + \theta + \omega\tau) \, dt \qquad (8\text{–}20)$$

Integration can be simplified by changing the variable from $\omega t + \theta$ to an arbitrary variable α:

$$\omega t + \theta = \alpha \qquad (8\text{–}21)$$

Substituting equation 8–21 into equation 8–20, we obtain

$$\phi_{ee}(\tau) = \frac{E^2}{2\pi} \int_\theta^{\theta+2\pi} \sin \alpha \sin(\alpha + \omega\tau) \, d\alpha \qquad (8\text{–}22)$$

The integral of equation 8–22 can be evaluated quite easily by standard expansion techniques with the following result:

$$\phi_{ee}(\tau) = \frac{E^2}{2} \cos \omega\tau \qquad (8\text{–}23)$$

Notice that the autocorrelation function of the sinusoidal waveform retains the amplitude and frequency information of the original waveform, but ignores the phase angle θ. Therefore, two sinusoidal signals having the same amplitude and frequency, but different phase angles, have the same autocorrelation functions.

White noise is usually defined as a random function having a frequency spectrum that is flat over the entire frequency spectrum. The autocorrelation function of this random function is an impulse at $\tau = 0$ and is zero at all other values of τ. In practical systems, white noise is considered a random function that has a flat frequency spectrum containing a finite amount of power over a relatively wide frequency range. The autocorrelation function corresponding to the theoretical case is an extremely narrow spike centered about $\tau = 0$. For the practical, it is a $(\sin x/x)$ function. The power-density spectrum and autocorrelation function for both cases of white noise are illustrated in Figure 8–3 and 8–4, respectively.

Figure 8–5 shows a *typical random function*, which may correspond to the motion of an airplane in a turbulent atmosphere or that of a ship in a rough sea. The corresponding autocorrelation function, shown in Figure 8–6, can be obtained by several methods, all based on the definition of $\phi_{xx}(\tau)$ given by equation 8–9. Although several devices can automatically compute the autocorrelation function, let us assume that they are unavailable to the reader and it is necessary to obtain $\phi_{xx}(\tau)$ graphically. The graphical evaluation consists of shifting the random function τ seconds, multiplying the functions $x(t)$ and $x(t + \tau)$, and then averaging over a

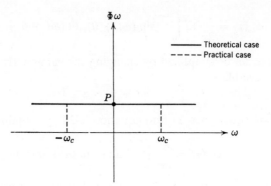

Figure 8–3.   Power-density spectrum for white noise.

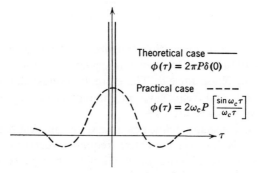

Figure 8–4.   Autocorrelation function for white noise.

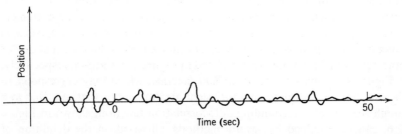

Figure 8–5.   Typical motion of an airplane in a turbulent atmosphere or that of a ship in a rough sea.

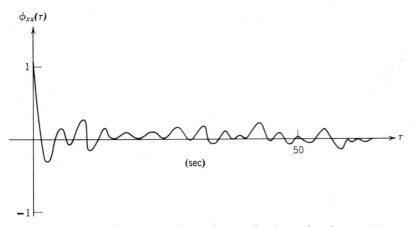

$\phi_{xx}(\tau)$

Figure 8–6.   Corresponding autocorrelation function for the random function shown in Figure 8–5.

finite interval Δt. In addition, the infinite limits of equation 8–9 must be replaced with finite limits. The autocorrelation function can be computed graphically from the following expression.

$$\phi_{xx}(\tau) = \frac{1}{N} \sum_{i=1}^{N} x(t)x(t + \tau) \Delta t \qquad (8\text{--}24)$$

The corresponding power-density spectrum, shown in Figure 8–7, can be obtained directly from the autocorrelation function by solving for its Fourier transform.

Since all techniques for obtaining the autocorrelation function and power-density spectrum are limited to a finite amount of time, the results obtained are not exact but only approximations. As the sampling time increases, the variations of the measured functions decrease. Practically, the sample length should be at least ten times the period of the smallest

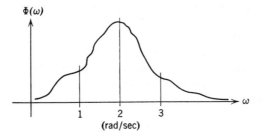

$\Phi(\omega)$

Figure 8–7.   Corresponding power-density spectrum for the random function shown in Figure 8–5.

significant frequency component present. However, since the power-density spectra of most signals found in control systems go all the way to zero radians/seconds, this is not always feasible. Generally it is necessary to evaluate several samples and compare the results. If an appreciable variation does not exist, it is safe to assume that the sampled length is sufficient. If the measured functions continue to fluctuate, however, it may not be possible to assume that the function has the properties of stationariness and ergodicity.

Detailed examination of Figures 8–5 and 8–6 indicates that the signal and autocorrelation function are somewhat periodic but have a random variation from a pure sine wave. Detailed examination of Figure 8–7 indicates that the power-density spectrum is concentrated in a narrow band of frequencies lying between 1 and 3 radians/second. About 80% of the energy is concentrated in this band of frequencies. In addition, the frequency band of interest is in the very low portion of the spectrum, and this introduces practical limitations in the determination of the statistical data.

It is important to emphasize that the motion of an airplane flying in turbulence or that of a ship in rough seas is not, strictly speaking, a stationary process. For example, location, direction, speed, wind, and atmospheric and sea conditions will change somewhat with time. This will result in changes of the characteristics of motion. For limited periods of time, however, which are long compared with the duration of the auto-correlation function, the random function is reasonably stationary.

8–6. BASIC STATISTICAL RELATIONS FOR LINEAR SYSTEMS

It is of great interest to the control engineer to determine the effect of a random signal having the properties of stationariness and ergodicity on a linear system. It is extremely difficult to determine this by utilizing the autocorrelation function in the time domain. However, by utilizing the power-density spectrum in the frequency domain, it is possible to apply transform methods in order to obtain relations between the input and the output of the linear system.

Consider the simple linear system illustrated in Figure 8–8. It has a transfer function $G(j\omega)$ and a random input $r(t)$, which has the statistical properties of stationariness and ergodicity. Assuming that the power-density spectrum of the input is $\Phi_r(\omega)$, the power-density spectrum of the

$$\xrightarrow[\Phi_r(\omega)]{r(t)} \boxed{G(j\omega)} \xrightarrow[\Phi_c(\omega)]{c(t)}$$

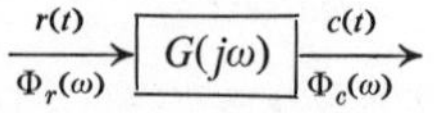

Figure 8–8. General linear system having a random input.

output is given by the following expression:

$$\Phi_c(\omega) = G(j\omega)\overline{(G(j\omega)}\Phi_r(\omega) \tag{8–25}$$

where $\overline{G(j\omega)}$ is the complex conjugate of $G(j\omega)$. This is usually written as

$$\Phi_c(\omega) = |G(j\omega)|^2\Phi_r(\omega) \tag{8–26}$$

In equation 8–26 $|G(j\omega)|^2$ may be interpreted as a weighting function which amplifies those frequency components about the resonant frequencies of the system and attenuates those component frequencies further removed. Observe from equation 8–26 that the phase of $G(j\omega)$ is not a factor in determining the power-density spectrum of the output.

If the amplitudes of the input to the linear system shown in Figure 8–8 have a Gaussian distribution, the distribution of the amplitudes of the output is also Gaussian. However, its mean-square value and variance will probably be different. In addition, if the amplitude distribution of the input is not Gaussian, the amplitude distribution of the output is generally not the same as that of the input.

By utilizing equation 8–17 and assuming that the signal exists across a 1-ohm resistor, the mean-square value, or average power, of the input to the linear system shown in Figure 8–8 can be obtained from the following expression:

$$\mathrm{MSV}_r = P_{\mathrm{avg}_r} = \frac{1}{2\pi} \int_{-\infty}^{\infty} \Phi_r(\omega)\, d\omega \tag{8–27}$$

Similarly, the mean-square value of the output can be obtained from the following expression:

$$\mathrm{MSV}_c = P_{\mathrm{avg}_c} = \frac{1}{2\pi} \int_{-\infty}^{\infty} \Phi_c(\omega)\, d\omega \tag{8–28}$$

The complex characteristics of the integrals in equations 8–27 and 8–28 usually make them very difficult to evaluate. However, when $\Phi_r(\omega)$ and/or $\Phi_c(\omega)$ are in rational form, these integrals may be evaluated using Table 8–1.

To illustrate the use of Table 8–1, let us consider the system illustrated in Figure 8–9. A simple linear feedback control system is subjected to a

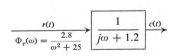

Figure 8–9.   Linear system having a random input.

Table 8–1. Table of integrals*

The following is a table of integrals of the type

$$I_n = \frac{1}{2\pi j} \int_{-\infty}^{\infty} dx \, \frac{g_n(x)}{h_n(x)h_n(-x)},$$

where

$$h_n(x) = A_0 x^n + A_1 x^{n-1} + \cdots + A_n,$$
$$g_n(x) = B_0 x^{2n-2} + B_1 x^{2n-4} + \cdots + B_{n-1},$$

and the roots of $h_n(x)$ all lie in the left half plane. The table lists the integrals I_n for values of n from 1 to 7 inclusive.

$$I_1 = \frac{B_0}{2A_0 A_1}$$

$$I_2 = \frac{-B_0 + A_0 B_1/A_2}{2A_0 A_1}$$

$$I_3 = \frac{-A_2 B_0 + A_0 B_1 - A_0 A_1 B_2/A_3}{2A_0(A_0 A_3 - A_1 A_2)}$$

$$I_4 = \frac{B_0(-A_1 A_4 + A_2 A_3) - A_0 A_3 B_1 + A_0 A_1 B_2 + (A_0 B_3/A_4)(A_0 A_3 - A_1 A_2)}{2A_0(A_0 A_3^2 + A_1^3 A_4 - A_1 A_2 A_3)}$$

$$I_5 = \frac{M_5}{2A_0 \, \Delta_5}$$

where

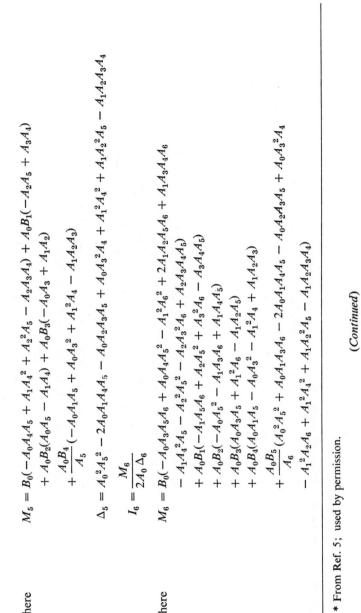

$$M_5 = B_0(-A_0A_4A_5 + A_1A_4^2 + A_2^2A_5 - A_2A_3A_4) + A_0B_1(-A_2A_5 + A_3A_4)$$
$$+ A_0B_2(A_0A_5 - A_1A_4) + A_0B_3(-A_0A_3 + A_1A_2)$$
$$+ \frac{A_0B_4}{A_5}(-A_0A_1A_5 + A_0A_3^2 + A_1^2A_4 - A_1A_2A_3)$$

$$\Delta_5 = A_0^2A_5^2 - 2A_0A_1A_4A_5 - A_0A_2A_3A_5 + A_0A_3^2A_4 + A_1^2A_4^2 + A_1A_2^2A_5 - A_1A_2A_3A_4$$

$$I_6 = \frac{M_6}{2A_0\,\Delta_6}$$

where

$$M_6 = B_0(-A_0A_3A_5A_6 + A_0A_4A_5^2 - A_1A_6^2 + 2A_1A_2A_5A_6 + A_1A_3A_4A_6$$
$$- A_1A_4^2A_5 - A_2^2A_5^2 - A_2A_3^2A_6 + A_2A_3A_4A_5)$$
$$+ A_0B_1(-A_1A_5A_6 + A_2A_5^2 + A_3^2A_6 - A_3A_4A_5)$$
$$+ A_0B_2(-A_0A_5^2 - A_1A_3A_6 + A_1A_4A_5)$$
$$+ A_0B_3(A_0A_3A_5 + A_1^2A_6 - A_1A_2A_5)$$
$$+ A_0B_4(A_0A_1A_5 - A_0A_3^2 - A_1^2A_4 + A_1A_2A_3)$$
$$+ \frac{A_0B_5}{A_6}(A_0^2A_5^2 + A_0A_1A_3A_6 - 2A_0A_1A_4A_5 - A_0A_2A_3A_5 + A_0A_3^2A_4$$
$$- A_1^2A_2A_6 + A_1^2A_4^2 + A_1A_2^2A_5 - A_1A_2A_3A_4)$$

(Continued)

* From **Ref. 5**; used by permission.

Table 8–1 (continued).   Table of integrals

$$\Delta_6 = A_0^2 A_5^3 + 3A_0 A_1 A_3 A_5 A_6 - 2A_0 A_1 A_4 A_5^2 - A_0 A_2 A_3 A_5^2 - A_0 A_3^3 A_6$$
$$+ A_0 A_3^2 A_4 A_5 + A_1^3 A_6^2 - 2A_1^2 A_2 A_5 A_6 - A_1^2 A_3 A_4 A_6 + A_1^2 A_4^2 A_5 + A_1 A_2^2 A_5^2$$
$$+ A_1 A_2 A_3^2 A_6 - A_1 A_2 A_3 A_4 A_5$$

$$I_7 = \frac{M_7}{2A_0 \, \Delta_7}$$

where

$$M_7 = B_0 m_0 + A_0 B_1 m_1 + A_0 B_2 m_2 + \cdots + A_0 B_6 m_6$$

$$m_0 = A_0^2 A_6 A_7^2 - 2A_0 A_1 A_6^2 A_7 - 2A_0 A_2 A_4 A_7^2 + A_0 A_2 A_5 A_6 A_7 + A_0 A_3 A_5 A_6^2$$
$$+ A_0 A_4^2 A_5 A_7 - A_0 A_4 A_5^2 A_6 + A_1^2 A_6^3 + 3A_1 A_2 A_4 A_6 A_7 - 2A_1 A_2 A_5 A_6^2$$
$$- A_1 A_3 A_4 A_6^2 - A_1 A_4^3 A_7 + A_1 A_4^2 A_5 A_6 + A_2^3 A_7^2 - 2A_2^2 A_3 A_6 A_7$$
$$- A_2^2 A_4 A_5 A_7 + A_2^2 A_5^2 A_6 + A_2 A_3 A_4^2 A_7 - A_2 A_3 A_4 A_5 A_6 + A_2 A_3^2 A_6^2$$

$$m_1 = A_0 A_4 A_7^2 - A_0 A_5 A_6 A_7 - A_1 A_4 A_6 A_7 + A_1 A_4 A_6 A_7 + A_1 A_5 A_6^2 - A_2^2 A_7^2 + 2A_2 A_3 A_6 A_7$$
$$+ A_2 A_4 A_5 A_7 - A_2 A_5^2 A_6 - A_3 A_4^2 A_7 + A_3 A_4 A_5 A_6$$

$$m_2 = A_0 A_2 A_7^2 - A_0 A_3 A_6 A_7 - A_0 A_4 A_5 A_7 + A_0 A_5^2 A_6 - A_1 A_2 A_6 A_7$$
$$+ A_1 A_3 A_6^2 + A_1 A_4^2 A_7 - A_1 A_4 A_5 A_6$$

$$m_3 = -A_0^2 A_7^2 + 2A_0 A_1 A_6 A_7 + A_0 A_3 A_4 A_7 - A_0 A_3 A_5 A_6 - A_1^2 A_6^2 - A_1 A_2 A_4 A_7$$
$$+ A_1 A_2 A_5 A_6$$

$$m_4 = A_0^2 A_5 A_7 - A_0 A_1 A_4 A_7 - A_0 A_1 A_5 A_6 - A_0 A_2 A_3 A_7 + A_0 A_3^2 A_6$$
$$+ A_1^2 A_4 A_6 + A_1 A_2^2 A_7 - A_1 A_2 A_3 A_6$$

$$m_5 = A_0^2 A_3 A_7 - A_0^2 A_5^2 - A_0 A_1 A_2 A_7 - A_0 A_1 A_3 A_6 + 2A_0 A_1 A_4 A_5$$
$$+ A_0 A_2 A_3 A_5 - A_0 A_3^2 A_4 + A_1^2 A_2 A_6 - A_1^2 A_4^2 - A_1 A_2^2 A_5 + A_1 A_2 A_3 A_4$$

$$m_6 = \frac{1}{A_7}(A_0^2 A_1 A_7^2 - 2A_0^2 A_3 A_5 A_7 + A_0^2 A_5^3 - 2A_0 A_1^2 A_6 A_7 + A_0 A_1 A_2 A_5 A_7$$
$$+ 3A_0 A_1 A_3 A_5 A_6 - 2A_0 A_1 A_4 A_5^2 + A_0 A_2 A_3^2 A_7 - A_0 A_2 A_3 A_5^2 - A_0 A_3^3 A_6$$
$$+ A_0 A_3^2 A_4 A_5 + A_1^3 A_6^2 + A_1^2 A_2 A_4 A_7 - 2A_1^2 A_2 A_5 A_6 - A_1^2 A_3 A_4 A_6$$
$$+ A_1^2 A_4^2 A_5 - A_1 A_2^2 A_3 A_7 + A_1 A_2^2 A_5^2 + A_1 A_2 A_3^2 A_6 - A_1 A_2 A_3 A_4 A_5)$$

$$\Delta_7 = -A_0^3 A_7^3 + 3A_0^2 A_1 A_6 A_7^2 + A_0^2 A_2 A_5 A_7^2 + 2A_0^2 A_3 A_4 A_7^2$$
$$- 3A_0^2 A_3 A_5 A_6 A_7 - A_0^2 A_4 A_5^2 A_7 + A_0^2 A_5^3 A_6 - 3A_0 A_1^2 A_6^2 A_7$$
$$- 3A_0 A_1 A_2 A_4 A_7^2 + A_0 A_1 A_2 A_5 A_6 A_7 + 3A_0 A_1 A_3 A_5 A_6^2 - A_0 A_1 A_3 A_4 A_6 A_7$$
$$+ 2A_0 A_1 A_4^2 A_5 A_7 - 2A_0 A_1 A_4 A_5^2 A_6 - A_0 A_2^2 A_3 A_7^2 + 2A_0 A_2^2 A_3 A_6 A_7$$
$$+ A_0 A_2 A_3 A_4 A_5 A_7 - A_0 A_3^2 A_5^2 A_6 - A_0 A_3^3 A_6^2 - A_0 A_3^2 A_4^2 A_7$$
$$+ A_0 A_3^2 A_4 A_5 A_6 + A_1^3 A_6^3 + 3A_1^2 A_2 A_4 A_6 A_7 - 2A_1^2 A_2 A_5 A_6^2$$
$$- A_1^2 A_3 A_4 A_6^2 - A_1^2 A_4^3 A_7 + A_1^2 A_4^2 A_5 A_6 + A_1 A_2^3 A_7^2 - 2A_1 A_2^2 A_3 A_6 A_7$$
$$- A_1 A_2^2 A_4 A_5 A_7 + A_1 A_2^2 A_5^2 A_6 + A_1 A_2 A_3^2 A_6^2 + A_1 A_2 A_3 A_4^2 A_7$$
$$- A_1 A_2 A_3 A_4 A_5 A_6$$

random input function described by a power-density spectrum given by the following expression.

$$\Phi_r(\omega) = \frac{2.8}{\omega^2 + 25} \tag{8-29}$$

The feedback control system has an overall response which is adequately described by the following transfer function:

$$\frac{C(j\omega)}{R(j\omega)} = \frac{1}{j\omega + 1.2} \tag{8-30}$$

We wish to determine and compare the average power of the input signal and the resulting output of the system. Both signals will be assumed to exist across 1-ohm resistances.

The average power, or mean-square value, of the input signal can be obtained by substituting equation 8–29 into equation 8–27:

$$P_{\text{avg}_r} = \frac{1}{2\pi} \int_{-\infty}^{\infty} \frac{2.8}{\omega^2 + 25} \, d\omega \tag{8-31}$$

In order to evaluate this integral utilizing Table 8–1, equation 8–31 is written as follows:

$$P_{\text{avg}_r} = \frac{1}{2\pi j} \int_{-\infty}^{\infty} \frac{j2.8}{(5 + j\omega)(5 - j\omega)} \, d\omega \tag{8-32}$$

In order to utilize Table 8–1 and obtain the constants necessary to evaluate this integral, we compare the numerator and denominator of equation 8–32 to the numerator and denominator of the general equation given in Table 8–1. The results are as follows:

$$h_n(x) = A_0 x^n + A_1 x^{n-1} + \cdots + A_n = 5 + j\omega$$
$$\therefore \quad A_0 = j$$
$$A_1 = 5 \tag{8-33}$$
$$n = 1$$

and

$$g_n(x) = B_0 x^{2n-2} + B_1 x^{2n-4} + \cdots + B_{n-1} = j2.8$$
$$\therefore \quad B_0 = j2.8 \tag{8-34}$$
$$n = 1$$

Since $n = 1$, the solution to equation 8–32 is obtained from I_1 of Table 8–1 as follows:

$$I_1 = \frac{B_0}{2A_0 A_1} \tag{8-35}$$

Substituting the constants, previously determined, into equation 8–35, we obtain

$$P_{avg_r} = I_1 = \frac{j2.8}{2(j)(5)} = 0.28 \text{ watts} \tag{8-36}$$

Therefore the average power of the input signal is 0.28 watts assuming that the signal is considered as the voltage across a 1-ohm resistor.

In order to obtain the average power, or mean-square value, of the output signal, we must first determine the power-density spectrum of the output. This can be obtained by substituting equations 8–29 and 8–30 into equation 8–26 as follows:

$$\Phi_c(\omega) = \left| \frac{1}{j\omega + 1.2} \right|^2 \frac{2.8}{\omega^2 + 25} \tag{8-37}$$

This can be rewritten as follows:

$$\Phi_c(\omega) = \frac{2.8}{(\omega^2 + 1.44)(\omega^2 + 25)} \tag{8-38}$$

The average power of the output signal can be obtained by substituting equation 8–38 into equation 8–28:

$$P_{avg_c} = \frac{1}{2\pi} \int_{-\infty}^{\infty} \frac{2.8}{(\omega^2 + 1.44)(\omega^2 + 25)} d\omega \tag{8-39}$$

In order to evaluate the integral using Table 8–1, we rewrite equation 8–39 as

$$P_{avg_c} = \frac{1}{2\pi j} \int_{-\infty}^{\infty} \frac{j2.8}{(5 + j\omega)(1.2 + j\omega)(5 - j\omega)(1.2 - j\omega)} d\omega \tag{8-40}$$

In order to use Table 8–1 and obtain the constants necessary to evaluate this integral, we compare the numerator and denominator of equation 8–40 to the numerator and denominator of the general equation given in Table 8–1, as follows:

$$h_n(x) = A_0 x^n + A_1 x^{n-1} + \cdots + A_n = (5 + j\omega)(1.2 + j\omega)$$
$$= -\omega^2 + 6.2j\omega + 6$$
$$\therefore \quad A_0 = -1$$
$$A_1 = j6.2 \tag{8-41}$$
$$A_2 = 6$$
$$n = 2$$

and

$$g_n(x) = B_0 x^{2n-2} + B_1 x^{2n-4} + \cdots + B_{n-1} = j2.8$$
$$\therefore \quad B_0 = 0$$
$$B_1 = j2.8 \tag{8-42}$$
$$n = 2$$

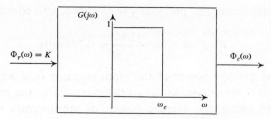

Figure 8–10. Ideal low-pass filter having an input of white noise.

Since $n = 2$, the solution to equation 8–40 is obtained from I_2 of Table 8–1 as

$$I_2 = \frac{-B_0 + A_0 B_1/A_2}{2A_0 A_1} \tag{8–43}$$

Substituting the constants, previously determined, into equation 8–43, we obtain

$$P_{\text{avg}_c} = I_2 = \frac{-0 - 1(j2.8)/6}{2(-1)(j6.2)} = 0.0376 \text{ watts} \tag{8–44}$$

Therefore the average power of the output signal is 0.0376 watts assuming that the signal is considered as the voltage across a 1-ohm resistor.

It is interesting to note that the average power of the input signal is 0.28 watts while that of the output from the linear feedback system is only 0.0376 watts. This is reasonable since the feedback system illustrated is basically a low-pass filter which attenuates most of the power of the random input signal. This very important result is physically justifiable.

We shall next demonstrate that the average power at the output of an idealized low-pass filter due to a random input is directly proportional to the bandwidth. Let us consider the system illustrated in Figure 8–10, where an ideal low-pass filter having a cutoff frequency ω_c has an input of white noise whose power-density spectrum is given by the expression

$$\Phi_r(\omega) = K \tag{8–45}$$

From equation 8–26, the power-density spectrum of the output is given by the following expression:

$$\Phi_c(\omega) = |G(j\omega)|^2 \Phi_r(\omega)]_{\omega = -\omega_c \text{ to } \omega_c} = (1)^2 K = K \tag{8–46}$$

Therefore, assuming that the signal exists across a 1-ohm resistor, the average power of the output, or mean-square value, is given by the expression

$$P_{\text{avg}_c} = \frac{1}{2\pi} \int_{-\omega_c}^{\omega_c} K \, d\omega = \frac{K\omega_c}{\pi} \tag{8–47}$$

and it can easily be seen that the average power at the output of a system due to a random input is directly proportional to the bandwidth. Feedback control systems should be designed to have a sufficiently wide bandwidth in order that they do not attenuate the desired portion of the frequency spectrum. However, once a sufficient response is obtained, increasing the bandwidth further will primarily increase the output due to random noise fluctuations and degrade the system's performance.

8-7. THE ROOT-MEAN-SQUARE ERROR CRITERION FOR MINIMIZING THE EFFECTS OF NOISE[6]

The root-mean-square error criterion for minimizing the effects of noise has been presented previously in Section 4–7 as a measure of performance. We shall review it briefly and extend the concept for practical application to control problems based on the statistical tools that have been presented in this chapter.

For a system having inputs of signal and noise, the root-mean-square error is defined as the average value of the square of the difference between the actual system output, $c_a(t)$, and the desired system output, $c_d(t)$. It is expressed by the following relation:

$$\overline{e^2} = \lim_{T \to \infty} \frac{1}{2T} \int_{-T}^{T} [c_a(t) - c_d(t)]^2 \, dt \tag{8-48}$$

Figure 8–11 gives a good pictorial insight into the fundamental relationship stated by equation 8–48. $G_r(j\omega)$ represents the transfer function of the

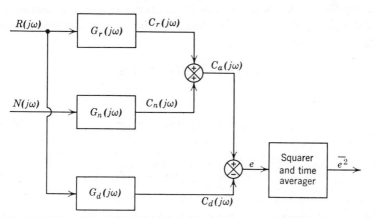

Figure 8–11. A system optimizing procedure to minimize the effects of noise.

control system to the signal component $R(j\omega)$, and $G_n(j\omega)$ represents the transfer function of the control system to the noise component, $N(j\omega)$. The outputs due to the signal component, $C_r(j\omega)$, and the noise components, $C_n(j\omega)$, combine to give an actual output, $C_a(j\omega)$. The desired control system transfer function to the signal component is defined as $G_d(j\omega)$. The time average of the square of the difference between the actual system response $C_a(j\omega)$ and the desired systems response $C_d(j\omega)$ is the factor to be minimized.

1. Derivation of the Root-Mean-Square Error

Let us derive the general expression of the root-mean-square error $\overline{e^2}$ for the system shown in Figure 8–11. Since the actual output is the sum of the outputs due to the signal component and the noise component, equation 8–48 may be rewritten in the following form:

$$\overline{e^2} = \lim_{T \to \infty} \frac{1}{2T} \int_{-T}^{T} [(c_r(t) - c_d(t)) + c_n(t)]^2 \, dt \tag{8–49}$$

Expansion of equation 8–49 results in

$$\overline{e^2} = \lim_{T \to \infty} \frac{1}{2T} \int_{-T}^{T} \{[c_r(t) - c_d(t)]^2 + c_n{}^2(t) + 2c_n(t)[c_r(t) - c_d(t)]\} \, dt \tag{8–50}$$

In order that the root-mean-square error may be obtained in terms of the input signals and the characteristics of the control system, it is necessary to express $c_r(t)$, $c_d(t)$, and $c_n(t)$ in forms of their respective superposition integrals as follows:

$$c_r(t) = \int_{-\infty}^{\infty} g_r(\tau) r(t - \tau) \, d\tau \tag{8–51}$$

$$c_d(t) = \int_{-\infty}^{\infty} g_d(\tau) r(t - \tau) \, d\tau \tag{8–52}$$

$$c_n(t) = \int_{-\infty}^{\infty} g_n(\tau) n(t - \tau) \, d\tau \tag{8–53}$$

Substituting equations 8–51, 8–52, and 8–53 into equation 8–50 yields the following:

$$
\begin{aligned}
\overline{e^2} = \lim_{T \to \infty} \frac{1}{2T} \int_{-T}^{T} & \left[\left(\int_{-\infty}^{\infty} g_r(\tau) r(t - \tau) \, d\tau - \int_{-\infty}^{\infty} g_d(\tau) r(t - \tau) \, d\tau \right)^2 \right. \\
& + \left(\int_{-\infty}^{\infty} g_n(\tau) n(t - \tau) \, d\tau \right)^2 \\
& + 2 \int_{-\infty}^{\infty} g_n(\tau) n(t - \tau) \, d\tau \left(\int_{-\infty}^{\infty} g_r(\tau) r(t - \tau) \, d\tau \right. \\
& \left. \left. - \int_{-\infty}^{\infty} g_d(\tau) r(t - \tau) \, d\tau \right) \right] dt
\end{aligned}
\tag{8-54}
$$

Expanding equation 8–54 and utilizing the variable μ for the second integrand in order to denote that the variable of integration is other than τ, results in the following expression:

$$
\begin{aligned}
\overline{e^2} = \lim_{T \to \infty} & \frac{1}{2T} \int_{-T}^{T} dt \int_{-\infty}^{\infty} r(t - \tau)[g_r(\tau) - g_d(\tau)] \, d\tau \\
& \times \int_{-\infty}^{\infty} r(t - \mu)[g_r(\mu) - g_d(\mu)] \, d\mu \\
+ \lim_{T \to \infty} & \frac{1}{2T} \int_{-T}^{T} dt \int_{-\infty}^{\infty} n(t - \tau) g_n(\tau) \, d\tau \\
& \times \int_{-\infty}^{\infty} n(t - \mu) g_n(\mu) \, d\mu \\
+ 2 \lim_{T \to \infty} & \frac{1}{2T} \int_{-T}^{T} dt \int_{-\infty}^{\infty} n(t - \tau) g_n(\tau) \, d\tau \\
& \times \int_{-\infty}^{\infty} r(t - \tau)[g_r(\tau) - g_d(\tau)] \, d\tau
\end{aligned}
\tag{8-55}
$$

By interchanging the order and processes of integration, we can rewrite equation 8–55 as follows:

$$
\begin{aligned}
\overline{e^2} = & \left[\int_{-\infty}^{\infty} [g_r(\tau) - g_d(\tau)] \, d\tau \right] \left[\int_{-\infty}^{\infty} [g_r(\mu) - g_d(\mu)] \, d\mu \right] \\
& \times \left[\lim_{T \to \infty} \frac{1}{2T} \int_{-T}^{T} r(t - \tau) r(t - \mu) \, dt \right] + \left[\int_{-\infty}^{\infty} g_n(\tau) \, d\tau \right] \\
& \times \left[\int_{-\infty}^{\infty} g_n(\mu) \, d\mu \right] \left[\lim_{T \to \infty} \frac{1}{2T} \int_{-T}^{T} n(t - \tau) n(t - \mu) \, dt \right] \\
& + \left[\int_{-\infty}^{\infty} g_n(\tau) \, d\tau \right] \left[\int_{-\infty}^{\infty} [g_r(\mu) - g_d(\mu)] \, d\mu \right] \\
& \times \left[\lim_{T \to \infty} \frac{1}{2T} \int_{-T}^{T} r(t - \tau) n(t - \mu) \, dt \right] + \left[\int_{-\infty}^{\infty} g_n(\mu) \, d\mu \right] \\
& \times \left[\int_{-\infty}^{\infty} [g_r(\tau) - g_d(\tau)] \, d\tau \right] \left[\lim_{T \to \infty} \frac{1}{2T} \int_{-T}^{T} n(t - \tau) r(t - \mu) \, dt \right]
\end{aligned}
\tag{8-56}
$$

Equation 8–56 may be simplified and written in terms of known system characteristics by recognizing the following relations:

$$\lim_{T \to \infty} \frac{1}{2T} \int_{-T}^{T} r(t - \tau)r(t - \mu) \, dt = \phi_{rr}(\tau - \mu) = \frac{1}{2\pi} \int_{-\infty}^{\infty} \Phi_{rr}(\omega) \, e^{j\omega(\tau - \mu)} \, d\omega$$

(8–57)

$$\lim_{T \to \infty} \frac{1}{2T} \int_{-T}^{T} n(t - \tau)n(t - \mu) \, dt = \Phi_{nn}(\tau - \mu)$$

$$= \frac{1}{2\pi} \int_{-\infty}^{\infty} \Phi_{nn}(\omega) \, e^{j\omega(\tau - \mu)} \, d\omega \quad (8–58)$$

$$\lim_{T \to \infty} \frac{1}{2T} \int_{-T}^{T} r(t - \tau)n(t - \mu) \, dt = \phi_{rn}(\tau - \mu)$$

$$= \frac{1}{2\pi} \int_{-\infty}^{\infty} \Phi_{rn}(\omega) \, e^{j\omega(\tau - \mu)} \, d\omega \quad (8–59)$$

$$\lim_{T \to \infty} \frac{1}{2T} \int_{-T}^{T} n(t - \tau)r(t - \mu) \, dt = \phi_{nr}(\tau - \mu)$$

$$= \frac{1}{2\pi} \int_{-\infty}^{\infty} \Phi_{nr}(\omega) \, e^{j\omega(\tau - \mu)} \, d\omega \quad (8–60)$$

Notice that equations 8–57 to 8–60 are based on definitions given in equations 8–9, 8–12, 8–14, and 8–16. Substituting equations 8–57 to 8–60 into equation 8–56 results in the following expression:

$$\overline{e^2} = \frac{1}{2\pi} \left[\int_{-\infty}^{\infty} [g_r(\tau) - g_d(\tau)] \, d\tau \right] \left[\int_{-\infty}^{\infty} [g_r(\mu) - g_d(\mu)] \, d\mu \right]$$

$$\times \left[\int_{-\infty}^{\infty} \Phi_{rr}(\omega) \, e^{j\omega(\tau - \mu)} \, d\omega \right] + \frac{1}{2\pi} \left[\int_{-\infty}^{\infty} g_n(\tau) \, d\tau \right]$$

$$\times \left[\int_{-\infty}^{\infty} g_n(\mu) \, d\mu \right] \left[\int_{-\infty}^{\infty} \Phi_{nn}(\omega) \, e^{j\omega(\tau - \mu)} \, d\omega \right]$$

$$+ \frac{1}{2\pi} \left[\int_{-\infty}^{\infty} g_n(\tau) \, d\tau \right] \left[\int_{-\infty}^{\infty} [g_r(\mu) - g_d(\mu)] \, d\mu \right]$$

$$\times \left[\int_{-\infty}^{\infty} \Phi_{rn}(\omega) \, e^{j\omega(\tau - \mu)} \, d\omega \right] + \frac{1}{2\pi} \left[\int_{-\infty}^{\infty} g_n(\mu) \, d\mu \right]$$

$$\times \left[\int_{-\infty}^{\infty} [g_r(\tau) - g_d(\tau)] \, d\tau \right] \left[\int_{-\infty}^{\infty} \Phi_{nr}(\omega) \, e^{j\omega(\tau - \mu)} \, d\omega \right] \quad (8–61)$$

When the exponential terms of equation 8–61 are interchanged, the following expression results:

$$\overline{e^2} = \frac{1}{2\pi}\left[\int_{-\infty}^{\infty}[g_r(\tau) - g_d(\tau)]\,e^{j\omega\tau}\,d\tau\right]\left[\int_{-\infty}^{\infty}[g_r(\mu) - g_d(\mu)]\,e^{-j\omega\mu}\,d\mu\right]$$

$$\times\left[\int_{-\infty}^{\infty}\Phi_{rr}(\omega)\,d\omega\right] + \frac{1}{2\pi}\left[\int_{-\infty}^{\infty}g_n(\tau)\,e^{j\omega\tau}\,d\tau\right]$$

$$\times\left[\int_{-\infty}^{\infty}g_n(\mu)\,e^{-j\omega\mu}\,d\mu\right]\left[\int_{-\infty}^{\infty}\Phi_{nn}(\omega)\,d\omega\right]$$

$$+ \frac{1}{2\pi}\left[\int_{-\infty}^{\infty}g_n(\tau)\,e^{j\omega\tau}\,d\tau\right]\left[\int_{-\infty}^{\infty}[g_r(\mu) - g_d(\mu)]\,e^{-j\omega\mu}\,d\mu\right]$$

$$\times\left[\int_{-\infty}^{\infty}\Phi_{rn}(\omega)\,d\omega\right] + \frac{1}{2\pi}\left[\int_{-\infty}^{\infty}g_n(\mu)\,e^{-j\omega\mu}\,d\mu\right]$$

$$\times\left[\int_{-\infty}^{\infty}[g_r(\tau) - g_d(\tau)]\,e^{j\omega\tau}\,d\tau\right]\left[\int_{-\infty}^{\infty}\Phi_{nr}(\omega)\,d\omega\right] \tag{8–62}$$

Equation 8–62 can be further simplified when we recognize the following relationships:

$$G_r(j\omega) - G_d(j\omega) = \int_{-\infty}^{\infty}[g_r(\mu) - g_d(\mu)]\,e^{-j\omega\mu}\,d\mu \tag{8–63}$$

where $G_r(j\omega)$ is the Fourier transform of $g_r(t)$, and $G_d(j\omega)$ is the Fourier transform of $g_d(t)$;

$$G_r(-j\omega) - G_d(-j\omega) = \int_{-\infty}^{\infty}[g_r(\tau) - g_d(\tau)]\,e^{j\omega\tau}\,d\tau \tag{8–64}$$

where $G_r(-j\omega)$ is the complex conjugate of $G_r(j\omega)$, and $G_d(-j\omega)$ is the complex conjugate of $G_d(j\omega)$;

$$G_n(j\omega) = \int_{-\infty}^{\infty}g_n(\mu)\,e^{-j\omega\mu}\,d\mu \tag{8–65}$$

where $G_n(j\omega)$ is the Fourier transform of $g_n(t)$;

$$G_n(-j\omega) = \int_{-\infty}^{\infty}g_n(\tau)\,e^{j\omega\tau}\,d\tau \tag{8–66}$$

where $G_n(-j\omega)$ is the complex conjugate of $G_n(j\omega)$.

Substituting equations 8–63 to 8–66 into equation 8–62 results in the following expression:

$$\overline{e^2} = \frac{1}{2\pi} \int_{-\infty}^{\infty} [G_r(-j\omega) - G_d(-j\omega)][G_r(j\omega) - G_d(j\omega)]\Phi_{rr}(\omega)\, d\omega$$

$$+ \frac{1}{2\pi} \int_{-\infty}^{\infty} [G_n(-j\omega)][G_n(j\omega)]\Phi_{nn}(\omega)\, d\omega$$

$$+ \frac{1}{2\pi} \int_{-\infty}^{\infty} [G_n(-j\omega)][G_r(j\omega) - G_d(j\omega)]\Phi_{rn}(\omega)\, d\omega$$

$$+ \frac{1}{2\pi} \int_{-\infty}^{\infty} [G_n(j\omega)][G_r(-j\omega) - G_d(-j\omega)]\Phi_{nr}(\omega)\, d\omega \qquad (8\text{–}67)$$

This is usually written

$$\overline{e^2} = \frac{1}{2\pi} \int_{-\infty}^{\infty} |G_r(j\omega) - G_d(j\omega)|^2\, \Phi_{rr}(\omega)\, d\omega$$

$$+ \frac{1}{2\pi} \int_{-\infty}^{\infty} |G_n(j\omega)|^2\, \Phi_{nn}(\omega)\, d\omega$$

$$+ \frac{1}{2\pi} \int_{-\infty}^{\infty} [G_n(-j\omega)][G_r(j\omega) - G_d(j\omega)]\Phi_{rn}(\omega)\, d\omega$$

$$+ \frac{1}{2\pi} \int_{-\infty}^{\infty} [G_n(j\omega)][G_r(-j\omega) - G_d(-j\omega)]\Phi_{nr}(\omega)\, d\omega \qquad (8\text{–}68)$$

Equation 8–68 illustrates that the root-mean-square error is the sum of four components. The first component is caused entirely by signal and the difference in transmission between the actual and desired system transfer functions. The second component is caused entirely by noise transmission through the system. The third and fourth terms are caused by the crosscorrelation relation existing in transmission of signal and noise. In practice, signal and noise are usually generated from independent sources and are uncorrelated. If we make this assumption, equation 8–68 reduces to

$$\overline{e^2} = \frac{1}{2\pi} \int_{-\infty}^{\infty} |G_r(j\omega) - G_d(j\omega)|^2\, \Phi_{rr}(\omega)\, d\omega + \frac{1}{2\pi} \int_{-\infty}^{\infty} |G_n(j\omega)|^2\, \Phi_{nn}(\omega)\, d\omega$$

$$(8\text{–}69)$$

Now the control engineer can approach the problem of minimizing the root-mean-square error from several directions. For example, he may desire to derive an optimum linear system which minimizes $\overline{e^2}$ regardless of its physical realizability. From a practical viewpoint, he may want to modify this optimum linear system so that a physically realizable system may be obtained. Another approach is to constrain the form of the system transfer function from the beginning and vary a particular parameter of the feedback control system until $\overline{e^2}$ is minimized. We shall consider each of these techniques and conclude that the last approach is usually the most practical.

2. Optimum Theoretical Filter

Let us consider the general case where signal and noise enter a feedback control system at the same point, as shown in Figure 8–12. Assuming that the signal and noise are both random and stationary functions whose cross-correlation is zero, it has been shown[4,7] that the optimum linear filter resulting in the least root-mean-square error is given by

$$G_{\text{opt}}(j\omega) = \frac{\Phi_{rr}(\omega)}{\Phi_{rr}(\omega) + \Phi_{nn}(\omega)} G_d(j\omega) \tag{8-70}$$

where $\Phi_{rr}(\omega)$ = power-density spectrum of the signal
$\Phi_{nn}(\omega)$ = power-density spectrum of the noise
$G_d(j\omega)$ = desired system transfer function

Since the impulsive response of $G_{\text{opt}}(j\omega)$ has values for $t < 0$, it is physically unrealizable.

The added constraint of a physically realizable $G_{\text{opt}}(j\omega)$ usually increases the root-mean-square error. The best possible physically realizable $G_{\text{opt}}(j\omega)$ has been derived by Bode and Shannon from equation 8–69, in the following manner.[6,7] The optimum system considered is made up of two tandem sections, as shown in Figure 8–13. The power-density spectrum

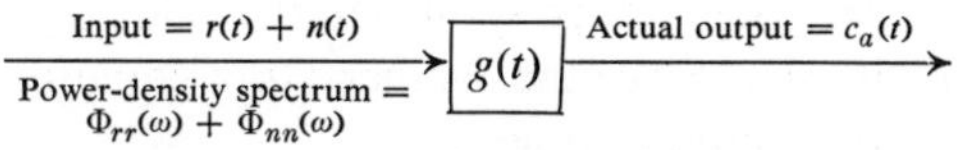

Figure 8–12. *Linear system having an input of signal and noise at the same point.*

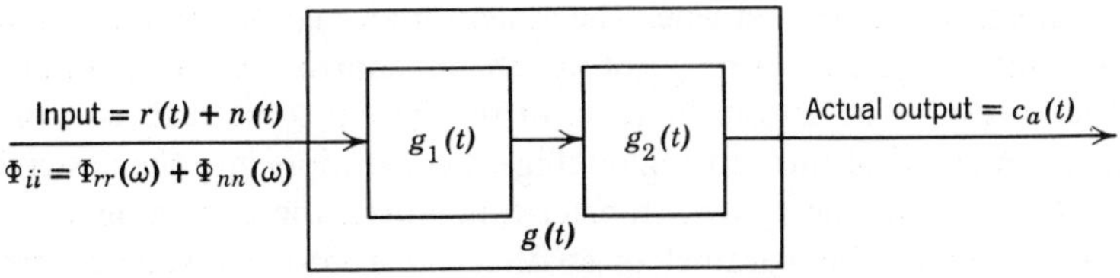

Figure 8–13. *Optimum system separated into two tandem sections.*

at the input is factored into two components $\Phi_{ii}^{+}(\omega)$, which has poles and zeros only in the left half plane, and $\Phi_{ii}^{-}(\omega)$, which has poles and zeros only in the right half plane. The positive superscript of $\Phi_{ii}(\omega)$ indicates that the corresponding inverse transform, $g(t)$, is finite for positive time and zero for negative time. The value of $G_1(j\omega)$ is given by the expression

$$G_1(j\omega) = \frac{1}{\Phi_{ii}^{+}(\omega)}$$

The transfer function $G_2(j\omega)$ is obtained from the physically realizable remaining portion of the optimum transfer function, $\Phi_{rr}(\omega)G_d(j\omega)/\Phi_{ii}^{-}$, where $G_d(j\omega)$ is the transfer function of the desired response. The transfer function of the complete physically realizable system is obtained from the product $G_1(j\omega)G_2(j\omega)$. Knowing $G_1(j\omega)G_2(j\omega)$, we may use conventional methods to synthesize a control system which approximates the optimum physically realizable response.

The value of $G_1(j\omega)G_2(j\omega)$ can also be evaluated from the Weiner-Hopf equation. This relationship, which gives the value of the optimum impulsive response in the time domain, is given by

$$\phi_{rr}(\tau) = \int_0^\infty \phi_{ii}(\tau - t)g_{\text{opt}}(t)\, dt \tag{8-71}$$

where $\phi_{rr}(\tau)$ = autocorrelation function of the signal
$\phi_{ii}(\tau - t)$ = autocorrelation function of the input
$g_{\text{opt}}(t)$ = optimum impulsive response
$\tau \geqslant 0$

The Weiner-Hopf equation is a necessary and sufficient condition that $g(t)$ is the optimum linear filter for the situation illustrated in Figure 8-12. The Fourier transform of $g(t)$ corresponds to the value $G_1(j\omega)G_2(j\omega)$ which was obtained previously. Since the Weiner-Hopf equation is very difficult to evaluate, it is rarely used in practice.

The techniques used for determining $G_{\text{opt}}(j\omega)$ permit the determination of the optimum linear system for a particular application. However, it leaves much to be desired when the system under consideration is a feedback control system. For most feedback control systems, additional restrictions must be set on the form of the system to be realized. A very practical method of introducing intelligent constraints into the design is to select the form of the system transfer function at the beginning and vary one or more of the parameters so that the root-mean-square error is minimized.[5,6] This will be illustrated next with two examples.

3. Example of Optimum Gain

Consider the system illustrated in Figure 8–14. At the very outset of the design, the form of $G(j\omega)$ will be set as

$$G(j\omega) = \frac{K}{j\omega} \qquad (8\text{–}72)$$

and

$$H(j\omega) = 1$$

The procedure for choosing the forward-loop gain K so that the root-mean-square error may be minimized will be demonstrated. Assume that the power-density spectrum of the signal input component $\Phi_{rr}(j\omega)$ is given by the expression

$$\Phi_{rr}(j\omega) = \frac{0.1}{0.09 + \omega^2} \qquad (8\text{–}73)$$

and that the power-density spectrum of the noise input component, $\Phi_{nn}(j\omega)$, is given by the expression

$$\Phi_{nn}(j\omega) = \frac{1}{1.2 + \omega^2} \qquad (8\text{–}74)$$

We further assume that the signal and noise sources are uncorrelated.

The root-mean-square error can be determined directly from equation 8–69. The closed-loop transfer function of the system, corresponding to the notation $G_r(j\omega)$ and $G_n(j\omega)$ of equation 8–69, is given by the following expression:

$$G_r(j\omega) = G_n(j\omega) = \frac{K/j\omega}{1 + K/j\omega} = \frac{K}{j\omega + K} \qquad (8\text{–}75)$$

The desired system response, $G_d(j\omega)$, is given by

$$G_d(j\omega) = 1 \qquad (8\text{–}76)$$

Substituting equations 8–73 to 8–76 into equation 8–69, we obtain the

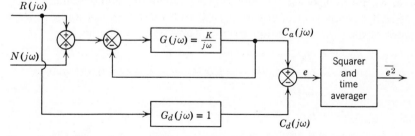

Figure 8–14. Illustrative example for the design of K in order that the root-mean-square error is minimized.

following expression for the root-mean-square error:

$$\overline{e^2} = \frac{1}{2\pi} \int_{-\infty}^{\infty} \left| \frac{K}{j\omega + K} - 1 \right|^2 \left(\frac{0.1}{0.09 + \omega^2} \right) d\omega$$

$$+ \frac{1}{2\pi} \int_{-\infty}^{\infty} \left| \frac{K}{j\omega + K} \right|^2 \left(\frac{1}{1.2 + \omega^2} \right) d\omega \quad (8\text{-}77)$$

This equation can be simplified to

$$\overline{e^2} = \frac{1}{2\pi j} \int_{-\infty}^{\infty} \left| \frac{-j\omega}{j\omega + K} \right|^2 \left(\frac{0.1j}{0.09 + \omega^2} \right) d\omega$$

$$+ \frac{1}{2\pi j} \int_{-\infty}^{\infty} \left| \frac{K}{j\omega + K} \right|^2 \left(\frac{j}{1.2 + \omega^2} \right) d\omega \quad (8\text{-}78)$$

Expansion of the complex-conjugate squared terms results in the following:

$$\overline{e^2} = \frac{1}{2\pi j} \int_{-\infty}^{\infty} \left(\frac{\omega^2}{\omega^2 + K^2} \right) \left(\frac{0.1j}{0.09 + \omega^2} \right) d\omega$$

$$+ \frac{1}{2\pi j} \int_{-\infty}^{\infty} \left(\frac{K^2}{\omega^2 + K^2} \right) \left(\frac{j}{1.2 + \omega^2} \right) d\omega \quad (8\text{-}79)$$

In order to evaluate this equation utilizing Table 8–1, we rearrange equation 8–78:

$$\overline{e^2} = \overline{e^2_{signal}} + \overline{e^2_{noise}} = \frac{1}{2\pi j} \int_{-\infty}^{\infty} \overbrace{\frac{0.1j\omega^2}{(K + j\omega)(0.3 + j\omega)(K - j\omega)(0.3 - j\omega)}}^{\text{signal}} d\omega$$

$$+ \frac{1}{2\pi j} \int_{-\infty}^{\infty} \underbrace{\frac{K^2 j}{(K + j\omega)(1.1 + j\omega)(K - j\omega)(1.1 - j\omega)}}_{\text{noise}} d\omega$$

$$(8\text{-}80)$$

The signal and noise components of equation 8–80 will be evaluated separately, as follows.

a. Signal Component. Comparing the numerator and denominator of the signal component of equation 8–80 with the numerator and denominator of the general equation given in Table 8–1, we obtain

$$h_n(x) = A_0 x^n + A_1 x^{n-1} + \cdots + A_n$$
$$= (K + j\omega)(0.3 + j\omega) = -\omega^2 + j(K + 0.3)\omega + 0.3K$$
$$\therefore \quad A_0 = -1$$
$$A_1 = j(K + 0.3) \quad (8\text{-}81)$$
$$A_2 = 0.3K$$
$$n = 2$$

and

$$g_n(x) = B_0 x^{2n-2} + B_1 x^{2n-4} + \cdots + B_{n-1} = 0.1j\omega^2 \qquad (8\text{--}82)$$

$$\therefore \quad B_0 = 0.1j$$

$$B_1 = 0$$

$$n = 2$$

Since $n = 2$, the solution to the signal component of equation 8–80 is obtained from I_2 of Table 8–1 as follows:

$$I_2 = \frac{-B_0 + A_0 B_1 / A_2}{2 A_0 A_1} \qquad (8\text{--}83)$$

Substituting the constants, previously determined, into equation 8–83, we obtain

$$\overline{e^2_{\text{signal}}} = \frac{-0.1j + (-1)(0)/0.3K}{2(-1)[j(K + 0.3)]} = \frac{0.05}{K + 0.3} \qquad (8\text{--}84)$$

b. Noise Component. Comparing the numerator and denominator of the noise component of equation 8–80 with the numerator and denominator of the general equation given in Table 8–1, we obtain

$$h_n(x) = A_0 x^n + A_1 x^{n-1} + \cdots + A_n$$

$$= (K + j\omega)(1.1 + j\omega) = -\omega^2 + j(K + 1.1)\omega + 1.1K$$

$$\therefore \quad A_0 = -1 \qquad (8\text{--}85)$$

$$A_1 = j(K + 1.1)$$

$$A_2 = 1.1K$$

$$n = 2$$

and

$$g_n(x) = B_0 x^{2n-2} + B_1 x^{2n-4} + \cdots + B_{n-1} = K^2 j \qquad (8\text{--}86)$$

$$\therefore \quad B_0 = 0$$

$$B_1 = K^2 j$$

$$n = 2$$

Since $n = 2$, the solution to the noise component of equation 8–80 is obtained from I_2 of Table 8–1 as given by equation 8–83. Substituting the constants, previously determined, into this equation, we obtain

$$\overline{e^2_{\text{noise}}} = \frac{0 + (-1)(K^2 j)/1.1K}{2(-1)[j(K + 1.1)]} = \frac{K}{2.2(K + 1.1)} \qquad (8\text{--}87)$$

The total value of the root-mean-square error is obtained by combining equations 8–84 and 8–87 as follows:

$$\overline{e^2} = \overline{e^2_{\text{signal}}} + \overline{e^2_{\text{noise}}} = \frac{0.05}{K + 0.3} + \frac{K}{2.2(K + 1.1)} \quad (8\text{–}88)$$

The root-mean-square error can be minimized with respect to the forward-loop gain, K, by differentiating equation 8–88 with respect to K and setting the resultant equation equal to zero, as follows:

$$\frac{d\overline{e^2}}{dK} = \frac{d}{dK}\left[\frac{0.05}{K + 0.3} + \frac{K}{2.2(K + 1.1)}\right] = 0 \quad (8\text{–}89)$$

$$\frac{d\overline{e^2}}{dK} = \frac{-(0.05)(1)}{(K + 0.3)^2} + \frac{2.2(K + 1.1) - K(2.2)}{[2.2(K + 1.1)]^2} = 0 \quad (8\text{–}90)$$

Solution of equation 8–90 indicates that the root-mean-square error is a minimum at a forward-loop gain setting K equal to 0.57.

4. Example of Optimum Rate Feedback Constant

Let us next consider a system containing rate and position feedback, like that shown in Figure 8–15. At the very beginning of the design, $G(j\omega)$ and $H(j\omega)$ will be specified as

$$G(j\omega) = \frac{2}{j\omega} \quad (8\text{–}91)$$

and

$$H(j\omega) = 1 + bj\omega$$

In contrast to the previous problem in which we had to choose the forward-loop gain in order to minimize the root-mean-square error, we now have to

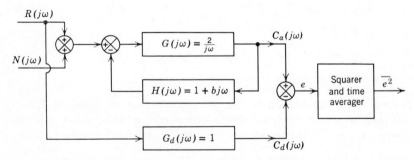

Figure 8–15.   Illustrative example for the design of b in order that the root-mean-square error is minimized.

choose the rate feedback constant b in order to minimize this error. Let us assume that the power-density spectrum of the signal input component, $\Phi_{rr}(j\omega)$, is given by the expression

$$\Phi_{rr}(j\omega) = \frac{0.08}{0.04 + \omega^2} \tag{8-92}$$

The power-density spectrum of the noise input component, $\Phi_{nn}(j\omega)$, is assumed to be given by the expression

$$\Phi_{nn}(j\omega) = \frac{0.46}{0.64 + \omega^2} \tag{8-93}$$

We assume that the signal and noise are uncorrelated.

The root-mean-square error can be determined directly from equation 8–69. The closed-loop transfer function of the system, corresponding to the notation $G_r(j\omega)$ and $G_n(j\omega)$ of equation 8–69, is given by the following expression:

$$G_r(j\omega) = G_n(j\omega) = \frac{2/j\omega}{1 + (2/j\omega)(1 + bj\omega)} = \frac{2}{j\omega + 2 + 2bj\omega}$$

$$= \frac{1}{1 + (0.5 + b)j\omega} \tag{8-94}$$

The desired system response $G_d(j\omega)$ is given by

$$G_d(j\omega) = 1 \tag{8-95}$$

Substituting equations 8–92 to 8–95 into equation 8–69, we obtain the following expression for the root-mean-square error:

$$\overline{e^2} = \frac{1}{2\pi} \int_{-\infty}^{\infty} \left| \frac{1}{1 + (0.5 + b)j\omega} - 1 \right|^2 \frac{0.08}{0.04 + \omega^2} \, d\omega$$

$$+ \frac{1}{2\pi} \int_{-\infty}^{\infty} \left| \frac{1}{1 + (0.5 + b)j\omega} \right|^2 \frac{0.46}{0.64 + \omega^2} \, d\omega \tag{8-96}$$

This equation can be simplified to

$$\overline{e^2} = \frac{1}{2\pi j} \int_{-\infty}^{\infty} \left| \frac{-(0.5 + b)j\omega}{1 + (0.5 + b)j\omega} \right|^2 \frac{0.08j}{0.04 + \omega^2} \, d\omega$$

$$+ \frac{1}{2\pi j} \int_{-\infty}^{\infty} \left| \frac{1}{1 + (0.5 + b)j\omega} \right|^2 \frac{0.46j}{0.64 + \omega^2} \, d\omega \tag{8-97}$$

Expansion of the complex-conjugate squared terms results in the following:

$$\overline{e^2} = \frac{1}{2\pi j} \int_{-\infty}^{\infty} \frac{(0.5 + b)^2 \omega^2 (0.08) j}{[1 + (0.5 + b)^2 \omega^2](0.04 + \omega^2)} \, d\omega$$

$$+ \frac{1}{2\pi j} \int_{-\infty}^{\infty} \frac{0.46 j}{[1 + (0.5 + b)^2 \omega^2](0.64 + \omega^2)} \, d\omega \quad (8\text{--}98)$$

In order to evaluate this integral utilizing Table 8–1, equation 8–78 is rearranged into the following form:

$$\overline{e^2} = \overline{e^2_{\text{signal}}} + \overline{e^2_{\text{noise}}}$$

$$\overbrace{= \frac{1}{2\pi j} \int_{-\infty}^{\infty} \frac{0.08(0.5 + b)^2 \omega^2 j}{[1 + (0.5 + b)j\omega](0.2 + j\omega)[1 - (0.5 + b)j\omega](0.2 - j\omega)} \, d\omega}^{\text{signal}}$$

$$\underbrace{+ \frac{1}{2\pi j} \int_{-\infty}^{\infty} \frac{0.46 j}{[1 + (0.5 + b)j\omega](0.8 + j\omega)[1 - (0.5 + b)j\omega](0.8 - j\omega)} \, d\omega}_{\text{noise}}$$

$$(8\text{--}99)$$

The signal and noise components of equation 8–99 will be evaluated separately, as follows.

a. Signal Component. Comparing the numerator and denominator of the signal component of equation 8–99 with the numerator and denominator of the general equation given in Table 8–1, we obtain

$$h_n(x) = A_0 x^n + A_1 x^{n-1} + \cdots + A_n$$
$$= [1 + (0.5 + b)j\omega](0.2 + j\omega)$$
$$= -(0.5 + b)\omega^2 + j(1.1 + 0.2b)\omega + 0.2$$
$$\therefore \quad A_0 = -(0.5 + b) \quad\quad\quad\quad (8\text{--}100)$$
$$A_1 = j(1.1 + 0.2b)$$
$$A_2 = 0.2$$
$$n = 2$$

and

$$g_n(x) = B_0 x^{2n-2} + B_1 x^{2n-4} + \cdots + B_{n-1}$$
$$= 0.08(0.5 + b)^2 j\omega^2$$
$$\therefore \quad B_0 = 0.08(0.5 + b)^2 j \quad\quad\quad (8\text{--}101)$$
$$B_1 = 0$$
$$n = 2$$

Since $n = 2$, the solution to the signal component of equation 8–99 is obtained from I_2 of Table 8–1 as given by equation 8–83. Substituting the constants, previously determined, into equation 8–83, we obtain

$$\overline{e^2_{\text{signal}}} = \frac{-0.08(0.5 + b)^2 j - (0.5 + b)(0)/0.2}{2[-(0.5 + b)][(1.1 + 0.2b)j]}$$

$$= \frac{0.04(0.5 + b)}{1.1 + 0.2b} \tag{8–102}$$

b. Noise Component. Comparing the numerator and denominator of the noise component of equation 8–99 with the numerator and denominator of the general equation given in Table 8–1, we obtain

$$\begin{aligned}
h_n(x) &= A_0 x^n + A_1 x^{n-1} + \cdots + A_n \\
&= [1 + (0.5 + b)j\omega](0.8 + j\omega) \\
&= -(0.5 + b)\omega^2 + (1.4 + 0.8b)j\omega + 0.8
\end{aligned}$$

$$\therefore \quad A_0 = -(0.5 + b) \tag{8–103}$$
$$A_1 = (1.4 + 0.8b)j$$
$$A_2 = 0.8$$
$$n = 2$$

and

$$g_n(x) = B_0 x^{2n-2} + B_1 x^{2n-4} + \cdots + B_{n-1} = 0.46j$$
$$\therefore \quad B_0 = 0 \tag{8–104}$$
$$B_1 = 0.46j$$
$$n = 2$$

Since $n = 2$, the solution to the noise component of equation 8–99 is obtained from I_2 of Table 8–1 as given by equation 8–83. Substituting the constants previously determined into this equation, we obtain

$$\overline{e^2_{\text{noise}}} = \frac{-0 + [-(0.5 + b)(0.46j)/0.8]}{2[-(0.5 + b)(1.4 + 0.8b)j]} = \frac{0.46}{1.6(1.4 + 0.8b)} \tag{8–105}$$

The total value of the root-mean-square error is obtained by combining equations 8–102 and 8–105 as follows:

$$\overline{e^2} = \overline{e^2_{\text{signal}}} + \overline{e^2_{\text{noise}}} = \frac{0.04(0.5 + b)}{(1.1 + 0.2b)} + \frac{0.46}{1.6(1.4 + 0.8b)} \tag{8–106}$$

The root-mean-square error can be minimized with respect to the rate feedback constant b by differentiating equation 8–106 with respect to b and setting the resultant equation equal to zero, as follows:

$$\frac{d\overline{e^2}}{db} = \frac{d}{db}\left[\frac{0.04(0.5 + b)}{1.1 + 0.2b} + \frac{0.46}{1.6(1.4 + 0.8b)}\right] = 0 \qquad (8\text{--}107)$$

Solution of equation 8–107 indicates that the root-mean-square error is minimized at a rate feedback constant setting b equal to 4.1.

8-8. SIGNAL-TO-NOISE POWER RATIO CONSIDERATIONS

The statistical tools presented in this chapter enable us to examine the very interesting problem of comparing the ratio of the signal-to-noise power at the input to a feedback control system with that at its output. Qualitatively, it would seem that the signal-to-noise power at the output would be larger than that at the input since a feedback control system is inherently a low-pass filter, which would attenuate much more of the noise component than signal component. This is what actually does occur, as is next demonstrated using the system in Figure 8–15 as a model. We assume that the root-mean-square error has been minimized and that the rate feedback constant has a value of 4.1.

By utilizing equation 8–17, and assuming that the signals exist across 1-ohm resistors, the mean-square value, or average power, of the signal and noise components at the input can be obtained from the following expressions:

$$\text{MSV}_{\text{signal}}]_{\text{input}} = P_{\text{avg}_{\text{signal}}}]_{\text{input}} = \frac{1}{2\pi}\int_{-\infty}^{\infty}\Phi_{rr}(\omega)\,d\omega \qquad (8\text{--}108)$$

and

$$\text{MSV}_{\text{noise}}]_{\text{input}} = P_{\text{avg}_{\text{noise}}}]_{\text{input}} = \frac{1}{2\pi}\int_{-\infty}^{\infty}\Phi_{nn}(\omega)\,d\omega \qquad (8\text{--}109)$$

Substituting equation 8–92 into equation 8–108, and equation 8–93 into equation 8–109, we obtain

$$P_{\text{avg}_{\text{signal}}}]_{\text{input}} = \frac{1}{2\pi}\int_{-\infty}^{\infty}\frac{0.08}{0.04 + \omega^2}\,d\omega \qquad (8\text{--}110)$$

and

$$P_{\text{avg}_{\text{noise}}}]_{\text{input}} = \frac{1}{2\pi}\int_{-\infty}^{\infty}\frac{0.46}{0.64 + \omega^2}\,d\omega \qquad (8\text{--}111)$$

Equations 8–110 and 8–111 can be directly evaluated using Table 8–1, as has been previously demonstrated in this chapter for similar equations. The results are

$$P_{\text{avg}_{\text{signal}}}]_{\text{input}} = 0.2 \text{ watts} \qquad (8\text{--}112)$$

and

$$P_{\text{avg}_{\text{noise}}}]_{\text{input}} = 0.287 \text{ watts} \qquad (8\text{--}113)$$

Dividing equation 8–112 by equation 8–113, we obtain the ratio of signal-to-noise power at the input as

$$\frac{P_{\text{avg}_{\text{signal}}}}{P_{\text{avg}_{\text{noise}}}}\bigg]_{\text{input}} = \frac{0.2}{0.287} = 0.7 \qquad (8\text{--}114)$$

In order to obtain expressions for the mean-square value, or average power, of the signal and noise components at the output, we must first calculate their respective autocorrelation functions at the output. This can easily be accomplished from the relationship given by equation 8-26 (Section 8–6) as follows:

$$\Phi_{rr}(\omega)]_{\text{output}} = \Phi_{rr_o}(\omega) = |G_r(j\omega)|^2 \, \Phi_{rr}(\omega) \qquad (8\text{--}115)$$

$$\Phi_{nn}(\omega)]_{\text{output}} = \Phi_{nn_o}(\omega) = |G_n(j\omega)|^2 \, \Phi_{nn}(\omega) \qquad (8\text{--}116)$$

Assuming that the signals exist across 1-ohm resistors, the mean-square value, or average power, corresponding to the autocorrelation functions given by equations 8–115 and 8–116 can be obtained as follows:

$$\text{MSV}_{\text{signal}}]_{\text{output}} = P_{\text{avg}_{\text{signal}}}]_{\text{output}} = \frac{1}{2\pi} \int_{-\infty}^{\infty} |G_r(j\omega)|^2 \, \Phi_{rr}(\omega) \, d\omega$$
$$(8\text{--}117)$$

$$\text{MSV}_{\text{noise}}]_{\text{output}} = P_{\text{avg}_{\text{signal}}}]_{\text{output}} = \frac{1}{2\pi} \int_{-\infty}^{\infty} |G_n(j\omega)|^2 \, \Phi_{nn}(\omega) \, d\omega$$
$$(8\text{--}118)$$

Substituting equations 8–92 to 8–94 into equations 8–117 and 8–118, and setting $b = 4.1$, we obtain

$$P_{\text{avg}_{\text{signal}}}]_{\text{output}} = \frac{1}{2\pi} \int_{-\infty}^{\infty} \frac{0.08}{(0.04 + \omega^2)(1 + 21.2\omega^2)} \, d\omega \quad (8\text{--}119)$$

and

$$P_{\text{avg}_{\text{noise}}}]_{\text{output}} = \frac{1}{2\pi} \int_{-\infty}^{\infty} \frac{0.46}{(0.64 + \omega^2)(1 + 21.2\omega^2)} \, d\omega \quad (8\text{--}120)$$

Equations 8–119 and 8–120 can be directly evaluated using Table 8–1, as has been previously demonstrated in this chapter for similar equations. The results are

$$P_{\text{avg}_{\text{signal}}}]_{\text{output}} = 0.105 \text{ watts} \qquad (8\text{--}121)$$

and

$$P_{\text{avg}_{\text{noise}}}]_{\text{output}} = 0.062 \text{ watts} \qquad (8\text{--}122)$$

Dividing equation 8–121 by equation 8–122, we obtain the ratio of signal-to-noise power, at the output, as

$$\left.\frac{P_{\text{avg}_{\text{signal}}}}{P_{\text{avg}_{\text{noise}}}}\right]_{\text{output}} = \frac{0.105}{0.062} = 1.7 \tag{8–123}$$

Comparing equations 8–114 and 8–123, we reach the interesting conclusion that the signal-to-noise power ratio is $1.7/0.7 = 2.43$ times as large at the output as it is at the input. This quantitative calculation agrees with the qualitative conclusion reached previously.

8–9. LIMITATIONS OF THE ROOT-MEAN-SQUARE ERROR CRITERION FOR MINIMIZING THE EFFECTS OF NOISE

Systems designed to minimize the root-mean-square error often exhibit large overshoots and a long settling time. This oscillatory system response is a direct result of the heavy weighting that this criterion places on large errors. For example, a feedback control system having a step input has a very large initial error, as was shown in Figures 4–3, 4–4, and 4–5, for type 0, 1, and 2 systems, respectively, and this results in a very rapid response and therefore a very large overshoot. However, the control engineer has a very important factor aiding him when employing the root-mean-square error criterion. This is the fact that the minimum resulting from the use of this technique is quite broad. Therefore an appreciably wide variation of characteristics is permitted without a serious change in the index of performance.

We should reemphasize the fact that optimization using the root-mean-square error criterion has been limited to inputs having the statistical properties of stationariness and ergodicity. Should the input of interest not have these properties, the optimum system would become non-stationary, or time-variable. If we know the characteristics of the time variation explicitly, then we may be able to design a system that exhibits a variable bandwidth. This is a very complex problem, however, and beyond the scope of this book.

In many applications, the time variation of the input's statistical characteristics are very slow compared with the response time of the feedback control system. When this is the situation, the nonstationary input can be expanded into a series of stationary segments. However, it is important to emphasize the fact that we cannot ignore the nonstationary statistical characteristic of the input if it varies at a rate that is of the same order of magnitude as the system's response time.

Minimization of the root-mean-square error is not necessarily the proper criterion of optimization for all feedback control systems. For example, in a gun-fire control system, the object is to maximize the probability of destroying a target. Furthermore, the statistical characteristics of the signal may vary greatly during a specific interval of time. In a gun-fire control system, the root-mean-square error of the noise is a function of range. Therefore we are not utilizing all the available information if the system is designed purely on the basis of average statistics. In addition, the signal component of the input to a gun-fire control system can usually be described by some analytic function over a specific interval of time. Therefore the signal component is not a random process possessing the statistical properties of stationariness and ergodicity; it is some known polynomial. The optimum filter for feedback control systems having an analytic signal component and some random noise input is usually non-linear. The problem of analyzing and synthesizing nonlinear filters of this nature is very complex and beyond the scope of this book.

Many attempts have been made to extend Wiener's fundamental statistical approach to systems with nonstationary inputs. Initial attempts depended greatly on analog computers. Their primary value was that they did permit practical study of problems which were otherwise completely unsolvable. The reader should consult Ref. 8 through 10, for some interesting initial approaches to the solution of this problem. Considerable research for a solution to this problem from the viewpoint of modern optimal control theory has recently produced some interesting results. These will be presented in Chapter 10 when optimal control systems are discussed.

8–10. MEASUREMENT OF STATISTICAL CHARACTERISTICS

The greatest practical problem in applying the tools of statistical analysis to actual control systems having random inputs is the measurement and determination of the input's characteristics. Several methods are available for determining the correlation functions and the power-density spectrum. The optimum method for a particular application depends on such factors as the form of the available data, accuracy desired, frequency range of the spectrum, length of the significant correlation, and availability of special-purpose computing equipment. In general, the statistical evaluation of experimental data involves considerable time and money, so careful study of the problem should precede a choice of the optimum technique. This section presents several methods of measuring and determining statistical characteristics together with their advantages and disadvantages.

Techniques for measuring the autocorrelation function are all based on the definition given by (see equation 8–9)

$$\phi_{xx}(\tau) = \lim_{T \to \infty} \frac{1}{2T} \int_{-T}^{T} x(t)x(t + \tau)\, dt \qquad (8\text{--}124)$$

The general procedure we shall describe could apply equally well to the determination of the crosscorrelation function. From the definition of the autocorrelation function, it can be observed that the computation of $\phi_{xx}(\tau)$ involves the following three steps:

1. Generation of $x(t + \tau)$ by shifting the time axis
2. Multiplication of $x(t)$ by $x(t + \tau)$
3. Averaging

Techniques using manual computations and computers are considered next.

If a graphical sample of the input signal is available, the autocorrelation function can be determined by manual calculation, as we discussed briefly in Section 8–5. It was shown there that the graphical evaluation consisted of shifting the random function τ seconds, multiplying the function $x(t)$ by $x(t + \tau)$, and then averaging over a finite interval, Δt. The autocorrelation function was then computed from the following expression:

$$\phi_{xx}(\tau) = \frac{1}{N} \sum_{i=1}^{N} x(t)x(t + \tau)\, \Delta t \qquad (8\text{--}125)$$

Any attempt to carry out this procedure raises certain logical questions. For example, the control engineer is interested in determining the spacing between sampling points, Δt, and the length of the graphical sample he should consider, $N\,\Delta t$. The samples Δt should be spaced sufficiently close together for the function $x(t)$ not to change significantly within the sampling interval. If the random signal is an input to a physical system, a good rule of thumb is that the sampling interval Δt should be about one-tenth the smallest significant time constant of the system. A guideline for choosing the sample length $N\,\Delta t$ is that it be long enough to indicate the lowest significant frequency components of the random signal. A good rule of thumb is that the sample length should be at least ten times the period of the lowest significant frequency component of the signal. Another good rule of thumb is that the total sample $N\,\Delta t$ should not be longer than ten times the value of τ at which $\phi_{xx}(\tau)$ becomes essentially zero. For example, if $\phi_{xx}(\tau)$ is essentially zero for all τ greater than 3 seconds, a 30-second sample should be sufficient since the values of the function more than 3 seconds apart are essentially independent.

From this discussion, it is obvious that the accuracy of the auto-correlation function computed manually increases as Δt is decreased and $N \Delta t$ is increased. However, the computations involved become quite cumbersome and the control engineer must make a compromise between accuracy and complexity of the calculations involved. In addition, the computations necessary to determine $\phi_{xx}(\tau)$ for a large number of τ's becomes extremely involved. For these reasons, control engineers have gone towards the direction of computers to aid in the calculations.

In order to simplify the complexity of the computations, control engineers have built special-purpose computers and have adapted general-purpose computers to solve equation 8–125. We shall use the IBM punched-card calculator as an example of a general-purpose computer that can calculate the autocorrelation function and power-density spectrum. We shall also illustrate the basic principle used by most special-purpose computers to determine the autocorrelation function.

General-purpose computers like the IBM punched-card calculators can be readily programmed to calculate the autocorrelation function on the basis of equation 8–125. The random signal is sampled every Δt seconds; the amplitude is converted into digital form and then punched into two decks of cards. A shift of τ seconds is achieved simply by removing one or more cards from one of the decks. The multiplication and averaging processes are standard operations for this type of machine. The same decks of cards can be used to calculate the power-density spectrum by merely programming the machine to perform a Fourier series analysis of the signal. The square of this amplitude spectrum is then an approximation to the power-density spectrum.

When this process is completely mechanized, it is possible to obtain high accuracy at a much faster speed than can be obtained by normal calculations. However, this general-purpose computer is still much slower than electronic correlation that utilizes a special-purpose computer.

The basic principle of special-purpose electronic correlators is illustrated in Figure 8–16. The random signal is recorded on magnetic tape, photographic film, or another storage device. Assuming that the magnetic tape is used, the tape is then played back through two recording heads which are spaced a fixed distance F apart. Recording head B receives the

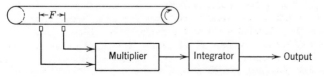

Figure 8–16. Special-purpose electronic correlator.

same signal as recording head A except that it is delayed by a time τ_s where

$$\tau_s = \frac{F}{\text{tape speed}} \qquad (8\text{–}126)$$

The outputs from the recording heads are then multiplied and integrated (averaged). The autocorrelation function, as defined by equations 8–9 and 8–124, can then be obtained by dividing the output from the integrator by the time interval over which the run was made. The accuracy of this technique is limited by the recording device, multiplier, and integrator. After the autocorrelation function is determined, the power-density spectrum can be directly evaluated by solving for its Fourier transform.

The relative accuracy obtainable from measuring the autocorrelation function as compared with that from measuring the power-density spectrum is an important consideration. The behavior of the autocorrelation function in the vicinity of $\tau = 0$ is of great importance in statistical design. Since the behavior of the autocorrelation function at $\tau = 0$ corresponds to the behavior of the power-density spectrum as ω approaches infinity, it is usually more accurate to measure the autocorrelation function for small shifts in τ than to measure the power-density spectrum at very high frequencies. There are certain cases, however, where the power-density spectrum can be obtained more accurately than the autocorrelation function. For example, a power-density spectrum having a sharp peak gives rise to a slowly damped cosine wave for the autocorrelation function. The amplitude of such a peak can be determined relatively easily by measuring the power-density spectrum, but this requires the calculation of a very long segment of the autocorrelation function for accurate results. Therefore it appears advisable to measure both the autocorrelation function and the power-density spectrum, independently, and to take advantage of the most accurate portions of each function.

REFERENCES

1. *Introduction to Mathematical Probability*, J. V. Uspensky, McGraw-Hill Book Co., New York, 1937.
2. *Mathematical Methods of Statistics*, Harold Cramer, Princeton University Press, Princeton, N. J., 1946.
3. *An Introduction to Probability Theory and Its Applications*, William Feller, John Wiley and Sons, New York, 1957, Vol. 1, second edition.
4. *The Extrapolation, Interpolation, and Smoothing of Stationary Time Series*, Norbert Wiener, MIT Technology Press, Cambridge, Mass., 1949.
5. *Theory of Servomechanisms*, H. M. James, N. G. Nichols, and R. J. Phillips, MIT Radiation Laboratory Series, Vol. 25, McGraw-Hill Book Co., New York, 1947.
6. *Automatic Feedback Control System Synthesis*, J. G. Truxal, McGraw-Hill Book Co., New York, 1955, Chapter 7.

7. A Simplified Derivation of Linear Least Square Smoothing and Prediction Theory, H. W. Bode and C. E. Shannon, *Proc. IRE*, **38,** 417 (April 1950).

8. An Extension of Wiener's Theory of Prediction, L. A. Zadeh and J. R. Ragazzini, *J. Appl. Phys.*, **21,** 645 (July 1950).

9. On the Theory of Prediction of Nonstationary Stochastic Processes, R. C. Davis, *J. Appl. Phys.*, **23,** 1047 (Sept. 1952).

10. A New Approach to Optimum Filtering, E. W. Pike, *Proceedings of the National Electronics Conference*, Vol. 8, 1953.

9 SAMPLED-DATA CONTROL SYSTEMS

9-1. INTRODUCTION

This chapter is concerned with a class of feedback control systems in which the signal at one or more points appears as a train of pulses rather than as a continuous function. Such a system is known as a sampled-data control system in contrast to a continuous control system where the signal is continuous everywhere. The controlling information, determined by the amplitude of the pulses, is present only at discrete moments of time, which are usually assumed to be equally spaced. Due to the inherent time delay introduced by the sampling operation, stabilization of the sampled-data control system becomes a serious problem requiring special techniques for analysis and synthesis.

A sampled-data control system functions in a manner similar to that of a human being in a feedback control system. In both cases, intelligence information occurs only at discrete instants of time. This results in control systems that have waiting intervals between the application of intelligence information. A very unfortunate result of this waiting period is a tendency of the particular closed-loop system to oscillate because it attempts to overcorrect errors which have accumulated during the interval between samples. However, this problem can be overcome in several ways by means of proper design.

Sampled-data systems are used in a wide variety of applications. Perhaps the device that has given the greatest impetus to the interest in sampled-data theory is the use of a digital computer in feedback control systems. Digital computers operate only on discrete numbers, and data transmitted through them occur as periodic recurring samples rather than as a continuous signal. Since digital computers operate only on one number at a time, any change in the actuating signal must present the digital computer with a new number, and the computation must be repeated periodically.

Since digitalized data can be transmitted with much greater accuracy than continuous-type data, digitalized data appears quite often in feedback

350

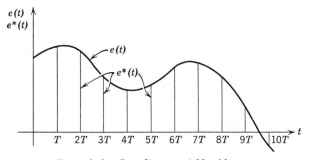

Figure 9–1.   Sampling a variable e(t).

control systems even though a complex digital computer is not actually used. For example, an analog-to-digital converter, or encoder, can be placed on a shaft to obtain angular-position data with much greater accuracy than could be obtained with a simple analog-type device as a synchro. This digitalized data can be used as the actuating signal to a feedback control system which reproduces the original shaft position with an accuracy primarily limited by the accuracy of the digitalized data transmitted. The feedback control system decodes the data and acts as a digital-to-analog converter.

Sampled data is also present in control systems that use time-shared data communication. For example, a guided missile transmitting several pieces of information to a ground station during its flight would most likely transmit the data on a time-shared basis. Therefore each piece of information would be in the form of sampled data. Guidance signals, which would also be in the form of sampled data, could be transmitted to the missile after the original sampled data were processed in a computer.

The sampling operation can best be described by considering a variable of interest, $e(t)$, which is sketched in Figure 9–1. Let us assume that this function is sampled at equal intervals of time, T, so that a sampled function can be described by the sequence of numbers

$$e(0), \ e(T), \ e(2T), \ e(3T), \ e(4T), \ \ldots, \ e(nT)$$

This series of numbers gives a limited description of the function $e(t)$. Specifically, the values of $e(t)$ at times 0, T, $2T$, $3T$, $4T$, and nT seconds are known. Its value at other times can only be approximated by means of extrapolation.

In practical control systems it is necessary that sampled data be reconstructed during the intervals between samples since most other control system components are continuous, or analog, types of device. Data extrapolators, or predictors, are usually quite simple devices; they predict

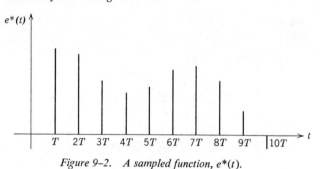

Figure 9–2.   A sampled function, e(t).*

values during sampling intervals based on the last one, two, or three pieces of data. Very rarely are more than three pieces of information used. Figure 9–2 illustrates the sampled information, which will be designated as $e^*(t)$. It is common practice in sampled-data theory to denote the sampled version of time with an asterisk. Figure 9–3 illustrates the information after it is reconstructed by means of a simple holding device which simply remembers the last piece of information until a new sample is obtained. This type of holding circuit is known as a zero-order hold. The reconstructed function is designated $e_R(t)$.

This chapter discusses the basic concepts and characteristics of sampled-data systems and illustrates the techniques of analyzing and synthesizing them. We analyze the sampling process, data extrapolators, stability, and compensation techniques. In addition, we shall obtain the relations between variables of the control system by using a form of transform calculus known as the z-transformation. The use of the Laplace transformation in sampled-data control systems is quite cumbersome since we are working with difference equations[1,2] rather than differential equations as in continuous systems. The transformation is very useful in the analysis and design of sampled-data control systems. Several practical design

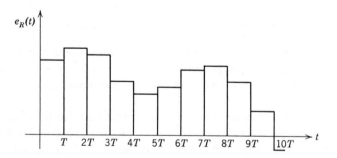

Figure 9–3.   Reconstruction of a sampled function by means of a zero-order hold.

problems are presented for illustrative purposes wherever appropriate. The design of sampled-data systems from the viewpoint of modern optimal control theory is presented in Chapter 10.

9–2. THE CHARACTERISTICS OF SAMPLING

Sampling can be accomplished by mechanical or electronic devices. For purposes of simplicity, we assume that the sampler is a simple mechanical switch which closes briefly every T seconds. This is commonly shown schematically as in Figure 9–4. We further assume that the closure of the switch is of very short duration as compared to the time between closures. Therefore the value of the function at the output of the switch is the instantaneous value of the function $e(t)$ when the switch is closed.

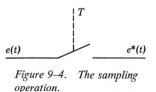

Figure 9–4. The sampling operation.

To obtain a clearer mathematical picture of the sampling process, we can think of the sampler as a device that multiplies some input intelligence signal $e(t)$ by a sampling function $s(t)$. This is mathematically equivalent to a modulation process where the sampling function represents the carrier that is being modulated by the input intelligence signal. This can be expressed as

$$e^*(t) = e(t)s(t) \tag{9–1}$$

From the viewpoint of mathematical simplicity, it is very desirable to define the sampling function as a series of unit impulses which are characterized by having an infinitely narrow width and an infinite amplitude. Its total area is defined as unity. However, practical samplers remain closed for a finite length of time and may result in an actual sampling pulse whose area may be a finite number A. For this case, the only modification necessary to the unit-impulse approximation is to replace the unit-area impulse with one whose area is A. In practice, the only real requirement for using the unit-impulse approximation is that the sampling duration be small compared to the time constant of the system. This is usually the case since feedback control systems generally represent low-pass filters. In the succeeding discussion, we assume that the sampling function is a series of unit impulses which can be expressed as

$$s(t) = \sum_{n=-\infty}^{n=+\infty} \delta(t - nT) \tag{9–2}$$

where $\delta(t - nT)$ represents an impulse having unit area at time $t = nT$.

The Laplace transform of the unit-impulse modulated function, $e*(t)$, can be easily determined. Assuming that the function $e(t)$ is zero for negative time, $e*(t)$ can be expressed as

$$e*(t) = \sum_{n=0}^{\infty} e(nT)\, \delta(t - nT) \tag{9–3}$$

where $e(nT)$ is the value of $e(t)$ at the sampling instant nT, and $\delta(t - nt)$ represents a unit impulse occurring at the instant nT. The Laplace transform of equation 9–3 can be written as

$$E*(s) = \sum_{n=0}^{\infty} e(nT)\, e^{-nTs} \tag{9–4}$$

Fortunately, the Laplace transform for a sampler having equal sampling intervals and whose switching function can be represented by a series of unit impulses is not an infinite summation and can be expressed in closed form. This is easily demonstrated by considering the case where the function $e(t)$ is a simple unit step, $U(t)$. For this case, all values of $e(nT)$ are equal to unity for positive time, and the Laplace transform of $E*(s)$, given by equation 9–4, can be expressed as

$$E*(s) = \sum_{n=0}^{\infty} e^{-nTs} = 1 + e^{-Ts} + e^{-2Ts} + e^{-3Ts} + \cdots + e^{-nTs} \tag{9–5}$$

Equation 9–5 is recognizable as a geometric progression in e^{-Ts} which can be expressed as

$$E*(s) = \frac{1}{1 - e^{-Ts}} \tag{9–6}$$

The Laplace transform for the unit-impulse sampling device can be obtained in another form which makes use of the fact that the sampling function $s(t)$ is periodic and can be expressed as a Fourier series. Expanding $s(t)$ into a Fourier series, we obtain

$$s(t) = \sum_{n=-\infty}^{\infty} C_n \exp\left(j\frac{2\pi n}{T} t\right) \tag{9–7}$$

where C_n represents the Fourier coefficients of the exponential series. These coefficients can be easily determined for the unit-impulse series from the integral

$$C_n = \frac{1}{T} \int_{-T/2}^{T/2} s(t) \exp\left(-j\frac{2\pi n}{T} t\right) dt \tag{9–8}$$

Since the area of any impulse equals unity, the integral also equals unity, and all the Fourier coefficients can be expressed by

$$C_n = \frac{1}{T} \qquad (9\text{–}9)$$

Substituting equation 9–9 into 9–7, we obtain the expression for the Fourier series of the sampling function.

$$s(t) = \frac{1}{T} \sum_{n=-\infty}^{\infty} \exp\left(j\,\frac{2\pi n}{T}\,t\right) \qquad (9\text{–}10)$$

The expression for the Fourier series of the sampled function, $e^*(t)$, can be easily obtained by substituting equation 9–10 into equation 9–1. The result is

$$e^*(t) = \frac{1}{T} \sum_{n=-\infty}^{\infty} e(t) \exp\left(j\,\frac{2\pi}{T}\,nt\right) \qquad (9\text{–}11)$$

Notice that the term $2\pi/T$ in the exponent of equation 9–11 represents the radian frequency of sampling. It will be defined as ω_s. Therefore $e^*(t)$ can be expressed as

$$e^*(t) = \frac{1}{T} \sum_{n=-\infty}^{\infty} e(t)\, e^{jn\omega_s t} \qquad (9\text{–}12)$$

The Laplace transform of equation 9–12 is

$$E^*(s) = \frac{1}{T} \sum_{n=-\infty}^{\infty} E(s - jn\omega_s) \qquad (9\text{–}13)$$

Let us now use equation 9–13 to determine $E^*(s)$ for the case where $e(t)$ is a unit step. The result will then be compared with that obtained previously, given by equation 9–6. Since the Laplace transform of a unit step is $1/s$, the Laplace transform of the sampled function is given by

$$E^*(s) = \frac{1}{T} \sum_{n=-\infty}^{\infty} \frac{1}{s - jn\omega_s} \qquad (9\text{–}14)$$

Equation 9–14 is an infinite summation and cannot be expressed in closed form as was equation 9–6, with the result that it is less useful to us. However, equation 9–14 does show very clearly the periodic properties of the Laplace transform of the sampled function. From equation 9–14, the frequency spectrum can be expressed as

$$E^*(j\omega) = \frac{1}{T} \sum_{n=-\infty}^{\infty} \frac{1}{j(\omega - n\omega_s)} \qquad (9\text{–}15)$$

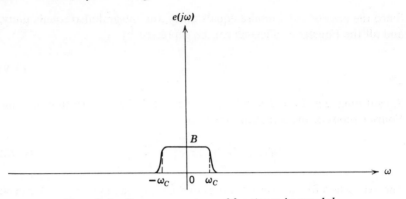

Figure 9–5.   Frequency spectrum of function to be sampled.

In general, the frequency spectrum of a sampled function can be expressed as

$$E^*(j\omega) = \frac{1}{T} \sum_{n=-\infty}^{\infty} E[j(\omega - n\omega_s)] \tag{9-16}$$

Notice that the frequency spectrum is periodic in ω_s. Figure 9–6 shows the effect of the sampler if the input intelligence signal $e(t)$ has a spectral distribution as shown in Figure 9–5. The cutoff frequency of the input signal is designated ω_c.

At this point in our development of sampled-data theory we shall consider the relation between ω_c and ω_s. Referring to Figure 9–6, we can see that the function $e(t)$ can be recovered if the sampled function $e^*(t)$ is passed through a low-pass filter, as shown by the dashed lines. Shannon[3]

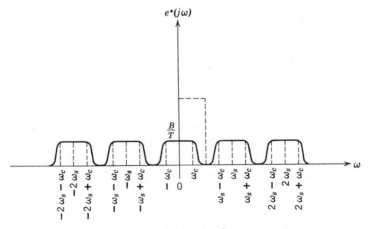

Figure 9–6.   Sampled function frequency spectrum.

has shown that if the highest input frequency is ω_c, the sampling frequency must be at least $2\omega_c$ in order that the input function, $e(t)$, can be recovered undistorted. If the sampling frequency is less than $2\omega_c$, the spectral distribution from 0 to ω_c would overlap partly the region from ω_s to $\omega_s - \omega_c$. This would result in the filter recovering the input signal distorted by the overlapped portion of the first sideband. As will be seen later in this chapter, practical considerations often dictate a sampling frequency much higher than twice the highest input frequency. In addition, since signals generally do not have finite frequency spectrums and filters do not have ideal frequency response characteristics, the recovered signal always has a certain amount of distortion. This distortion is called ripple. It occurs at the sampling frequency, and its harmonics should be treated as noise of the sampled-data control system.

9–3. DATA EXTRAPOLATORS

A data extrapolator is a device which reconstructs a sampled function into a continuous signal based on a knowledge of past samples. This device, which is also called a data hold, follows the sampler in practical feedback control systems. Figure 9–7 illustrates a simple system having a sampler, a data hold, and a process which is to be controlled. The reconstructed signal, $E_R(s)$, is continuous and is applied to the process.

Data extrapolators are classified according to the number of prior samples required for predicting the sampled function during waiting intervals. As was illustrated in Figure 9–3, an extrapolator that only depends on the value of the sampled function at the beginning of a sampling interval is known as a zero-order hold. It is similar in operation to an electronic clamping circuit which keeps its output level equal to the magnitude of an input pulse and then resets itself when a new pulse is applied. An extrapolator that depends on two prior samples is known as a first-order hold. Figure 9–8 illustrates a reconstructed time function, $e_R(t)$, produced by such an extrapolation from a signal $e(t)$. Practical systems usually do not use data extrapolators that are higher than first-order, since they

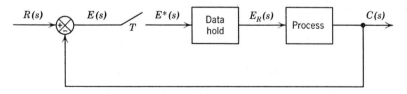

Figure 9–7. Simple sampled-data feedback control system.

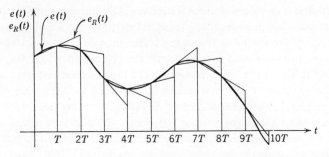

Figure 9–8.   Reconstruction of a signal by means of a first-order hold.

introduce an excessive phase lag into the feedback control system. In addition, they usually increase the effects of noise and are more complex and costly.

The transfer function of a zero-order hold can be easily determined from the impulsive response. This can be obtained from the superposition of a positive step at zero time and a negative step T seconds later, where T is the sampling period. This is illustrated in Figure 9–9. The impulsive response can be expressed in the time domain as

$$g_h(t) = U(t) - U(t - T) \tag{9–17}$$

The Laplace transform of equation 9–17 is

$$G_h(s) = \frac{1}{s} - \frac{1}{s} e^{-Ts} \tag{9–18}$$

This can be simplified to

$$G_h(s) = \frac{1 - e^{-Ts}}{s} \tag{9–19}$$

Equation 9–19 is quite useful for studying the effects of a zero-order hold in a feedback control system.

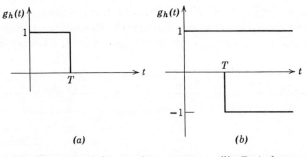

Figure 9–9.   (a) Zero-order hold impulsive response.   (b) Equivalent step function components.

The frequency response of the zero-order hold can be expressed as

$$G_h(j\omega) = \frac{1 - e^{-j\omega T}}{j\omega} \tag{9-20}$$

To obtain an expression for the amplitude and phase characteristics of a zero-order hold we rearrange equation 9–20 successively as follows:

$$G_h(j\omega) = \frac{\exp\left(-j\dfrac{\omega T}{2}\right)\left[\exp\left(j\dfrac{\omega T}{2}\right) - \exp\left(-j\dfrac{\omega T}{2}\right)\right]}{j\omega} \tag{9-21}$$

$$G_h(j\omega) = \frac{2}{\omega} \frac{\exp\left(-j\dfrac{\omega T}{2}\right)\left[\exp\left(j\dfrac{\omega T}{2}\right) - \exp\left(-j\dfrac{\omega T}{2}\right)\right]}{2j}. \tag{9-22}$$

Observing that

$$\frac{\exp\left(j\dfrac{\omega T}{2}\right) - \exp\left(-j\dfrac{\omega T}{2}\right)}{2j} \quad \text{equals} \quad \sin\frac{\omega T}{2}$$

equation 9–22 can be simplified to

$$G_h(j\omega) = \frac{2}{\omega}\left[\exp\left(-j\frac{\omega T}{2}\right)\right]\sin\frac{\omega T}{2} \tag{9-23}$$

Multiplying numerator and denominator by $T/2$, a familiar $(\sin X)/X$ term results:

$$G_h(j\omega) = T\frac{\sin(\omega T/2)}{\omega T/2}\,\bigg/\!-\frac{\omega T}{2} \tag{9-24}$$

The amplitude and phase of $G_h(j\omega)$ are sketched in Figure 9–10. The frequency characteristics of this extrapolating device are similar to those of a low-pass filter where full cutoff occurs at $2\pi n/T$ radians/second. Of primary concern to the control engineer is the phase shift introduced by the zero-order hold. This appreciable phase lag may cause a feedback system that might ordinarily be stable in its continuous form to become unstable.

Let us next determine the characteristics of a first-order holding device. Figure 9–8 shows that the extrapolated function of a first-order hold is linear and has a slope determined by the last two samples. The transfer function of such an extrapolating device can be obtained in a manner similar to that used for the zero-order hold. The impulsive response of a first-order hold is shown in Figure 9–11a. Its equivalent step and ramp function components are sketched in Figure 9–11b. By superposition the

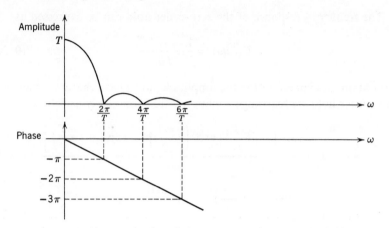

Figure 9–10.   Amplitude and phase response of a zero-order hold.

Laplace transform of the impulsive response can be expressed as

$$G_h(s) = \frac{1}{s} + \frac{1}{Ts^2} - \frac{2}{s} e^{-Ts} - \frac{2}{Ts^2} e^{-Ts} + \frac{1}{s} e^{-2Ts} + \frac{1}{Ts^2} e^{-2Ts} \quad (9\text{–}25)$$

This can be simplified to

$$G_h(s) = T(1 + Ts)\left(\frac{1 - e^{-Ts}}{Ts}\right)^2 \quad (9\text{–}26)$$

Equation 9–26 is quite useful for studying the effects of a first-order hold in a feedback control system.

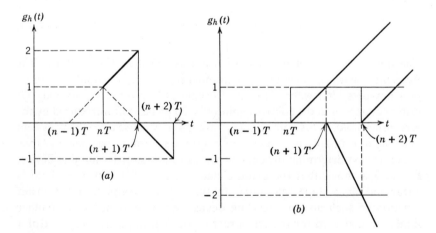

Figure 9–11.   (a) First-order hold impulsive response.   (b) Equivalent step and ramp function components.

The frequency characteristics of the first-order hold can be expressed as

$$G_h(j\omega) = T(1 + j\omega T)\left(\frac{1 - e^{-j\omega T}}{j\omega T}\right)^2 \tag{9–27}$$

In order to obtain the amplitude and phase characteristics, equation 9–27 is rearranged as follows:

$$G_h(j\omega) = T\sqrt{1 + \omega^2 T^2}(e^{-j\omega T})\frac{4}{\omega^2 T^2}$$

$$\times \left[\frac{\exp\left(j\dfrac{\omega T}{2}\right) - \exp\left(-j\dfrac{\omega T}{2}\right)}{2j}\right]^2 \bigg/\tan^{-1}\omega T \tag{9–28}$$

Observing that

$$\left[\frac{\exp\left(j\dfrac{\omega T}{2}\right) - \exp\left(-j\dfrac{\omega T}{2}\right)}{2j}\right]^2 \quad \text{equals} \quad \sin^2\frac{\omega T}{2}$$

we can simplify equation 9–28 to

$$G_h(j\omega) = T\sqrt{1 + \omega^2 T^2}\left[\frac{\sin(\omega T/2)}{\omega T/2}\right]^2 \bigg/\tan^{-1}\omega T - \omega T \tag{9–29}$$

The amplitude and phase of $G_h(j\omega)$ are sketched in Figure 9–12.

Observe that the amplitude response of this extrapolating device is similar to that of the zero-order hold. However, the phase shift introduced by the first-order hold is approximately twice that of the zero-order hold.

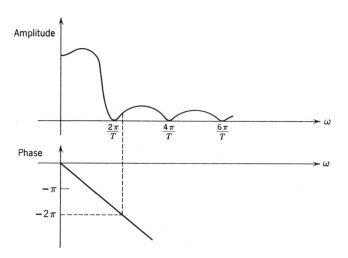

Figure 9–12. Amplitude and phase response of a first-order hold.

For example, at $\omega = 2\pi/T$, the first-order hold introduces a phase shift of $-2\pi + \tan^{-1} 2\pi$ (about $-279°$) while the zero-order hold introduces a phase shift of $-180°$. This greatly affects the stability and is a serious disadvantage of the more complex extrapolator. In addition, the higher-order extrapolator transmits a greater amount of the higher frequency components with a resultant higher noise level in the system. For these reasons, higher-order holding devices are not usually included in practical feedback control systems. Their only advantage is that they are capable of perfectly reproducing functions which are higher-order derivatives of time. For example, a zero-order hold is only capable of reproducing a step function perfectly; a first-order hold can reproduce a ramp function perfectly. However, the zero-order hold is adequate for most practical applications.

9–4. z-TRANSFORM THEORY

The analysis of continuous feedback control systems is considerably simplified by the use of the Laplace transform. The transfer function of simple networks and complicated processes can be represented by an algebraic function which is a ratio of two polynomials in s. A sampler, however, produces an equivalent transfer function which is the ratio of two polynomials in e^{Ts}. This was shown in equation 9–4, which is basically a transcendental function. This result[4] stems from the fact that we are working with difference equations[1,2] in sampled-data control systems instead of differential equations as in continuous systems. It is possible to obtain an algebraic relationship, similar in form to the Laplace transform, if e^{Ts} is replaced by some arbitrary symbol z. This is the basis of the z-transform theory.[5,6,7,14] The analysis of sampled-data control systems is very similar to that of continuous systems when the z-transform is employed.

The z-transform of a sampler can be simply obtained by substituting $z = e^{Ts}$ into equation 9–4. This results in a power series of $1/z$ as follows:

$$E(z) = \sum_{n=0}^{\infty} e(nT)z^{-n} \tag{9–30}$$

Notice that the z-transform describes the values of the time function at the sampling instants only. It offers no information on the behavior of the function between the sampled times. Therefore, instead of thinking of the variable z as equal to e^{Ts}, it may be thought of as an ordinary variable whose exponent represents a particular pulse of $e^*(t)$. From this viewpoint, the z-transform is basically the transform of the sampled function.

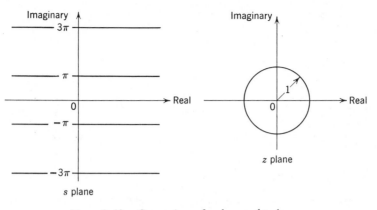

Figure 9–13.   Comparison of s plane and z plane.

In order to analyze or synthesize a feedback control system containing a sampler, it is also necessary to obtain the z-transform of all other elements in the closed loop. Stability can then be determined using the complex z plane, just as the complex s plane was used for continuous systems. For purposes of clarity, a brief comparison of the conditions for stability will next be made for these two planes.

Figure 9–13 illustrates the s and z planes. The imaginary axis of the s plane appears as a unit circle in the z plane by virtue of the definition of the variable z:

$$z = e^{Ts} = e^{j\omega T} \tag{9-31}$$

Notice from equation 9–31 that z is a complex number whose magnitude is unity and whose phase angle is ωT. Therefore the z plane illustrates the periodicity of e^{Ts} by repeating the same values whenever the angle ωT increases by 2π radians. The poles and zeros of $E^*(s)$ repeat themselves in horizontal strips of the s plane separated by 2π radians. Since $E^*(s)$ is periodic in $j\omega_s$, as is illustrated in equation 9–13, this seemingly ambiguous way of representing the properties of $E(z)$ presents no problems. Basically, the poles and zeros of $E^*(s)$ are those of $E(s)$, with infinite repetitions displaced by $j\omega_s$. This results in having points which are similarly located in each of the strips appearing as the same point in the z plane.

When desiring to determine stability, the control engineer ordinarily examines the s plane to see whether any poles are in the right half plane. Since the imaginary axis serves as the dividing line between the right and left halves of the s plane, stability can be determined in the z plane by determining whether poles lie outside or inside the unit circle. Notice that all points in the right half of the s plane lie outside the unit circle in the z plane, while all points in the left half of the s plane lie inside the unit

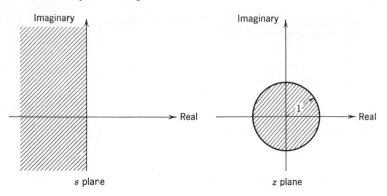

Figure 9–14.   Areas of stability in the s and z planes are shown crosshatched.

circle of the z plane. Therefore, the condition of stability in the z plane is that all poles lie inside the unit circle. This is illustrated in Figure 9–14.

The z-transforms for various types of time functions will now be considered. These are readily obtainable through a direct application of equation 9–4 or 9–30. Attention will be focused on those types of functions which are common to feedback control systems. We use several examples to illustrate the techniques prior to tabulating several useful transform pairs.

1.   Techniques of z-Transformation

a.   The z-Transform of a Unit Step

$$r(t) = U(t) = 1 \qquad [e(t) = 0 \text{ for } t \leqslant 0]$$

$$R^*(s) = \sum_{n=0}^{\infty} e(nT)e^{-nTs}$$

where $e(nT) = 1$

$$\therefore \; R^*(s) = \sum_{n=0}^{\infty} e^{-nTs} = 1 + e^{-Ts} + e^{-2Ts} + e^{-3Ts} + \cdots \, ;$$

$$R(z) = 1 + z^{-1} + z^{-2} + z^{-3} + \cdots$$

This series is convergent for $|z| > 1$, and it yields

$$R(z) = \frac{1}{1 - z^{-1}}$$

$$R(z) = \frac{z}{z - 1} \tag{9–32}$$

b. The z-Transform of a Unit Ramp

$$r(t) = t$$

$$R^*(s) = \sum_{n=0}^{\infty} e(nT)\, e^{-nTs}$$

where $e(nT) = 0, T, 2T, 3T, 4T$, and so on.

$$\therefore\ R^*(s) = T e^{-Ts} + 2T e^{-2Ts} + 3T e^{-3Ts} + 4T e^{-4Ts} + \cdots$$
$$R(z) = Tz^{-1} + 2Tz^{-2} + 3Tz^{-3} + 4Tz^{-4} + \cdots$$

This series is convergent for $|z| > T$, and it yields

$$R(z) = \frac{Tz}{(z-1)^2} \qquad (9\text{-}33)$$

c. The z-Transform of an Exponential Decay

$$r(t) = e^{-at}$$

$$R^*(s) = \sum_{n=0}^{\infty} e(nT)\, e^{-nTs}$$

where $e(nT) = e^{-anT}$

$$\therefore\ R^*(s) = \sum_{n=0}^{\infty} e^{-nT(a+s)}$$
$$= 1 + e^{-aT} e^{-Ts} + e^{-2aT} e^{-2Ts} + e^{-3aT} e^{-3Ts} + \cdots$$
$$R(z) = 1 + e^{-aT}z^{-1} + e^{-2aT}z^{-2} + e^{-3aT}z^{-3} + \cdots$$

This series is convergent for $|z| > e^{-aT}$, and it yields

$$R(z) = \frac{1}{1 - e^{-aT}z^{-1}}$$

$$R(z) = \frac{z}{z - e^{-aT}} \qquad (9\text{-}34)$$

Once the z-transform for any function is obtained and tabulated, it need not be derived again. A tabulation of the foregoing results, and other transform pairs useful to the control engineer, appears in Table 9–1.

Since it is necessary for the control engineer to obtain the z-transform for all the elements of a feedback control system when analyzing a sampled-data system, it is a useful exercise to obtain the z-transform for a typical transfer function that the process may have. Attention will be focused on the technique of application for the z-transform of a type 2, third-order process whose transfer function is given by

$$G(s) = \frac{1}{s^2(s+1)} \qquad (9\text{-}35)$$

Table 9–1.   z-transforms

Number	Time Function	Laplace Transform	z-Transform
1	$\delta(t)$	1	1
2	$\delta(t - nT)$	e^{-nTs}	$\dfrac{1}{z^n}$
3	$U(t)$	$\dfrac{1}{s}$	$\dfrac{z}{z-1}$
4	t	$\dfrac{1}{s^2}$	$\dfrac{Tz}{(z-1)^2}$
5	$\dfrac{t^2}{2}$	$\dfrac{1}{s^3}$	$\dfrac{T^2 z(z+1)}{2(z-1)^3}$
6	$\displaystyle\lim_{a\to 0}\dfrac{(-1)^{m-1}}{(m-1)!}\dfrac{\delta^{m-1}}{\delta a^{m-1}}e^{-at}$	$\dfrac{1}{s^m}$	$\displaystyle\lim_{a\to 0}\dfrac{(-1)^{m-1}}{(m-1)!}\dfrac{\delta^{m-1}}{\delta a^{m-1}}\dfrac{z}{z-e^{-aT}}$
7	e^{-at}	$\dfrac{1}{s+a}$	$\dfrac{z}{z-e^{-aT}}$
8	te^{-at}	$\dfrac{1}{(s+a)^2}$	$\dfrac{Tz\,e^{-aT}}{(z-e^{-aT})^2}$
9	$\frac{1}{2}t^2 e^{-at}$	$\dfrac{1}{(s+a)^3}$	$\dfrac{T^2 z\,e^{-aT}(z+e^{-aT})}{2(z-e^{-aT})^3}$
10	$\dfrac{(-1)^{m-1}}{(m-1)!}\dfrac{\delta^{m-1}}{\delta a^{m-1}}e^{-at}$	$\dfrac{1}{(s+a)^m}$	$\dfrac{(-1)^{m-1}}{(m-1)!}\dfrac{\delta^{m-1}}{\delta a^{m-1}}\dfrac{z}{z-e^{-aT}}$
11	$\sin at$	$\dfrac{a}{s^2+a^2}$	$\dfrac{z\sin aT}{z^2-2z\cos aT+1}$
12	$\cos at$	$\dfrac{s}{s^2+a^2}$	$\dfrac{z^2-z\cos aT}{z^2-2z\cos aT+1}$
13	$e^{-at}f(t)$	$F(s+a)$	$F(e^{aT}z)$

By means of partial function expansion, as discussed in Chapter 2, this transfer function can be expressed as

$$G(s) = \frac{1}{s^2} - \frac{1}{s} + \frac{1}{s+1} \tag{9-36}$$

The z-transform can be obtained, by inspection, from Table 9–1:

$$G(z) = \frac{Tz}{(z-1)^2} - \frac{z}{z-1} + \frac{z}{z-e^{-T}} \tag{9-37}$$

2.   Obtaining the Inverse z-Transform

In general, there are three methods for obtaining the inverse z-transform. These are partial fraction expansion, power series expansion, and the real inversion integral. Each of these techniques is outlined as follows.

a.   Partial Fraction Expansion.   The z-transform is factored into its components so that each term of the expansion can be obtained, by inspection, from Table 9–1.   The technique for partial fraction expansion, discussed in Chapter 2, is also applicable to the z-transform.

b.   Power Series Expansion.   The z-transform can be expanded into an inverse power series in z by expanding equation 9–30.   The result is

$$E(z) = \sum_{n=0}^{\infty} e(nT)z^{-n} = \frac{e(0)}{z^0} + \frac{e(T)}{z^1} + \frac{e(2T)}{z^2} + \frac{e(3T)}{z^3} + \cdots \quad (9\text{–}38)$$

The coefficient of z^{-n}, $e(nT)$, is the value of the variable at the nth sensing instant, and the coefficients can be used directly to plot the time function at the sampling instants.

c.   The Inversion Integral.   The inversion integral for the z-transform is given by

$$e(nT) = \frac{1}{2\pi j} \oint E(z)z^{n-1}\, dz \quad (9\text{–}39)$$

where the line integration is made large enough to enclose all roots of the integral.   Since the poles of $E(z)$ must lie inside the unit circle for the system to be stable, the line integral is usually taken as the unit circle.   This integral, which may be evaluated by the usual residue methods, is rarely used in practice.

3.   A Simple, Open-Loop, Sampled-Data System

Let us now extend our development of z-transform theory to the case of a simple, open-loop, sampled-data system illustrated in Figure 9–15a.   The input function $r(t)$, illustrated in Figure 9–15b, is a pulse lasting for 5 seconds.   The sampling time T is 1 second.   The output $c^*(t)$ is to be assumed sampled by an imaginary chopper synchronized with the real one. Let us apply the techniques of z-transform theory in order to obtain $R(z)$, $C(z)$, and $c^*(t)$.

a.   Computation of $R(z)$

$$r(t) = U(t) - U(t - 5T)$$

$R(z)$ can be obtained by application of equation 9–30.   Since

$$R(z) = \sum_{n=0}^{\infty} r(nT)z^{-n}$$

and

$$r(nT) = U(nT) - U(nT - 5T)$$

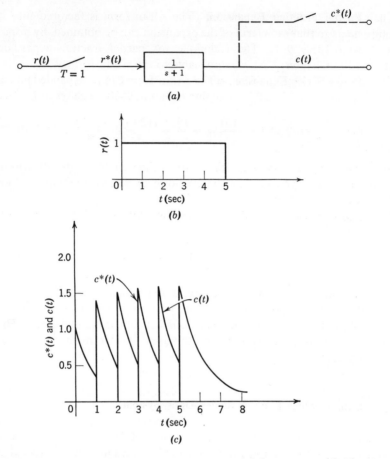

Figure 9–15. *Analysis of a simple, open-loop, sampled-data system.* (a) *The circuit.* (b) *The input function.* (c) *Sketch of* $c^*(t)$ *and* $c(t)$.

then

$$R(z) = \sum_{n=0}^{\infty} [U(nT) - U(nT - 5T)]z^{-n}$$

$$= \sum_{n=0}^{\infty} U(nT)z^{-n} - \sum_{n=0}^{\infty} U(nT - 5T)z^{-n}$$

$$R(z) = 1 + z^{-1} + z^{-2} + z^{-3} + \cdots - (z^{-6} + z^{-7} + z^{-8} + z^{-9} + \cdots)$$

$$\therefore \quad R(z) = 1 + z^{-1} + z^{-2} + z^{-3} + z^{-4} + z^{-5} \tag{9-40}$$

b. Computation of $C(z)$. It has been shown that the z-transform of the output of a network is equal to the z-transform of the input multiplied by the z-transfer function of the network.

$$\therefore\ C(z) = G(z)R(z) \tag{9–41}$$

The z-transform of the network shown in Figure 9–15a, $G(z)$, can be easily obtained from Table 9–1.

$$G(z) = \frac{z}{z - e^{-T}} = \frac{1}{1 - e^{-T}z^{-1}} \tag{9–42}$$

Substituting equations 9–40 and 9–42 into equation 9–41, we obtain the expression

$$C(z) = \frac{1}{1 - e^{-T}z^{-1}} (1 + z^{-1} + z^{-2} + z^{-3} + z^{-4} + z^{-5})$$

Dividing denominator into numerator, we obtain the series given by

$$
\begin{aligned}
C(z) = 1 &+ (1 + e^{-1})z^{-1} + (1 + e^{-1} + e^{-2})z^{-2} \\
&+ (1 + e^{-1} + e^{-2} + e^{-3})z^{-3} \\
&+ (1 + e^{-1} + e^{-2} + e^{-3} + e^{-4})z^{-4} \\
&+ (1 + e^{-1} + e^{-2} + e^{-3} + e^{-4} + e^{-5})z^{-5} \tag{9–43}
\end{aligned}
$$

c. Computation of $c^*(t)$. The value of $c^*(t)$ can be obtained from the power series expansion given by equation 9–43. Utilizing Table 9–1 we obtain

$$
\begin{aligned}
c^*(t) = 1 &+ (1 + e^{-1})\delta(t - 1) + (1 + e^{-1} + e^{-2})\delta(t - 2) \\
&+ (1 + e^{-1} + e^{-2} + e^{-3})\delta(t - 3) \\
&+ (1 + e^{-1} + e^{-2} + e^{-3} + e^{-4})\delta(t - 4) \\
&+ (1 + e^{-1} + e^{-2} + e^{-3} + e^{-4} + e^{-5})\delta(t - 5) \tag{9–44}
\end{aligned}
$$

The outputs $c^*(t)$ and $c(t)$ are illustrated in Figure 9–15c. Notice that the time function between sampling points equals the value of the function at the sampling instant times e^{-T}. After $t = 5$ seconds, the value of $c(t)$ is obtained by multiplying its value at $t = 5$ seconds by e^{-KT} where $K = 1$ at $T = 6$ seconds, $K = 2$ at $t = 7$ seconds, and so on.

For this simple example, the time function between sampling instants is obtained by inspection. For complex systems, however, it is necessary to use more sophisticated techniques as the advanced z-transform. This method is presented at the conclusion of this section.

4. Other Properties

Certain other properties of the z-transform are worthy of mention. The initial- and final-value theorems relate the initial and final values of a time function to its associated z-transform. They are given by

$$c(0) = \lim_{z \to \infty} C(z) \tag{9–45}$$

and

$$c(\infty) = \lim_{z \to 1} (1 - z^{-1})C(z) \tag{9–46}$$

Applying the initial and final-value theorems as given by equations 9–45 and 9–46, respectively, to the problem illustrated in Figure 9–15, we obtain

a. Initial Value

$$c(0) = \lim_{z \to \infty} C(z)$$

where $C(z)$ is given by equation 9–43.

$$\therefore \quad c(0) = 1$$

This result agrees with the sketch of Figure 9–15c.

b. Final Value

$$c(\infty) = \lim_{z \to 1} (1 - z^{-1})C(z)$$

where $C(z)$ is given by equation 9–43.

$$\therefore \quad c(\infty) = 0$$

This result also agrees with the sketch of Figure 9–15c.

5. The Advanced z-Transform Method

A very powerful tool for evaluating the response between sampling instants is the advanced z-transform method. This technique essentially consists of modifying the ordinary z-transform by inserting a fictitious time delay into the sampled-data control system. The resulting transform describes pulse sequences that are delayed from the time functions by nonintegral multiples of the sampling frequency. By varying the amount of delay, we can study the information contained in the continuous signal between sampling instants.

The advanced z-transform can best be understood by referring to the time function, which is delayed by αT seconds, in Figure 9–16. If α is an integral, the result is redundant since the z-transform of the resulting function is merely $z^{-\alpha}C(z)$. The value of n is chosen as the next highest integer after α. The difference between nT and αT is defined as ΔT where

$$\Delta T = nT - \alpha T \tag{9–47}$$

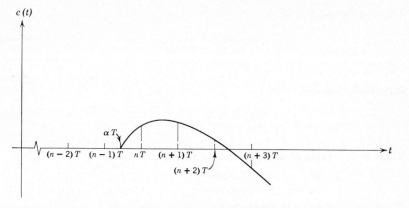

Figure 9–16.   Delayed sampled function.

or

$$\Delta = n - \alpha \qquad (9\text{–}48)$$

Δ is assumed to be a positive number between zero and unity.

Assuming that $C(s)$ is the Laplace transform of $c(t)$, then the Laplace transform of the delayed function $C(s, \alpha)$ is given by

$$\mathscr{L}[c(t - \alpha T)] = C(s, \alpha) = C(s)\, e^{-\alpha Ts} \qquad (9\text{–}49)$$

Substituting equation 9–48 into equation 9–49, we can obtain the expression

$$C(s, \Delta) = e^{-nTs}C(s)\, e^{\Delta Ts} \qquad (9\text{–}50)$$

The advanced z-transform corresponding to equation 9–50 is given by

$$C(z, \Delta) = z^{-n}\mathscr{Z}[C(s)\, e^{\Delta Ts}] \qquad (9\text{–}51)$$

where the symbol $\mathscr{Z}$ indicates the z-transform corresponding to the bracketed Laplace transform term. From the definition of the z-transform, the advanced z-transform can be expressed in the following general form:

$$C(z, \Delta) = \sum_{n=0}^{\infty} c(n + \Delta)Tz^{-n} \qquad (9\text{–}52)$$

As an example of the advanced z-transform let us consider an exponential decay, e^{-aT}, that is delayed by $0.2T$ seconds. For this problem,

$$c(t - 0.2T) = e^{-a(t+0.2T)} \qquad (9\text{–}53)$$

Utilizing equation 9–52, the advanced z-transform corresponding to this expression is given by

$$C(z, 0.2) = \sum_{n=0}^{\infty} e^{-a(n+0.2)T}z^{-n} \qquad (9\text{–}54)$$

This can be simplified to

$$C(z, 0.2) = e^{-0.2aT} \sum_{n=0}^{\infty} e^{-anT} z^{-n} \tag{9-55}$$

The infinite geometric progression corresponding to equation 9–55 can be expressed in closed form by

$$C(z, 0.2) = \frac{e^{-0.2aT}}{1 - e^{-aT} z^{-1}} \tag{9-56}$$

Table 9–2.   Table of advanced z-transforms

	Time Function	Laplace Transform	Advanced z-Transform
1	$\delta(t)$	1	0
2	$\delta(t - nT)$	e^{-nTs}	$z^{-n-1+\Delta}$
3	$U(t)$	$\dfrac{1}{s}$	$\dfrac{1}{1 - z^{-1}}$
4	t	$\dfrac{1}{s^2}$	$\dfrac{\Delta T}{z - 1} + \dfrac{T}{(z - 1)^2}$
5	e^{-at}	$\dfrac{1}{s + a}$	$\dfrac{z e^{-a\Delta T}}{z - e^{-aT}}$
6	$t\, e^{-at}$	$\dfrac{1}{(s + a)^2}$	$\dfrac{T e^{-a\Delta T}[e^{-aT} + \Delta(z - e^{-aT})]}{(z - e^{-aT})^2}$
7	$\sin at$	$\dfrac{a}{s^2 + a^2}$	$\dfrac{z \sin a\,\Delta T + \sin(1 - \Delta)\,aT}{z^2 - 2z \cos aT + 1}$
8	$\cos at$	$\dfrac{s}{s^2 + a^2}$	$\dfrac{z \cos a\,\Delta T - \cos(1 - \Delta)\,aT}{z^2 - 2z \cos aT + 1}$

Utilizing this approach, a table of advanced z-transforms for several functions can be derived. Table 9–2 lists the advanced z-transforms for some commonly found functions.

The inverse of the advanced z-transform enables the control-system engineer to evaluate the system's response between samples directly. For example, let us consider a system of the form shown in Figure 9–15a and let us further assume that the input is a unit step. From Table 9–2, the corresponding advanced z-transform corresponding to the input $R(s)$ is given by

$$R(z, \Delta) = \frac{1}{1 - z^{-1}} \tag{9-57}$$

and that for the control element, $G(s)$, is given by

$$G(z, \Delta) = \frac{e^{-\Delta T}}{1 - e^{-T}z^{-1}} \tag{9-58}$$

The advanced z-transform of the output, $C(z, \Delta)$, is given by

$$C(z, \Delta) = R(z, \Delta)G(z, \Delta) \tag{9-59}$$

or

$$C(z, \Delta) = \frac{e^{-\Delta T}}{(1 - z^{-1})(1 - e^{-T}z^{-1})} \tag{9-60}$$

By keeping Δ as a constant parameter, the inversion of equation 9-60 results in the following expression:

$$c(nT, \Delta) = \left(\frac{1 - e^{-T}e^{-nT}}{1 - e^{-T}} \right) e^{-\Delta T} \tag{9-61}$$

Therefore, if the response following the nth sampling interval is desired, the appropriate value of n is substituted into this expression and Δ is allowed to vary from zero to unity. As would be expected, the continous function between any sampling interval is an exponential decaying term whose initial value is that in the parentheses. It is left as an exercise for the reader to check the results illustrated in Figure 9-15c for the specific input of Figure 9-15b by use of the advanced z-transform method.

9-5. z-TRANSFORM BLOCK DIAGRAM ALGEBRA

The procedure for determining the z-transfer function of sampled-data systems is complicated by the absence of samplers between elements, and it is impossible to obtain a direct analogy with the rules governing the reduction of continuous systems.

Let us initially consider two elements in cascade separated by a sampler as is illustrated in Figure 9-17. The z-transform of the output from the

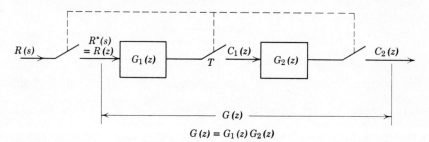

$$G(z) = G_1(z) G_2(z)$$

Figure 9-17. Cascaded continuous elements separated by a synchronous sampler.

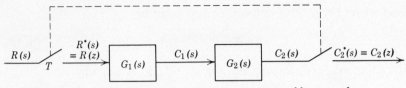

Figure 9–18.   Cascaded continuous elements not separated by a sampler.

second sampler, $C_1(z)$, is

$$C_1(z) = R(z)G_1(z) \tag{9-62}$$

The z-transform of the output from the last sampler, in terms of $C_1(z)$, is

$$C_2(z) = C_1(z)G_2(z) \tag{9-63}$$

Substituting equation 9–63 into equation 9–62, we obtain

$$C_2(z) = R(z)G_1(z)G_2(z) \tag{9-64}$$

and conclude that the z-transform of cascaded elements separated by samplers equals the product of the z-transforms of the individual cascaded elements.

Let us next consider the configuration where a sampler does not separate cascaded elements, as is illustrated in Figure 9–18. Notice that the second element is driven by the value $c_1(t)$ at the sampling instants, and also between the sampling instants. For this case, the z-transform of the output is given by

$$C_2(z) = R(z)G_1G_2(z) \tag{9-65}$$

where $G_1G_2(z)$ represents the z-transform of the cascaded combination corresponding to the transfer function $G_1(s)G_2(s)$. It is very important to emphasize here that $G_1G_2(z)$ is very different from $G_1(z)G_2(z)$ A very simple example will illustrate the difference implied by equations 9–64 and 9–65. Consider that

$$G_1(s) = \frac{1}{s + a}$$

and

$$G_2(s) = \frac{1}{s + b}$$

For the connection illustrated in Figure 9–17,

$$G(z) = G_1(z)G_2(z) \tag{9-66}$$

From Table 9–1, the individual z-transforms are

$$G_1(z) = \frac{z}{z - e^{-aT}}$$

and

$$G_2(z) = \frac{z}{z - e^{-bT}}$$

Substituting these z-transforms into equation 9–66, we obtain

$$G(z) = \frac{z^2}{(z - e^{-aT})(z - e^{-bT})} \qquad (9\text{–}67)$$

For the connection illustrated in Figure 9–18,

$$G(z) = G_1 G_2(z) \qquad (9\text{–}68)$$

The term $G_1 G_2(z)$ corresponds to the z-transform of $G_1(s)G_2(s)$, where

$$G_1(s)G_2(s) = \frac{1}{(s + a)(s + b)} \qquad (9\text{–}69)$$

By means of partial fraction expansion, equation 9–69 can be written as

$$G_1(s)G_2(s) = \frac{1}{b - a} \cdot \frac{1}{s + a} + \frac{1}{a - b} \cdot \frac{1}{s + b} \qquad (9\text{–}70)$$

The z-transform of equation 9–70, $G_1 G_2(z)$, can be obtained by inspection from Table 9–1:

$$G_1 G_2(z) = \frac{1}{b - a} \cdot \frac{z}{z - e^{-aT}} + \frac{1}{a - b} \cdot \frac{z}{z - e^{-bT}} \qquad (9\text{–}71)$$

Observe the great difference between equations 9–67 and 9–71!

Let us next determine the z-transform of the output for several versions of sampled-data feedback control systems. We shall specifically derive $C(z)$ for the systems illustrated in Figure 9–19a, b, c, and d.

a. Sampler in Error Channel. The closed-loop transfer function can be derived in the following manner:

$$E(s) = R(s) - H(s)G(s)E^*(s) \qquad (9\text{–}72)$$

Since the sampler is a linear device and superposition is valid, we can write

$$E^*(s) = R^*(s) - HG^*(s)E^*(s) \qquad (9\text{–}73)$$

Solving equation 9–73 for $E^*(s)$, we obtain

$$E^*(s) = \frac{R^*(s)}{1 + HG^*(s)} \qquad (9\text{–}74)$$

Since

$$C(s) = E^*(s)G(s) \qquad (9\text{–}75)$$

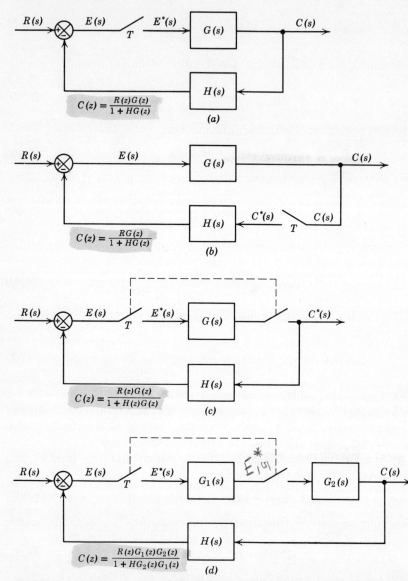

Figure 9–19. Various versions of sampled-data control systems. (a) Sampler in error channel. (b) Sampler in feedback loop. (c) Synchronous samplers in forward loop. (d) Synchronous samplers and cascaded elements in forward loop.

we obtain the value of $C(s)$ as

$$C(s) = \frac{R^*(s)G(s)}{1 + HG^*(s)} \qquad (9\text{--}76)$$

Taking the z-transform of equation 9–76, we obtain the following:

$$C(z) = \frac{R(z)G(z)}{1 + HG(z)} \qquad (9\text{--}77)$$

Equation 9–77 gives the value of the output at the sampling instants for the configuration of Figure 9–19*a*.

b. Samplers in Feedback Loop. The z-transfer function of the output can be derived in the following manner:

$$E(s) = R(s) - H(s)C^*(s) \qquad (9\text{--}78)$$

and

$$C(s) = G(s)E(s) \qquad (9\text{--}79)$$

Substituting equation 9–78 into equation 9–79, we obtain

$$C(s) = R(s)G(s) - H(s)G(s)C^*(s) \qquad (9\text{--}80)$$

Taking the z-transform of equation 9–80, we obtain the following:

$$C(z) = RG(z) - HG(z)C(z) \qquad (9\text{--}81)$$

Simplifying, we obtain

$$C(z) = \frac{RG(z)}{1 + HG(z)} \qquad (9\text{--}82)$$

Equation 9–82 gives the value of the output at the sampling instants for the configuration of Figure 9–19*b*.

c. Synchronous Samplers in Forward Loop. The z-transfer function of the output can be derived in the following manner:

$$E(s) = R(s) - H(s)G^*(s)E^*(s) \qquad (9\text{--}83)$$

Since the sampler is a linear device, and superposition is valid, we can write

$$E^*(s) = R^*(s) - H^*(s)G^*(s)E^*(s) \qquad (9\text{--}84)$$

Solving equation 9–84 for $E^*(s)$, we obtain

$$E^*(s) = \frac{R^*(s)}{1 + H^*(s)G^*(s)} \qquad (9\text{--}85)$$

In addition, since

$$C^*(s) = E^*(s)G^*(s) \qquad (9\text{--}86)$$

we obtain the relation between $C^*(s)$ and $R^*(s)$ as

$$C^*(s) = \frac{R^*(s)G^*(s)}{1 + H^*(s)G^*(s)} \qquad (9-87)$$

Taking the z-transform of equation 9–87, we obtain the following:

$$C(z) = \frac{R(z)G(z)}{1 + H(z)G(z)} \qquad (9-88)$$

Equation 9–88 gives the value of the output at the sampling instants for the configuration of Figure 9–19c.

d. Synchronous Samplers and Cascaded Elements in Forward Loop. The z-transfer function of the output can be derived in the following manner:

$$E(s) = R(s) - H(s)G_2(s)G_1^*(s)E^*(s) \qquad (9-89)$$

Since the sampler is a linear device and superposition is valid, we can write

$$E^*(s) = R^*(s) - HG_2^*(s)G_1^*(s)E^*(s) \qquad (9-90)$$

Solving equation 9–90 for $E^*(s)$ we obtain

$$E^*(s) = \frac{R^*(s)}{1 + HG_2^*(s)G_1^*(s)} \qquad (9-91)$$

In addition, since

$$C(s) = E^*(s)G_1^*(s)G_2(s) \qquad (9-92)$$

we obtain the value of $C(s)$ as

$$C(s) = \frac{R^*(s)G_1^*(s)G_2(s)}{1 + HG_2^*(s)G_1^*(s)} \qquad (9-93)$$

Taking the z-transform of equation 9–93, we obtain the following:

$$C(z) = \frac{R(z)G_1(z)G_2(z)}{1 + HG_2(z)G_1(z)} \qquad (9-94)$$

Equation 9–94 gives the value of the output at the sampling instants for the configuration of Figure 9–19d.

9–6. CHARACTERISTIC RESPONSE OF A SAMPLER AND ZERO-ORDER HOLD COMBINATION

The tools developed so far have made it possible for us to determine the characteristic response of the sampler and zero-order hold combination illustrated in Figure 9–20 to various types of input. We shall apply the

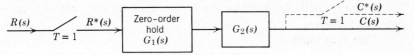

Figure 9–20. Sampler and zero-order hold in cascade.

z-transform theory in order to determine its response to inputs of a unit step and ramp. We assume that the sampling time is 1 second and that the transfer function $G_2(s)$ is given by

$$G_2(s) = \frac{1}{s+1} \tag{9-95}$$

The z-transfer function of this open-loop system, corresponding to the transfer function $G_1(s)G_2(s)$, is denoted by $G_{12}(z)$. The zero-order hold transfer function $G_1(s)$ was derived previously and is given by equation 9–19 as

$$G_1(s) = \frac{1 - e^{-Ts}}{s} \tag{9-96}$$

Since $T = 1$, equation 9–96 reduces to

$$G_1(s) = \frac{1 - e^{-s}}{s} \tag{9-97}$$

Therefore

$$G_1(s)G_2(s) = \frac{1 - e^{-s}}{s} \frac{1}{s+1} \tag{9-98}$$

By means of partial fraction expansion, equation 9–98 can be written as

$$G_1(s)G_2(s) = (1 - e^{-s})\left(\frac{1}{s} - \frac{1}{s+1}\right) \tag{9-99}$$

The z-transform of equation 9–99 can be obtained from Table 9–1 by inspection. Its value is

$$G_{12}(z) = (1 - z^{-1})\left(\frac{z}{z-1} - \frac{z}{z - e^{-1}}\right) \tag{9-100}$$

This relation can be simplified to the following:

$$G_{12}(z) = \frac{0.63}{z - 0.37} \tag{9-101}$$

For a given input whose z-transform is $R(z)$ the z-transform of the output can be expressed as

$$C(z) = R(z)G_{12}(z) \tag{9-102}$$

The characteristic response to inputs of a unit step and ramp are computed as follows:

a. Unit Step Input

$$r(t) = U(t)$$

From Table 9–1,

$$R(z) = \frac{z}{z - 1} \tag{9-103}$$

Substituting equations 9–101 and 9–103 into equation 9–102, we obtain

$$C(z) = \frac{0.63z}{(z - 1)(z - 0.37)} \tag{9-104}$$

This can also be expressed as

$$C(z) = \frac{0.63z}{z^2 - 1.37z + 0.37} \tag{9-105}$$

The inverse z-transform can be obtained by expanding equation 9–105 into a power series expansion in z and then taking the inverse z-transform by utilizing Table 9–1. The expression for a power series expansion in z is given by

$$C(z) = 0.63z^{-1} + 0.86z^{-2} + 0.95z^{-3} + 0.98z^{-4}$$
$$+ z^{-5} + z^{-6} + z^{-7} + \cdots \tag{9-106}$$

By using Table 9–1 we can express the inverse z-transform as

$$c^*(t) = 0.63\delta(t - 1) + 0.86\delta(t - 2) + 0.95\delta(t - 3)$$
$$+ 0.98\delta(t - 4) + \delta(t - 5) + \delta(t - 6)$$
$$+ \delta(t - 7) + \cdots \tag{9-107}$$

The result is plotted in Figure 9–21. It represents the output as seen by the fictitious sampler shown dashed in Figure 9–20.

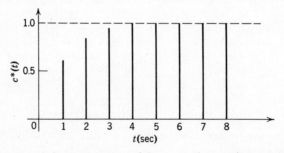

Figure 9–21.   Sampled output response of the circuit shown in Figure 9–20 to a unit step input.

b. Unit Ramp Input

$$r(t) = t$$

From Table 9–1,

$$R(z) = \frac{Tz}{(z-1)^2} \qquad (9\text{–}108)$$

Since $T = 1$, equation 9–108 reduces to

$$R(z) = \frac{z}{(z-1)^2} \qquad (9\text{–}109)$$

Substituting equation 9–101 and 9–109 into equation 9–102, we obtain

$$C(z) = \frac{0.63z}{(z-1)^2(z-0.37)} \qquad (9\text{–}110)$$

This can also be expressed as

$$C(z) = \frac{0.63z}{z^3 - 2.37z^2 + 1.74z - 0.37} \qquad (9\text{–}111)$$

The inverse z-transform can be obtained by expanding equation 9–111 into a power series expansion in z and then taking the inverse z-transform by utilizing Table 9–1. The expression for a power series expansion in z is given by

$$C(z) = 0.63z^{-2} + 1.5z^{-3} + 2.45z^{-4} + 3.43z^{-5} + 4.4z^{-6} + \cdots \quad (9\text{–}112)$$

By using Table 9–1, we can express the inverse z-transform as

$$c^*(t) = 0.63\delta(t-2) + 1.5\delta(t-3) + 2.45\delta(t-4)$$
$$+ 3.43\delta(t-5) + 4.4\delta(t-6) + \cdots \qquad (9\text{–}113)$$

The result is plotted in Figure 9–22.

From the results illustrated in Figures 9–21 and 9–22, we conclude that the zero-order hold circuit can respond with zero steady-state error to a

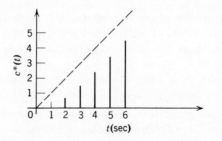

Figure 9–22. *Sampled output response of the circuit shown in Figure 9–20 to a unit ramp input.*

step input but not to higher-order inputs as a ramp. This is to be expected from our previous discussion of data extrapolators in Section 9–3.

9–7. STABILITY ANALYSIS USING THE SYSTEM TRANSFER FUNCTION

It is interesting to observe from Figure 9–19 that the system transfer functions for the various versions of sampled-data control systems can generally be written as

$$T(z) = \frac{C(z)}{R(z)} = \frac{M(z)}{1 + N(z)} \qquad (9\text{-}114)$$

where $N(z) = z$-transform of the loop. For the configuration of Figure 9–19a, where the sampler is in the error channel, $M(z) = G(z)$ and $N(z)$ corresponds to the z-transform of the continuous Laplace transfer function $G(s)H(s)$. Therefore,

$$T(z) = \frac{C(z)}{R(z)} = \frac{G(z)}{1 + GH(z)} \qquad (9\text{-}115)$$

For purposes of analyzing stability from the system transfer function, we study the form given in equation 9–115. It should be emphasized, however, that the technique used is applicable to any configuration of sampled-data control system.

The characteristic equation of a sampled-data control system, given by the denominator of equation 9–114, is

$$1 + N(z) = 0 \qquad (9\text{-}116)$$

For the case of the sampled-data control system having a sampler in the error channel, the characteristic equation is given by

$$1 + GH(z) = 0 \qquad (9\text{-}117)$$

In accordance with the discussion of stability in Section 9–4, a closed contour having a radius of unity is examined in the z plane. The area enclosed by the contour covers the entire region outside the unit circle, as shown in Figure 9–23. The map of this contour, in the $1 + GH(z)$ plane, indicates by its enclosure of the origin the difference between the zeros and poles of this function in accordance with Cauchy's theorem. Specifically, the number of times the map of this contour encloses the origin equals the difference between the numbers of poles and zeros.

It is important to realize that if $GH(z)$ is a stable function then $1 + GH(z)$ will also be stable. Another way of stating this is that the poles of $GH(z)$

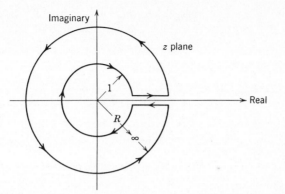

Figure 9–23. Contour used to enclose poles in the z plane outside the unit circle.

are the same as those of $1 + GH(z)$. In sampled-data systems it is convenient to shift the imaginary axis to the point $(1, 0)$ just as was done for continuous systems. When the axis is shifted in this manner, it is necessary to consider only $GH(z)$ and study the enclosure of the point $(-1, 0)$ rather than the origin.

Practical sampled-data control systems usually contain one or more integrations among the continuous elements. From Table 9–1 it can be seen that the z-transform of an integration results in a pole in the z plane at the point $(1, 0)$. This pole would cause a discontinuity if the contour being mapped were exactly the one shown in Figure 9–23. Therefore it is necessary to generate a small semicircular detour around the pole in order to establish a connection between the segments of the contour. This is illustrated in Figure 9–24. The detour is conventionally oriented to include

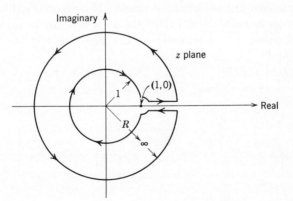

Figure 9–24. Contour used to enclose poles in the z plane outside the unit circle when integrations are present.

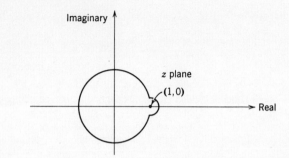

Figure 9–25.   Reduced contour for mapping practical values of GH(z).

the pole inside the unit circle. Since practical values of $GH(z)$ vanish for infinite values of z, and since the segment of the contour along the real axis cancels itself in the limit, only the unit circle and its detours are usually mapped. This is illustrated in Figure 9–25.

We next apply the stability theory we have developed to several practical systems. To show that the stability analysis developed is general and applicable to any configuration shown in Figure 9–19, we determine whether systems having the configuration illustrated in Figures 9–19a and 9–19b are stable. In addition, we attempt to determine the degree of system stability.

1.   The System of Figure 9–26

The sampled-data control system given in Figure 9–26 contains a sampler in the error channel followed by a zero-order circuit and a pure integrator. We wish to determine whether the system is stable when $K = 1$, the maximum value of K before the system becomes unstable, and the system's response to a unit step input. The sampling time is assumed to be 1 second.

a. System Stability. $K = 1$. The system stability can be determined by examining the locus of $GH(z)$ in the $GH(z)$ plane. The Laplace transfer

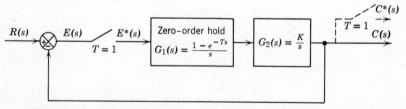

Figure 9–26.   Sampled-data control system around an integrating process.

function, corresponding to $GH(z)$, is $G_1(s)G_2(s)H(s)$ and equals

$$G_1(s)G_2(s)H(s) = \frac{1 - e^{-Ts}}{s} \frac{1}{s} 1 = \frac{1 - e^{-s}}{s^2} \qquad (9\text{--}118)$$

From Table 9–1, the z-transfer function $GH(z)$ corresponding to equation 9–118 is

$$GH(z) = \frac{1}{z - 1} \qquad (9\text{--}119)$$

The locus of $GH(z)$ in the $GH(z)$ plane is shown in Figure 9–27. Since the locus does not encircle the $-1, 0$ point, the Nyquist stability criterion is satisfied and the system is stable.

b. Maximum Value of Gain. The maximum value of gain, K, that is theoretically possible before the system becomes unstable can also be found from the locus of $GH(z)$ in the $GH(z)$ plane. This is illustrated in Figure 9–27. It can easily be seen that if the gain were doubled, the locus would pass through the $-1, 0$ point. Therefore, the maximum value of K before the system becomes unstable is 2.

c. System Response to a Unit Step. From Figure 9–19a, the z-transform of the system output equals

$$C(z) = \frac{R(z)G(z)}{1 + HG(z)} \qquad (9\text{--}120)$$

From Table 9–1, the z-transform of a unit step equals

$$R(z) = \frac{z}{z - 1} \qquad (9\text{--}121)$$

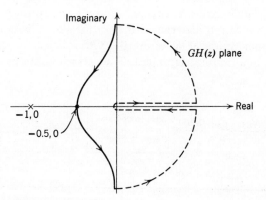

Figure 9–27. Locus in GH(z) plane of the system shown in Figure 9–26.

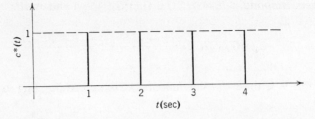

Figure 9–28.   Sampled output response of the system shown in Figure 9–26 to a unit step input.

Substituting equations 9–119 and 9–121 into equation 9–120 we obtain

$$C(z) = \frac{1}{z - 1} \qquad (9\text{–}122)$$

By expanding equation 9–122 into a power series in z and then taking the inverse z-transform, the output response can be plotted. The result is

$$C(z) = z^{-1} + z^{-2} + z^{-3} + z^{-4} + \cdots \qquad (9\text{–}123)$$

or

$$c^*(t) = \delta(t - 1) + \delta(t - 2) + \delta(t - 3) + \delta(t - 4) + \cdots \qquad (9\text{–}124)$$

and is plotted in Figure 9–28.

2.   The System of Figure 9–29

Let us next consider the sampled-data control system illustrated in Figure 9–29. It contains a sampler in the error channel followed by a zero-order hold circuit and a type 1, second-order process. For this configuration we wish to determine whether the system is stable when $K = 1$, the maximum value of K before the system becomes unstable, and the system's response to a step input. The sampling rate is assumed to be 1 second.

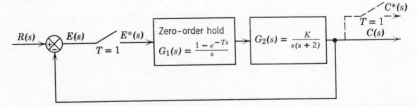

Figure 9–29.   Sampled-data control system containing type 1, second-order process.

a. System Stability. $K = 1$. The solution to this problem is similar to the previous one. The Laplace transformation function $G_1(s)G_2(s)H(s)$ equals

$$G_1(s)G_2(s)H(s) = \frac{1 - e^{-Ts}}{s} \frac{1}{s(s+2)} 1 = \frac{1 - e^{-s}}{s^2(s+2)} \qquad (9\text{--}125)$$

By utilizing a partial fraction expansion of the denominator and Table 9–1, we can obtain the z-transfer function $GH(z)$ corresponding to equation 9–125. Its value is

$$GH(z) = \frac{0.284(z + 0.524)}{(z - 1)(z - 0.136)} \qquad (9\text{--}126)$$

The locus of $GH(z)$ in the $GH(z)$ plane is shown in Figure 9–30. Since the locus does not encircle the $-1, 0$ point, the Nyquist stability criterion is satisfied and the system is stable.

b. Maximum Value of Gain. The maximum value of gain K that is theoretically possible before the system becomes unstable can be found from the locus of $GH(z)$ in the $GH(z)$ plane. This is illustrated in Figure 9–30. It can be easily seen that if the gain were increased by a factor of $1/0.160 = 6.26$, the locus would pass through the $-1,0$ point. Therefore, the maximum value of K before the system becomes unstable is 6.26.

c. System Response to a Unit Step. The system response to a unit step can be easily determined by substituting equations 9–121 and 9–126

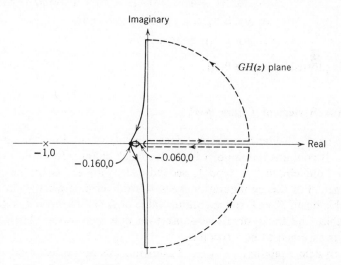

Figure 9–30. Locus in GH(z) plane of the system shown in Figure 9–29.

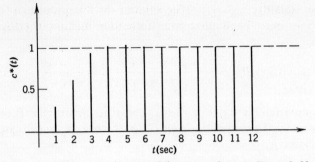

Figure 9–31. Sampled output response of the system shown in Figure 9–29 to a unit step input.

into equation 9–120. The result is

$$C(z) = \frac{0.284z^2 + 0.148z}{z^3 - 1.85z^2 + 1.13z - 0.284} \tag{9–127}$$

By expanding equation 9–122 into a power series in z and then taking the inverse z-transform we can plot the output response. The result is

$$
\begin{aligned}
C(z) = {} & 0.284z^{-1} + 0.674z^{-2} + 0.92z^{-3} + 1.02z^{-4} \\
& + 1.03z^{-5} + 1.015z^{-6} + z^{-7} + z^{-8} \\
& + z^{-9} + z^{-10} + z^{-11} + \cdots
\end{aligned} \tag{9–128}
$$

or,

$$
\begin{aligned}
c^*(t) = {} & 0.284\delta(t - 1) + 0.674\delta(t - 2) + 0.92\delta(t - 3) \\
& + 1.02\delta(t - 4) + 1.03\delta(t - 5) + 1.015\delta(t - 6) \\
& + \delta(t - 7) + \delta(t - 8) + \delta(t - 9) \\
& + \delta(t - 10) + \delta(t - 11) + \cdots
\end{aligned} \tag{9–129}
$$

and is plotted in Figure 9–31.

3. The System of Figure 9–32

We next consider the sampled-data control system illustrated in Figure 9–32. It contains the sampler in the feedback channel followed by a zero-order hold circuit. A type 1, second-order process is in the forward channel. For this configuration we wish to determine whether the system is stable when $K = 1$, the maximum value of K before the system becomes unstable, and the system's response to a unit step input. The sampling time is assumed to be 1 second.

a. System Stability. $K = 1$. Following the procedure used to solve the two previous problems, we determine the Laplace transfer function

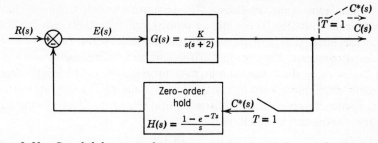

Figure 9–32. *Sampled-data control system containing a type 1, second-order process and featuring the sampler in the feedback path.*

$G(s)H(s)$ first. Its value is

$$G(s)H(s) = \frac{1}{s(s + 2)} \frac{1 - e^{-Ts}}{s} = \frac{1 - e^{-s}}{s^2(s + 2)} \qquad (9\text{--}130)$$

By utilizing a partial fraction expansion of the denominator and Table 9–1, the z-transfer function $GH(z)$ corresponding to equation 9–130 can be obtained. Its value is

$$GH(z) = \frac{0.284(z + 0.524)}{(z - 1)(z - 0.136)} \qquad (9\text{--}131)$$

The locus of $GH(z)$ in the $GH(z)$ plane is shown in Figure 9–33. Since the locus does not encircle the $-1, 0$ point, the Nyquist stability criterion is satisfied and the system is stable.

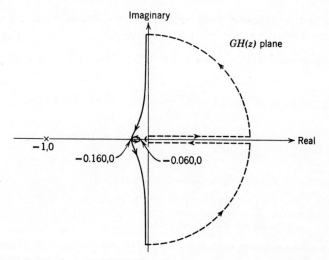

Figure 9–33. *Locus in GH(z) plane for system shown in Figure 9–32.*

b. Maximum Value of Gain. The maximum value of gain K that is theoretically possible before the system becomes unstable can be found from the locus $GH(z)$ in the $GH(z)$ plane. This is illustrated in Figure 9–33. It can easily be seen that if the gain were increased by a factor of $1/0.160 = 6.26$, the locus would pass through the $-1,0$ point. Therefore, the maximum value of K before the system becomes unstable is 6.26.

c. System Response to a Unit Step. From Figure 9–19b, the z-transform of the system output equals

$$C(z) = \frac{RG(z)}{1 + HG(z)} \qquad (9\text{–}132)$$

The z-transform $RG(z)$ corresponds to the z-transform of the function whose Laplace transform is

$$R(s)G(s) = \frac{1}{s}\frac{1}{s(s+2)} = \frac{1}{s^2(s+2)} \qquad (9\text{–}133)$$

By utilizing a partial fraction expansion of the denominator and Table 9–1, the z-transfer function $GH(z)$ corresponding to equation 9–133 can be obtained. Its value is

$$RG(z) = \frac{0.284z(z + 0.524)}{(z - 1)^2(z - 0.136)} \qquad (9\text{–}134)$$

Substituting equations 9–131 and 9–134 into equation 9–132, we obtain

$$C(z) = \frac{0.284z^2 + 0.148z}{z^3 - 1.850z^2 + 1.13z - 0.284} \qquad (9\text{–}135)$$

By expanding equation 9–135 into a power series in z and then taking the inverse z-transform, the output response can be plotted. The result is

$$\begin{aligned}
C(z) = {} & 0.284z^{-1} + 0.674z^{-2} + 0.920z^{-3} + 1.02z^{-4} + 1.03z^{-5} \\
& + 1.015z^{-6} + z^{-7} + z^{-8} + z^{-9} + z^{-10} \\
& + z^{-11} + z^{-12} + z^{-13} + \cdots
\end{aligned} \qquad (9\text{–}136)$$

or,

$$\begin{aligned}
c^*(t) = {} & 0.284\delta(t - 1) + 0.674\delta(t - 2) + 0.920\delta(t - 3) \\
& + 1.02\delta(t - 4) + 1.03\delta(t - 5) + 1.015\delta(t - 6) \\
& + \delta(t - 7) + \delta(t - 8) + \delta(t - 9) \\
& + \delta(t - 10) + \delta(t - 11) + \delta(t - 12) \\
& + \delta(t - 13) + \cdots
\end{aligned} \qquad (9\text{–}137)$$

and is plotted in Figure 9–34.

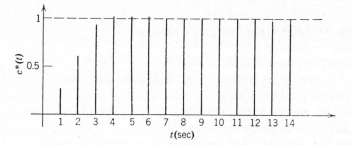

Figure 9–34. Sampled output response of the system shown in Figure 9–32 to a unit step input.

It is interesting to examine the similar results obtained for the systems of Figures 9–29 and 9–32. Identical $GH(z)$ loci and values of maximum gain are due to identical values of $GH(z)$. Other conditions being equal, $GH(z)$ is obviously the same whether the sampler and data extrapolator are in the forward or feedback paths. In addition, both systems have identical responses to step inputs since $R(z)G(z)$ and $RG(z)$ happen to be the same in this example. In general, these two quantities are not always the same and we should not expect the output response from these two systems to always equal each other.

In order to answer the question of how stable the sampled-data control system is, we should attempt to find an analogous criterion to that used for continuous systems. The gain and phase margins are indications of the degree of safety that a continuous feedback control system has in avoiding the $-1,0$ point in the complex plane. In addition, we can relate the gain and phase margins to the transient response. It is not conventional to use analogous margins in the design of sampled-data control systems. However, a general rule of thumb is that the greater the margin of avoidance of the point $-1,0$ in the $GH(z)$ plane, the higher the damping in the sampled-data control system.

9–8. STABILITY DETERMINATION USING MATHEMATICAL TESTS

Stability of sampled-data control systems can also be determined through the application of several mathematical tests. This section will specifically present the modified Routh-Hurwitz criterion, the Schur-Cohn stability criterion, and Jury's stability criterion.

1.   The Modified Routh-Hurwitz Criterion

Stability of sampled-data control systems cannot be determined by means of a direct application of the Routh-Hurwitz criterion. However, it is possible to apply a transformation to the characteristic equation in z that will transform the region outside the unit circle in the z plane to the right half of an auxiliary plane, and the region inside the unit circle to the left half of this plane. This transformation, known as the bilinear transformation, has been applied to control problems by Oldenbourg and Sartorius.[4] An auxiliary plane called the ω plane is defined by the following relationship:

$$z = \frac{\omega + 1}{\omega - 1} \tag{9-138}$$

or

$$\omega = \frac{z + 1}{z - 1} \tag{9-139}$$

If the Routh-Hurwitz criterion is applied to the characteristic equation, that is, subjected to the transformation of equation 9–138, conditions can be found that cause the roots of the transformed equation to lie in the left half of the ω plane. Therefore it is possible to determine whether roots of the characteristic equation lie within the unit circle of the z plane using this transformation. This procedure is illustrated next for the system having the form shown in Figure 9–19a.

Consider a system whose over-all system transfer function $T(z)$ is

$$T(z) = \frac{C(z)}{R(z)} = \frac{0.092(z + 0.718)}{(z - 0.8)(z - 0.04)} \tag{9-140}$$

Multiplying both factors of the denominator, we obtain the expression

$$T(z) = \frac{0.092(z + 0.718)}{z^2 - 1.20z + 0.320} \tag{9-141}$$

Setting the denominator of $T(z)$ equal to zero, the system's characteristic equation is

$$z^2 - 1.20z + 0.320 = 0 \tag{9-142}$$

Using the bilinear transformation on equation 9–142, we obtain

$$\left(\frac{\omega + 1}{\omega - 1}\right)^2 - 1.20\frac{\omega + 1}{\omega - 1} + 0.320 = 0 \tag{9-143}$$

Simplifying this expression, we obtain

$$\omega^2 + 11.30\omega + 21.0 = 0 \qquad (9\text{-}144)$$

Application of the Routh-Hurwitz criterion to equation 9–144 yields the following array (see Section 5–3):

$$
\begin{array}{ll}
1 & 21.0 \\
11.30 & 0 \qquad (9\text{-}145) \\
21.0 &
\end{array}
$$

Since there are no sign inversions in the left column of the resulting array, this system has no poles in the right half of the ω plane, or outside of the unit circle in the z plane, and it is stable. Actually, for this simple case we know from equation 9–140 that the system had no poles outside the unit circle in the z plane since it is given in factored form. However, this criterion is quite useful for polynomials that are not easily factorable.

2. The Schur-Cohn Stability Criterion

Although the modified Routh-Hurwitz criterion is simple to apply in principle, it is quite laborious for higher-order systems. For these cases, the Schur-Cohn[8,9] stability criterion and Jury's[8,9,14] stability criterion are quite useful.

The Schur-Cohn stability criterion states that a sampled-data control system is stable if the sequence of Schur-Cohn determinants, 1, Δ_1, $\Delta_2, \ldots, \Delta_j, \ldots, \Delta_n$, has n variations in sign. Another way of stating this particular stability criterion is that

$$\Delta_j < 0 \quad \text{for} \quad j \text{ odd}$$

and

$$\Delta_j > 0 \quad \text{for} \quad j \text{ even}$$

in order for the system to be stable.

Assuming that the characteristic equation of the linear sampled-data control system is given by

$$
\begin{aligned}
A_n z^n + A_{n-1} z^{n-1} + A_{n-2} z^{n-2} + A_{n-3} z^{n-3} + \cdots \\
+ A_3 z^3 + A_2 z^2 + A_1 z + A_0 = 0 \quad (9\text{-}146)
\end{aligned}
$$

Then the *j*th Schur-Cohn determinant is defined as in equation 9-147.

$$
\Delta_j =
\left|
\begin{array}{ccccccc|ccccccc}
A_0 & 0 & 0 & 0 & \cdots & 0 & A_n & A_{n-1} & A_{n-2} & A_{n-3} & \cdots & A_{n-j+1} \\
A_1 & A_0 & 0 & 0 & \cdots & 0 & 0 & A_n & A_{n-1} & A_{n-2} & \cdots & A_{n-j+2} \\
A_2 & A_1 & A_0 & 0 & \cdots & 0 & 0 & 0 & A_n & A_{n-1} & \cdots & A_{n-j+3} \\
A_3 & A_2 & A_1 & A_0 & \cdots & 0 & 0 & 0 & 0 & A_n & \cdots & A_{n-j+4} \\
\vdots & & & & & \vdots & \vdots & & & & & \vdots \\
A_{j-1} & A_{j-2} & A_{j-3} & A_{j-4} & \cdots & A_0 & 0 & 0 & 0 & 0 & \cdots & A_n \\
\hline
\bar{A}_n & 0 & 0 & 0 & \cdots & 0 & \bar{A}_0 & \bar{A}_1 & \bar{A}_2 & \bar{A}_3 & \cdots & \bar{A}_{j-1} \\
\bar{A}_{n-1} & \bar{A}_n & 0 & 0 & \cdots & 0 & 0 & \bar{A}_0 & \bar{A}_1 & \bar{A}_2 & \cdots & \bar{A}_{j-2} \\
\bar{A}_{n-2} & \bar{A}_{n-1} & \bar{A}_n & 0 & \cdots & 0 & 0 & 0 & \bar{A}_0 & \bar{A}_1 & \cdots & \bar{A}_{j-3} \\
\bar{A}_{n-3} & \bar{A}_{n-2} & \bar{A}_{n-1} & \bar{A}_n & \cdots & 0 & 0 & 0 & 0 & \bar{A}_0 & \cdots & \bar{A}_{j-4} \\
\vdots & & & & & \vdots & \vdots & & & & & \vdots \\
\bar{A}_{n-j+1} & \bar{A}_{n-j+2} & \bar{A}_{n-j+3} & \bar{A}_{n-j+4} & \cdots & \bar{A}_n & 0 & 0 & 0 & 0 & \cdots & \bar{A}_0
\end{array}
\right| \tag{9-147}
$$

where $j = 1, 2, 3, 4, \ldots, n$ and $\bar{A}_j$ is the conjugate of A_j

Assuming that all the coefficients of the characteristic equation are real, then the determinant Δ_j is symmetrical with respect to its principle diagonal. Although the reader has probably been exposed to matrix algebra somewhere in his education, it is probably worthwhile at this point to review its principles, which are outlined in Appendix A.

It is interesting to observe that if the conditions of the Schur-Cohn stability criterion are not satisfied, we merely know that the characteristic equation has at least one root which lies outside the unit circle in the z plane. Unlike the Routh-Hurwitz criterion, this criterion does not indicate the number of roots which lie on or outside the unit circle.

The Schur-Cohn stability criterion will next be applied to a simple system of the form shown in Figure 9-19a where

$$
T(z) = \frac{C(z)}{R(z)} = \frac{2(z + 1)}{(z - 0.5)(z - 2)} \tag{9-148}
$$

Multiplying both factors of the denominator together and setting the result equal to zero, we obtain the following characteristic equation:

$$
z^2 - 2.5z + 1 = 0 \tag{9-149}
$$

The Schur-Cohn determinant Δ_1 of this equation is given by:

$$
\Delta_1 =
\left|
\begin{array}{c|c}
A_0 & A_n \\
\hline
\bar{A}_n & \bar{A}_0
\end{array}
\right|
=
\left|
\begin{array}{cc}
1 & 1 \\
1 & 1
\end{array}
\right|
= 0 \tag{9-150}
$$

Therefore, the sequence of Schur-Cohn determinants for this simple case is:

$$1, 0$$

Since Δ_1 is not less than zero, this system is unstable according to the Schur-Cohn stability criterion. Actually, for this simple case, we know from equation 9–148 that the system had one pole outside the unit circle in the z plane since it was given in factored form. However, this criterion is quite useful for high-order polynomials that are not easily factorable.

3. Jury's Stability Criterion

The stability criterion devised by Jury[8,9] is much simpler to apply than the Schur-Cohn stability criterion. The first step in Jury's stability criterion is the formation of the following table from the characteristic equation 9–146:

Row	z^0	z^1	$\cdots$	z^{n-j}	$\cdots$	z^{n-1}	z^n
1	A_0	A_1	$\cdots$	A_{n-j}	$\cdots$	A_{n-1}	A_n
2	A_n	A_{n-1}	$\cdots$	A_j	$\cdots$	A_1	A_0
3	B_0	B_1	$\cdots$	B_{n-j}	$\cdots$	B_{n-1}	
4	B_{n-1}	B_{n-2}	$\cdots$	B_j	$\cdots$	B_0	
5	C_0	C_1	$\cdots$	C_{n-2}			
6	C_{n-2}	C_{n-3}	$\cdots$	C_0			
.	.	.					
.	.	.					
.	.	.					
$2n-5$	P_0	P_1 P_2 P_3					
$2n-4$	P_3	P_2 P_1 P_0					
$2n-3$	Q_0	Q_1					

Note that the elements of even rows consist of the coefficients of odd rows written in reverse order. The terms B_j, C_j, and Q_0 are defined as

$$B_j = \begin{vmatrix} A_0 & A_{n-j} \\ A_n & A_j \end{vmatrix}$$

$$C_j = \begin{vmatrix} B_0 & B_{n+j} \\ B_{n-1} & B_j \end{vmatrix}$$

$$Q_0 = \begin{vmatrix} P_0 & P_3 \\ P_3 & P_0 \end{vmatrix}$$

If the characteristic equation

$$1 + GH(1) > 0$$
$$1 + GH(-1) > 0 \quad \text{for} \quad n \text{ even}$$
$$< 0 \quad \text{for} \quad n \text{ odd}$$

and the coefficients

$$|A_0| < A_n$$
$$|B_0| < |B_{n-1}|$$
$$|C_0| > |C_{n-2}| \qquad n - 1 \text{ constraints}$$
$$\cdot \qquad \cdot$$
$$\cdot \qquad \cdot$$
$$\cdot \qquad \cdot$$
$$|Q_0| > |Q_2|$$

then this is a sufficient and necessary condition for all the roots of the characteristic equation to lie inside the unit circle in the z plane.

The Jury stability criterion is applied next, to a simple system of the form shown in Figure 9–19a, where the overall system transfer function $T(z)$ is given by

$$T(z) = \frac{C(z)}{R(z)} = \frac{2(z + 2)}{(z - 0.5)(z + 4)} \tag{9–151}$$

Multiplying both factors of the denominator together and setting the result equal to zero, we obtain the following characteristic equation:

$$z^2 + 3.5z - 2 = 0 \tag{9–152}$$

Using Jury's stability method, we observe that $1 + GH(1) = 2.5 > 0$, but $1 + GH(-1) = -4.5$, which violates the condition that $1 + GH(-1)$ must be greater than zero for $n = 2$. Therefore, the characteristic equation has at least one root lying on or outside the unit circle. Actually, for this simple case, we know from equation 9–151 that the system has one pole outside the unit circle in the z plane since $T(z)$ was given in factored form. However, Jury's criterion is the most useful method for determining the stability of sampled-data systems whose characteristic equation is a high-order polynomial which is not easily factorable.

9–9. APPLICATION OF CONVENTIONAL TECHNIQUES TO THE STABILIZATION OF SAMPLED-DATA CONTROL SYSTEMS

Continuous, tandem stabilizing elements can be used to provide compensation for sampled-data control systems. However, it is difficult to

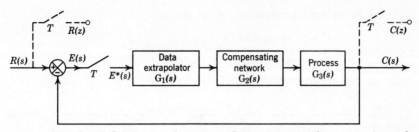

Figure 9–35. *Sampled-data control system utilizing conventional compensation techniques.*

determine their effect on the system analytically, because such a network results in a complex closed-loop z-transform. This difficulty ordinarily might not justify seeking other methods of compensation. However, better results can be achieved by the use of digital controllers. These devices have a synchronous sampler at both input and output terminals, and their characteristics are described by a relatively simple z-transfer function which permits a relatively simple system analysis. A block diagram of a sampled-data control system utilizing conventional, or continuous, network compensation techniques is shown in Figure 9–35, and one utilizing digital-controller compensation is shown in Figure 9–36. We consider the system illustrated in Figure 9–35 in this section and that of Figure 9–36 in the next.

The z-transfer function for the system shown in Figure 9–35 can be written as

$$\frac{C(z)}{R(z)} = \frac{G_1 G_2 G_3(z)}{1 + G_1 G_2 G_3(z)} \tag{9–153}$$

where $G_1 G_2 G_3(z)$ corresponds to the z-transform of the Laplace transfer function $G_1(s) G_2(s) G_3(s)$. The relations between the roots of $1 + G_1 G_2 G_3(z)$ and the characteristics of $G_2(s)$ are very complicated. This is the primary source of difficulty in system analysis. From equation 9–76, the transfer

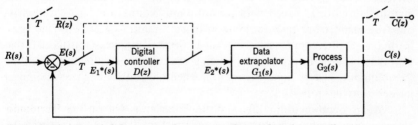

Figure 9–36. *Sampled-data control system utilizing digital controller compensation techniques.*

function in the time domain can be written as

$$\frac{C(j\omega)}{R^*(j\omega)} = \frac{G_1(j\omega)G_2(j\omega)G_3(j\omega)}{1 + G_1G_2G_3^*(j\omega)} \tag{9-154}$$

This can be rewritten as

$$\frac{C(j\omega)}{R^*(j\omega)} = \frac{G_1(j\omega)G_2(j\omega)G_3(j\omega)}{1 + \dfrac{1}{T}\sum_{-\infty}^{\infty} G_1(j\omega + jn\omega_s)G_2(j\omega + jn\omega_s)G_3(j\omega + jn\omega_s)} \tag{9-155}$$

where ω_s corresponds to the radian frequency of sampling. In order to analyze system stability by conventional techniques as the Nyquist and Bode diagrams, it is necessary to plot the function

$$A(j\omega) = \frac{1}{T}\sum_{-\infty}^{\infty} G_1(j\omega + jn\omega_s)G_2(j\omega + jn\omega_s)G_3(j\omega + jn\omega_s) \tag{9-156}$$

Obviously, from equation 9–156, the complications introduced by the harmonics of the sampling frequency forbid the simple addition of vectors or logarithms needed to examine the effect of a change in $G_2(j\omega)$ on the overall system vector or logarithmic plot. Each new compensating network requires a completely new frequency plot for the determination of its effect on system stability.

These facts lead us to conclude that when using a continuous tandem compensating network in a sampled-data control system the system analysis is very tedious, complex, and difficult. However, the control engineer can take advantage of several possible approximations. The reader is referred to Ref. 6 for an excellent discussion of possible approximations that can simplify the analysis, together with their validity. We briefly review these techniques. Because of their practical limitations, however, we do not present any practical problems that use these techniques.

a. Approximation of Sampled-Data Control System as a Continuous System. This is the simplest approximation. The sampler and data extrapolator are replaced with a continuous connection. The system is then designed from the viewpoint of a continuous system, and the performance of the compensated system is checked by means of the z-transform analysis. This procedure, which gives accurate results only when the sampling rate is very high, is common when the control engineer designs a pulsed tracking radar.

b. Approximation of the Effects of the Sampler by Only a Few Harmonic Terms. This technique, first proposed by Linvill,[10,11] is as accurate as the number of harmonic components included in the approximation. The procedure is to sketch a polar plot of $G(j\omega)H(j\omega)$ and then add vectorially a few harmonic terms of the sampled transfer function given by

$$\frac{1}{T}\sum_{-\infty}^{\infty}G(j\omega + jn\omega_s)H(j\omega + jn\omega_s) \tag{9-157}$$

Using conventional techniques, a compensating network having a transfer function given by $N(j\omega)$ is chosen, and the compensated loop transfer function

$$\frac{1}{T}\sum_{-\infty}^{\infty}G(j\omega + jn\omega_s)H(j\omega + jn\omega_s)N(j\omega + jn\omega_s) \tag{9-158}$$

is replotted with only a few harmonic terms, again, being used. The performance of the compensated system is checked by the z-transform analysis. The advantage of this technique is that we can use conventional design techniques by considering only the primary effects of the sampler.

c. Simplify the Analysis by Introducing a Sampler and Data Extrapolator between the Compensating Network and Process. This technique, first proposed by Sklansky,[12] attempts to use a fictitious sampler and data extrapolator between the compensating network and process. This provides the necessary separation of transfer functions required in order to apply conventional shaping techniques directly. The procedure is comparable in accuracy and applicability with Linvill's method.

d. Solution for a Continuous Network Compensation in the Time Domain. This technique, first proposed by Truxal,[7] is a method of specifying a continuous network to realize a time response specification. The procedure is to specify the loop z-transform, $GHN(z)$, based on the closed-loop transfer function. A continuous transfer function $F(s)$ corresponding to $GHN(z)$ is then obtained. The Laplace transform of the compensating network can then be obtained from the relation given by

$$N(s) = \frac{F(s)}{G(s)H(s)} \tag{9-159}$$

However, the complex relation that exists between $N(s)$ and $GHN(z)$ precludes a simple guide for the initial choice of $GHN(z)$ that will cause a practical network to result. Unfortunately, a trial-and-error procedure does not converge very quickly when using this method. Perhaps, with more development, this technique will become more practical in the future.

9-10. STABILIZING SAMPLED-DATA CONTROL SYSTEMS BY USING DIGITAL TECHNIQUES

Let us next consider stabilizing a sampled-data control system by means of a digital controller, as is illustrated in Figure 9-36. The object of this device is to compute a sequence of output numbers $E_2*(s)$ which are linearly related to the input number sequence $E_1*(s)$, in order to obtain a desired system response. The digital controller may contain active elements or simple passive networks. When this device contains active elements, the control engineer is completely free in choosing any stabilizing function in order that the desired system response may be obtained.

We assume that the digital controller is a linear device. Therefore the output and input number sequences are related linearly. The linear relationship between the input and output sequences, $e_1*(t)$ and $e_2*(t)$, respectively, can be expressed as

$$X_0 e_1(nT) + X_1 e_1[(n-1)T] + X_2 e_1[(n-2)T] + X_3 e_1[(n-3)T] + \cdots$$
$$+ X_l e_1[(n-l)T] = e_2(nT) + Y_1 e_2[(n-1)T]$$
$$+ Y_2 e_2[(n-2)T] + \cdots + Y_m e_2[(n-m)T] \qquad (9\text{--}160)$$

where X_l and Y_m are constant terms. The z-transform of this equation can be written as

$$E_1(z)(X_0 + X_1 z^{-1} + X_2 z^{-2} + X_3 z^{-3} + \cdots + X_l z^{-l})$$
$$= E_2(z)(1 + Y_1 z^{-1} + Y_2 z^{-2} + \cdots + Y_m z^{-m}) \qquad (9\text{--}161)$$

The z-transfer function of the digital controller, $D(z)$, is defined as

$$D(z) = \frac{E_2(z)}{E_1(z)} \qquad (9\text{--}162)$$

From equation 9–161, $D(z)$ can be expressed as

$$D(z) = \frac{X_0 + X_1 z^{-1} + X_2 z^{-2} + \cdots + X_l z^{-l}}{1 + Y_1 z^{-1} + Y_2 z^{-2} + \cdots + Y_m z^{-m}} \qquad (9\text{--}163)$$

For the digital controller to be physically reliable, the denominator of equation 9–163 must contain the term 1.

For the system shown in Figure 9–36, the system transfer function $T(z)$ can be expressed as

$$T(z) = \frac{C(z)}{R(z)} = \frac{D(z)G(z)}{1 + D(z)G(z)} \qquad (9\text{--}164)$$

The term $G(z)$ is the z-transform corresponding to the Laplace transfer function $G_1(s)G_2(s)$. For a specified system transfer function $T(z)$ to be realized, the various constants of $D(z)$ must be appropriately chosen. From equation 9–164, the value of $D(z)$ corresponding to a specified value of $T(z)$ can be expressed as

$$D(z) = \frac{1}{G(z)} \frac{T(z)}{1 - T(z)} \qquad (9\text{--}165)$$

It is important to realize that the primary purpose of the digital controller is to cancel any undesirable poles and zeros of the uncompensated system and replace them with poles and zeros which will result in a desired system response. It is obvious from equation 9–164 that this can be accomplished by designing $D(z)$ so that its zeros correspond to the poles of $G(z)$ and its poles correspond to the zeros of $G(z)$, which lie on or outside the unit circle of the z plane. It has been shown,[6] however, that this method of compensation is not practical, since any slight change in the parameters of $D(z)$ or $G(z)$ may result in having the poles and zeros of $G(z)$ lying on or outside the unit circle of the z plane being uncancelled.

A better method for compensation may be obtained by considering equation 9–165. Poles and zeros of $G(z)$ that lie on or outside the unit circle in the z plane may be cancelled by specifying $1 - T(z)$ and $T(z)$ in order that they cancel the poles and zeros, respectively. The following four rules must be pursued when specifying a system transfer function $T(z)$ that will result in a stable system.

RULE 1. The specified system transfer function $T(z)$ must contain as its zeros all the zeros of $G(z)$ that lie on or outside the unit circle in the z plane.

RULE 2. $1 - T(z)$ must contain as its zeros all the poles of $G(z)$ that lie on or outside the unit circle in the z plane.

RULE 3. For $D(z)$ to be physically realizable, the specified system transfer function must be of the form

$$T(z) = \frac{K_m z^{-m} + \cdots + K_p z^{-p}}{L_0 + L_1 z^{-1} + \cdots + L_q z^{-q}} \left[\begin{array}{c} \text{zero cancelling} \\ \text{terms} \end{array} \right] \qquad (9\text{–}166)$$

where m is the lowest order in z^{-1} of the z-transform

$$G(z) = \frac{P_m z^{-m} + \cdots + P_n z^{-n}}{Q_0 + Q_1 z^{-1} + \cdots + Q_b z^{-b}} \qquad (9\text{–}167)$$

In addition the term L_0 cannot be zero.

RULE 4. $T(z)$ must be specified in order that the steady-state error resulting from the application of an input having the form

$$R(z) = \frac{A(z)}{(1 - z^{-1})^m} \qquad (9\text{–}168)$$

is zero. From Table 9–1, this type of input can represent a step, ramp, or acceleration, and so on, depending on the value of m. Here $A(z)$ represents a polynomial in z^{-1} which does not contain factors of the form $1 - z^{-1}$.

From the relationships given by

$$E_1(z) = R(z) - C(z) \qquad (9\text{–}169)$$

and

$$T(z) = \frac{C(z)}{R(z)} \tag{9-170}$$

the z-transform of the system error can be expressed as

$$E_1(z) = R(z)[1 - T(z)] \tag{9-171}$$

Applying the final-value theorem to equation 9–171, we obtain

$$e_1(\infty) = \lim_{z \to 1} \{(1 - z^{-1})R(z)[1 - T(z)]\} \tag{9-172}$$

Substituting equation 9–168 into equation 9–172, the following expression results:

$$e_1(\infty) = \lim_{z \to 1} \left\{ (1 - z^{-1}) \frac{A(z)}{(1 - z^{-1})^m} [1 - T(z)] \right\} \tag{9-173}$$

It is easily seen from equation 9–173 that the steady-state error for inputs of the form given by equation 9–168 will be zero if $1 - T(z)$ satisfies the relationship

$$1 - T(z) = (1 - z^{-1})^m F(z) \tag{9-174}$$

where $F(z)$ is an unspecified ratio of polynomials in z^{-1} and m is the order of the denominator of the input, $R(z)$. When $F(z)$ is unity, a "minimal prototype" response function results and the order of $T(z)$ in z^{-1} is a minimum. However, a minimal prototype response function can only be utilized when $T(z)$ does not contain any zeros on or outside the unit circle of the z plane. A little further thought reveals that a system in which $m = 1$ will respond to a unit step with zero steady-state error, and when $m = 2$ it will respond to a unit ramp with zero steady-state error, and so on. In addition, a system using a minimal prototype will respond with zero steady-state error to lower-order input functions.

We next apply the theory to several systems of the type shown in Figure 9–36, where the data extrapolator is a zero-order hold. The sampling rate is one sample per second. The techniques used to choose the value of $D(z)$ and the system's response to various impulses will be illustrated.

1. System with an Integrating Process

The first system we consider contains a process which is an integrator and may be represented by the transfer function

$$G_2(s) = \frac{1}{s} \tag{9-175}$$

a. Design of $D(z)$. The first step of the procedure is to determine the z-transform $G(z)$ corresponding to the Laplace transfer function given by

$$G(s) = G_1(s)G_2(s) = \frac{1 - e^{-s}}{s}\frac{1}{s} = \frac{1 - e^{-s}}{s^2} \qquad (9\text{--}176)$$

From Table 9–1,

$$G(z) = \frac{z^{-1}}{1 - z^{-1}} \qquad (9\text{--}177)$$

Examination of $G(z)$ shows that it contains only a finite pole at $z = 1$. Applying rules 1 and 3, we can specify the system transfer function as

$$T(z) = K_1 z^{-1} \qquad (9\text{--}178)$$

Assuming that zero steady-state error to a unit step input is desired, the following relationship is obtained from rule 4.

$$1 - T(z) = (1 - z^{-1})F(z) \qquad (9\text{--}179)$$

From rule 4 $F(z)$ is set equal to one to obtain a minimal prototype system. Therefore, equation 9–179 can be expressed as

$$1 - T(z) = 1 - z^{-1} \qquad (9\text{--}180)$$

Substitution of equation 9–178 into equation 9–180 results in

$$1 - K_1 z^{-1} = 1 - z^{-1} \qquad (9\text{--}181)$$

From equation 9–181, the solution for K_1 is

$$K_1 = 1 \qquad (9\text{--}182)$$

Substitution of equation 9–182 into equation 9–178 results in

$$T(z) = z^{-1} \qquad (9\text{--}183)$$

It is now possible to compute the value of $D(z)$. Substituting equations 9–177 and 9–183 into equation 9–165, we obtain

$$D(z) = \frac{1 - z^{-1}}{z^{-1}}\frac{z^{-1}}{1 - z^{-1}} \qquad (9\text{--}184)$$

This expression reduces to

$$D(z) = 1 \qquad (9\text{--}185)$$

which is easily implemented.

b. System Response to a Unit Step. The z-transfer function of the system is given by

$$T(z) = \frac{C(z)}{R(z)} \qquad (9\text{--}186)$$

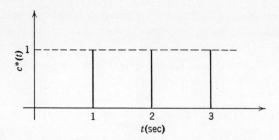

Figure 9–37. *Sampled response of a digitally stabilized sampled-data system containing an integrating process to a unit step input.*

From Table 9–1, the z-transform of a unit step input is

$$R(z) = \frac{1}{1 - z^{-1}} \qquad (9\text{–}187)$$

By substituting equations 9–183 and 9–187 into equation 9–186, we obtain the z-transform of the output response. This expression can be reduced to

$$C(z) = \frac{z^{-1}}{1 - z^{-1}} \qquad (9\text{–}188)$$

By expanding equation 9–188 into a power series in z, and then taking the inverse z-transform, the output response can be obtained. The results are

$$C(z) = z^{-1} + z^{-2} + z^{-3} + \cdots \qquad (9\text{–}189)$$

or

$$c^*(t) = \delta(t - 1) + \delta(t - 2) + \delta(t - 3) + \cdots \qquad (9\text{–}190)$$

and it is plotted in Figure 9–37. Observe that this system follows a unit step input with zero steady-state error based on our previous choice of $1 - T(z)$ in accordance with rule 4.

An analog computer can be extremely useful for determining the performance of such a sampled-data control system. Figure 9–38 illustrates

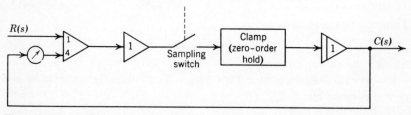

Figure 9–38. *Analog computer circuit for simulating the system shown in Figure 9–36 when $G_2(s) = 1/s$, $D(z) = 1$, and the data extrapolator is a zero-order hold.*

the analog-computer circuitry required for simulating the system whose block diagram was shown in Figure 9–36 with $G_2(s) = 1/s$ and $D(z) = 1$. This circuit can study the effects of varying the gain K, and sampling time T, on the transient response to various inputs at R. A simple analog simulation circuit of this type can easily indicate the direction the control engineer should follow and can save much design time. It is recommended that the reader determine the effect of varying the sampling time T on the system's performance (see Problem 9–24).

2. System with a Double Integrating Process

The next system we consider contains a process which is a double integrator and may be represented by the transfer function

$$G_2(s) = \frac{1}{s^2} \tag{9–191}$$

a. Design of $D(z)$. Using the same procedure as in the previous problem, we first obtain $G(z)$. The expression for $G(s)$ is

$$G(s) = \frac{1 - e^{-s}}{s^3} \tag{9–192}$$

Using Table 9–1, we obtain the z-transform as

$$G(z) = \frac{(1 + z^{-1})z^{-1}}{2(1 - z^{-1})^2} \tag{9–193}$$

Examination of $G(z)$ shows that it contains a zero at $z = -1$ and 2 poles at $z = 1$. Applying rules 1 and 3, we can specify the system transfer function as

$$T(z) = (1 + z^{-1})(K_1 z^{-1} + K_2 z^{-2}) \tag{9–194}$$

Assuming that zero steady-state error to a unit ramp input is desired, the following relationship is obtained from rule 4.

$$1 - T(z) = (1 - z^{-1})^2 F(z) \tag{9–195}$$

Observe from rule 4 that this expression automatically insures that the system will respond to a unit ramp with zero steady-state error. However, a minimal prototype response function cannot be specified since $G(z)$ contains a zero on the unit circle in the z plane. Instead, a longer minimum finite settling time response will be obtained. Therefore, equation 9–195 can be rewritten as

$$1 - T(z) = (1 - z^{-1})^2(1 + \gamma_1 z^{-1} + \gamma_2 z^{-2} + \gamma_3 z^{-3} + \cdots) \tag{9–196}$$

Substituting equation 9–194 into equation 9–196, we obtain the expression

$$1 - (1 + z^{-1})(K_1 z^{-1} + K_2 z^{-2}) = (1 - z^{-1})^2(1 + \gamma_1 z^{-1} + \gamma_2 z^{-2} + \cdots)$$
$$(9\text{–}197)$$

Here γ_2, γ_3, and so on, are considered to be zero in order to obtain a solution for the constants of the equation. Equating coefficients of terms having the same power of z together, we then obtain three simultaneous equations, relating the constants of equation 9–197. If γ_2, γ_3, and so on, were considered, we would have more unknowns than equations and we would obtain a non-minimum finite settling time. The results are as follows:

$$K_1 = 1.25$$
$$K_2 = -0.75 \qquad (9\text{–}198)$$
$$\gamma_1 = 0.75$$

Substituting equation 9–198 into equations 9–194 and 9–196, we obtain

$$T(z) = (1 + z^{-1})(1.25z^{-1} - 0.75z^{-2}) \qquad (9\text{–}199a)$$
$$1 - T(z) = (1 - z^{-1})^2(1 + 0.75z^{-1}) \qquad (9\text{–}199b)$$

It is now possible to compute the value of $D(z)$. Substituting equations 9–193 and 9–199 into equation 9–165, we obtain the expression

$$D(z) = \left[\frac{2(1 - z^{-1})^2}{(1 + z^{-1})(z^{-1})}\right]\left[\frac{(1 + z^{-1})(1.25z^{-1} - 0.75z^{-2})}{(1 - z^{-1})^2(1 + 0.75z^{-1})}\right] \qquad (9\text{–}200)$$

This expression can be reduced to

$$D(z) = \frac{2.5 - 1.5z^{-1}}{1 + 0.75z^{-1}} \qquad (9\text{–}201)$$

The response can be implemented by utilizing two number storage devices (time delays).

  b.   System Response to a Unit Step.   By substituting equations 9–187 and 9–199a into equation 9–186, we can obtain the z-transform of the output response. The resulting expression can be reduced to

$$C(z) = \frac{1.25z^{-1} + 0.5z^{-2} - 0.75z^{-3}}{1 - z^{-1}} \qquad (9\text{–}202)$$

By expanding equation 9–202 into a power series in z and then taking the inverse z-transform, we can obtain the output response. The results are

$$C(z) = 1.25z^{-1} + 1.75z^{-2} + z^{-3} + z^{-4} + \cdots \qquad (9\text{–}203)$$

or

$$c^*(t) = 1.25\,\delta(t - 1) + 1.75\,\delta(t - 2) + \delta(t - 3) + \delta(t - 4) + \cdots$$
$$(9\text{–}204)$$

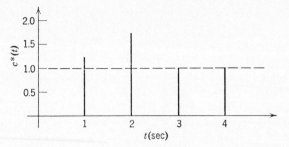

Figure 9–39. Sampled response of a digitally stabilized sampled-data system containing a double integrating process to a unit step input.

and it is plotted in Figure 9–39. Notice that the steady-state error of this system to a unit step input is zero. This is what we should expect from our previous choice of $1 - T(z)$ in accordance with rule 4.

c. System Response to a Unit Ramp. From Table 9–1, the z-transform of a unit ramp is given by the expression

$$R(z) = \frac{Tz^{-1}}{(1 - z^{-1})^2} \tag{9–205}$$

Since we are assuming a sampling time of 1 second, equation 9–205 reduces to

$$R(z) = \frac{z^{-1}}{(1 - z^{-1})^2} \tag{9–206}$$

By substituting equations 9–199a and 9–206 into equation 9–186 we obtain the z-transform of the output response. The resulting expression can be reduced to

$$C(z) = \frac{2.5z^{-2} + z^{-3} - 1.5z^{-4}}{2 - 4z^{-1} + 2z^{-2}} \tag{9–207}$$

By expanding equation 9–207 into a power series in z and then taking the inverse z-transform, we can obtain the output response. The results are

$$C(z) = 1.25z^{-2} + 3z^{-3} + 4z^{-4} + 5z^{-5} + 6z^{-6} + \cdots \tag{9–208}$$

or

$$c^*(t) = 1.25\, \delta(t - 2) + 3\, \delta(t - 3) + 4\, \delta(t - 4) + 5\, \delta(t - 5) + \cdots \tag{9–209}$$

and it is plotted in Figure 9–40.

A comparison of Figures 9–39 and 9–40 indicates that the system responds relatively smoothly to the type of input it was designed for, specifically a ramp, and poorly for lower-order inputs, such as a step. For

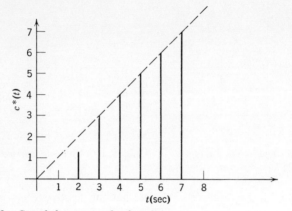

Figure 9–40. Sampled response of a digitally stabilized sampled-data system containing a double integrating process to a unit ramp input.

example, it exhibits an overshoot of 75% when responding to a step input before finally settling to its steady-state value. It is interesting to note that in the first example, which consisted of a sampled-data system containing a single integrator, the response did not exhibit an overshoot to a step input since we originally designed it to respond specifically to this type of input.

The control engineer can obtain much useful information about this sampled-data control system when it is simulated on an analog computer. In particular, it is possible to determine the affects of varying the gain and the sampling time T on the transient response to various inputs at R. Figure 9–41 illustrates the computer circuitry required for simulating the system whose block diagram was shown in Figure 9–36 with

$$G_2(s) = \frac{1}{s^2}$$

and

$$D(z) = \frac{2.5 - 1.5z^{-1}}{1 + 0.75z^{-1}}$$

The circuitry associated with the digital controller is obtained from the difference equation associated with

$$D(z) = \frac{E_2(z)}{E_1(z)} = \frac{2.5 - 1.5z^{-1}}{1 + 0.75z^{-1}} \tag{9–210}$$

or

$$(1 + 0.75z^{-1})E_2(z) = (2.5 - 1.5z^{-1})E_1(z) \tag{9–211}$$

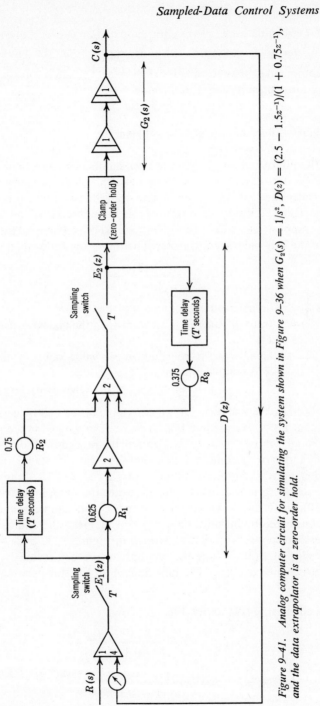

Figure 9–41. Analog computer circuit for simulating the system shown in Figure 9–36 when $G_2(s) = 1/s^2$, $D(z) = (2.5 - 1.5z^{-1})/(1 + 0.75z^{-1})$, and the data extrapolator is a zero-order hold.

The difference equation corresponding to equation 9–211 is given by

$$e_2(n) = -0.75e_2(n-1) + 2.5e_1(n) - 1.5e_1(n-1) \qquad (9\text{–}212)$$

It is recommended that the reader determine the affect of varying the sampling rate on the system's performance (see Problem 9–25).

3. Damping Effect of the Staleness Factor

A method of overcoming the severe overshoots of sampled-data control systems to inputs of a lower order than those they are specifically designed for is to introduce a term to the system transfer function known as the "staleness factor." Implementation of this factor results in softening the system's response to a wide variety of inputs. The "staleness factor" term is added to the original system transfer function in the following manner:

$$T_s(z) = \frac{T(z)}{(1 - Cz^{-1})^N} \qquad (9\text{–}213)$$

where $T(z)$ = original z-transfer function of the system

$T_s(z)$ = z-transfer function of system with the staleness factor term added

C = staleness factor constant whose value ranges from $+1$ to -1 for stable systems

N = exponent which can be any positive value

Since Bertram[13] has shown that not very much is gained by designing N greater than unity, we assume that $N = 1$. The value for the staleness factor C can be chosen by analytical optimizing procedures[13] or by laboratory trial-and-error techniques. Generally, it can be stated that as C approaches unity maximum damping is produced, and as C approaches zero the damping is decreased. We illustrate the damping effect of the staleness factor term on the response of the second sampled-data control system considered by introducing a staleness factor of 0.3 and comparing the system's response with that illustrated in Figures 9–39 and 9–40.

a. Design of $D(z)$. Using the same procedure as previously, we first compute the value of $D(z)$. The introduction of the staleness factor term

$$1 - 0.3z^{-1} \qquad (9\text{–}214)$$

modifies equation 9–194 and 9–196 as follows:

$$T_s(z) = \frac{(1 + z^{-1})(K_1 z^{-1} + K_2 z^{-2})}{1 - 0.3z^{-1}} \qquad (9\text{–}215)$$

$$1 - T_s(z) = \frac{(1 - z^{-1})^2(1 + \gamma_1 z^{-1} + \gamma_2 z^{-2} + \gamma_3 z^{-3} + \ldots)}{1 - 0.3z^{-1}} \qquad (9\text{–}216)$$

Substituting equation 9–215 into 9–216, we obtain the expression

$$1 - \frac{(1 + z^{-1})(K_1 z^{-1} + K_2 z^{-2})}{1 - 0.3z^{-1}}$$

$$= \frac{(1 - z^{-1})^2(1 + \gamma_1 z^{-1} + \gamma_2 z^{-2} + \cdots)}{1 - 0.3z^{-1}} \quad (9\text{–}217)$$

As in the previous example, the constants γ_2, γ_3, and so on, need not be considered. Equating coefficients of terms having the same power of z together, we obtain three simultaneous equations relating the constants of equation 9–217. The results are as follows:

$$K_1 = 1.025$$
$$K_2 = -0.675 \quad (9\text{–}218)$$
$$\gamma_1 = 0.675$$

Substituting equation 9–218 into equations 9–215 and 9–216, we obtain

$$T_s(z) = \frac{(1 + z^{-1})(1.025z^{-1} - 0.675z^{-2})}{1 - 0.3z^{-1}} \quad (9\text{–}219a)$$

$$1 - T_s(z) = \frac{(1 - z^{-1})^2(1 + 0.675z^{-1})}{1 - 0.3z^{-1}} \quad (9\text{–}219b)$$

The value of $D(z)$ can now be computed by substituting equations 9–193 and 9–219 into equation 9–165. The resulting expression is

$$D(z) = \left[\frac{2(1 - z^{-1})^2}{(1 + z^{-1})(z^{-1})} \right]$$

$$\times \left[\frac{(1 + z^{-1})(1.025z^{-1} - 0.675z^{-2})/(1 - 0.3z^{-1})}{(1 - z^{-1})^2(1 + 0.675z^{-1})/(1 - 0.3z^{-1})} \right] \quad (9\text{–}220)$$

This can be reduced to

$$D(z) = \frac{2.05 - 1.35z^{-1}}{1 + 0.675z^{-1}} \quad (9\text{–}221)$$

A comparison of equations 9–201 and 9–221 shows that the values of the various coefficients are different but that the required number of storage stages of the digital controller is the same. Therefore the introduction of the staleness factor term may be obtained by merely readjusting the programming of the digital controller; it does not require a more complex device.

In order to present the digital-computer circuitry associated with equation 9–221, we first obtain the difference equation corresponding to the

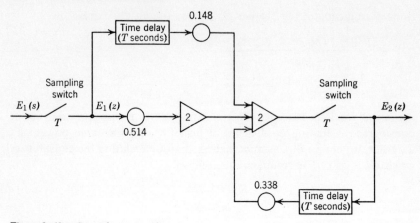

Figure 9–42. Special-purpose digital computer for obtaining $D(z) = (2.05 - 1.35z^{-1})/$
$(1 + 0.675z^{-1})$.

digital controller. Since

$$D(z) = \frac{E_2(z)}{E_1(z)} \tag{9–222}$$

equation 9–221 can be expressed as

$$D(z) = \frac{E_2(z)}{E_1(z)} = \frac{2.05 - 1.35z^{-1}}{1 + 0.675z^{-1}} \tag{9–223}$$

or

$$(1 + 0.675z^{-1})E_2(z) = (2.05 - 1.35z^{-1})E_1(z) \tag{9–224}$$

The difference equation corresponding to equation 9–224 is given by

$$e_2(n) = -0.675e_2(n - 1) + 2.05e_1(n) - 1.35e_1(n - 1) \tag{9–225}$$

A special-purpose digital computer which realizes equation 9–225 by means of samplers, summers, storage devices (time delays), and attenuators is shown in Figure 9–42.

  b.   System Response to a Unit Step.   By substituting equations 9–187 and 9–219a into equation 9–186, we obtain the z-transform of the output response. The resulting expression can be reduced to

$$C(z) = \frac{1.025z^{-1} + 0.35z^{-2} - 0.675z^{-3}}{1 - 1.3z^{-1} + 0.3z^{-2}} \tag{9–226}$$

By expanding equation 9–226 into a power series in z and then taking the inverse z-transform, we can obtain the output response. The results are

$$C(z) = 1.025z^{-1} + 1.68z^{-2} + 1.2z^{-3} + 1.07z^{-4} + 1.02z^{-5}$$
$$+ 1.01z^{-6} + z^{-7} + z^{-8} + \cdots \tag{9–227}$$

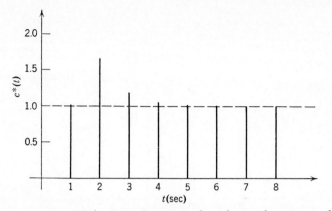

Figure 9–43. Use of the staleness factor term for softening the response of a digitally stabilized sampled-data system containing a double integrating process to a unit step input.

or

$$c^*(t) = 1.025 \, \delta(t - 1) + 1.68 \, \delta(t - 2) + 1.2 \, \delta(t - 3)$$
$$+ 1.07 \, \delta(t - 4) + 1.02 \, \delta(t - 5) + 1.01 \, \delta(t - 6)$$
$$+ \delta(t - 7) + \delta(t - 8) + \cdots \qquad (9\text{–}228)$$

and is sketched in Figure 9–43. Comparing Figures 9–39 and 9–43 we can clearly see the damping or "softening" effect of the staleness factor on the system's response. By varying C between ± 1, an optimum value can be found.

c. System Response to a Unit Ramp. The z-transform of the output response to a unit ramp input can be obtained by substituting equations 9–206 and 9–219a into equation 9–186. The expression can be reduced to

$$C(z) = \frac{1.025z^{-2} + 0.35z^{-3} - 0.675z^{-4}}{1 - 2.3z^{-1} + 1.6z^{-2} - 0.3z^{-3}} \qquad (9\text{–}229)$$

By expanding equation 9–229 into a power series in z and then taking the inverse z-transform, we can obtain the output response. The results are

$$C(z) = 1.025z^{-2} + 2.71z^{-3} + 3.93z^{-4} + 5z^{-5}$$
$$+ 6z^{-6} + 7z^{-7} + \cdots \qquad (9\text{–}230)$$

or

$$c^*(t) = 1.025 \, \delta(t - 2) + 2.71 \, \delta(t - 3) + 3.93 \, \delta(t - 4)$$
$$+ 5 \, \delta(t - 5) + 6 \, \delta(t - 6) + 7 \, \delta(t - 7) + \cdots \quad (9\text{–}231)$$

and is plotted in Figure 9–44. Comparing Figures 9–40 and 9–44, we can clearly see the damping or "softening" effect of the staleness factor on the

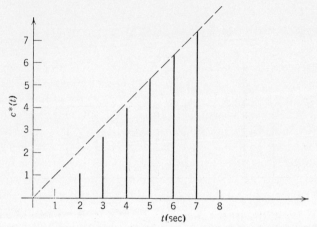

Figure 9–44. Use of the staleness factor term, for softening the response of a digitally stabilized sampled-data system containing a double integrating process to a unit ramp input.

system's response. Although it is true that the implementation of the staleness factor term results in the system taking a little longer time to respond finally to a ramp input, it must be remembered that this solution is a compromise which enables the system to respond less sharply to a step input.

This sampled-data control system can be studied using the analog-computer circuitry shown in Figure 9–41 with the following attenuator setting changes:

$$R_1 = 0.514$$

$$R_2 = 0.148$$

$$R_3 = 0.338$$

The reader should determine the effect on the system's performance of sampling rate changes (see Problem 9–26).

Digital controllers have been used in practice to stabilize both continuous and sampled-data control systems. Their use for the former type of system stems from the fact that the system characteristics resulting from this form of compensation are desirable and advantageous compared to those from conventional continuous techniques. Certainly, when the system contains sampled data to start with, a digital controller is a simple way not only of processing the data but also of compensating the system. Practical digital controllers[6,14] are rather simple devices which can be implemented quite easily.

9–11. RANDOM SIGNALS IN SAMPLED-DATA SYSTEMS

Statistical concepts developed in Chapter 8 for linear continuous systems, having random signals present, can be extended to the design of linear sampled-data systems with random signals. This section will assume that the random signals have the properties of stationariness and ergodicity. Specifically, statistical expressions for sampled-data systems, analogous to those for linear continuous systems, will be presented. Consideration of sampled-data systems having random signals present which do not possess the properties of stationariness and ergodicity is reserved for Chapter 10 when modern optimal control theory is discussed.

To obtain expressions analogous to the autocorrelation function and power-density spectrum of linear continuous functions, it is necessary to analyze the case of a random function which is modulating the amplitude of a rectangular pulse series. This can be visualized from Figure 9–1 if $e(t)$ is assumed to be a stationary random function and $e^*(t)$ as the stationary sampled-random variable.

The *sampled-autocorrelation function* of the sampled random function can be obtained by finding the time average of the product of $e^*(t)$ and $e^*(t + \tau)$ as follows.

$$\phi_{e^*e^*}(\tau) = \lim_{T \to \infty} \frac{1}{2T} \int_{-T}^{T} e^*(t)e^*(t + \tau)\, dt \qquad (9\text{–}232)$$

This expression reduces to a series of impulses which can be expressed as

$$\phi_{e^*e^*}(\tau) = \frac{1}{T} \sum_{N=-\infty}^{\infty} \phi_{ee}(NT)\, \delta(\tau - NT) \qquad (9\text{–}233)$$

This expression shows that the autocorrelation function of a stationary and ergodic sampled impulse series $e^*(t)$ is an impulse series in τ modulated by $1/T$ times the autocorrelation function of the stationary and ergodic continuous random function $e(t)$. It is analogous to equation 8–9 for linear continuous systems.

The *sampled-power-density spectrum* of the random function, whose sampled-autocorrelation function is given by equation 9–233, is the Fourier transform of this equation. It is given by

$$\Phi_{e^*e^*}(\omega) = \int_{-\infty}^{\infty} \sum_{N=-\infty}^{\infty} \phi_{e^*e^*}(NT)\, \delta(\tau - NT)e^{-j\omega\tau}\, d\tau \qquad (9\text{–}234)$$

This expression reduces to

$$\Phi_{e^*e^*}(\omega) = \sum_{N=-\infty}^{\infty} \phi_{e^*e^*}(NT)e^{-j\omega NT} \qquad (9\text{–}235)$$

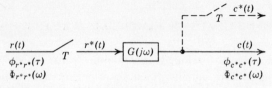

Figure 9–45. *Sampled-data system having a random input.*

In terms of the z transform, the sampled-power density is

$$\Phi_{e^*e^*}(z) = \sum_{N=-\infty}^{\infty} \phi_{e^*e^*}(NT)z^{-N} \qquad (9\text{–}236)$$

Equations 9–235 and 9–236 define the expressions for the sampled-power-density spectrum of the random function, $e(t)$. It is analogous to equation 8–14 for linear continuous systems.

The statistical relationships of a sampled-data system can be illustrated by considering the system shown in Figure 9–45. The input $r(t)$ is assumed to be a random function having the properties of stationariness and ergodicity. In a manner analogous to the linear continuous case, it can be shown that the sampled-power-density spectrum of the input to this system $\Phi_{r^*r^*}(\omega)$ is related to the sampled-power-density spectrum of the output $\Phi_{c^*c^*}(\omega)$ by the following expressions:

$$\Phi_{c^*c^*}(\omega) = |G(j\omega)|^2 \, \Phi_{r^*r^*}(\omega) \qquad (9\text{–}237)$$

$$\Phi_{c^*c^*}(z) = G(z)G(z^{-1})\Phi_{r^*r^*}(z) \qquad (9\text{–}238)$$

It is interesting to compare the similarity of these two equations with equation 8–26.

The sampled-autocorrelation function and the sampled-power-density spectrum are the basic tools for the design of linear sampled-data systems having random inputs. All previously developed statistical concepts, including the root-mean-square error performance criterion, can be obtained using these basic relationships.[14] This discussion has been limited to random functions having the properties of stationarity and ergodicity. Sampled-data systems containing random signals which do not possess the properties of stationariness and ergodicity are considered in the following chapter from the viewpoint of modern optimal control theory.

REFERENCES

1. *Transients in Linear Systems*, M. F. Gardner and J. L. Barnes, John Wiley and Sons, New York, 1942, Vol. 1, Chapter 9.
2. *Laplace Transformation*, W. T. Thomson, Prentice-Hall, New York, 1950, Chapter 7.

3. The Philosophy of Pulse Code Modulation, C. Shannon, *Proc. IRE*, **36**, No. 11, 1324 (Nov. 1948).

4. *The Dynamics of Automatic Controls*, R. C. Oldenbourg and R. Sartorius, *Am. Soc. Mech. Eng.*, New York, 1948, Chapter 5.

5. The Analysis of Sampled-data Systems, J. R. Ragazzini and L. A. Zadeh, *Trans. AIEE*, **71, Pt. 2,** *Appl. Ind.*, 225 (1952).

6. *Sampled-Data Control Systems*, J. R. Ragazzini and G. F. Franklin, McGraw-Hill Book Co., New York, 1958.

7. *Automatic Feedback Control System Synthesis*, J. G. Truxal, McGraw-Hill Book Co., New York, 1955, Chapter 9.

8. A Stability Test for Linear Discrete Systems in Table Form, E. I. Jury and J. Blanchard, *Proc. IRE*, **49**, 1947 (1961).

9. A Simplified Stability Criterion for Linear Discrete Systems, E. I. Jury, *Proc. IRE*, **50**, 1493 (1962).

10. Sampled-Data Control Systems Studied through Comparison with Amplitude Modulation, W. K. Linvill, *Trans. AIEE*, **70, Pt. 2,** *Appl. Ind.*, 1779 (1951).

11. Analysis of Control Systems Involving a Digital Computer, W. K. Linvill and J. M. Salzer, *Proc. IRE*, **41**, No. 7, 901 (1953).

12. Network Compensation of Error-Sampled Feedback Control Systems, J. Sklansky, *Technical Report* T-7/B, Dept. of Electrical Engineering, Columbia University, New York, April 4, 1955.

13. Factors in the Design of Digital Controllers for Sampled-Data Feedback Control Systems, J. E. Bertram, *Trans. AIEE*, *Paper* 56–209, 1956.

14. *Analysis and Synthesis of Sampled-Data Control Systems*, B. C. Kuo, Prentice-Hall, Inc., Englewood Cliffs, 1963.

10 OPTIMAL CONTROL SYSTEMS

10-1. INTRODUCTION

During the presentation of linear, nonlinear, sampled-data, and stochastic (statistical) systems in Chapters 6 through 9, the word "optimum" has been used rather loosely. For example, a typical statement in Chapter 6 was that a feedback control system whose phase margin was 60° and gain margin was 6 db resulted in a transient performance which was "optimum" for the application of the system. We have used this wording purposely in order to introduce the concepts of this chapter more easily. The task of designing control systems which are optimal, in some sense, is one of the most important and complex problems facing control engineers today.

McDonald[1] first developed the concept of optimal theory for control systems in 1950. His objective was to minimize the transient response time of a relay-type feedback control system to step inputs. In 1957, Draper and Li[2] wrote a booklet discussing the theoretical concepts of optimal control for an internal combustion engine. Their system, which is discussed further in Chapter 11, attempted to minimize (or optimize) the consumption of fuel. Since that time many papers have been written on optimal control systems both in this country and abroad.

The theory of optimal control has had some difficulty in being accepted by the practicing control engineer primarily because it is general and its use in solving specific problems is usually not too clear. However, theory creates understanding, and from understanding better designs will evolve. The purpose of this chapter is to present the principle of this new theory, its necessary tools of application, and some simple examples of its use.

It is important to emphasize to the reader that the theory of optimal control systems is at present just a theory. Extremely little of the theory has been converted into practice. As a matter of fact, it is my opinion that the situation will probably not change in the near future. There are many reasons for this. Perhaps the primary reason is that most of the work in this field has been performed in the universities and the research areas of industry. So far, very little of this effort has filtered down to the area of practical development engineering.

Therefore, unlike previous chapters, this chapter is quite general in nature. However, we feel that it is important enough to include, since it is a concept and tool which will play a very important role in the design of the complex control systems of tomorrow.

In order to better understand the very important and complex problem of optimal control, a unified theory utilizing the state-variable approach has evolved. This theory has been developed primarily from the efforts of Bellman,[3,4] Bertram,[5,6] and Kalman[5,6] in this country, and Boltyanskii,[7] Gamkrelidge,[7] and Pontryagin[7,8] abroad.

The concepts of the state-variable approach applied to control systems have been borrowed from classical mechanics and utilize the calculus of variations as the primary analytical tool. In addition, the state-variable concept assumes that the control engineer has a thorough knowledge of and facility in using matrix algebra. Although the reader has probably been exposed to matrix algebra somewhere in his education, it is probably a worthwhile idea to review its principles. Appendix A has been included to serve this function.

The following section is entirely devoted to the presentation of the state-variable, or state-space, concept. To those control engineers who have been educated with the conventional tools—block diagrams, transfer functions, and signal flow graphs—the state-space concept will appear at first to be quite complex. It is important to emphasize at this point, however, that this tool is quite useful and powerful for problems associated with optimal control.

10–2. STATE-SPACE CONCEPTS

The analysis and design of automatic control systems can be approached either by means of the block diagram, transfer function, and signal flow diagram approach, or it can be carried out by means of the state-space concept. In the latter approach, the feedback control system is characterized by a set of first-order differential or difference[9] equations that describe the "state" variables of the system. System analysis and design is then accomplished by solving a set of first-order equations rather than a single higher-order equation.

Although the state-space concept may appear difficult initially, it is well worth while:[10]

1. The solution to a set of first-order differential or difference equations

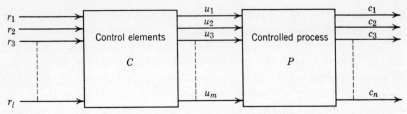

Figure 10–1.   The optimal control problem.

is much easier to obtain than the solution to one higher-order differential equation.

2. The state-space concept can greatly simplify the mathematical notation by utilizing vector matrix notation for the set of first-order equations.

3. Although the inclusion of initial conditions in the analysis of control systems using conventional techniques is quite difficult, the state-space approach readily lends itself to the inclusion of the system's initial conditions as part of the solution.

4. The state-space approach can be readily applied to the solution of certain nonlinear and time-varying systems. In addition, it can be applied to the solution of all sampled-data system configurations (multirate sampling, nonstationary, random sampling and so on).

In order to define certain terms and notations,[11] let us consider the block diagram in Figure 10–1. This simple, open-loop control system will be used to introduce the optimal control problem. The basic optimal control problem concerns the determination of the control elements C such that the controlled process P performs optimally with respect to a selected performance criterion S for the anticipated inputs $r_1, r_2, r_3, \ldots, r_l$ subject to limitations on the controlled process' inputs $u_1, u_2, u_3, \ldots, u_m$. For the present, attention will be focused only on the controlled process.

Let us assume that the u's and c's are time functions, where the notations $u_i(t)$ and $c_j(t)$ represent the values of u_i and c_j at time t. It is often convenient to represent the inputs $u_1, u_2, u_3, \ldots, u_m$ by an *input vector*, $\mathbf{u}$, where

$$\mathbf{u} = (u_1, u_2, u_3, \ldots, u_m) \qquad (10\text{–}1)$$

and the outputs $c_1, c_2, c_3, \ldots, c_n$ by an *output vector*, $\mathbf{c}$, where

$$\mathbf{c} = (c_1, c_2, c_3, \ldots, c_n) \qquad (10\text{–}2)$$

The *input function space* of P is defined as the set of all possible input functions $\mathbf{u}$ that can be applied to P. The *input space* of P is defined as the set of all possible values the vector $\mathbf{u}$ can have at some time T. The *initial state* of P refers to the initial conditions of P at the start of some time interval of interest, t_0.

In general $\mathbf{c}$, the output of P, will be a function of the input $\mathbf{u}$ and the initial conditions of P. For purposes of clarification, let us assume that an input $\mathbf{u}$ is applied to P from t_0 to T seconds, where $T \geqslant t_0$. The segments of the time functions $\mathbf{u}$ and $\mathbf{c}$ over the observation interval (t_0, T) are denoted by $\mathbf{u}_{(t_0, T)}$ and $\mathbf{c}_{(t_0, T)}$. In addition, the initial state of P will be denoted by $\mathbf{p}(t_0)$. Therefore, in state-space terminology, we can say that $\mathbf{c}_{(t_0, T)}$ depends on $\mathbf{u}_{(t_0, T)}$ and $\mathbf{p}(t_0)$.

The procedure to be used for associating a state vector with the controlled process, and then finding the state equations for P, is first to associate with P a vector $\mathbf{x}(0)$ such that $c(t)$ is uniquely determined by $\mathbf{x}(0)$ and $\mathbf{u}_{(t_0, T)}$. The state equations, which are satisfied by $\mathbf{x}$, $\mathbf{u}$, and $\mathbf{c}$, are then determined. If these resulting equations have the property that $\mathbf{x}$ and $\mathbf{c}$ are uniquely determined by $\mathbf{x}(0)$ and $\mathbf{u}_{(t_0, T)}$, then $\mathbf{x}$ will qualify as a state vector for P.

In order to derive the state equations for the system considered in Figure 10–1, let us assume that P is a linear, time-invariant system characterized by the following scalar differential equation:

$$A_n \frac{d^n c}{dt^n} + A_{n-1} \frac{d^{n-1} c}{dt^{n-1}} + \cdots + A_0 c = u \tag{10-3}$$

where all the coefficients are constants and $A_n \neq 0$. We further assume that the time reference point t_0 is zero. Taking the Laplace transformation of equation 10–3, we obtain

$$(A_n s^n + A_{n-1} s^{n-1} + \cdots + A_0) C(s) = U(s) + A_n c^{(n-1)}(0)$$
$$+ (A_n s + A_{n-1}) c^{(n-2)} + \cdots + (A_n s^{n-1} + \cdots + A_1) c(0) \tag{10-4}$$

where $c^{(m)}(0)$ represents the initial value of $c^{(m)}$ at $t = 0$. For convenience this equation is rearranged into the form

$$C(s) = D(s)U(s) + \frac{A_n c^{(n-1)}(0) + (A_n s^n + A_{n-1}) c^{(n-2)}(0) + \cdots + (A_n s^{n-1} + \cdots + A_1) c(0)}{E(s)} \tag{10-5}$$

where
$$E(s) = A_n s^n + A_{n-1} s^{n-1} + \cdots + A_0$$

and
$$D(s) = \frac{1}{E(s)} = P(s)$$

Notice from this last expression that the Laplace transform of the output $C(s)$, and certainly the output in the time domain $c(t)$ (for $t > 0$), is completely determined by the input $\mathbf{u}$ (for $t > 0$) and the values of the output **c** and all its derivatives up to and including order $n - 1$ at $t = 0$. We associate with the initial state $\mathbf{x}(0)$ an n vector, where

$$\mathbf{x}(0) = (c(0), \ldots, c^{(n-1)}(0)) \tag{10-6}$$

Carrying this one step further, the vector $\mathbf{x}(t)$ can be represented by

$$\mathbf{x}(t) = (c(t), \ldots, c^{(n-1)}(t)) \tag{10-7}$$

It will next be proven that this is the state vector of P.

The mathematical model, which describes the dynamic relationships between the inputs and outputs of the controlled process, can be derived from equation 10–7. Rewriting equation 10–7 as

$$
\begin{aligned}
x_1 &= c \\
x_2 &= \dot{c} \\
&\cdot \quad \cdot \quad \cdot \\
x_n &= c^{(n-1)}
\end{aligned}
\tag{10-8}
$$

we notice that equation 10–8 can also be written in the following form:

$$
\begin{aligned}
\dot{x}_1 &= x_2 \\
&\cdot \quad \cdot \quad \cdot \\
\dot{x}_n &= c^{(n)} = \frac{1}{A_n}(u - A_0 x_1 - \cdots - A_{n-1} x_n)
\end{aligned}
\tag{10-9}
$$

Therefore, we can obtain the following relationships:

$$\dot{\mathbf{x}} = \mathbf{Px} + \mathbf{bu} \tag{10-10}$$

$$\mathbf{c} = \mathbf{Lx} \tag{10-11}$$

where

$$
\mathbf{P} = \left[
\begin{array}{ccccc}
0 & 1 & 0 & \cdots & 0 \\
0 & 0 & 1 & \cdots & 0 \\
0 & & \cdots & & 1 \\
-A_0/A_n & & \cdots & - & -A_{n-1}/A_n
\end{array}
\right],
$$

$$
\mathbf{b} = \left[
\begin{array}{c}
0 \\
0 \\
\cdot \\
\cdot \\
\cdot \\
1/A_n
\end{array}
\right], \quad \mathbf{L} = [1, 0, \ldots, 0] \tag{10-12}
$$

Since equation 10-10 is a first-order vector differential equation, its solution $\mathbf{x}(t)$ is uniquely determined by $\mathbf{x}(0)$ and $\mathbf{u}_{(t_0, T)}$. It can be shown[11] that this is a necessary and sufficient condition to qualify $\mathbf{x}(t)$ as the state vector for P.

Equations 10-10 and 10-11 may also be found in the following form in some of the recent literature:

$$\dot{\mathbf{x}} = \mathbf{f}(\mathbf{x}, \mathbf{u}, t) \tag{10-13}$$

$$\mathbf{c} = \mathbf{g}(\mathbf{x}, t) \tag{10-14}$$

Hereafter, we refer to $\mathbf{u}$ as an m vector, $\mathbf{x}$ as an n vector, and $\mathbf{c}$ as a p vector.

The time behavior of the controlled process is described by the solution to the differential equation 10-10 (or 10-13). Convenient terminology for its solution, or motion, is

$$x(t) = \phi_u(T; \mathbf{x}, t_0) \tag{10-15}$$

Equation 10-15 is to be interpreted as the motion of $x(t)$ observed at time T after starting at time t_0 in state $\mathbf{x}$, and influenced by the control input $\mathbf{u}$, which is defined for the interval from t_0 to T. The output of the controlled process P at every instant is assumed to be a continuous function of the state at that instant.

Having defined certain terms and notations concerning the state-space concept, we can now define the state of this system. It can be simply defined[12] as the minimum set of variables, denoted by $x_1, \ldots, x_n$ and specified at times $t \leqslant t_0$, which, together with the given inputs $u_1, \ldots, u_m$, determine the outputs $c_1, \ldots, c_p$ at any future time $t > t_0$.

Before leaving this section, we give an example[12] for converting the plant dynamics, given in any of several forms, into the state-space form given by

$$\dot{x}_1 = f_1(x_1, \ldots, x_n; u_1, \ldots, u_m)$$
$$\cdot$$
$$\cdot \tag{10-16}$$
$$\cdot$$
$$\dot{x}_n = f_n(x_1, \ldots, x_n; u_1, \ldots, u_m)$$

or in vector state-space form given by

$$\dot{\mathbf{x}} = \mathbf{f}(\mathbf{x}, \mathbf{u}, t) \tag{10-17}$$

In general, equation 10-16 (or 10-17) must be solved on an anaolg computer in order to obtain a continuous-time solution. However, if the equations are linear and time-invariant, then an explicit solution is possible utilizing the Laplace transformation. The linear, time-invariant, forms of equations 10–16 and 10–17 are as follows:

$$\dot{x}_1 = A_{11}x_1 + \cdots + A_{1n}x_n + B_{11}u_1 + \cdots + B_{1m}u_m$$

$$\cdot$$
$$\cdot \tag{10-18}$$
$$\cdot$$

$$\dot{x}_n = A_{n1}x_1 + \cdots + A_{nn}x_n + B_{n1}u_1 + \cdots + B_{nm}u_m$$

and

$$\dot{\mathbf{x}} = \mathbf{Px} + \mathbf{bu} \tag{10-19}$$

In equation 10–19, $\mathbf{x}$ represents a column matrix (vector) whose components are $x_1, \ldots, x_n$; $\mathbf{u}$ is a column matrix whose components are $u_1, \ldots, u_m$; $\mathbf{P}$ is an $n \times m$ matrix with entries A_{ij}, and $\mathbf{b}$ is an m matrix with entries B_i. The notation $\dot{\mathbf{x}}$ indicates that each component of the vector $\mathbf{x}$ is differentiated with respect to time once.

As an example of expressing the plant dynamics of a system in state-space form, let us consider the case of rocket flight in two dimensions, with the vertical axis represented by c and the horizontal axis by x.[12,13] The describing equations are given by

$$\ddot{x} = F \cos \psi \tag{10-20}$$
$$\ddot{c} = F \sin \psi - g \tag{10-21}$$

where F = thrust force and ψ = thrust direction. The control inputs will be considered F and ψ. Assuming that

$$x_1 = x, \quad x_2 = \dot{x}$$
$$x_3 = c, \quad x_4 = \dot{c} \tag{10-22}$$
$$u_1 = F, \quad u_2 = \psi$$

the plant dynamics then become

$$\dot{x}_1 = x_2$$
$$\dot{x}_2 = \quad u_1 \cos u_2$$
$$\dot{x}_3 = x_4 \tag{10-23}$$
$$\dot{x}_4 = \quad u_1 \sin u_2 - g$$

Equation 10–23 represents the expression of the plant dynamics in state-space form.

As a second example, consider an open-loop control system whose transfer function is given by

$$P(s) = \frac{C(s)}{U(s)} = \frac{4}{s^3 + 6s^2 + 7s + 3} \tag{10-24}$$

The differential equation corresponding to this system is given by

$$\frac{d^3c}{dt^3} + 6\frac{d^2c}{dt^2} + 7\frac{dc}{dt} + 3c = 4u \tag{10–25}$$

Defining the three-state variable as

$$x_1 = c, \qquad x_2 = \dot{c}, \qquad x_3 = \ddot{c} \tag{10–26}$$

the system can now be described by the following three first-order differential equations:

$$\dot{x}_1 = x_2 = \dot{c} \tag{10–27}$$
$$\dot{x}_2 = x_3 = \ddot{c} \tag{10–28}$$
$$\dot{x}_3 = -3x_1 - 7x_2 - 6x_3 + 4u \tag{10–29}$$

Therefore, the entire system can be described in state-space matrix form by

$$\dot{\mathbf{x}} = \mathbf{Px} + \mathbf{bu} \tag{10–30}$$
$$\mathbf{c} = \mathbf{Lx} \tag{10–31}$$

where
$$\mathbf{P} = \begin{bmatrix} 0 & 1 & 0 \\ 0 & 0 & 1 \\ -3 & -7 & -6 \end{bmatrix}$$

$$\mathbf{b} = \begin{bmatrix} 0 \\ 0 \\ 4 \end{bmatrix}$$

$$\mathbf{x} = \begin{bmatrix} x_1 \\ x_2 \\ x_3 \end{bmatrix}$$

$$\mathbf{L} = \begin{bmatrix} 1 & 0 & 0 \end{bmatrix}$$

10–3. OBJECTIVES FOR DESIGNING AN OPTIMAL CONTROL SYSTEM

The previous section has illustrated that any physical system describable by an nth order differential equation can also be represented by n first-order related differential equations whose variables are considered to constitute the coordinates of a state-space. If the input $\mathbf{u}(t)$ and the initial state $\mathbf{x}(t_0)$ are given, then the behavior of the system, as described by equations 10–13 and 10–14, uniquely defines the motion of the point $\mathbf{x}(t)$ in the state-space. Certain restrictions that must be imposed on the control system to obtain optimization are considered next. This section considers the basic problem of optimal control theory, which is to choose the control input $\mathbf{u}(t)$ such that the performance of the system is optimum from the viewpoint of some performance criterion, utilizing the state-space concepts.

The basic objective of optimal control theory is to make available techniques for the design of the control elements (see Figure 10–1), which best meets a wide variety of requirements. All the problems considered by optimal control theory must possess the following:

1. A controlled process (or plant) whose dynamics are of the form

$$\dot{\mathbf{x}} = \mathbf{f}(\mathbf{x}, \mathbf{u}, t) \tag{10–32}$$

2. Limitations on the input $\mathbf{u}$ and/or the plant, $\mathbf{x}$.
3. A reference signal $\mathbf{r}$ which represents the desired output response.
4. A performance criterion having the form given by

$$S = \int_0^T G(\mathbf{c}(t), \mathbf{u}(t), \mathbf{r}(t), t)\, dt \tag{10–33}$$

The integrand G of equation 10–33, which is referred to in the literature[13] as the loss function, represents a measure of the instantaneous change from ideal performance. Therefore the performance criterion can be viewed as the cumulative loss. The optimal control problem basically consists of determining the control input $\mathbf{u}$ that minimizes the performance criterion S, subject to certain constraints on $\mathbf{u}$ and $\mathbf{x}$.

As a typical problem of the type of control system which can be readily formulated using optimal control theory, let us consider the simple unity feedback positioning control system (servomechanism).[12] The object is to determine the input $\mathbf{u}$ that causes the output $\mathbf{c}$ to follow a given reference signal $\mathbf{r}$ as closely as possible. For this case, the loss function is generally considered to be the squared norm of the magnitude of the error vector $\mathbf{e} = |(\mathbf{c} - \mathbf{r})|$:

$$G = |(\mathbf{c} - \mathbf{r})|^2 \tag{10–34}$$

Therefore, from the definition given by equation 10–33 for the performance criterion of optimal controlled systems, we obtain

$$S = \int_0^T [|(\mathbf{c} - \mathbf{r})|^2]\, dt \tag{10–35}$$

The optimization interval from $t = 0$ to $t = T$ seconds is generally specified and may be either finite or infinite. It is usually desirable to modify the performance criterion, given by equation 10–35, to include the effects of excessive control effort (small and large error amplitudes). Therefore, by modifying equation 10–35 to the following form

$$S = \int_0^T [|(\mathbf{c} - \mathbf{r})|^2 + \lambda(\mathbf{u})^2] \, dt \tag{10–36}$$

a compromise between small and large error control amplitudes can be obtained by a proper choice of λ.

The specification of a particular input $\mathbf{u}$, over the operating interval from $t = 0$ to $t = T$ seconds, is referred to in the literature as the control law.[14] If the input $\mathbf{u}$ is designed so that it minimizes the performance criterion S, then the policy is referred to as being optimal. For this case, the input is denoted by $\mathbf{u}^o$ and the performance criterion is denoted by S^o.

An optimum policy can be specified in either of the following two manners:

1. Open-loop policy
2. Feedback (closed-loop) policy

The optimal policy is called an open-loop policy if the controlled input is specified as a function of the reference input and only the initial state of the output:

$$\mathbf{u}^o(t) = \mathbf{\Psi}(\mathbf{c}(0), \mathbf{r}(t), t) \tag{10–37}$$

The optimal policy is called a feedback policy if the controlled input is specified as a function of the reference signal and the current state of the plant:

$$\mathbf{u}^o(t) = \mathbf{\Psi}(\mathbf{c}(t), \mathbf{r}(t), t) \tag{10–38}$$

Policy is a very important concept since it indicates how $\mathbf{u}^o(t)$ is to be generated from $\mathbf{r}$ and $\mathbf{c}$. Figure 10–2 illustrates the configuration for optimal control systems having open-loop and feedback policies.

A feedback policy is usually the preferred mode of operation for optimal control systems for the reasons given in Chapters 1, 3, and 4 using conventional methods of analysis. For example, feedback operation tends to make the system less sensitive to variations of the plant parameters. In addition, the feedback case makes use of the most up-to-date information on the state of the plant. Therefore, if a disturbance of the system occurs in the feedback case, the system operates on the latest measurement of $\mathbf{c}$ from an optimal viewpoint. In an open-loop system, however, the entire input is preprogrammed on the basis of an initial-state value. There any subsequent disturbances of the output destroy the optimality of operation.

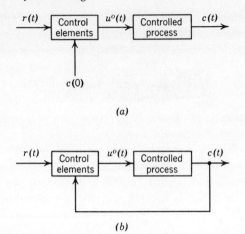

Figure 10–2. Open-loop and feedback optimal control systems. (a) Open-loop optimal system. (b) Feedback optimal control system.

10–4. THEORETICAL APPLICABILITY OF OPTIMAL CONTROL THEORY

Optimal control theory has the potential of applicability to a great variety of control systems. The discussion of this chapter so far has considered only the case of the linear continuous control system, In this section we consider the optimization of sampled-data (discrete) control systems, control systems having random inputs (stochastic), and non-linear control systems. The optimal control theory approach to linear, discrete, stochastic, and nonlinear systems should enhance the reader's understanding of the conventional approaches presented in previous chapters. Optimal control theory is more general and, therefore, less restrictive than the conventional approach. In many cases it can be used to solve problems that do not lend themselves to conventional solutions. For example, we can use optimal control theory to solve problems in continuous and discrete stochastic systems whose random variables do not possess the properties of stationariness and ergodicity.

Discrete control systems are very important because they have many uses, as was discussed extensively in Chapter 9. This class of control system can be easily treated from the optimal control theory viewpoint by considering difference equations[9] instead of differential equations as in the case of continuous systems.

Let us consider the solution of the vector differential equation given by

$$\dot{\mathbf{x}} = \mathbf{f}(\mathbf{x}, \mathbf{u}) \tag{10–39}$$

This differential equation can be written as follows, if the time axis is divided into sufficiently small time intervals Δt:

$$\frac{\mathbf{x}(K\,\Delta t + \Delta t) - \mathbf{x}(K\,\Delta t)}{\Delta t} = \mathbf{f}[\mathbf{x}(K\,\Delta t), \mathbf{u}(K\,\Delta t)] \qquad (10\text{–}40)$$

The left-hand side of equation 10–40 represents the approximation $\dot{\mathbf{x}}$ at time $t = K\,\Delta t$. The notation

$$\mathbf{x}_K = \mathbf{x}(K\,\Delta t) \qquad (10\text{–}41)$$

will be used wherever possible for convenience. Therefore, equation 10–40 can be written as

$$\mathbf{x}_{K+1} = \mathbf{g}(\mathbf{x}_K, \mathbf{u}_K) \qquad (10\text{–}42)$$

where

$$\mathbf{g}(\mathbf{x}_K, \mathbf{u}_K) = \mathbf{x}_K + \Delta t\mathbf{f}(\mathbf{x}_K, \mathbf{u}_K) \qquad (10\text{–}43)$$

Equation 10–43 is basically a difference equation in vector form. A solution for $\mathbf{x}$ at the discrete time values $0, \Delta t, 2\Delta t, \ldots, K\,\Delta t$ can be obtained directly from repeated use of equation 10–42.

Table 10–1. Comparison of expressions for continuous and discrete control systems

No.	Item	Continuous	Discrete
A	Dynamics of a Plant (see eqs. 10–32 and 10–42)	$\dot{\mathbf{x}} = \mathbf{f}(\mathbf{x}, \mathbf{u}, t)$	$\mathbf{x}_{K+1} = \mathbf{g}(\mathbf{x}_K, \mathbf{u}_K)$
B	General Performance Criterion (see eq. 10–33)	$S = \displaystyle\int_0^T G[\mathbf{c}(t), \mathbf{u}(t), \mathbf{r}(t), t]\,dt$	$S = \displaystyle\sum_{K=0}^{n-1} G_K(\mathbf{c}_K, \mathbf{u}_K, \mathbf{r}_K)$
C	Servomechanism Performance Criterion (see eq. 10–35)	$S = \displaystyle\int_0^T [|(\mathbf{c} - \mathbf{r})|^2]\,dt$	$S = \displaystyle\sum_{K=0}^{n-1} |(\mathbf{c}_K - \mathbf{r}_K)|^2$
D	Input for an Open-Loop Policy (see eq. 10–37)	$\mathbf{u}^o(t) = \boldsymbol{\psi}(\mathbf{c}(0), \mathbf{r}(t), t)$	$\mathbf{u}_K{}^o = \boldsymbol{\psi}_K(\mathbf{c}_0, \mathbf{r}_K)$
E	Input for a Feedback Policy (see eq. 10–38)	$\mathbf{u}^o(t) = \boldsymbol{\psi}(\mathbf{c}(t), \mathbf{r}(t), t)$	$\mathbf{u}_K{}^o = \boldsymbol{\psi}_K(\mathbf{c}_K, \mathbf{r}_K)$

It is important to emphasize at this point that the solution of complicated differential equations can be reduced to the simpler problem of repeated evaluation of an algebraic function by means of introducing discrete time (or sampling) values. As a matter of fact, this is precisely the approach taken by digital computers in the solution of differential equations.

All the theory developed in previous sections for linear continuous systems is also true for linear discrete systems, except for changes in the notation. Table 10–1 compares the expressions of linear continuous systems with the corresponding expressions of discrete systems.

The optimal control theory presented so far is based on the assumption that the control engineer has exact information regarding the plant and reference signal. .In order to take account of the uncertainty in optimal control theory, some of the concepts have to be modified. The resulting theory is often called the "*stochastic*" (*or probabilistic*) *optimal control theory* in order to distinguish it from the "deterministic" optimal control theory discussed previously. The basic concept of the stochastic approach modifies the expressions for the plant's dynamics of the linear continuous and discrete cases (see A of Table 10–1) as follows:

$$\dot{\mathbf{x}} = \mathbf{f}(\mathbf{x}, \mathbf{u}, \mathbf{a}, t) \qquad \text{for the continuous case} \qquad (10\text{–}44)$$

$$\dot{\mathbf{x}}_{K+1} = \mathbf{g}(\mathbf{x}_K, \mathbf{u}_K, \mathbf{a}_K) \quad \text{for the discrete case} \qquad (10\text{–}45)$$

The vector $\mathbf{a}$ (or $\mathbf{a}_K$) is referred to as the "environmental parameter" and represents the uncertainty concerning the nature of the plant or some additive disturbance (noise).

Optimal control theory is still in its developmental stages and has not accounted to any great extent for *nonlinearities*. Although some academic attempts have appeared in the literature,[15,16,17] an adequate theory does not exist today.

10–5. PRACTICAL CONSIDERATIONS FOR DESIGNING AN OPTIMAL CONTROL SYSTEM[12]

In most practical systems, the state $\mathbf{x}$ cannot be measured directly but must be estimated from the output $\mathbf{c}$. At this time a complete and rigorous method for solving this problem has not yet been achieved. The current engineering practice is to treat this problem in the following manner.

1. Compute the "best approximation" $\hat{x}(t)$ of the state $x(t)$ from the measured output $c(\tau)$ for $t_0 \leqslant \tau \leqslant T$.
2. Compute the optimal control law assuming that the state $x(t)$ is known and then use the "best approximation" $\hat{x}(t)$ in the control policy.

This method can be readily justified for the linear case with a few minor assumptions.

Other practical problems encountered by the control engineer when attempting to use the principle of optimal control theory are enumerated. We shall consider each of them in this section.

1. Definition of the optimal control objective
2. Derivation of an adequate model
3. Computation of the optimal control policy
4. Stability

It is very rare that a practical optimal control problem is presented to the control engineer in which the performance criterion, as given by equation 10–33, is explicitly defined. As a matter of fact, the *definition of the optimal control objective* is a major practical problem. For example, if we attempted to apply equation 10–33 to a chemical process for the purpose of, perhaps, maximizing the efficiency of the process, it may take a great amount of time, effort, and cost to accomplish. This is usually typical, since a number of objectives are required simultaneously. For example, in the chemical process case, it may be required to minimize equation 10–33 while producing a certain amount of the product. In addition, the temperature and pressure may be limited to certain ranges by safety considerations.

The problem of *deriving an adequate model* is closely related to the problem of defining the control objective. Because of the complexity of modern plants; because the operation of many plants is dependent on empirical techniques; because sufficient operating data are unavailable, it is usually impossible to derive equations 10–13 and 10–14 for a plant. Therefore, an expensive and time-consuming period of experimentation is necessary to collect the necessary data. Furthermore, the process of developing an adequate dynamic model from this collection of data is art, not science.

After the optimal control problem is defined and an adequate model is obtained, the important practical problem of *computing the optimal control policy* remains. An analytic solution in closed form is not possible except in the simplest of cases. The classical technique using the calculus of variations is limited in range and definitely inadequate when it comes to providing numerical answers. Therefore, it has been necessary to develop new methods for the computation of the optimal control policy using digital computers. The techniques of dynamic programming probably present the most straightforward method of computation. Although modern digital computers are limited by their memory capacity, various methods of overcoming this limitation are available to the control engineer.[18] Dynamic programming is discussed in the following section.

A system designed in accordance with optimal control theory is not necessarily *stable*. At present the problem of determining stability of an optimal control system is a difficult task dependent on conventional techniques.

10-6. DESIGN OF A TYPICAL OPTIMAL CONTROL SYSTEM UTILIZING CONVENTIONAL AND DYNAMIC PROGRAMMING TECHNIQUES[12]

This section illustrates the procedure for designing a typical optimal control system utilizing conventional and dynamic programming techniques. The object of this exercise is to illustrate the inadequacies of the conventional approach and the possibilities of dynamic programming.

The system to be considered is a simple regulator, which can be considered to be a special case of the servomechanism problem discussed in Section 10–3. The objective in the regulator problem is to maintain the output at a fixed value. Therefore, its main difference compared to the servomechanism problem is that $\mathbf{r} = 0$. The problem will be considered in discrete time.

The controlled process is assumed to be a first-order linear plant whose dynamics are given by

$$c_{K+1} = Ac_K + Bu_K \tag{10-46}$$

The performance criterion is assumed to have the form

$$S_2 = \sum_{K=0}^{2} (c_K)^2 = (c_0)^2 + (c_1)^2 + (c_2)^2 \tag{10-47}$$

In addition, the controlled input must satisfy the following limitations:

$$-1 \leqslant u_K \leqslant 1$$

The problem is to determine the optimal input sequence $u_0{}^o$, $u_1{}^o$. The value of $u_2{}^o$ is not included as part of the optimal input sequence since it cannot effect the value of c_K during the interval from $0 < K < 2$.

The values of c_1 and c_2 can easily be determined from the dynamics of the controlled process in terms of the initial state c_0 and controlled input sequence u_0, u_1 as follows:

$$c_1 = Ac_0 + Bu_0 \tag{10-48}$$

$$c_2 = Ac_1 + Bu_1 \tag{10-49}$$

The value of c_2 can be expressed in terms of A, B, c_0, u_0 and u_1 by substituting equation 10–48 into equation 10–49 as follows:

$$c_2 = A^2c_0 + ABu_0 + Bu_1 \tag{10-50}$$

Substituting equations 10–48 and 10–50 into equation 10–47, the performance criterion then becomes

$$S_2 = (c_0)^2 + (Ac_0 + Bu_0)^2 + (A^2c_0 + ABu_0 + Bu_1)^2 \quad (10\text{–}51)$$

The problem has now resolved itself to the point where we wish to determine the values of u_0 and u_1 which minimize S_2. These values can be obtained in several ways, including ordinary calculus, by taking partial derivatives of S_2 with respect to u_0 and u_1, and then setting the resulting expressions equal to zero. However, a conventional method that can illustrate better the complexity involved, as compared to dynamic programming, is the "direct approach."[13]

The direct approach requires the calculation and tabulation of all possible values of S_2. The minimum value of S_2 is then obtained by comparing all the values tabulated. Since u_0 and u_1 are continuous variables, it is necessary to divide the unit square in the (u_0, u_1) plane into a finite number of grid points in order that there be only a finite number of possibilities. In order to minimize the computations, and yet obtain sufficient resolution for S_2, a compromise is to choose a grid that contains five discrete points along the u_0 and u_1 axes. The value of S_2 must then be computed for each grid point P_i, as is illustrated in Figure 10–3.

For this problem there are $5 \times 5 = 25$ grid points to calculate. Obviously, the number of grid points increases geometrically with the number of controlled inputs (decisions). For example, a problem having N controlled inputs $u_0, u_1, u_2, \ldots, u_N$ would require a total number of grid points 5^N in order to obtain the same resolution as for the sample problem. Another disadvantage of the conventional approach is the open-loop nature of the solution.

Let us next consider the same problem using dynamic programming.[3] In general, this technique requires substantially fewer computations than

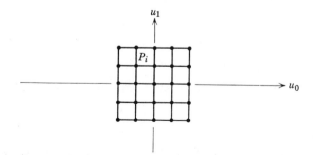

Figure 10–3. Conventional direct approach for calculating the optimal control system.

the direct approach. In addition, this technique always leads to a closed-loop control system since the choice of controlled input, at any instant, is based on the most currently available information of the output (state).

Since c_0 cannot be affected by any controlled input during the interval $(0, 2)$, this parameter is omitted from the optimization process. Therefore it will be assumed that a choice of u_0 has already been made and the corresponding state is c_1. This means that the only controlled input which can be optimized is u_1. Therefore, for this case, there is only one control decision (stage) to be made. The corresponding performance criterion is given by

$$S_1 = (c_2)^2 \tag{10-52}$$

Substituting equation 10–49 into equation 10–52, we obtain

$$S_1 = (Ac_1 + Bu_1)^2 \tag{10-53}$$

The remaining problem is to select u_1, which minimizes S_1.

Let us consider equation 10–53 in the following, more convenient, form:

$$S_1 = \left[B\left(\frac{Ac_1}{B} + u_1 \right) \right]^2 \tag{10-54}$$

From equation 10–54 it is obvious that the value of u_1 which minimizes S_1 is given by the following:

$$u_1 = -1 \qquad \text{for} \quad \frac{Ac_1}{B} > 1$$

$$u_1 = 1 \qquad \text{for} \quad \frac{Ac_1}{B} < -1 \tag{10-55}$$

$$u_1 = -\frac{Ac_1}{B} \quad \text{for} \quad -1 \leqslant \frac{Ac_1}{B} \leqslant 1$$

In order to simplify the notation, equation 10–55 will be written in terms of the sat function, which is defined as

$$\text{sat } z = -1 \quad \text{for} \quad z < -1$$
$$\text{sat } z = 1 \quad \text{for} \quad z > 1 \tag{10-56}$$
$$\text{sat } z = z \quad \text{for} \quad -1 \leqslant z \leqslant 1$$

Therefore, in terms of the sat function, equation 10–55 is given by

$$u_1 = -\text{sat} \frac{Ac_1}{B} \tag{10-57}$$

Equation 10–57, which is a fixed decision rule for all possible states c_1, is optimal only for the last stage of operation. The corresponding minimum value of S_1 is given by

$$S_1^0 = \left(Ac_1 - B \text{ sat} \frac{Ac_1}{B} \right)^2 \tag{10-58}$$

Let us next proceed one step backwards in time. The performance criterion is then given by

$$S_2 = (c_1)^2 + (c_2)^2 = (c_1)^2 + S_1^0 \tag{10-59}$$

We substitute S_1^0 into equation 10-59 since the last decision rule has been fixed. Proceeding as before, the function which must be minimized is given by

$$S_2 = (Ac_0 + Bu_0)^2 + \left[A(Ac_0 + Bu_0) - B \text{ sat} \frac{A}{B} (Ac_0 + Bu_0) \right]^2 \tag{10-60}$$

We wish to minimize this function with respect to u_0. A similar analysis of this function indicates that the value of u_0, which minimizes S_2, has a similar form:

$$u_0 = -\text{sat} \frac{Ac_0}{B} \tag{10-61}$$

Therefore, the optimal control policy for this problem is given by

$$u_K^0 = -\text{sat} \frac{Ac_K}{B} \tag{10-62}$$

It is interesting to note that the optimal control solution has resulted in a feedback policy. In addition, notice that each step of the optimization process involved minimization with respect to only one variable as compared with the two-dimensional minimization required using the conventional direct approach.

To illustrate the reduction in the number of computations required using the dynamic programming technique, as compared to the conventional direct approach, let us consider the optimization of S_2 as given by equation 10-60. As before, the u_0 axis would be divided into five discrete points in order to obtain sufficient resolution. For a fixed value of c_0, the dynamic programming minimization of S_2 would require that S_2 be evaluated at each discrete value of u_0. However, since u_0 must be obtained as a function of c_0, it is necessary to repeat the procedure for all possible values of c_0. Assuming that the c_0 axis is divided into ten points, $10 \times 5 = 50$ computations would be required for the minimization of S_2. Since an equal amount of computation would be required for the minimization of S_1, the total amount of computation required for this two-stage process using dynamic programming is $2 \times 50 = 100$. In contrast, a conventional direct minimization would require $10 \times 5^2 = 250$ computations. The factor of 10 must be included if the initial state is not known in an a priori manner. Therefore the dynamic programming approach has resulted in a reduction in the total number of computations required.

It is interesting to note that if the initial state c_0 is known a priori, then only $5^2 = 25$ computations would be required when using the conventional direct optimization approach. However, an exact knowledge of c_0 does not reduce the number of computations with the dynamic programming approach since the controlled input is always determined at each stage for all possible values of the current state. For such cases, it is possible that the conventional direct approach can result in fewer computations than the dynamic programming technique. As the number of stages increases, however, the dynamic programming technique will quickly result in less computations, even in the cases when c_0 is known a priori. For example, if $N = 6$, a conventional direct approach requires $5^6 = 15,625$ computations, while the dynamic programming technique would require only $6 \times 10 \times 5 = 300$ computations.

It can be shown[3,12] that the concept of dynamic programming, as developed by Bellman, is based on an imbedding principle and an optimality principle. The *imbedding principle* states that a system having fixed initial states and a fixed operation interval $(0, N - 1)$ can always be considered a special case of a more general system when the initial state and operation interval $(n', N - 1)$ are both variable. Therefore, the original system is imbedded into a whole class of problems. The *optimality principle* states that any policy which is optimal over the interval $(0, N - 1)$ is necessarily optimal over any subinterval $(n', N - 1)$, where $0 \leqslant n' \leqslant N - 1$.

Both of these principles were used in the solution to the illustration. The imbedding principle was used in this problem since the original problem involved a fixed initial state c_0 and a fixed operation interval $(0, 2)$, while we chose a variable state c_1 and a reduced operation interval $(1, 2)$. The optimality principle was involved in the second optimization step since the optimization over the interval $(0, 2)$ assumed that the policy over the subinterval $(1, 2)$ had already been chosen to be optimal.

10–7. PONTRYAGIN'S MAXIMUM PRINCIPLE

Another tool which can be used for analyzing problems in optimal control is Pontryagin's Maximum Principle. It is very closely related to dynamic programming. The main difference between the two methods is the basic viewpoint: Dynamic programming is concerned with minimizing the performance criterion, S; the maximum principle is concerned with maximizing a scalar H which will also result in minimizing the performance criterion, S.

The original maximum principle, as formulated by Pontryagin, states that a control input, $\mathbf{u}$, which minimizes the performance criterion

$$S = \sum_{i=0}^{n} c_i x_i(T) \tag{10-63}$$

maximizes the Hamiltonian function H (a scalar quantity)

$$H = \sum_{i=0}^{n} p_i f_i(\mathbf{x}, \mathbf{u}) \tag{10-64}$$

where $\dot{x}_i$ and $\dot{p}_i$ are defined as

$$\dot{x}_i = f_i(\mathbf{x}, \mathbf{u}^o) \tag{10-65}$$

and

$$\dot{p}_i = \sum_{j=0}^{n} \frac{\partial f_j}{\partial x_i}\bigg]_{\mathbf{u}=\mathbf{u}^o} p_j; \qquad i = 0, 1, 2, \ldots, n \tag{10-66}$$

$\mathbf{u}^o$ is used to designate the permissible value of the control input $\mathbf{u}$ which maximizes the scalar H.

In the discrete-time case, the maximum principle has the following form:

$$S = \sum_{i=0}^{n} c_i x_{N-1}^i \tag{10-67}$$

and

$$\mathbf{x}_{K+1} - \mathbf{x}_K = \mathbf{f}(\mathbf{x}_K, \mathbf{u}_K); \qquad K = 0, 1, 2, \ldots, n \tag{10-68}$$

The control input sequence, $\mathbf{u}_K$, which minimizes the performance criterion, S, must necessarily maximize H where

$$H = \sum_{i=0}^{n} p_K{}^i f^i(\mathbf{x}_K, \mathbf{u}_K) \tag{10-69}$$

and

$$p_{K+1}^i - p_K{}^i = -\sum_{j=0}^{n} \frac{\partial f^j}{\partial x^i}\bigg]_{\mathbf{u}_K=\mathbf{u}_K^o} p_K{}^j \tag{10-70}$$

$\mathbf{u}_K{}^o$ is used to designate the permissible value of the discrete control input which maximizes the scalar H.

Pontryagin's maximum principle can be looked on in a more useful manner if we consider a performance criterion that is a function of the controlled process' dynamics, inputs, and desired output. For the continuous case, let us assume that we have a process whose dynamics are given by

$$\dot{x}_i = f_i(\mathbf{x}, \mathbf{u}) \tag{10-71}$$

The modified maximum principle states that the control input **u** which minimizes the performance criterion

$$S = \int_0^T G[\mathbf{x}, \mathbf{u}, \mathbf{r}, t] \, dt \tag{10-72}$$

will at the same time maximize a modified scalar, H', with respect to **u**. The modified scalar is defined as

$$H' = \sum_{i=0}^{n} p_i f_i(\mathbf{x}, \mathbf{u}) - F(\mathbf{x}, \mathbf{u}, \mathbf{r}) \tag{10-73}$$

The function, $\dot{p}_i$, is defined as

$$\dot{p}_i = -\frac{\partial H'}{\partial x_i}; \qquad i = 1, 2, \ldots n \tag{10-74}$$

It can be shown that a very close relationship exists between Pontryagin's maximum principle and dynamic programming. I like to look at the maximum principle as another tool which can be used to optimize control systems from a slightly different viewpoint. References 3, 7, and 19 have more complete discussions of Pontryagin's maximum principle.

10–8.   OPTIMAL FILTER THEORY—KALMAN FILTERING

A subject of current interest in the optimal control field is design of the best possible filter for predicting discrete data that is corrupted with random noise. A complete description of the stochastic properties of such a train of pulses is very difficult. To describe the stochastic properties of such a random pulse train completely requires a K-dimensional point probability distribution which defines the properties of sample K in terms of the previous $K - 1$ samples. This has the general form of a conditional probability distribution function:

$$p(x_K/x_{K-1}, x_{K-2}, \ldots, x_1) \tag{10-75}$$

Equation 10–75 states that the probability characteristics of sample K can be determined if the values of all preceding samples are known. Some problems may require only a few of the preceding samples, depending on the statistics of the signal and the nature of the problem. Unfortunately, even for the simple case of a Gaussian random variable, the distribution function is a $K - 1$ dimensional covariance matrix. This results in extremely complex expressions that are very difficult to evaluate.

The very practical problem of making a decision based on an observation or group of observations which is corrupted by additive noise is illustrated in Figure 10–4. If an estimate of x_K is to be made on the basis of the noisy information y_K, it is necessary to utilize the statistical characteristics of x_K in the decision making process. Useful illustrative results can be obtained if certain reasonable assumptions are made. First, we will assume that the values of y_K and all its previous values are known. In addition, the noise will be assumed to have a zero-mean Gaussian density distribution. The expected value of x_K, denoted by $\hat{x}_K$, can be evaluated from the conditional estimate

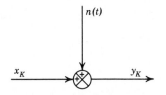

Figure 10–4. Additive noise corrupting a discrete function.

$$E[x_K \mid y_K, y_{K-1}, y_{K-2}, \ldots, y_1] \qquad (10\text{--}76)$$

which minimizes the loss function

$$E\{(x_K - E[x_K \mid y_K, y_{K-1}, y_{K-2}, \ldots, y_1])^2\} \qquad (10\text{--}77)$$

that represents the mean-square error of the estimate.

R. E. Kalman[20–22] has shown that the mean value of the conditional probability distribution function is the best possible estimate of x_K for this problem in terms of a restricted class of loss functions which contain the least mean-square error. Another interesting result of Kalman's is that the best estimate of x_K is a linear function of the data $y_K, y_{K-1}, \ldots, y_1$ when Gaussian additive noise is present. Therefore, the best least mean-square error estimate of x_K, $\hat{x}_K$, is given by

$$\hat{x}_K = \sum_{i=K}^{K-N} a_i y_i \qquad (10\text{--}78)$$

where N represents the total number of observations available. The coefficients a_i may be evaluated directly from the discrete form of the Weiner-Hopf equation (see equation 8–71). This yields $K - N$ linear equations with $K - N$ unknowns. Standard matrix techniques can be applied to evaluate this problem.

If the optimum estimate of x_K is considered to be a function of the new information y_K and the previous estimates of x_K, then it can be shown that

$$\hat{x}_K = \hat{x}_{K-1} + a_K y_K \qquad (10\text{--}79)$$

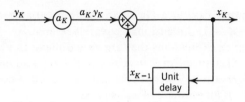

Figure 10–5.   Computer simulation of a linear prediction filter.

where

$$a_K = \frac{P_{K-1}}{P_{K-1} + \sigma_n^{\,2}}$$

$$P_K = (1 - a_K)P_{K-1}$$

$$P_0 = \sigma_y^{\,2}$$

The term P_K is defined as the mean-square error of the Kth estimate of the zero-mean random variable y:

$$P_K = E[(\hat{y}_K - y_K)^2] \qquad (10\text{–}80)$$

The terms $\sigma_n^{\,2}$ and $\sigma_y^{\,2}$ represent the variances of the zero-mean of the corruptive Gaussian noise and the observable function y_K, respectively. Figure 10–5 illustrates the computer representation of Equation 10–79. Observe that this optimum estimate results in a feedback policy since the estimate depended on the new observable information y_K in addition to the previous estimates of x_K. Kalman has shown that equations 10–78 and 10–79 are equivalent for zero-mean Gaussian noise.

The basic concepts for optimizing the estimate of a noisy observation presented in this section can be extended to considerably more complex systems. The reader is referred to some interesting results in References 20, 21, 22, and 23.

10–9.   CONCLUSION

The theory of optimal control is an extremely powerful technique. Its concepts have had a profound impact on the philosophy of feedback control system design. At the present time optimal control theory is still in its developmental stages, and a more complete treatment cannot be presented.

Optimal control theory represents an important area of research in the feedback control field. Unfortunately, a large gap has developed between research and practice in this area, primarily because the concept is novel and the practicing control engineer is unfamiliar with the radically different language (state-space notations). This large gap is sure to shrink in the very near future.

The important concept that the reader should have gained from this chapter is the principle of optimality. This is certainly very important in modern, complex, control systems. The extension of the principle of optimality to adaptive control systems is presented in Chapter 11. It will be shown there that optimal control systems are a special class of the broader classification of adaptive control systems, and several practical applications will be illustrated.

REFERENCES

1. Nonlinear Techniques for Improving Servo Performance, D. McDonald, *Proceedings of the National Electronics Conference*, Vol. 6, 1950.
2. Principles of Optimalizing Control Systems and an Application to Internal Combustion Engine, C. S. Draper and Y. T. Li, Am. Soc. Mech. Engrs., New York, Sept. 1951.
3. *Dynamic Programming*, R. Bellman, Princeton University Press, Princeton, N.J., 1959.
4. *Adaptive Control Processes—A Guided Tour*, R. Bellman, Princeton University Press, Princeton, N.J., 1961.
5. General Synthesis Procedure for Computer Control of Single-Loop and Multiloop Linear Systems, R. E. Kalman and J. E. Bertram, *Trans. AIEE*, **77, Pt. 2, *Appl. Ind.*, 602 (1958).
6. Control System Analysis and Design via the Second Method of Lyapunov, R. E. Kalman and J. E. Bertram, *J. Trans. ASME*, **82, Pts. 1 and 2,** 371 (June 1960).
7. The Theory of Optimal Processes, I. The Maximum Principle, V. G. Boltyanskii, R. V. Gamkrelidge, and L. J. Pontryagin, *Izv. Akad. Nauk SSSR, Ser. Mat.*, **24,** 3 (1960).
8. Optimal Control Processes, L. S. Pontryagin, *Usp. Mat. Nauk*, **14,** 3 (1959).
9. *Transients in Linear Systems*, M. F. Gardner and J. L. Barnes, John Wiley and Sons, New York, 1942, Vol. 1.
10. State Transition Flow Graphs of Continuous and Sampled Dynamic Systems, Benjamin C. Kuo, presented at the 1962 Western Electronic Show and Convention, August 21–24, 1962, Los Angeles, Calif.
11. An Introduction to State-Space Techniques, L. A. Zadeh, presented at the 1962 Joint Automatic Control Conference, New York.
12. Optimal Control Theory—A Short Course, presented at the Polytechnic Institute of Brooklyn, Jan. 7–11, 1963.
13. Optimization Techniques, G. Leitmann, editor, Academic Press, New York, 1962.
14. The Theory of Optimal Control and the Calculus of Variations, R. E. Kalman, *RIAS Technical Report* 61–3, 1961.
15. Dynamic Optimization of a Distillation Column, R. L. Zhradnik, D. H. Archer, and R. R. Rothfus, *Proc. of the Joint Automatic Control Conference*, 1962.
16. Some Optimization Problems in Chemical Engineering, R. Aris, R. E. Bellman, and R. Kalaba, *Chem. Eng. Progr., Symp. Ser., Adv. in Comp. & Math. Tech. in Chem. Eng.*, **56,** No. 31, 95 (1960).

17. Dynamic Programming Formulation of Catalyst Replacement Problems, S. M. Roberts, *Chem. Eng. Progr.*, *Symp. Ser.*, *Adv. in Comp. & Math. Tech. in Chem. Eng.*, **56**, No. 31, 103 (1960).
18. *Applied Dynamic Programming*, R. E. Bellman, Princeton University Press, Princeton, N.J., 1962.
19. *Statistical Analysis and Optimization of Systems*, E. L. Peterson, John Wiley and Sons, New York, 1961.
20. Optimal Synthesis of Linear Sampling Control Systems Using Generalized Performance Indices, R. E. Kalman and R. W. Koepcke, *ASME Trans.*, **80**, 1820 (Nov. 1958).
21. A New Approach to Linear Filtering and Prediction Problems, R. E. Kalman, *ASME Trans.*, *Series D, Jour. Basic. Eng.*, **82**, 35 (March 1960).
22. New Results in Linear Filtering and Prediction Theory, R. S. Bucy and R. E. Kalman, *ASME Trans.*, *Series D, Jour. Basic Eng.*, **95** (March 1961).
23. Optimal Stochastic Control Theory—A Short Course, P. Dorato, R. F. Drenick, and L. Shaw, Presented at the Polytechnic Institute of Brooklyn, Jan. 6–10, 1964.

11 ADAPTIVE CONTROL SYSTEMS

11-1. INTRODUCTION

So that the reader may fully comprehend the concept of adaptivity he has first been introduced to the concept of optimality. This philosophy plays an important role in the generation of the adaptive control system concept. As a matter of interest, the first form of adaptive control system was referred to as an "optimal control system" by Draper and Li.[1,2]

An adaptive control system is basically a feedback control system that automatically achieves a desired response in the presence of extreme changes in the controlled system's parameters and major external disturbances. Adaptive control systems are usually characterized by devices which automatically measure the dynamics of the controlled system and other devices which automatically adjust the characteristics of the controlled elements based on a comparison of these measurements with some optimum figure of merit.

A good question the control engineer can ask at this point is: Wouldn't a conventional control system compensate for variations due to changes in the parameters of the controlled system and to disturbances? Certainly the answer is affirmative. However, the reason that the control engineer resorts to an adaptive control system is that a conventional feedback control system is not capable of high performance in the presence of extreme changes of the controlled system's parameters and large external disturbances. For example, a very large change in the parameter values of the controlled system may easily degrade the performance of a conventional feedback control system. In addition, a conventional feedback control system designed to respond in an optimum manner to simple inputs such as steps and ramps, may not respond in an optimum manner to these signals if they are contaminated with noise. However, an adaptive control can be designed to overcome the limitations of ordinary feedback control systems.

It is not always simple to distinguish between an optimal and an adaptive control system, and the control engineer should not attempt to

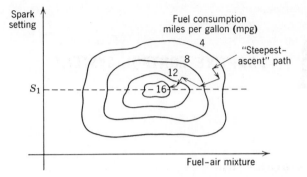

Figure 11–1. Contours of constant miles per gallon (figures of merit) for an internal combustion engine with a "steepest-ascent" path superimposed.

separate these two concepts. In order to clarify this further, the operating phases that comprise an adaptive control system will be outlined. From its definition, an adaptive control system can be considered to be composed of the following three stages of operation:

1. Determine a figure of merit, or operating point, for optimum performance in an a priori manner.
2. Continuously compare the desired performance of the system with actual system performance.
3. Automatically, and continuously, adjust the feedback control system's parameters in order to minimize the difference between desired and actual system performance.

Based on this interpretation of an adaptive control system, my feeling is that an optimal control system is a class of adaptive control systems where the figure of merit can be measured directly. This difference will be further clarified with some simple illustrations.

Let us assume that our problem is to minimize the fuel consumption of an internal combustion engine.[1,3] There are two controls available to the engineer which he may adjust: spark setting and fuel-air mixture. An entire family of contours for constant miles per gallon, which is the figure of merit for this particular example, is possible as these two controls are varied. This is illustrated in Figure 11–1. The difference in operation between an adaptive and optimal control system for this particular example is quite clear:

1. An adaptive control system would continually compare the actual system figure of merit, fuel consumption in miles per gallon (mpg), with the ideal maximum figure of merit (16 mpg for this example). In addition, it would continuously and automatically adjust the

fuel-air mixture and spark setting to achieve an actual fuel consumption of 16 mpg.

2. An optimal control system would depend on a priori information, based on experience, to determine the optimum spark setting. This system, for example, might assume that a spark setting of S_1 is optimum, as shown in Figure 11–1. A plot of the fuel consumption, in mpg, versus the corresponding fuel-air mixture for this spark setting is shown in Figure 11–2. This optimal control system would, therefore, only adjust the fuel-air mixture with the spark setting at its optimum value, S_1.

From this example it is quite clear that optimal control systems are a form of adaptive control systems.

The interrelation between adaptive and optimal control systems can be further illustrated by considering the control system for a photographic reconnaissance satellite.[4] Since a primary requirement for such a system is minimum fuel consumption, it is necessary to choose a certain desired attitude based on a priori data. Therefore it is necessary to incorporate an optimal control system to minimize fuel consumption. However, this quiescent operating point is a function of the particular orbit of the satellite and its spin rate. Since the process dynamics and the desired attitude of the satellite, with respect to the Earth's gravitational field, will slowly change as it traverses its orbit, the control system must also utilize an adaptive control system to maintain satisfactory dynamic control.

It is my very strong feeling that a textbook should make every effort not to confuse the control engineer with semantics. The important thing is to convey concepts in order that the reader may understand the principles involved. If the reader attempts to go through the vast volume of literature in this particular phase of automatic control theory, he will find that some authors have used the terms self-adaptive, computer-controlled,

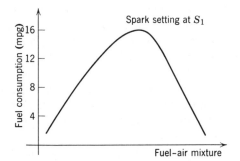

Figure 11–2. Variation of fuel consumption with the fuel-air mixture of an internal combustion engine for a specific spark setting.

preprogrammed, and final-value control systems to describe the different types of control system which feature the adaptive concept. Without belaboring the semantics of this concept any further, I consider any system that continually measures and compares a system's performance with some reference and then automatically adjusts the system's parameters in order to achieve optimum performance to be an adaptive control system. Furthermore, an optimal control system is considered to be a form of adaptive control system.

The problem of obtaining maximum cruising range of long-range aircraft per pound of fuel used in their internal combustion engines stimulated the original work in adaptive control systems.[1] Before the use of adaptive flight controls, both throttle setting and fuel-air mixture were determined experimentally for each type of aircraft. This was a tedious task involving extensive testing. The results of these tests were then tabulated for use by the flight engineer. However, this extensive tabulation could not account for changes in all the variables, which included humidity, pressure, temperature, wear of the engines, variations of the engines, and errors due to improper settings. Furthermore, the flight engineer could not continuously monitor and recheck all the variations. The use of adaptive flight control systems has increased the cruising range of some long-range aircraft by as much as 25%. Most of these systems monitor and control the manifold pressure ratio which has been found to have a very close relationship to actual fuel consumption.

In addition to its use for aircraft and space vehicles, the adaptive concept lends itself readily for problems in precision instrument radar tracking systems. An adaptive radar tracking system[5] is a necessity when the control system's requirements conflict with either the angular tracking dynamics or the type of received signal.

Ballistic missile dynamics, with which a modern instrument radar tracking loop must contend, usually requires that the servo bandwidth be wide enough to handle high-speed, close-in targets in order to achieve a high gain constant. However, such a wide bandwidth is very undesirable when noise considerations are brought into focus. In order to meet the simultaneous and apparently contradictory requirements of wide bandwidths and low sensitivity to noise, a computer is usually required to augment the tracking performance through an adaptive configuration. Here the effect of computer augmentation is to increase all gain constants of the radar tracking system without requiring that the intrinsic bandwidth of the servo be increased.

If the received radar signal of a tracking radar is heavily contaminated with noise, a large amount of filtering may be required with a resultant sluggish track loop response. Therefore, in order to obtain an optimum response of the tracking loop under these conditions, it is necessary to adjust the loop gain of the feedback control system as a function of the signal-to-noise ratio.

Other applications of adaptive control systems are for missile control, chemical-process control, and machine tool control. In the next section, an attempt to categorize adaptive control systems in accordance with their configurations will be made. In addition, several examples will be used for illustrative purposes.

11–2. TYPES OF ADAPTIVE CONTROL SYSTEMS

From the qualitative examples presented in the previous section, the reader should have been left with the impression that adaptivity can be achieved using several configurations depending on the specific application. In this section, we attempt to categorize most forms of adaptive control systems into the following four general classes:

1. Model-reference adaptive control system
2. Nonlinear adaptive control system
3. Impulse-response adaptive control system
4. Digital-computer-controlled adaptive control system

The main attempt in the following discussion is to convey ideas and concepts rather than specific systems. In the next section the design philosophy for adaptive control systems is generalized. A design example for a specific adaptive control system is illustrated in Section 11–4.

Any attempt to limit the classification of adaptive control systems to only four categories is a very "short-sighted" approach. I recognize this, but feel that it is worthwhile, since it is an attempt to unify most of the work that has been done in the adaptive control field up to the present time. Certainly this classification will need revision and modification in the future.

The block diagram of a *model-reference adaptive control system*[6] is shown in Figure 11–3. The elements that change the conventional feedback control system to an adaptive one for this configuration are the addition of the model, comparator, and adaptor. The model-reference adaptive control system applies the input to both the conventional feedback control system and the model, whose output represents the desired or optimum response. If a difference exists between the actual and desired responses, an error signal is generated by the comparator. The resulting error signal is then operated on by the adaptor in an a priori fashion in order to adjust the control elements, which attempt to achieve optimum

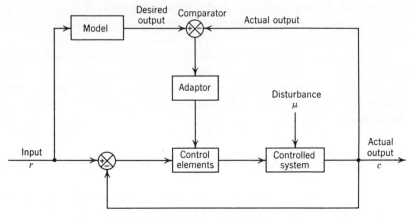

Figure 11–3.   Model-reference adaptive control system.

control. The model furnishes this system with an optimum criterion for adaptivity. Any changes caused by variations of the parameters of the controlled system or external disturbances are compensated for by the adaptive feature.

The system in Figure 11–3 has been designed by the MIT Instrumentation Laboratory for use in adaptive autopilots. Besides being adaptive, this system has certain other attractive features. For example, if the adaptive portion should fail, the system would continue to operate with the conventional feedback control system portion operating with the control elements set at some nominal values. In addition, the model can adapt itself to obtain the best possible responses if the available control forces in the adaptive system are limited to the extent of being unable to obtain the optimum response physically. Therefore this model "learns" from previous experience and exhibits a very high degree of adaptivity.

The block diagram of a *nonlinear adaptive control system* is shown in Figure 11–4. This general configuration has been used by Minneapolis-Honeywell[7] as an adaptive flight control system for the F-94C aircraft. Its adaptive feature incorporates a high linear gain together with a nonlinear element (relay). The nonlinear characteristics of the relay are modified by an a-c sinusoidal dither signal in order that the effective relay characteristic is a function of the waveform. The limiter, which follows the relay, has its limiting levels adjusted in accordance with the adaptor's actuating signal. When the error is above allowable limits, full output from the relay is applied to the system; conversely, the adaptor attenuates the relay's output when the error is below a prescribed level.

Since this nonlinear configuration is capable of extremely high gain loops, responses to abrupt inputs would be undesirable for the pilot.

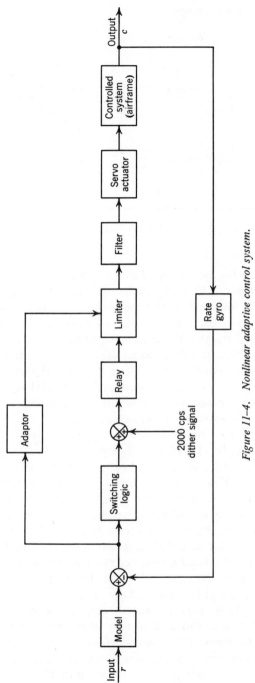

Figure 11–4. Nonlinear adaptive control system.

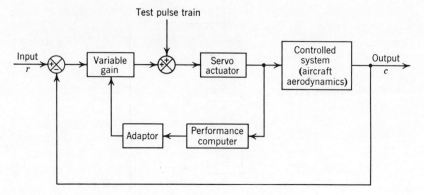

Figure 11–5. Impulsive response adaptive control system proposed by the Sperry Gyroscope Co.

Therefore, an analog model is used to shape the input in order to prevent this from occurring. The model effectively "smoothes" the input.

The nonlinear adaptive control system configuration illustrated offers the advantage of a fairly high degree of performance, simplicity, and reliability. However, it has the disadvantage that it is capable of operation for only a limited range of parameter variations. In addition, since the adaptation of this system is to each signal or disturbance as it occurs, it does not learn from previous experience as does the MIT system previously described. Therefore, the system in Figure 11–4 exhibits a lower degree of adaptivity than the system in Figure 11–3.

The block diagram of an *impulsive response adaptive control system* is shown in Figure 11–5. This configuration attempts to determine the damping of the overall system by measuring the response of the system to a test pulse train. This excitation signal consists essentially of a low-amplitude pulse having a relatively narrow width. The damping factor can be determined by counting the number of half cycles of the resulting output transient, which has the form of a decaying oscillation. The performance computer actually counts the number of half cycles of the resulting oscillation. Based on the determination of damping by the performance computer, the adaptor adjusts the system's gain in order to achieve a damping that is considered optimum.

An adaptive system proposed by the Sperry Gyroscope Co.[7] for adaptive flight control falls into this general type of adaptive control system. It assumes that the form of the controlled system is known in advance. Specifically, this system attempts to measure the exact location of a pair of variable high-frequency poles which move in the complex plane as a function of the flight conditions. The adaptive feature overcomes this problem by adjusting the gain in order to keep the location of these sensitive poles fixed in the complex plane. Another feature of the Sperry system is to vary the rate of the test pulse as a function of the frequency of parameter variation.

This adaptive system represents a solution to a specific problem. It cannot be used for a different system than the one for which it was specifically designed.

The application of test pulses, large enough to have their resulting responses sensed above the noise level, may change the desired quiescent operation of a system and be intolerable. For these cases, correlation techniques are utilized in order to determine the impulsive response of the system. The Aeronutronic Division of the Ford Motor Co.[8] has proposed an adaptive control system based on this principle. The block diagram of this configuration is illustrated in Figure 11–6. This system uses the principle that the crosscorrelation function between the system input and output is the impulsive response of the system when it is excited by a signal whose bandwidth is several times that of the controlled system.[9] White noise is a signal that satisfies this requirement quite well. The perturbing test signal can be of the same order of magnitude as the

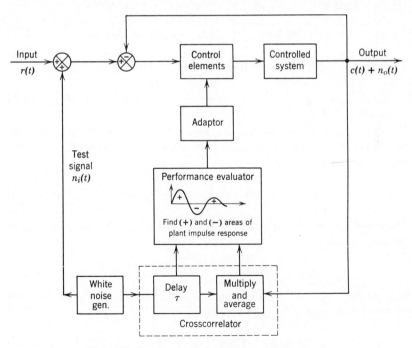

Figure 11–6.   Aeronutronic adaptive control system.

feedback control system's noise since the correlating technique can sense the effects of the test signal from the ambient noise.

The configuration of Figure 11–6 functions by having the white noise generator supply a wideband test signal that is mixed with the input to the feedback control system. It can be small enough so that its overall effect on normal operation of the system is negligible. The test signal is also delayed by τ seconds and is fed to the crosscorrelator, where it is multiplied by the system's output and averaged. The output from the correlator, which represents the crosscorrelation between the white noise test signal and the system's output, is basically the impulsive response of the system due to the fact that the autocorrelation function for white noise is an impulse (see Section 8–5).

Consider the noise input to be represented by $n_i(t)$ and the noise output of the basic control system to be $n_0(t)$, as indicated in Figure 11–6. From the definition of the crosscorrelation function (see equation 8–12), the crosscorrelation between the input noise and the system output is given by

$$\phi_{io}(\tau) = \lim_{T \to \infty} \frac{1}{2T} \int_{-T}^{T} n_i(t)[c(t + \tau) + n_0(t + \tau)]\, dt \qquad (11\text{–}1)$$

For this particular proof, the following form is more useful:

$$\phi_{io}(\tau) = \lim_{T \to \infty} \frac{1}{2T} \int_{-T}^{T} n_i(t - \tau)[c(t) + n_0(t)]\, dt \qquad (11\text{–}2)$$

This can be simplified to the form

$$\phi_{io}(\tau) = \lim_{T \to \infty} \frac{1}{2T} \left[\int_{-T}^{T} n_i(t - \tau)n_0(t)\, dt + \int_{-T}^{T} n_i(t - \tau)c(t)\, dt \right] \qquad (11\text{–}3)$$

The second term of equation 11–3 is zero since it is assumed that the input noise and output due to signal $c(t)$ arise from separate sources and are uncorrelated. Therefore,

$$\phi_{io}(\tau) = \lim_{T \to \infty} \frac{1}{2T} \left[\int_{-T}^{T} n_i(t - \tau)n_0(t)\, dt \right] \qquad (11\text{–}4)$$

The output noise is related to the input noise by means of the convolution integral as follows:

$$n_0(t) = \int_{-\infty}^{\infty} g(t')n_i(t - t')\, dt' \qquad (11\text{–}5)$$

Substituting equation 11–5 into equation 11–4, and interchanging the order of integration, yields the following result:

$$\phi_{io}(\tau) = \int_{-\infty}^{\infty} g(t') \left[\lim_{T \to \infty} \frac{1}{2T} \int_{-T}^{T} n_i(t - \tau)n_i(t - t')\, dt \right] dt' \qquad (11\text{–}6)$$

Notice that the bracketed term of equation 11–6 is the autocorrelation function $\phi_{ii}(\tau - t')$ of the input noise (see equation 8–9 for the definition of the autocorrelation function). Therefore, equation 11–6 may be simplified to the following expression:

$$\phi_{io}(\tau) = \int_{-\infty}^{\infty} g(t')\phi_{ii}(\tau - t')\, dt' \qquad (11\text{--}7)$$

Recall the derivation of the autocorrelation function for white noise in Section 8–5, where it was shown that the autocorrelation function of white noise is an impulse. Therefore, equation 11–7 can be expressed as

$$\phi_{io}(\tau) = \int_{-\infty}^{\infty} g(t')\,\delta(\tau - t')\, dt' = g(\tau) \qquad (11\text{--}8)$$

Equation 11–8 proves that the output of the crosscorrelation results in a point on the impulse response for the system. Additional points on the impulse response may be obtained by introducing additional crosscorrelator channels having appropriate delays.

A performance evaluator, shown in Figure 11–6, then determines the relative ratio of the positive to negative areas of the impulsive response in order to determine the actual value of the damping factor. From the decision of the performance evaluator the adaptor adjusts the system's parameters to keep the damping factor at a constant, optimum value. See Problems 11–1 and 11–2 for a mathematical description of the operation.

The disadvantage of this system is that it requires considerable hardware. In addition, if the system has multiple inputs and outputs, the extension of this technique requires a very complex information-handling system.

The block diagram of a *digital-computer-controlled adaptive control system* is shown in Figure 11–7. The function of the digital computer is to compute the forcing function required to obtain the desired response of the system, and to compute the latest information on the dynamic response of the system. By applying a forcing function which is based on the computed dynamic response of the system, the system possesses the adaptive property.

There exists today an entire class of systems which can be classified as being digital-computer-controlled adaptive control systems. Extensive

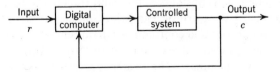

Figure 11–7. Digital-computer-controlled adaptive control system.

literature has been written[10-21] about this general class of adaptive systems. Basically, all have the configuration illustrated in Figure 11-6.

R. E. Kalman of RIAS has made some interesting attempts to apply digital-computer-controlled adaptive systems in practice. Reference 10 discusses his approach to optimizing a chemical process using a special-purpose, combination analog-digital computer. In Ref. 15, Kalman suggests a technique for using a general-purpose digital computer in order to achieve adaptive control. The program for the general-purpose computer uses the concepts of Bellman's dynamic programming.[16]

The "steepest-ascent method" is an interesting approach which has recently been applied to digital-computer-controlled adaptive systems. References 17 to 21 give the details of this method. We briefly outline the basic principles of the steepest-ascent method by reconsidering the adaptive internal-combustion engine[1] discussed in Section 11-1. Our purpose is to design an adaptive digital-computer-controlled system which will optimize the fuel consumption at 16 mpg for the internal combustion engine considered in Figure 11-1.

The steepest-ascent approach measures the slopes of the constant miles per gallon contours shown in Figure 11-1 by perturbing the spark setting and the fuel-air mixture adjustments. The procedure is repeated until an optimum consumption of 16 mpg is obtained. A typical response pattern for a moderate gain system is shown by the path in Figure 11-1. A lower-gain system results in a smoother path; a higher-gain system results in a path containing more and wider excursions.

A very good analogy of the steepest-ascent adaptive system is a boat using depth-sounding instruments to search for the deepest point in a gently sloping body of water. The boat makes small excursions in each of two perpendicular directions and observes the results. Depending on the measured slope, the boat then proceeds in the optimum direction for a short distance. The process is then repeated until the deepest point is found.

The recent literature indicates that many practical adaptive digital-computer-controlled systems have been developed. As an example, the Sperry Gyroscope Company has developed an adaptive tracking loop for the instrumentation radars used on the Advanced Range Instrumentation Ships (ARIS). By utilizing a digital computer as part of the tracking loop, the inherent gain constants of the radar tracking system are increased without increasing the intrinsic bandwidth of the servo. This technique meets the simultaneous and contradictory requirements of wide bandwidth due to accuracy considerations, and narrow bandwidth to minimize the tracking jitter due to noise. The reader is referred to Reference 5 for a more detailed description of this system.

11-3. DESIGN PHILOSOPHY FOR ADAPTIVE CONTROL SYSTEMS

In conventional feedback control systems, the performance criterion may concern rise time, overshoot, bandwidth, relative stability, accuracy, the integral of time and error (ITAE) and/or the root-mean-square error (rms). All have been discussed previously in Chapter 4 for conventional feedback control systems. Adaptive control systems also have certain performance criteria that must be met. The choice of the proper performance criterion for an adaptive control system is extremely important and plays a very important role in determining the adaptive configuration.

All adaptive control systems attempt to optimize some index performance. In the internal combustion engine example, discussed in Section 11-1, the figure of merit was maximizing the miles per gallon of fuel. Other adaptive systems may attempt to optimize the ITAE criterion. As discussed in Chapter 4, minimizing the ITAE results in very desirable responses to step functions. As a matter of fact, many practical adaptive control systems have been designed from this viewpoint. It is very important to emphasize at this point that all adaptive control systems characterize the performance of a feedback control system by one number. This number may refer to any of the performance criteria discussed previously: rise time, overshoot, ITAE, rms error, and so on. It is this number that the adaptive feature attempts to optimize. A very important function of an adaptive control system is the determination, or measurement, of the performance index it is trying to optimize.

From what has been presented so far, it is obvious that adaptive control systems always have the following two characteristics present:

1. Identification
2. Actuation

Identification refers to the measurement of the characteristics of the control system to be optimized. *Actuation* refers to the generation of a command which varies some parameter in order to optimize the adaptive control systems. These two characteristics are fundamental features found in all adaptive control systems.

In general, the design of adaptive control systems is basically the same as design of conventional feedback control systems, once the configuration and logic of the adaptive feature is established. All the tools we have developed for linear, nonlinear, sampled-data, and statistical analysis of feedback control systems apply equally well to adaptive control systems. In addition, the concept of optimal control theory plays a very important role in determining the logic and configuration for the adaptive control system desired. For example, the control engineer must determine what factor he wishes to optimize. Is it the conservation of fuel in an aircraft or missile, or is it the transient response of the autopilot where the ITAE criterion is to be minimized? Is it the minimization of the magnitude of error between the line-of-sight and radar beam axis of a tracking radar in a fire control system, or is it maximizing the probability of kill of the fire control system? These are important questions; the answers will determine the form of the adaptive control system.

In the following section the design of a typical adaptive control system is chosen to illustrate the procedure. As will be observed, the techniques used for the design of adaptive control systems consist of adding the properties of identification and actuation, and using the basic tools previously developed.

11-4. DESIGN OF A TYPICAL ADAPTIVE CONTROL SYSTEM

The impulsive-response adaptive control system proposed by the Sperry Gyroscope Co. has been considered qualitatively in Section 11–2. We shall illustrate the actual design of this system using the root locus approach. Figure 11–8 shows a detailed block diagram of the configuration. Its root locus plot is given in Figure 11–9.

As can be observed from the root locus plot, the response of this system is determined primarily by the actuator's poles. Optimum system response is obtained when the variable gain K_v is maintained between K_1 and K_2. The function of this adaptive system is to measure the impulsive response and adjust K_v in order to maintain an optimum damping factor.

The natural resonant frequency for the system, ω_n, remains essentially constant when $K_1 < K_v < K_2$. Therefore, the number of sign changes of δ_o is proportional to the damping factor of the closed-loop poles. From the analysis of the response of a type 1, second-order system in Section 3–7, it was shown that the period of oscillation was given by (see equation 3–114)

$$t_m = \frac{2\pi}{\omega_n\sqrt{1 - \zeta^2}} \tag{11-9}$$

A simple extension of this result indicates that the response changes sign whenever

$$t = \frac{t_m}{2} m \quad \text{where} \quad m = 1, 2, 3, \ldots \tag{11-10}$$

Substituting equation 11–9 into equation 11–10, we find that the impulsive

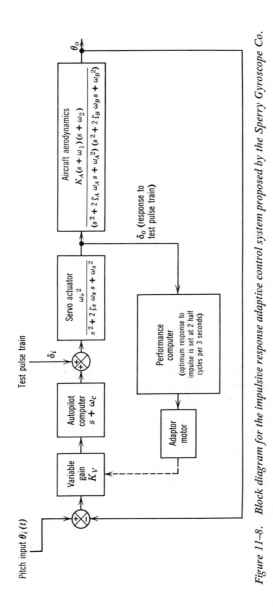

Figure 11–8.   Block diagram for the impulsive response adaptive control system proposed by the Sperry Gyroscope Co.

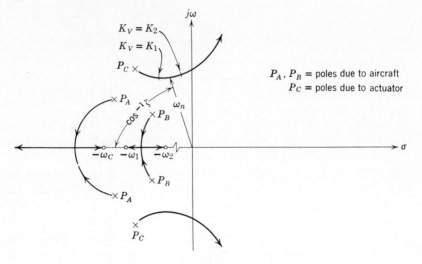

Figure 11–9.   Root locus plot for the system shown in Figure 11–8.

response changes sign whenever

$$t = \frac{\pi m}{\omega_n \sqrt{1 - \zeta^2}} \quad \text{where} \quad m = 1, 2, 3, \ldots \qquad (11\text{--}11)$$

If the actual damping factor ζ_a is less than an optimum desired damping factor ζ_{opt}, then the number of sign reversals will be greater than an optimum predetermined number. Conversely, if $\zeta_a > \zeta_{\text{opt}}$, then the number of sign reversals will be less than the optimum predetermined number. This adaptive control system, which has been simulated for an F-100C aircraft, appeared to give optimum results when 2 half cycles were measured in a period of 3 seconds. The performance computer is designed so that a count less than 2 over a 3 second period will cause the adaptor motor to increase K_v, while a count greater than 2 over a 3 second period will cause the adaptor motor to decrease K_v.

The system operation described is valid only when the pitch input signal $\theta_i(t)$ is zero. If there is an input command signal, the validity of the relation between the number of changes of sign of δ_o and the damping ratio is questionable. This difficulty is overcome by applying the test impulse only when the input signal is zero or when the transients due to an input signal have subsided. Any quiescent d-c level which might exist in δ_o is removed at the input to the performance computer by means of a capacitor.

11–5. CONCLUSION

The adaptive control system concept enables the control engineer to design a large variety of complex systems which could never be achieved using conventional techniques. As control problems become more complex, the control engineer will resort more and more to adaptive control systems which automatically sense and correct themselves against extreme disturbances and a wide range of parameter changes. In addition, this class of control system will ultimately be able to do part of the control engineer's design task by initially establishing the limits and boundaries for the operation of a process and, thereafter, permitting a conventional or simplified adaptive control system to take over.

Perhaps the greatest promise of adaptive control systems lies in the possibility of introducing a simple learning mechanism into the adaptive part of the control system. This possibility was discussed for the MIT model reference adaptive control system. Control systems utilizing the features of adaptivity and learning will approach the capabilities and flexibilities of human controllers in certain tasks.

REFERENCES

1. Principles of Optimalizing Controls and an Application to the Internal Combustion Engine, C. S. Draper and Y. T. Li, Am. Soc. Mech. Engrs., New York, Sept. 1951.
2. The Philosophy of Adaptive Control, Y. T. Li, presented at the First International Congress of International Federation on Automatic Control, Moscow, June 1960.
3. Making Sense Out of the Adaptive Principle, John E. Gibson, *Control Eng.*, 113 (Aug. 1960).
4. *Adaptive Control Systems*, Eli Mishkin and Ludwig Braun, Jr., editors, McGraw-Hill Book Co., New York, 1961, Chapter 1.
5. Automatic Tracking Consideration for Ballistic Targets, S. Adelman and S. M. Shinners, in the *1961 Conference Proceedings of the Fifth National Convention on Military Electronics*, McGregor and Werner, Washington, D.C.
6. Design of Model-Reference Adaptive Control Systems for Aircraft, H. P. Whitaker, J. Yamron, and A. Kezer, *MIT Instrumentation Laboratory Report* R-164, Sept. 1958.
7. Proceedings of the Self-Adaptive Flight Control Systems Symposium, Lt. F. C. Gregory, editor, *WADC Technical Report* 59–49, *ASTIA Document No.* AD 209389, March 1959.
8. Aeronutronic Self-Optimizing Automatic Control Systems, G. W. Anderson, R. N. Buland, and G. R. Cooper, Adaptive Control Systems Symposium, Jan. 1959.
9. *Digital and Sampled-Data Control Systems*, J. T. Tou, McGraw-Hill Book Co., New York, 1959.
10. Design of Self-Optimizing Control Systems, R. E. Kalman, *Trans. ASME*, **80**, 468 (1958).
11. On the Measurement Problem in Adaptive Systems Utilizing Analog Computer

Techniques, R. M. Corbin and E. Mishkin, *Research Report* R-699-58, P13-627, Polytechnic Institute of Brooklyn, Microwave Research Institute, 1958.

12. Use of Mathematical Error Criterion in the Design of Adaptive Control Systems, C. W. Merriam III, *Trans. AIEE*, **78, Pt. 2,** *Appl. Ind.*, 506 (1959).

13. On Adaptive Control Systems, L. Braun, Jr., Doctoral dissertation, Polytechnic Institute of Brooklyn, 1959.

14. Executive-Controlled Adaptive Systems, R. Staffin, *Trans. AIEE*, **78, Pt. 2,** *Appl. Ind.*, 523 (1959).

15. The Role of Digital Computers in the Dynamic Organization of Chemical Reactions, R. E. Kalman and R. W. Koepcke, Western Joint Computer Conference, March 1959.

16. *Dynamic Programming*, R. E. Bellman, Princeton University Press, Princeton, N. J., 1957.

17. A Steepest Ascent Method for Solving Optimum Programming Problems, A. E. Bryson and W. F. Denham, *Raytheon Co. Technical Report* BR-1303, August 1961.

18. Gradient Theory of Optimal Flight Paths, H. J. Kelley, *ARS Journal*, **30,** No. 10, 947 (Oct. 1960).

19. A Parametric Perturbation Adaptive Control System, R. J. McGrath, V. Rajaraman, and V. C. Rideout, *IRE Trans. PGAC*, **AC-6,** No. 2, 154 (May 1961).

20. *Computational Methods in Automatic Control*, A. A. Feldbaum, State Publishing House of Physical and Mathematical Literature, Moscow, 1959.

21. A Multichannel Automatic Optimizer for Solving Variational Problems, R. I. Stakhovskii, *Automation and Remote Control*, **20,** No. 11, 1435 (Nov. 1959).

APPENDIX

A

ELEMENTS OF MATRIX AND

DETERMINANT ANALYSIS

A-1. INTRODUCTION

A *matrix* is a rectangular array of elements. It is usually denoted by **A** and is defined by

$$\mathbf{A} = \begin{bmatrix} a_{11} & a_{12} & \cdots & a_{1n} \\ a_{21} & a_{22} & \cdots & \cdot \\ \cdot & \cdot & & \cdot \\ \cdot & \cdot & & \cdot \\ \cdot & \cdot & & \cdot \\ a_{m1} & a_{m2} & \cdots & a_{mn} \end{bmatrix} \tag{A-1}$$

A matrix having m rows and n columns is referred to as an $m \times n$ matrix. A *square matrix* refers to the condition where $m = n$. A *column matrix*, or *vector*, which refers to the condition where $m = 1$, is usually represented by small letters in the following manner:

$$\mathbf{a} = \begin{bmatrix} a_1 \\ a_2 \\ \cdot \\ \cdot \\ \cdot \\ a_n \end{bmatrix} \tag{A-2}$$

The number of elements of a vector is referred to as the dimension of the vector. Therefore, equation A-2 represents an n-dimensional vector.

A *determinant* is a number that is associated with a square matrix **A**. It is usually denoted by det **A** or |**A**|. A determinant of nth order consists of a square $n \times n$ array of elements a_{ij} whose total number is n^2, as

461

follows:

$$
\begin{vmatrix}
a_{11} & a_{12} & \cdots & a_{1n} \\
a_{21} & a_{22} & \cdots & a_{2n} \\
\cdot & \cdot & & \cdot \\
\cdot & \cdot & & \cdot \\
\cdot & \cdot & & \cdot \\
a_{n1} & a_{n2} & \cdots & a_{nn}
\end{vmatrix}
\tag{A-3}
$$

The determinant of **A** may be evaluated from the row expansion given by

$$
\det \mathbf{A} = \sum_{i=1}^{n} a_{ki} A_{ki}
\tag{A-4}
$$

where k is an integer having a value from 1 to n. A_{ki} is termed the *cofactor* of the element a_{ki} and is defined as the determinant of the matrix that results when the kth row and ith column of the **A** matrix are struck out and the resultant matrix is multiplied by $(-1)^{k+1}$. A *minor* is defined as a cofactor without the sign term.

Having reviewed the basic definitions of matrices and determinants, this appendix will next present the basic rules and properties for these powerful mathematical tools. The reader should treat the following material as a supplement to the state space concept presented during the discussion of optimal control theory in Chapter 10.

A–2. PROPERTIES OF MATRIX ANALYSIS

In order to present the basic properties of matrix analysis, three matrices **A**, **B**, and **C** will be considered whose respective components are a_{ij}, b_{ij}, and c_{ij}. Thirteen basic rules and properties, which govern matrix analysis, follow:

RULE 1.   Matrix **A** equals matrix **B** if element a_{ik} equals element b_{ik}.

RULE 2.   The sum (or difference) of two matrices **A** and **B** is obtained by adding (or subtracting) similar elements. The result is a new matrix **C** where

$$
\mathbf{C} = \mathbf{A} + \mathbf{B}
$$

and

$$
c_{ij} = a_{ij} + b_{ij}
$$

$$\tag{A-5}$$

RULE 3.   Multiplication of a matrix **A** by a scalar d is equivalent to multiplying each element of the matrix by d. The result is a new matrix

C, where

$$C = d\mathbf{A}$$

and
$$c_{ij} = da_{ij}$$
(A–6)

RULE 4. Multiplication of matrix **A** by matrix **B** results in a new matrix **C** where

$$\mathbf{C} = \mathbf{A} \cdot \mathbf{B}$$

and
$$c_{ij} = \sum_{l=1}^{K} a_{il}b_{lj}$$
(A–7)

In order to multiply the matrices **A** and **B** the number of columns in matrix **A** must equal the number of rows in matrix **B**.

RULE 5. The element c_{ij} of the matrix obtained when the matrices **A** and **B** are multiplied is obtained by multiplying the elements of the ith row of matrix **A** by the corresponding elements of the jth column of matrix **B** and adding the resulting products.

RULE 6. In general

$$\mathbf{A} \cdot \mathbf{B} \neq \mathbf{B} \cdot \mathbf{A}$$
(A–8)

RULE 7. The transpose of matrix **A** is a matrix **C** whose rows and columns are interchanged with those of the original matrix as follows:

$$a_{ij} = c_{ji}$$
(A–9)

The transpose of matrix **A** is designated by $\mathbf{A}^{T}$.

RULE 8. The identity matrix is a square matrix whose principal diagonal elements are unity and whose other elements are zero. This matrix, which is denoted by **I**, is given by

$$\mathbf{I} = \begin{bmatrix} 1 & 0 & 0 & \cdots & 0 \\ 0 & 1 & 0 & & \cdot \\ 0 & 0 & 1 & & \cdot \\ \cdot & & & & \cdot \\ \cdot & & & & \\ \cdot & & & & \\ 0 & & \cdots & & 1 \end{bmatrix}$$
(A–10)

Multiplication of any matrix **A** by an identity matrix **I** results in the original matrix **A**:

$$\mathbf{A} \cdot \mathbf{I} = \mathbf{A}$$
(A–11)

RULE 9.   A diagonal matrix is a more general case of an identity matrix. This matrix, which is denoted by Λ, is given by

$$\Lambda = \begin{bmatrix} x_1 & 0 & 0 & \cdots & 0 \\ 0 & x_2 & 0 & & \cdot \\ 0 & 0 & x_3 & & \cdot \\ \cdot & & & & \cdot \\ \cdot & & & & \\ \cdot & & & & \\ 0 & & \cdots & & x_n \end{bmatrix} \qquad (A-12)$$

It is often written as

$$\Lambda = \mathrm{diag}(x_1, x_2, x_3, \ldots, x_n) \qquad (A-13)$$

RULE 10.   A symmetric matrix is defined by the condition

$$a_{ij} = +a_{ji} \qquad (A-14)$$

This matrix, which is denoted by $\mathbf{A}_s$, is represented by

$$\mathbf{A}_s = \begin{bmatrix} a_{11} & a_{12} & a_{13} & \cdots & a_{1n} \\ a_{12} & a_{22} & a_{23} & & \cdot \\ a_{13} & a_{23} & a_{33} & & \cdot \\ \cdot & & & & \cdot \\ \cdot & & & & \\ \cdot & & & & \\ a_{1n} & & \cdots & & a_{nn} \end{bmatrix} \qquad (A-15)$$

RULE 11.   A skew-symmetric matrix is defined by the condition

$$a_{ij} = -a_{ji}; a_{ii} = 0 \qquad (A-16)$$

This matrix, which is denoted by $\mathbf{A}_a$, is represented by

$$\mathbf{A}_a = \begin{bmatrix} 0 & a_{12} & a_{13} & \cdots \\ -a_{12} & 0 & a_{23} & \\ -a_{13} & -a_{23} & 0 & \\ \cdot & & & \\ \cdot & & & \\ \cdot & & & \end{bmatrix} \qquad (A-17)$$

RULE 12.   The zero matrix, denoted by $\mathbf{0}$, is defined as a matrix whose elements are all zero. It has the property that

$$\mathbf{A} + \mathbf{0} = \mathbf{A} \qquad (A-18)$$

RULE 13.   The matrix **A** may be portioned (or subdivided) into various submatrices as follows:

$$
\mathbf{A} =
\begin{bmatrix}
\mathbf{A}_{11} & \mathbf{A}_{12} & \cdots \\
\mathbf{A}_{21} & \mathbf{A}_{22} & \\
\cdot & & \\
\cdot & & \\
\cdot & &
\end{bmatrix}
\qquad\qquad (\text{A--19})
$$

where $\mathbf{A}_{ij}$ represents a matrix (not a scaler). The properties and operations of matrix analysis carry over to the portioned case except that some care must be taken when multiplication is involved since $\mathbf{A} \cdot \mathbf{B} \neq \mathbf{B} \cdot \mathbf{A}$.

A–3.   PROPERTIES OF DETERMINANTS

Eight basic rules for simplifying, manipulating, and determining the values of determinants are presented in this section as follows.

RULE 1.   Interchanging any row or column of a determinant with its immediately adjacent row or column does not change the magnitude of the original determinant but does change its sign.

RULE 2.   Interchanging any row of a determinant with its corresponding column, or any column with its corresponding row, does not change the value or sign of the determinant.

RULE 3.   The value of a determinant is unchanged if the elements of any row or column of a determinant are added to or subtracted from the elements of any row or column.

RULE 4.   Dividing or multiplying any single row or column of a determinant by a constant is equivalent to dividing or multiplying the entire determinant by the same constant.

RULE 5.   The value of a determinant is zero if any two rows or columns are identical.

RULE 6.   The value of a determinant is zero if all the elements of any row or column equal zero.

RULE 7.   The value of a determinant is unity if all of the elements along the principal diagonal are unity and all other elements are zero.

RULE 8.   Determinants and cofactors are related to the inverse square matrix **A**, denoted by **A**$^{-1}$, by the following relationship:

$$\mathbf{A}^{-1} = \frac{1}{\det \mathbf{A}} \begin{bmatrix} A_{11} & A_{21} & A_{31} & \cdots \\ A_{12} & A_{22} & A_{32} \\ A_{13} & A_{23} & A_{33} \\ \cdot \\ \cdot \\ \cdot \end{bmatrix} \tag{A–20}$$

The portioned and transposed matrix of this relationship is defined as the adjoint matrix. By means of this equation, division by a matrix reduces to the multiplication of its inverse square matrix.

APPENDIX

B CONVERSION FACTORS FOR CONTROL SYSTEM CALCULATIONS

Given	Multiply by	To Obtain
Btu	777.97	ft-lb
	3.929×10^{-4}	hp-hr
	1054.8	joules
Centimeters	0.3937	inches
	0.01	meters
Centimeter-dyne	1	ergs
	0.7376×10^{-7}	ft-lb
Centimeters/sec	0.1943×10^{-1}	knots
	0.2237×10^{-1}	mph
Cubic feet	2.8317×10^{4}	cubic centimeters
	1.728×10^{3}	cubic inches
Cycles	10^{-3}	kilocycles
	10^{-6}	megacycles
	10^{-9}	G_c
	10^{-12}	T_c
Degrees	17.453	milliradians
	1.7453×10^{-2}	radians
	3600	angular seconds
Dynes	1.0197×10^{-3}	grams
	10^{-7}	joules/cm
	10^{-5}	joules/meter (Newtons)
	0.2248×10^{-5}	pounds
Dyne-cm	1.416×10^{-5}	oz-in.
Ergs	1	dyne-cm
	0.73756×10^{-7}	ft-lb
	0.3722×10^{-13}	hp-hr
	10^{-7}	joules
	0.27778×10^{-10}	watt-hr

467

Given	Multiply by	To Obtain
Feet	0.30479×10^{-3}	kilometers
	0.30479	meters
	0.16447×10^{-3}	nautical miles
	0.18939×10^{-3}	miles
Feet/min	11.364×10^{-3}	mph
Feet/sec	0.5921	knots
Foot/lb	1.3558	joules
Foot-lb/min	3.0303×10^{-5}	hp
	2.2597×10^{-5}	kilowatts
Foot-lb/rad/sec	20.106	in.-oz/rpm
Grams	35.274×10^{-3}	ounces
Gram-cm	0.98066×10^{-4}	joules
	0.13887	oz-in.
Horse-power	0.7457	kilowatts
Horse-power-hr	26.856×10^{5}	joules
Inches	2.54	centimeters
	2.54×10^{-2}	meters
	0.15783×10^{-4}	miles
	27.778×10^{-3}	yards
Joules	0.2778×10^{-3}	w-hr
Kilograms	2.2046	lb
Kilowatt-hr	3.6×10^{6}	joules
Knots	6080.2	ft/hr
	1.1516	mph
Meters	1.0936	yards
Meters/sec	1.9425	knots
Miles (nautical)	1.1516	miles
Miles	1760	yards
Milliradians	3.43775	angular minutes
	10^{-3}	radians
Minutes (angular)	1.6667×10^{-2}	degrees
	2.9089×10^{-4}	radians
Newtons	10^{5}	dynes
Oz-in.	7.201	gram-centimeters
Radians	2.06265×10^{5}	angular seconds
Radians/second	57.3	degrees/second
	9.549	rpm
Revolutions	6.2832	radians

Given	Multiply by	To Obtain
Slugs	32.174	lb
Square feet	929.03	square centimeters
Square inches	6.4516	square centimeters
Square meters	1.196	square yards
Watts	44.254	ft-lb/min
	1.3596×10^{-3}	hp
	1	joules/sec
Watt-hr	2655.3	ft-lb

APPENDIX

 USEFUL MATHEMATICAL RELATIONSHIPS

C–1. GENERAL TRIGONOMETRIC FUNCTIONS

$$\sin^2 \phi + \cos^2 \phi = 1$$

$$\sec^2 \phi = 1 + \tan^2 \phi$$

$$\csc^2 \phi = 1 + \cot^2 \phi$$

$$\sin \phi = \frac{e^{j\phi} - e^{-j\phi}}{2j}$$

$$\cos \phi = \frac{e^{j\phi} + e^{-j\phi}}{2}$$

$$\tan \phi = \frac{1}{j}\frac{e^{j2\phi} - 1}{e^{j2\phi} + 1}$$

C–2. TRIGONOMETRIC FUNCTIONS OF THE SUM AND DIFFERENCE OF TWO ANGLES

$$\sin (\phi \pm \theta) = \sin \phi \cos \theta \pm \cos \phi \sin \theta$$

$$\cos (\phi \pm \theta) = \cos \phi \cos \theta \mp \sin \phi \sin \theta$$

$$\tan (\phi \pm \theta) = \frac{\tan \phi \pm \tan \theta}{1 \mp \tan \phi \tan \theta}$$

$$\sin \phi \pm \sin \theta = 2 \sin \tfrac{1}{2}(\phi \pm \theta) \cos \tfrac{1}{2}(\phi \mp \theta)$$

$$\cos \phi + \cos \theta = 2 \cos \tfrac{1}{2}(\phi + \theta) \cos \tfrac{1}{2}(\phi - \theta)$$

$$\cos \phi - \cos \theta = -2 \sin \tfrac{1}{2}(\phi + \theta) \sin \tfrac{1}{2}(\phi - \theta)$$

$$\tan \phi \pm \tan \theta = \frac{\sin (\phi \pm \theta)}{\cos \phi \cos \theta}$$

C–3. TRIGONOMETRIC FUNCTIONS OF HALF AND MULTIPLE ANGLES

$$\sin \tfrac{1}{2}\phi = \pm \, [\tfrac{1}{2}(1 - \cos \phi)]^{\frac{1}{2}}$$

$$\cos \tfrac{1}{2}\phi = \pm \, [\tfrac{1}{2}(1 + \cos \phi)]^{\frac{1}{2}}$$

$$\tan \tfrac{1}{2}\phi = \pm \, \left(\frac{1 - \cos \phi}{1 + \cos \phi}\right)^{\frac{1}{2}}$$

$$\sin 2\phi = 2 \sin \phi \cos \phi$$

$$\cos 2\phi = \cos^2 \phi - \sin^2 \phi$$

$$\tan 2\phi = \frac{2 \tan \phi}{1 - \tan^2 \phi}$$

C–4. HYPERBOLIC FUNCTIONS

$$\sinh \phi = \tfrac{1}{2}(e^\phi - e^{-\phi})$$

$$\cosh \phi = \tfrac{1}{2}(e^\phi + e^{-\phi})$$

$$\tanh \phi = \frac{\sinh \phi}{\cosh \phi}$$

$$\cosh^2 \phi - \sinh^2 \phi = 1$$

$$1 - \coth^2 \phi = -\operatorname{csch}^2 \phi$$

C–5. EXPONENTIAL AND LOGARITHMIC SERIES EXPANSIONS

$$e^x = 1 + \frac{x}{1!} + \frac{x^2}{2!} + \frac{x^3}{3!} + \frac{x^4}{4!} + \cdots \quad \text{where} \quad -\infty < x < \infty$$

$$A^x = 1 + x \log A + \frac{(x \log A)^2}{2!} + \frac{(x \log A)^3}{3!} + \cdots$$

$$\text{where} \quad A > 0, \quad -\infty < x < \infty$$

$$\log (1 + x) = x - \frac{x^2}{2} + \frac{x^3}{3} - \frac{x^4}{4} + \frac{x^5}{5} - \cdots \quad \text{where} \quad -1 < x < 1$$

$$\log (1 - x) = -x - \frac{x^2}{2} - \frac{x^3}{3} - \frac{x^4}{4} - \frac{x^5}{5} - \cdots \quad \text{where} \quad -1 < x < 1$$

C–6. TRIGONOMETRIC SERIES EXPANSIONS

$$\sin \phi = \phi - \frac{\phi^3}{3!} + \frac{\phi^5}{5!} - \frac{\phi^7}{7!} + \cdots \quad \text{where} \quad -\infty < \phi < \infty$$

$$\cos \phi = 1 - \frac{\phi^2}{2!} + \frac{\phi^4}{4!} - \frac{\phi^6}{6!} + \frac{\phi^8}{8!} - \cdots \quad \text{where} \quad -\infty < \phi < \infty$$

$$\tan \phi = \phi + \frac{\phi^3}{3} + \frac{2\phi^5}{15} + \frac{17\phi^7}{315} + \frac{62\phi^9}{2835} + \cdots$$

$$\text{where} \quad -\frac{\pi}{2} < \phi < \frac{\pi}{2}$$

C–7. HYPERBOLIC SERIES EXPANSION

$$\sinh \phi = \phi + \frac{\phi^3}{3!} + \frac{\phi^5}{5!} + \frac{\phi^7}{7!} + \cdots \quad \text{where} \quad -\infty < \phi < \infty$$

$$\cosh \phi = 1 + \frac{\phi^2}{2!} + \frac{\phi^4}{4!} + \frac{\phi^6}{6!} + \cdots \quad \text{where} \quad -\infty < \phi < \infty$$

PROBLEMS

CHAPTER 1

1–1. Figure P1–1 illustrates the control system for controlling the angular position of a ship's rudder. The desired heading, which is determined by the gyroscope setting, is the reference. An electrical signal proportional to the reference is obtained from a resistor that is fixed to the ship's frame. Qualitatively explain how this open-loop control system operates in following a command for a southbound direction.

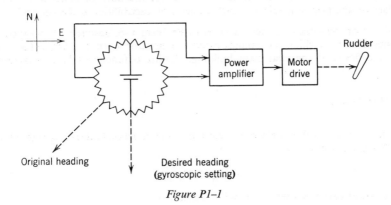

Figure P1–1

1–2. Explain how the system discussed in Problem 1–1 can be modified to become a closed-loop control system.

1–3. An electric hot-water heater is illustrated in Figure P1–3. The heating element is turned on and off by a thermostatic switch in order to maintain a desired temperature. Any demand for hot water results in hot water leaving the tank and cold water entering. Draw the simple functional block diagram for this closed-loop control system and qualitatively explain how it operates if the reference temperature of the thermostat is changed.

1–4. Explain how the system discussed in Problem 1–3 operates if the ambient temperature surrounding the tank suddenly changes. Refer to the block diagram.

1–5. Devise a system that can control the speed of an internal combustion

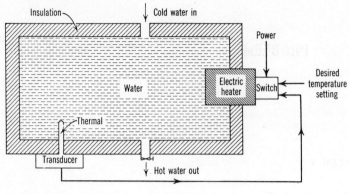

Figure P1–3

engine in accordance with a command in the form of a voltage. Explain the operation of your system.

1–6. Devise a system that can control the position, rate, and acceleration of an elevator used in an apartment house. What specifications or limits would you place on the position, velocity, and acceleration capabilities of the system?

1–7. For the control system devised in Problem 1–6, describe what happens when a man weighing 200 pounds enters the elevator when it is stopped at one of the floors of the apartment building. Utilize a functional block diagram.

CHAPTER 2

2–1. Prove that the Laplace transform of an exponentially decaying sine wave, $e^{-\alpha t} \sin \omega t$, is given by

$$\frac{\omega}{(s + \alpha)^2 + \omega^2}$$

This transform is shown as item 9 in Table 2–1.

2–2. Obtain the direct Laplace transform for the following differential and integral equations:

(a)
$$L\frac{di(t)}{dt} + Ri(t) + \frac{1}{C}\int i(t)\,dt = e(t)$$

(b)
$$M\frac{d^2x(t)}{dt^2} + B\frac{dx(t)}{dt} + Kx(t) = 3t$$

(c)
$$J\frac{d^2\theta(t)}{dt^2} + B\frac{d\theta(t)}{dt} + K\theta(t) = 10\sin \omega t$$

2–3. Obtain the inverse Laplace transform for the following expressions:

(a)
$$F_A(s) = \frac{20}{(s + 2)^2(s^2 + 12s + 16)}$$

(b)
$$F_B(s) = \frac{10(s + 2)}{(s^2 - 16)(s + 1)}$$

(c)
$$F_C(s) = \frac{2(s + 1)}{s(s^2 + 8s + 4)}$$

2–4. Prove that the transfer function for the network illustrated in Table 2–2, item 3, is given by the expression shown.

2–5. Prove that the transfer function for the network illustrated in Table 2–2, item 6, is given by the expression shown.

2–6. Prove that the transfer function for the network illustrated in Table 2–2, item 9, is given by the expression shown.

2–7. By means of block diagram reduction techniques, find the transfer function of the system $C(s)/R(s)$ for the configuration illustrated in Figure P2–7.

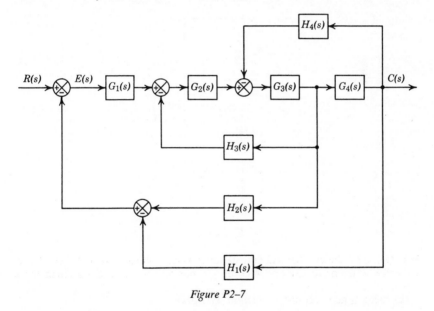

Figure P2–7

2–8. For the system illustrated in Figure P2–7, what is the effect on the system transfer function of inserting a sign reverser in series with $H_3(s)$.

2–9. Determine the transfer function of the system shown in Figure P2–7 relating error $E(s)$ and input $R(s)$.

2–10. Repeat Problem 2–9 with a sign reverser inserted in series with $H_3(s)$. What is the significance of this result as compared to that obtained in Problem 2–9?

2–11. Repeat Problem 2–7 using the signal flow diagram method.

2–12. Repeat Problem 2–8 using the signal flow diagram method.

2-13. Repeat Problem 2-9 using the signal flow diagram method.

2-14. Repeat Problem 2-10 using the signal flow diagram method.

CHAPTER 3

3-1. (a) For the mechanical translational system illustrated in Figure P3-1, write the differential equation relating the position $y(t)$ and the applied force $f(t)$.
   (b) Determine the transfer function $Y(s)/F(s)$.

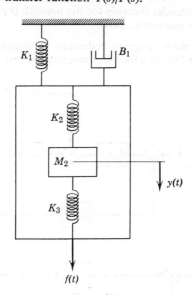

Figure P3-1

3-2. (a) For the mechanical translational system illustrated in Figure P3-2, write the differential equation relating the position $y(t)$ and the applied force $f(t)$.
   (b) Determine the transfer function $Y(s)/F(s)$.

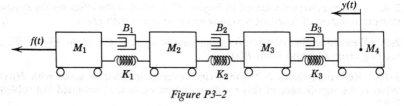

Figure P3-2

3-3. (a) For the mechanical rotational system illustrated in Figure P3-3, write the differential equation relating $T(t)$ and $\theta(t)$.
   (b) Determine the transfer function $\theta(s)/T(s)$.

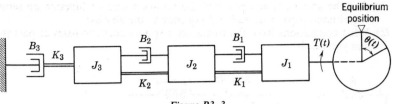

Equilibrium
position

Figure P3–3

3–4. Figure P3–4 represents the diagram of a gyroscope which is used quite frequently in autopilots, stabilized fire control systems, and so on. Assume that the rotor speed is constant, that the total developed torque about the output axis is given by

$$T_o = K \frac{d\theta_i(t)}{dt}$$

where K is a constant, and that the inner gimbal exerts a moment of inertia J about the output axis.
  (a) Write the differential equation relating $\theta_i(t)$ and $\theta_o(t)$.
  (b) Determine the transfer function $\theta_o(s)/\theta_i(s)$.

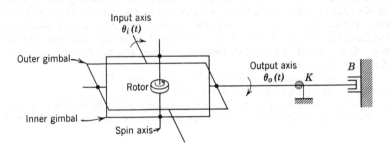

Figure P3–4

3–5. The Ward-Leonard system shown in Figure 3–19 has the following constants and characteristics:

Generator	Motor
$R_f = 1.1$ ohms	$R_m = 2$ ohms
$L_f = 0.25$ henries	$L_m = 0.05$ henries
$R_g = 0.20$ ohms	$K_e = 0.1$ volt/radian/second
$L_g = 0.01$ henries	$K_T = 2$ ft-lb/ampere
$K_g = 1$ volt/radian/second	$J = 0.1$ slug-ft^2
	$B = $ negligible

  (a) Derive the transfer function for the system, $\theta_o(s)/E_f(s)$.

(b) Plot the amplitude and phase of the resultant transfer function on semi-logarithmic paper with radian frequency as the abscissa.
(c) What conclusions from the frequency response characteristics of part (b) can you reach?

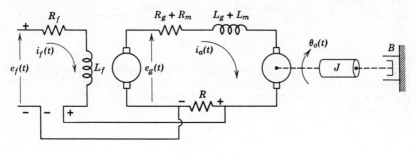

Figure P3–6

3–6. The time constant for highly inductive devices such as the armature circuit of the Ward-Leonard system shown in Figure 3–19 is usually too long for high performance control systems. A simple technique for decreasing the time constant of such a system uses feedback, which controls the current of the inductive device. Figure P3–6 illustrates how this can be practically accomplished for a Ward-Leonard system by inserting a resistor R in series with the armature circuit. Other notations used in this diagram are the same as those used in Section 3–3 of Chapter 3.

(a) Write the differential equation relating $e_f(t)$ and $\theta_o(t)$.
(b) Determine the transfer function $\theta_o(s)/E_f(s)$.
(c) Compare the answer to part (b) with equation 3–47 and conclusively show that the armature time constant has been reduced by means of feedback.

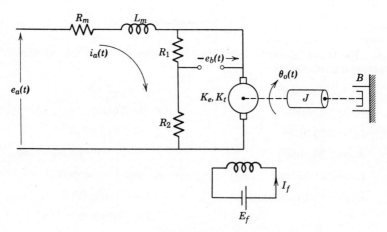

Figure P3–7

3–7. Since it is proportional to velocity, the back emf of a motor is sometimes directly used as a stabilizing voltage. Figure P3–7 illustrates a practical bridge-type circuit which can be used for this purpose. R_1 and R_2, which have very high relative resistance, are adjustable in order to obtain the desired value of $e_b(t)$. R_m, L_m, K_e, K_T, J, and B have the same significance as they did in Chapter 3.
  (a) Write the differential equation relating $e_a(t)$ and $e_b(t)$.
  (b) Determine the transfer function $E_b(s)/E_a(s)$.

3–8. If the armature current of the field-controlled d-c servomotor is not held constant, the developed torque is proportional to both the field and the armature currents (see equation 3–57). This essentially results in a nonlinear device because of the multiplication effect of field and armature current.
  (a) Draw the signal flow diagram for the system.
  (b) Determine the transfer function of this device relating the output $\theta_o(s)$ to the field circuit input $E_f(s)$ and the armature circuit input $E_a(s)$.
  (c) What approximations can be made to linearize the operation?

3–9. Draw the signal flow diagram and analog-computer simulation circuitry for the following devices:
  (a) d-c generator
  (b) The Ward-Leonard system
  (c) Two-phase a-c servomotor

3–10. Derive the transfer function $C(s)/R(s)$ for the valve-controlled hydraulic transmission system shown in Figure 3–29 if a spring in parallel with a viscous damper is attached between the right end of the valve control rod and some stationary reference point. Assume that the spring stiffness factor is K pounds/foot and the viscous damping factor is B pounds/foot/second.

3–11. A two-phase a-c servomotor has the following specifications: 115/115 volts; 60 cycles/second; 2 phases; 4 poles; rotor moment of inertia, 0.09 oz.-in.^{2}, rated stalled torque, 6 oz.-in.; no-load speed, 2500 rpm; load inertia and coefficient of viscous friction are negligible. Calculate the transfer function for this servomotor, $\theta_o(s)/E_c(s)$.

3–12. It is common practice to place a gear reduction between a servomotor and the load in order to convert the high-speed, low-torque motor characteristics to a low-speed, high-torque device. Assuming a gear reduction of N:1 and a load inertia of J_2, derive the transfer function $\theta_o(s)/E_c(s)$ for this system and compare it with equation 3–64. Use the same terminology and motor characteristics as in Section 3–3, part 5.

3–13. Based on the derivation of Problem 3–12, repeat Problem 3–11 if the load has an inertia of 0.40 oz.-in.^{2} and a gear ratio of 36:1 is used.

3–14. The two-phase a-c induction motor of Problem 3–11 is used in a simple positioning system as shown in Figure 3–34. Assume that a difference amplifier, whose gain is 10, is used as the error detector and also supplies power to the control field.
  (a) What are the undamped natural frequency ω_n and the damping factor ζ?
  (b) What are the percent overshoot and rise time resulting from the application of a unit step input?
  (c) Plot the error as a function of time on the application of a unit step input.

CHAPTER 4

4-1. Assume that the system shown in Figure 4–1 has the following characteristics:

$$K_1 = 10 \text{ volts/radian}$$

$$K_2 = 10 \text{ volts/radian}$$

$$G = \frac{100}{s(s + 1)}$$

(a) Determine the sensitivity of the system's transmittance T with respect to the input transducer, K_1.
(b) Determine the sensitivity of the system's transmittance T with respect to the output transducer, K_2.
(c) Determine the sensitivity of the system's transmittance T with respect to G.

4-2. For the system illustrated in Figure P4–2, assume the following characteristics:

$$K_1 = 10 \text{ volts/radian} \qquad G_1 = \frac{10}{100 + s}$$

$$K_2 = 10 \text{ volts/radian} \qquad G_2 = \frac{20}{s(s + 2)}$$

$$K_3 = 2 \text{ volts/radian} \qquad H = 4s$$

(a) Determine the sensitivity of the system's transmittance T with respect to G_1.
(b) Determine the sensitivity of the system's transmittance T with respect to G_2.
(c) Determine the sensitivity of the system's transmittance T with respect to H.
(d) Determine the sensitivity of the system's transmittance T with respect to K_3.
(e) List the answers of parts (a) through (d) in tabular form with the lowest value first and the largest value last. Normalize your table. What conclusions can you reach?

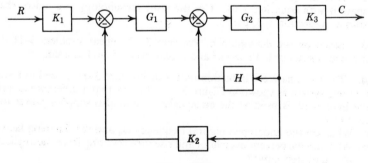

Figure P4–2

4-3. The block diagram of a simple instrument servomechanism is shown in Figure P4-3.

(a) Determine the steady-state error resulting from the input of a ramp which may be represented by

$$r(t) = 10t$$

(b) Determine the steady-state error resulting from the following input:

$$r(t) = 4 + 6t + 3t^2$$

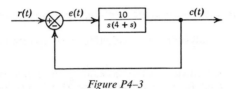

Figure P4-3

4-4. For the system shown in Figure P4-4, determine the following:

(a) Steady-state error resulting from an input

$$r(t) = 10t$$

(b) Steady-state error resulting from an input

$$r(t) = 4 + 6t + 3t^2$$

(c) Steady-state error resulting from an input

$$r(t) = 4 + 6t + 3t^2 + 1.8t^3$$

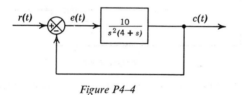

Figure P4-4

4-5. A servomechanism, shown in Figure P4-5, is used to drive an inertia load through gearing of negligible inertia.

1. A-c motor characteristics:

$$\text{Torque-speed slope} = 4.5 \times 10^{-6} \frac{\text{lb-ft}}{\text{rad/sec}}$$

$$\text{Stall torque constant} = 8.5 \times 10^{-6} \text{ lb-ft/volt}$$

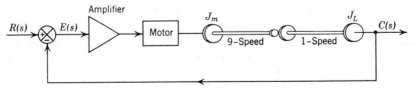

Figure P4-5

2. Load inertia $= J_L = 40 \times 10^{-6}$ slug-ft^2
3. Amplifier gain $= 10$
4. Gear ratio $= 9:1$ (steps motor speed down)
(a) What is the transfer function $G(s)$ relating $C(s)$ and $E(s)$ of the system?
(b) What are the undamped natural frequency ω_n and the damping factor ζ?
(c) What is the percent overshoot and rise time resulting from the application of a unit step input?
(d) What is the steady-state error resulting from application of a unit step input?
(e) What is the steady-state error resulting from application of a unit ramp input?
(f) What is the steady-state error resulting from application of a parabolic input?

4–6. A third-order feedback system containing three feedback paths is illustrated in Figure P4–6. In order to satisfy the ITAE criterion, determine the values of K_1, β_1, and β_2. Solve this problem utilizing block diagram reduction techniques and the signal flow diagram method. Which technique do you prefer?

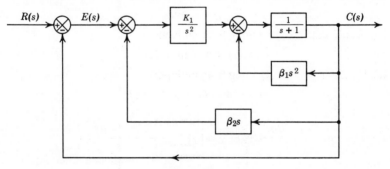

Figure P4–6

4–7. An analog computer will be used to study the transient response of the system considered in Problem 4–6 as certain parameters are varied from their ITAE criterion condition values.
(a) Determine the circuitry required to simulate the system shown in Figure P4–6 on an analog computer.
(b) Utilizing an analog computer, determine the overshoot and rise time of the system's transient response to a step input as K_1, β_1, and β_2 are each varied $\pm 100\%$.

4–8. A sixth-order feedback system containing four feedback paths is illustrated in Figure P4–8. In order to satisfy the ITAE criterion, determine the values of β_1, β_2, β_3, and α. It is suggested that you use the signal flow diagram method for the solution.

4–9. An analog computer will be used to study the transient response of the system considered in Problem 4–8 as certain parameters are varied from their ITAE criterion condition values.
(a) Determine the circuitry required to simulate the system shown in Figure P4–8 on an analog computer.

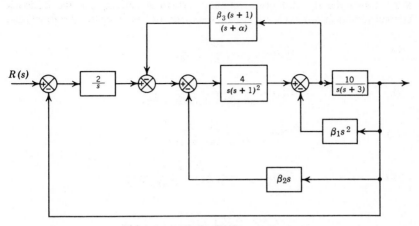

Figure P4–8

(b) Utilizing an analog computer, determine the overshoot and rise time of the system's transient response to a step input as β_1, β_2, β_3, and α are each varied $\pm100\%$.

4–10. Repeat Problem 4–6 using the integral of the absolute value of the error as the performance criterion. (See Ref. 1 of Chapter 4 for the details of this performance criterion.)

4–11. Repeat Problem 4–6 using the integral of time and multiplied by the error squared as the performance criterion. (See Ref. 1 of Chapter 4 for the details of this performance criterion.)

4–12. Repeat Problem 4–6 using the integral of time squared multiplied by the error squared as the performance criterion. (See Ref. 1 of Chapter 4 for the details of this performance criterion.)

CHAPTER 5

5–1. The differential equation expressing the output $y(t)$ of a mechanical system in terms of its input $x(t)$ is given by

$$A \frac{d^2y(t)}{dt^2} + B \frac{dy(t)}{dt} + Cy(t) = x(t)$$

(a) Find the ratio of $Y(j\omega)/X(j\omega)$ for a sinusoidal input motion in terms of A, B, and C.
(b) Plot the ratio $Y(j\omega)/X(j\omega)$ in the complex plane when

$$A = 1$$
$$B = 4$$
$$C = 16$$

5–2. Using the Routh-Hurwitz stability criterion, determine if the feedback control system shown in Figure P5–2 is stable for the following transfer functions:

(a)
$$G(s) = \frac{100}{s(s^2 + 8s + 24)}$$

(b)
$$G(s) = \frac{3s + 1}{s^2(300s^2 + 600s + 50)}$$

(c)
$$G(s) = \frac{24}{s(s + 2)(s + 4)}$$

(d)
$$G(s) = \frac{0.2(s + 2)}{s(s + 0.5)(s + 0.8)(s + 3)}$$

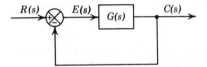

Figure P5–2

5–3. By means of complex-plane plots, determine whether feedback systems represented by the following values of $G(j\omega)H(j\omega)$ are stable.

(a)
$$G(j\omega)H(j\omega) = \frac{10}{(1 + j\omega)(1 + 2j\omega)(1 + 3j\omega)}$$

(b)
$$G(j\omega)H(j\omega) = \frac{10}{j\omega(1 + j\omega)(1 + 10j\omega)}$$

(c)
$$G(j\omega)H(j\omega) = \frac{10}{(j\omega)^2(1 + 0.1j\omega)(1 + 0.2j\omega)}$$

(d)
$$G(j\omega)H(j\omega) = \frac{2}{(j\omega)^2(1 + 0.1j\omega)(1 + 10j\omega)}$$

Do not attempt to plot the exact values of $G(j\omega)H(j\omega)$ for all values of frequency. It should only be necessary to determine a few values of frequency exactly.

5–4. The positive-frequency portions of the complex-plane plots for several transfer functions are shown in Figure P5–4. Complete the Nyquist diagram and determine stability, assuming that $G(j\omega)$ has no poles in the right half plane.

5–5. A feedback control system has a block diagram as shown in Figure P5–5.
  (a) Determine the required gain K for a steady-state velocity-lag error of 30° with an input velocity of 10 radians/second.
  (b) What are the values of M_p and ω_p?

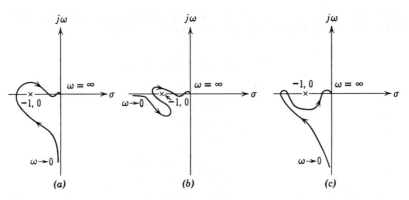

Figure P5–4

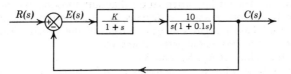

Figure P5–5

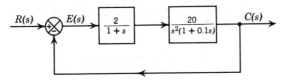

Figure P5–6

5–6. For the feedback control system shown in Figure P5–6, plot the amplitude and phase of the closed-loop frequency response.

5–7. Repeat Problem 5–6 if one of the pure integrations is removed.

5–8. A unity feedback control system has a forward transfer function given by

$$G(s) = \frac{10}{s(1 + 0.1s)(1 + 0.05s)}$$

(a) Plot the transfer locus $G(j\omega)$ on the inverse plane.
(b) What are the values of M_p and ω_p?

5–9. Repeat Problem 5–8 if

$$G(s) = \frac{2}{s(1 + s)(1 + 10s)}$$

5–10. Draw the straight-line attenuation diagrams, showing the magnitude in decibels, and the phase characteristics, showing the phase angle in degrees, as a function of frequency for the following transfer functions:

(a)
$$G_A = \frac{20}{s(1 + 0.5s)(1 + 0.1s)}$$

(b)
$$G_B = \frac{2s^2}{(1 + 0.4s)(1 + 0.04s)}$$

(c)
$$G_C = \frac{50(0.6s + 1)}{s^2(4s + 1)}$$

(d)
$$G_D = \frac{7.5(0.2s + 1)(s + 1)}{s(s^2 + 16s + 100)}$$

5-11. A feedback control system has a configuration shown in Figure P5–11.
(a) Draw the frequency loci of the loop gain function.
(b) Draw the straight-line attenuation diagram showing the magnitude, in decibels, and phase angle, in degrees, as a function of frequency.
(c) Find the phase margin and gain margin of the system. Illustrate these points on the graphs for parts (a) and (b).
(d) Find the values of K_p, K_v, and K_a.
(e) What is the steady-state velocity-lag error for a velocity input of 5 radians/second?

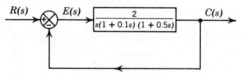

Figure P5–11

5-12. A feedback control system has the configuration shown in Figure P5–12.
(a) Plot the Bode diagram for this system.
(b) What is the gain crossover frequency? What is the phase margin at gain crossover? Is the system stable?
(c) Find the values of K_p, K_v, K_a.
(d) What is the steady-state velocity-lag error for a velocity input of 40 radians/second?

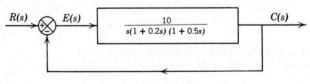

Figure P5–12

5-13. A tank level control is shown in Figure P5–13. It is desired to hold the tank level C within limits even though the outlet flow rate V is varied. If the level is not correct, an error voltage E_n is developed which is amplified and applied

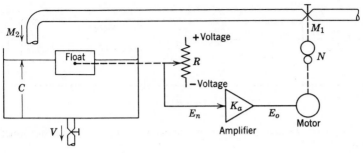

Figure P5–13

to a servomotor. This in turn adjusts a valve through appropriate gearing N and thereby restores balance by adjusting the inlet rate, M_2.

The following relations are valid from this figure:

$$E_n = R - C = \text{error in level (inches)}$$
$$E_0 = K_a E_n = \text{voltage applied to motor (volts)}$$
$$M_1 = G_1 E_0 = \text{valve position (radians)}$$
$$M_2 = K_v M_1 = \text{tank feed flow (ft}^3\text{/sec)}$$
$$C = G_2 M_2 = \text{tank level (inches)}$$

The pertinent constants and transfer functions are as follows:

$$G_1 = \frac{1}{s(0.1s + 1)} \qquad \text{radians of valve motion per volt}$$

$G_2 = 0.5/s$ inches of level per ft^3/sec

$K_v = 0.1$ ft^3/sec per radian of valve motion

$K_a = $ amplifier gain to be set

Error detector $= 1$ volt per foot of error

(a) Draw the system block diagram showing all transfer functions.
(b) Using a Bode diagram for the solution, determine the amplifier gain K_a required to meet a required gain crossover frequency of 1.5 radians/second.
(c) With the gain set at the value determined in part (b), what are the resulting phase and gain margins?

5–14. A feedback control system has the configuration shown in Figure P5–14, where $U(s)$ represents an extraneous signal appearing at the input to the plant.
(a) Assuming that $G_1(s) = 1$, plot the decibel-log frequency diagram for this system.
(b) It is desired that the steady-state error resulting from an extraneous step input signal at $U(s)$ shall be 0.1 unit. Assuming $G_1(s) = K$, determine K to meet this specification.
(c) A plot of the decibel-log frequency diagram for part (b) results in a 0-db gain line ____ db (above, below) that for part (a).
(d) Determine the crossover frequency and phase margin resulting from part (b).

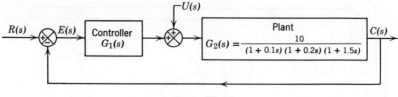

Figure P5–14

5–15. A type 1, second-order servomechanism has a forward transfer function given by

$$G(s) = \frac{16}{s(2 + s)}$$

The feedback function is unity.
  (a) Draw the Bode diagram showing the magnitude and the phase characteristics as a function of frequency.
  (b) Using the Nichols chart, plot a curve of frequency response of the overall system.
  (c) What are ω_p and M_p?
  (d) Can this system ever be unstable no matter how large the forward gain is made? Explain.

5–16. Repeat Problem 5–15 when

$$G(s) = \frac{60(1 + 0.5s)}{s(1 + 5s)}$$

5–17. Repeat Problem 5–15 when

$$G(s) = \frac{60(1 + s)}{s^2(1 + 0.1s)}$$

5–18. A unity feedback control system has a forward transfer function given by

$$G(s) = \frac{K}{s(1 + 0.1s)(1 + s)}$$

  (a) Sketch the root locus giving all pertinent characteristics of the locus.
  (b) At what value of gain does the system become unstable?

5–19. Repeat Problem 5–18 for the following transfer functions:

(a) $$G(s) = \frac{K}{s^2}$$

(b) $$G(s) = \frac{K(1 + s)}{s^2(1 + 0.1s)}$$

(c) $$G(s) = \frac{K(s + 1)}{s(s^2 + 8s + 16)}$$

(d) $$G(s) = \frac{K(s + 0.1)^2}{s^2(s^2 + 9s + 20)}$$

5–20. Sketch the root locus for a feedback control system having the following forward and feedback transfer functions:

$$G(s) = \frac{K(s + 0.1)}{s^2(s + 0.01)}$$

$$H(s) = 1 + 0.6s$$

5–21. The rules for determining the root locus must be modified if positive feedback is considered. Determine which rules must be modified to take this into account.

5–22. Based on the rule changes determined in Problem 5–21, sketch the root locus of a unity feedback system, where

$$G(s) = \frac{K(1 + 0.1s)}{s(1 + 0.25s)^2(1 + s)}$$

for positive and negative values of gain.

CHAPTER 6

6–1. Determine the network structure, the values of resistance and capacitance, and the complex-plane plot for networks having the following characteristics:
  (a) Phase lead of 60° at $\omega = 4$ radians/second, a minimum input impedance of 50,000 ohms, an attenuation of 10 db at d-c.
  (b) Phase lag of 60° at $\omega = 4$, a minimum input impedance of 50,000 ohms, and a high-frequency attenuation of -10 db.
  (c) A lag-lead network having an attenuation of 10 db for a frequency range of $\omega = 1$ to $\omega = 10$ radians/second and an input impedance of 50,000 ohms.
In all cases, limit the maximum values of resistance to 1 megohm and capacitance to 10 μf. Furthermore, assume that the loads on the networks have essentially infinite impedance.

6–2. The system illustrated in Figure P6–2 consists of a unity feedback loop containing a minor rate feedback loop.
  (a) Without any rate feedback ($b = 0$), determine the damping factor, natural resonant frequency, overshoot of the system to a unit step input, and the steady-state error resulting from a unit ramp input.

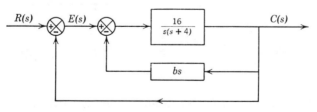

Figure P6–2

(b) Determine the rate feedback constant *b* which will increase the equivalent damping factor of the system to 0.8.

(c) With rate feedback and a damping factor of 0.8, determine the overshoot of the system to a unit step input and the steady-state error resulting from a unit ramp input.

(d) Illustrate how the resulting steady-state error of the system with rate feedback to ramp inputs can be reduced to the same level, if rate feedback were not used, and still maintain a damping factor of 0.8.

6–3.   An error-measuring system that does not result in voltage interaction between inputs is shown in Figure P6–3.

(a) Show that the transfer characteristics of this error-measuring device are given by

$$e_o = \frac{z}{2}\left(\frac{e_I}{z + z_I} + \frac{e_{II}}{z + z_{II}}\right)$$

(b) What are the limitations of this circuit?

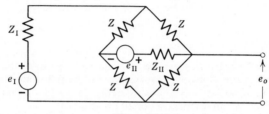

Figure P6–3

6–4.   Find the spectrum at the output of the modulator circuit shown in Figure P6–4. Determine e_o in both the time and frequency domains. Assume that the mechanical chopper arm is up one-half the time and down the remaining time of each cycle.

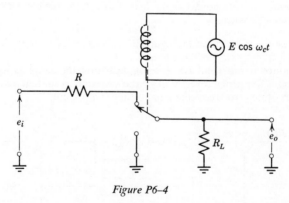

Figure P6–4

6–5.   Repeat Problem 6–4 for the modulator circuit shown in Figure P6–5. What are the advantages of the circuit of Figure P6–5 over that of Figure P6–4?

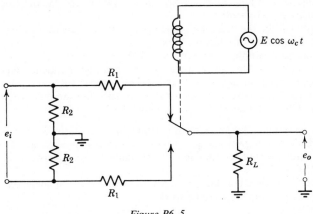

Figure P6-5

6-6. Prove that the transfer function of a parallel-T network is given by equation 6–58.

6-7. (a) For the parallel-T network shown in Figure 6–18a, determine the output for the following conditions:

    1. Input $= V \cos a\omega_c t \cos \omega_c t$

    2. Input $= V \cos a\omega_c t \cos (1 + \delta)\omega_c t$ where $\delta \ll 1$

  (b) What is the effect of δ on the carrier phase shaft? Explain.

6-8. A unity feedback system has a forward transfer function given by

$$G(s) = \frac{28(1 + 0.05s)}{s(1 + s)}$$

It is desired to compensate this system so that the resulting damping factor is unity (critically damped).

  (a) Using the classical approach, determine the time constant of a cascaded lead network which can achieve this.

  (b) Repeat part (a) utilizing a lag network.

  (c) Using the classical approach, determine the rate feedback constant of a minor rate feedback loop which can achieve critical damping.

6-9. It is desired to add cascade compensation to the system considered in Problem 5–5 in order that $M_p = 1.2$ while the same steady-state error is maintained.

  (a) Design a phase-lag network to achieve this.

  (b) Repeat part (a) for a phase-lead network.

  (c) With the compensation networks chosen in parts (a) and (b), determine the closed-loop amplitude and phase frequency responses for each part.

  (d) What conclusions can you reach from part (c)?

6-10. It is desired that the system considered in Problem 6–9 have an overshoot of approximately 15% to a step input.

(a) Utilizing a minor rate feedback loop, specify the tachometer constant which can achieve this.

(b) What will be the resulting system steady-state error to a unit ramp input with the minor rate feedback loop added?

(c) Utilizing a simple, high-pass, RC filter in cascade with the tachometer, determine the time constant of the network and the tachometer constant which will result in a 15% overshoot to a step input.

(d) What will the system's steady-state error to a unit ramp be when the high-pass filter is cascaded with the tachometer?

6–11. It is desired that the system considered in Problem 5–12 have a phase margin of 65° and a gain margin of 6 db. Cascade compensation is to be employed where the transfer function of the compensating network is given by $(1 + T_1s)/(1 + T_2s)$.

(a) Specify the time constants of a lead network that can achieve this.

(b) Repeat part (a) for a lag network.

6–12. It is desired that the system considered in Problem 5–13 have a phase margin of 45° at the crossover frequency. Determine the stabilizing element required to achieve this.

6–13. It is desired that the system considered in Problem 5–14 have a phase margin of 45° at the crossover frequency. In order to achieve this, a phase-lead network is introduced into the controller. This results in the controller having a transfer function given by

$$G_1(s) = K \frac{1 + T_1s}{1 + T_2s}$$

where K is the value of gain found in part (b) of Problem 5–14. Determine T_1, T_2, and the resulting new crossover frequency to meet this specification.

6–14. It is desired to add cascade compensation to the system considered in Problem 5–16 in order that its overshoot to a step input be approximately 10%.

(a) Using the Nichols chart, design a phase-lead network which can achieve this.

(b) Repeat part (a) using a phase-lag network.

(c) With the compensation networks chosen in parts (a) and (b), determine the closed-loop amplitude and phase frequency response for each part.

(d) What conclusions can you reach from part (c)?

6–15. It is desired that the system considered in Problem 5–18 have a damping factor of 0.75 for the dominant complex roots. Using the root locus method,

(a) Determine the lag network

$$\frac{s + n\alpha}{s + \alpha}$$

which can achieve this. Assume $n = 15$.

(b) Determine the lead network

$$\frac{s + n\alpha}{s + \alpha}$$

which can achieve this. Assume $n = 0.15$.

  (c) Determine the steady-state error coefficients, ω_p and M_p for parts (a) and (b).

6–16. Repeat Problem 6–15 for the system considered in Problem 5–19(b).

6–17. Repeat Problem 6–15 for the system considered in Problem 5–19(c).

6–18. Repeat Problem 6–15 for the system considered in Problem 5–19(d).

CHAPTER 7

7–1. The torque-speed characteristics of a two-phase, a-c instrument servo-motor are illustrated in Figure P7–1. Assume that the inertia of the rotor is 0.1 oz-in.^{2} and that the load inertia and coefficient of viscous friction are negligible.
  (a) Derive the transfer function of the motor using linearizing approximations. Approximate the characteristics by one straight line that is tangent to the exact characteristics at 1000 rpm, and by one straight line that goes through the two end points. Compare your results.
  (b) How do the time constants derived in part (a) change if the torque-speed characteristics are approximated with two straight lines: one at low speed that is tangent to the exact characteristics at 250 rpm, and one at high speed that is tangent to the exact characteristics at 1750 rpm?
  (c) Comparing your answers to parts (a) and (b), what conclusions can you reach?

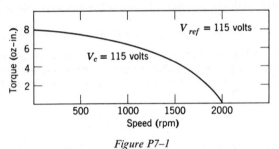

Figure P7–1

7–2. Derive the describing function corresponding to the combined nonlinear characteristics of staturation and dead zone.

7–3. Derive the describing function of a 2-position contactor which does not exhibit any hysteresis effect.

7–4. An amplifying device in a feedback loop has the following nonlinear characteristics:
  1. No output signal for all inputs whose magnitude is less than $|E_1|$ volts.

$$e_o(t) = 0 \quad \text{when} \quad e_i(t) < |E_1|$$

  2. Input signals whose magnitude is greater than E_1 volts but less than E_2 volts are amplified according to the relation

$$e_o(t) = K[e_i(t) - |E_1|]$$

where

$$|E_1| < e_i(t) < |E_2|$$

3. For all input signals whose magnitude is greater than E_2 volts, the output is given by

$$e_o(t) = K|E_2|$$

when

$$e_i(t) > |E_2|$$

Sketch the input-output characteristics and derive the describing function.

7-5. A unity feedback system consists of cascaded elements which include a relay, pure integration, an amplifier which saturates, a two-phase, a-c servomotor and a gear train containing backlash.
  (a) Draw the block diagram and show the linear transfer functions and the describing functions for the nonlinear elements, symbolically.
  (b) Qualitatively illustrate how you would predict stability on a polar plot and a gain-phase diagram.

7-6. A unity feedback instrument servo with a spring-loaded shaft has a dead zone of 2°. The transfer function for the linear portion of the system is given by

$$G(j\omega) = \frac{20}{j\omega(j\omega + 0.05)(j\omega + 0.1)}$$

  (a) Investigate stability utilizing the describing-function method on a gain-phase diagram.
  (b) Investigate stability utilizing the describing-function method on a polar plot.
  (c) Compare the results of parts (a) and (b). What conclusions can you reach?

7-7. A unity feedback instrument servo is driven by an amplifier which saturates at 70% of rated voltage. Assume that the gain of the unsaturated amplifier is 40. The transfer function of the linear portion of the system, excluding the amplifier, is given by

$$G(j\omega) = \frac{0.25}{j\omega(j\omega + 2)}$$

  (a) Investigate stability utilizing the describing-function method on a gain-phase diagram.
  (b) Investigate stability utilizing the describing-function method on a polar plot.

7-8. An instrument servo contains a three-position contactor which has a pull-in point at an error of 0.03 radian and a drop-out point at 0.01-radian error. The transfer function of the linear portion is given by

$$G(j\omega) = \frac{10}{j\omega(j\omega + 4)}$$

Determine whether the system is stable utilizing the describing-function analysis on a gain-phase diagram.

7-9. An instrument servo system used for positioning a load may be adequately represented by the block diagram shown in Figure P7-9.

(b)
$$\frac{d^2\theta(t)}{dt^2} + 0.8\frac{d\theta(t)}{dt} + 0.4\theta(t) = 0.6$$

(c)
$$\frac{d^2\theta(t)}{dt^2} + 0.8\frac{d\theta(t)}{dt}\left|\frac{d\theta(t)}{dt}\right| + 0.4\theta(t) = 0$$

(d)
$$\frac{d^2\theta(t)}{dt^2} + 0.8\frac{d\theta(t)}{dt}\left|\frac{d\theta(t)}{dt}\right| + 0.4\theta(t) = 0.6$$

7–17. Construct the phase portraits for each of the differential equations of Problem 7–16 using the method of isoclines.

7–18. The differential equation of a typical second-order system containing both viscous and coulomb friction is given by

$$\frac{d^2y}{dx^2} + 0.8\frac{dy}{dx} + 0.4y + A\sin\frac{dy}{dx} = 0$$

Determine and construct the phase portraits for $A = 0.2, 0.4$, and 0.8.

7–19. Determine and construct the phase trajectory for a second-order system containing rate limiting where $\theta(0) = 0.7$. Assume that the differential equation for the system is given by

$$\frac{d^2\theta(t)}{dt^2} + 0.8\frac{d\theta(t)}{dt} + 0.4\frac{d\theta(t)}{dt} = 0$$

and that

$$\left.\frac{d\theta(t)}{dt}\right|_{\max} = 0.3$$

7–20. Determine and construct the phase trajectory of a torque-saturated system for which the describing equations are given by

$$\frac{d^2\theta(t)}{dt^2} + 0.8\frac{d\theta(t)}{dt} = 0.5 \quad \text{where} \quad \theta(t) > 0$$

and

$$\frac{d^2\theta(t)}{dt^2} + 0.8\frac{d\theta(t)}{dt} = -0.5 \quad \text{where} \quad \theta(t) < 0$$

Assume that the initial conditions are $\theta(0) = 0.5$ and $d\theta(0)/dt = 0$.

7–21. Prove that the total energy stored in a second-order linear system is proportional to the square of the radial distance to any point in the normalized phase plane (the ordinate is $\dot{x}/\omega_n$).

7–22. Linear systems containing time-varying parameters are much more difficult to analyze than systems having constant parameters. For such systems nonlinear techniques are often helpful. For the system whose differential equation is given by

$$(t^2 + 0.5t + 1)\frac{d^2\theta(t)}{dt^2} + (t^2 + 0.5t - 0.2)\frac{d\theta(t)}{dt} + (t + 1)\theta(t) = t^2 + 1$$

determine and construct the phase portrait. Indicate its transient response to a step input.

7–23. Utilizing Liapunov's second method, determine the stability of the following nonlinear differential equation

$$\frac{d^2x}{dt^2} + \left[K_1 + K_2\left(\frac{dx}{dt}\right)^2\right]\frac{dx}{dt} + x^2 = 0$$

if

(a) $K_1 > 0$; $K_2 > 0$

(b) $K_1 > 0$; $K_2 < 0$

(c) $K_1 < 0$; $K_2 > 0$

(d) $K_1 = K_2 = 0$

7–24. Repeat Problem 7–23 for the nonlinear differential equation

$$\frac{d^2x}{dt^2} + \left[1 + K_1\left(\frac{dx}{dt}\right)^2\right]\frac{dx}{dt} + K_2x^2 = 0$$

7–25. Utilizing step-by-step numerical computation techniques, determine the solution to the differential equations listed below. Assume that $\Delta t = 0.02$ seconds. It is recommended that part (a) be done both by hand and with the aid of a desk calculator (or digital computer); and all of the other parts only with the aid of a desk calculator (or digital computer).

(a) $$\frac{dx}{dt} + x^2 = 1$$

where $x_0 = \left(\frac{dx}{dt}\right)_0 = 0$

(b) $$\frac{d^2x}{dt^2} + x\frac{dx}{dt} + x = 2$$

where $x_0 = 1$

$$\left(\frac{dx}{dt}\right)_0 = 2$$

$$\left(\frac{d^2x}{dt^2}\right)_0 = 1$$

(c) $$\frac{d^3x}{dt^3} + x^2\frac{d^2x}{dt^2} + 6\frac{dx}{dt} + 1 = 0$$

where $x_0 = 1$

$$\left(\frac{dx}{dt}\right)_0 = 10$$

$$\left(\frac{d^2x}{dt^2}\right)_0 = 1$$

$$\left(\frac{d^3x}{dt^3}\right)_0 = 0$$

(d) $$\frac{d^3x}{dt^3} + 6\frac{d^2x}{dt^2} + x^2 + 1 = 0$$

where $x_0 = \left(\frac{dx}{dt}\right)_0 = \left(\frac{d^2x}{dt^2}\right)_0 = \left(\frac{d^3x}{dt^3}\right)_0 = 0$

7-26. Repeat Problem 7–25 if Δt is varied in the following manner:

(a) $\Delta t = 0.01$ second

(b) $\Delta t = 0.04$ second

(c) $\Delta t = 0.1$ second

(d) $\Delta t = 1$ second

What conclusions can you reach from your results?

7-27. Utilizing the equivalent constant-coefficient method, in conjunction with the Routh-Hurwitz criterion, determine the stability of the following time-variable linear differential equations at $t = 0.1$, 1.0, 10, and 100 seconds:

(a) $$\frac{d^2y(t)}{dt^2} + t\frac{dy(t)}{dt} + y(t) = 10$$

(b) $$\frac{d^2y(t)}{dt^2} + (4t + 6)\frac{dy(t)}{dt} + ty(t) = 1$$

(c) $$\frac{d^3y(t)}{dt^3} + \frac{d^2y(t)}{dt^2} + (2t + 1)\frac{dy(t)}{dt} + ty(t) = 1$$

(d) $$\frac{d^3y(t)}{dt^3} + t\frac{d^2y(t)}{dt^2} + t\frac{dy(t)}{dt} + y(t) = 10$$

(e) What conclusions can you reach from your results?

CHAPTER 8

8-1. A recording of the roll of a ship in a rough sea is shown in Figure P8–1.

(a) Determine and sketch the autocorrelation function of this signal utilizing a $\tau = 5$ seconds.

(b) Determine and sketch the power-density spectrum for the random function.

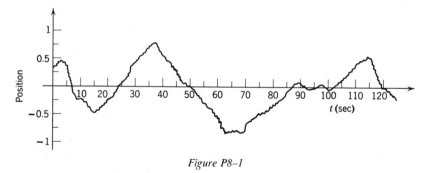

Figure P8–1

8-2. Repeat Problem 8–1 if $\tau = 2$, 10, and 30 seconds. What conclusions can you reach from your results?

8-3. A random signal, whose power-density spectrum is given by

$$\Phi_R(\omega) = \frac{20}{\omega^2 + 4}$$

is to be transmitted through a low-pass filter whose transfer function is adequately described by

$$G(j\omega) = \frac{1}{1 + Tj\omega}$$

Determine the time constant T necessary to transmit 80% of the input power.

8-4. Repeat Problem 8-3 if it is required that the filter block 80% of the input power. What conclusions can you draw from your results?

8-5. An instrument servo positioning system, whose block diagram is shown in Figure P8-5, has an input consisting of signal and white noise. The power-density spectra of the signal and noise inputs are given by

$$\Phi_{rr}(j\omega) = \frac{0.2}{0.09 + \omega^2}$$

$$\Phi_{nn}(j\omega) = N^2$$

Assuming that the signal and noise are statistically independent, find the value of K which minimizes the root-mean-square error.

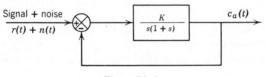

Figure P8-5

8-6. For Problem 8-5, determine the ratio of signal-to-noise power at the input and compare it with that at the output if the root-mean-square error is minimized. Assume that the signals appear across 1-ohm resistances.

8-7. Repeat Problem 8-5 if the power-density spectrum of the input noise is given by

$$\Phi_{nn}(j\omega) = \frac{1}{0.4 + \omega^2}$$

8-8. Repeat Problem 8-6 for the condition specified in Problem 8-7.

8-9. A positioning control system can be represented by the block diagram shown in Figure P8-9. The signal input is a random time function which is stationary and described by the power-density spectrum given by

$$\Phi_{rr}(j\omega) = \frac{1}{1 + \omega^2}$$

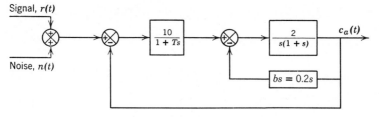

Figure P8–9

The disturbance, or noise, which is applied at the same point, is stationary and is described by the power density spectrum given by

$$\Phi_{nn}(j\omega) = \frac{10}{9 + \omega^2}$$

(a) What value of time constant T will minimize the root-mean-square error?
(b) With the value of T determined in part (a) determine the ratio of signal-to-noise power at the input and compare it with the signal-to-noise power at the output. Assume that the signals appear across 1-ohm resistances.

8–10.   Repeat Problem 8–9 if the time constant T is chosen to be 0.1 seconds and it is desired to vary the rate feedback constant, b.

CHAPTER 9

9–1.   Prove item 8 of Table 9–1.

9–2.   Prove item 12 of Table 9–1.

9–3.   A pulse input, $r^*(t)$, is applied to the low-pass filter as shown in Figure P9–3.
(a) What is the z-transform of $r^*(t)$?
(b) What is the z-transform of $c^*(t)$?
(c) Compute the pulse train, $c^*(t)$, carrying out the computation to 8 pulses.
(d) Using the advanced z-transform, determine the time function between sampling points. In your calculations, assume $\Delta = 0.25, 0.5$, and 0.75.
(e) Apply the initial- and final-value theorem to obtain $c^*(0)$ and $c^*(\infty)$.

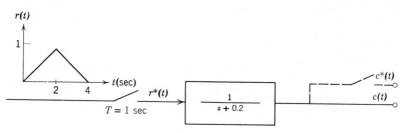

Figure P9–3

9–4. Repeat Problem 9–3 if the input $r(t)$ is given by Figure P9–4.

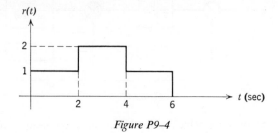

Figure P9–4

9–5. Determine the z-transforms corresponding to the following transfer functions:

(a)
$$G(s) = \frac{1}{s(s + 1)^2}$$

(b)
$$G(s) = \frac{se^{st}}{s(s + 1)(s + 2)}$$

(c)
$$G(s) = \frac{1}{s^2 + 10s + 25}$$

9–6. Derive the z-transform of the output, $C(z)$, for the sampled-data feedback control system shown in Figure P9–6.

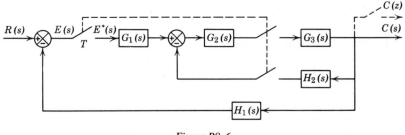

Figure P9–6

9–7. The linear system shown in Figure P9–7 is subjected to an input which is sampled and held by a zero-order holding circuit. Assume that the impulse sampling approximation is applicable for this problem and that the sampling interval T is 1 second.

   (a) Determine the z-transfer function relating the sampled input $R(z)$ and the sampled output $C(z)$.

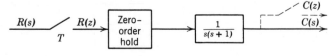

Figure P9–7

(b) For a step function at the input $R(s)$, determine the z-transform of the output $C(z)$. Compute the pulse sequence $C(z)$ and sketch your result.

(c) For a unit ramp at the input, determine the z-transform of the output $C(z)$. Compute the pulse sequence $C(z)$ and sketch your result.

(d) Compute and sketch the value of $c(t)$ in parts (b) and (c) using the advanced z-transform. In your calculations, assume $\Delta = 0.25, 0.5,$ and 0.75.

(e) What conclusions can you reach from your results to parts (b), (c), and (d)?

9–8. Repeat Problem 9–7 if the sampling interval is varied to 0.1, 0.5, 2, and 10 seconds. It is recommended that a desk calculator (or digital computer) be used as a computational aid. What conclusions can you reach from your results?

9–9. Repeat Problem 9–7 if the extrapolating circuit is a first-order hold.

9–10. Repeat Problem 9–8 for the condition of Problem 9–9.

9–11. The sampled-data control system illustrated in Figure P9–11 contains a sampler in the error channel followed by a zero-order holding circuit and a linear continuous plant whose transfer function is $G_2(s)$. Assuming that $G_2(s)$ is given by

$$G_2(s) = \frac{K}{s^2(s + 4)}$$

determine the following:

(a) Is the system stable when $K = 1$?

(b) What is the maximum value of K before the system becomes unstable?

(c) What is the system's response to a unit step input?

(d) What is the system's response to a unit ramp input?

It is recommended that a desk calculator (or digital computer) be used as a computational aid.

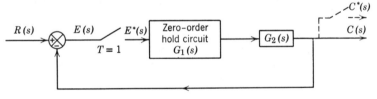

Figure P9–11

9–12. Repeat Problem 9–11 if

$$G_2(s) = \frac{K(s + 2)}{s(s + 4)(s + 8)}$$

9–13. A feedback control system has a forward transfer function given by

$$G(s) = \frac{K}{s^2(s + 1)}$$

The error channel and feedback channel are sampled at a sampling interval of 1 second as shown in the block diagram of Figure P9–13. The error and output pulse trains are extrapolated by means of zero-order holding circuits (clamps).

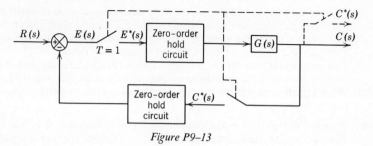

Figure P9–13

(a) Determine the loop z-transfer function $GH*(z)$.
(b) Is this system stable when $K = 1$?
(c) At what value of gain K does the system become unstable?
(d) Determine the system's response to a unit step input assuming that $K = 0.2$.
(e) Determine the system's response to a unit ramp input assuming that $K = 0.2$.

It is recommended that a desk calculator (or digital computer) be used as a computational aid.

9–14. Repeat Problem 9–13 if the forward transfer function $G(s)$ is given by

$$G(s) = \frac{K(s + 0.1)}{s^2(s + 1)}$$

9–15. Utilizing a desk calculator (or digital computer), determine the effect of varying the sampling rate of the systems considered in Problems 9–13 and 9–14 to 0.1, 0.5, 2, and 10 seconds. What conclusions can you reach from your results?

9–16. It is desired to compensate a sampled-data control system utilizing digital compensation techniques. For the system shown in Figure 9–36, assume that the data extrapolation is a zero-order hold circuitry, the sampling rate is one second, and $G_2(s)$ is given by

$$G_2(s) = \frac{2}{s(s + 1)}$$

(a) Applying rules 1 through 4, design $D(z)$ in order to obtain a minimal response function.
(b) Determine and sketch the response of this system to a unit step input.
(c) Determine and sketch the response of this system to a unit ramp input.

9–17. Repeat Problem 9–16 if $G_2(s)$ is given by

$$G_2(s) = \frac{2}{s^2(s + 1)}$$

9–18. Illustrate how the response of the problem considered in Figure 9–16 is softened by the addition of a staleness factor term where the staleness factor c is given by

(a) $c = 0.2$

(b) $c = -0.2$

(c) $c = 0.8$

(d) $c = -0.8$

What conclusions can you reach from your results?

9–19. Repeat Problem 9–18 for the modification specified in Problem 9–17.

9–20. Find $f(0)$ and $f(\infty)$ in each case:

(a)
$$F(z) = \frac{z(z+1)(z+2)}{(z-\frac{1}{3})(z^2 - z/2 + \frac{1}{2})}$$

(b)
$$F(z) = \frac{(z-2)^2}{(z+\frac{1}{3})(z+\frac{1}{2})(z-\frac{2}{3})}$$

(c)
$$F(z) = \frac{z(z-1)}{z^2 - 3z + 1}$$

9–21. Utilizing the bilinear transformation, determine the stability of sampled-data control systems whose characteristic equations are given by

(a) $z^2 + 1.5z - 1 = 0$

(b) $z^2 - z + 0.25 = 0$

(c) $z^3 - 3z^2 + 2.25z - 0.5 = 0$

(d) $z^4 - 3.1z^3 + 2.55z^2 - 2.75z + 0.05 = 0$

9–22. Repeat Problem 9–21 utilizing the Schur-Cohn stability criterion.

9–23. Repeat Problem number 9–21 utilizing Jury's stability test.

9–24. The choice of a suitable sampling frequency in a sampled-data control system is a very interesting and stimulating problem. Consider the digitally compensated system shown in Figure 9–36 with

$$G_2(s) = \frac{K}{s}$$

Utilizing the analog computer simulation circuit shown in Figure 9–38, determine the effect of varying the sampling to $T = 0.1, 0.5, 2,$ and 10 seconds on the following system characteristics:
(a) Stability when $K = 1$
(b) Maximum value of gain K before system becomes unstable
(c) System's response to a unit step
(d) What conclusions can you reach from your results?

9–25. Repeat Problem 9–24 for the case where

$$G_2(s) = \frac{K}{s^2}$$

and utilizing the analog computer simulation circuitry shown in Figure 9–41.

9–26. Repeat Problem 9–25 if a staleness factor term of $1 - .3z^{-1}$ is implemented into the digital controller.

CHAPTER 10

10–1. Determine the state equations for the systems characterized by the following differential equations:

(a)
$$\frac{d^2c}{dt^2} + 2\frac{dc}{dt} + c = 0$$

(b)
$$\frac{d^2c}{dt^2} + 2\frac{dc}{dt} + c = A$$

(c)
$$\frac{d^3c}{dt^3} + 3\frac{d^2c}{dt^2} + 2\frac{dc}{dt} + 2c = 0$$

(d)
$$\frac{d^3c}{dt^3} + 3\frac{d^2c}{dt^2} + 2\frac{dc}{dt} + 2c = A$$

10–2. The approximate linear equations of a spherical satellite are given by

$$I\ddot{\theta}_1 + \omega_0 I\dot{\theta}_3 = L_1$$
$$I\ddot{\theta}_2 \qquad\quad = L_2$$
$$I\ddot{\theta}_3 - \omega_0 I\dot{\theta}_1 = L_3$$

where θ_1, θ_2, θ_3 represent angular deviations of the satellite from a set of axes with fixed orientation; L_1, L_2, L_3 represent applied torques; I represents the moment of inertia; and ω_0 represents the angular frequency of the oriented axis. Determine the state space form of the system's dynamics.

10–3. The voltage build-up of a simple vacuum tube oscillator is given by the Van der Pol equation as follows:

$$\ddot{v} - \mu(1 - v^2)\dot{v} + v = 0$$

Determine the state space form for the dynamics.

10–4. Show that the state space equation for the system shown in Figure P10–4 is given by

$$\dot{c}(t) = Ac(t) + br(t)$$

where
$$A = \begin{vmatrix} -4 & 1 \\ -3 & 0 \end{vmatrix}; \qquad b = \begin{vmatrix} 0 \\ 3 \end{vmatrix}$$

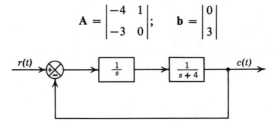

Figure P10–4

10–5. The terminal control problem is a special case of the servomechanism problem, where the only error that is important is the final error. Express the performance criterion and loss function for continuous and discrete systems which obey this law.

10–6. The minimum time problem consists of determining a control input **u** which drives the output **c** from some initial state $c(0)$ or c_0 to some prescribed final state $x(t)$ or x_N in a minimum amount of time. Express the performance criterion and loss functions for continuous and discrete systems obeying this law.

10–7. The object of the minimum control effort problem is to go from an initial state to a final state with the minimum amount of control effort (energy). Express the performance criterion and loss functions for continuous and discrete systems obeying this law.

10–8. Determine the optimal control policy for a simple regulator problem, where

$$S = \int_0^{T} (c^2 + \mu^2)\, dt$$

if the plant dynamics are given by

$$\dot{c} = -2c + \mu$$

Assume that there are no constraints on the input.

10–9. Repeat Problem 10–8 if $T \to \infty$.

10–10. Determine the optimal control policy for a second-order system where

$$\ddot{c} + 4\dot{c} + c = \mu$$

$$S = \int_0^{\infty} c^2\, dt$$

Assume that the magnitude of the controlled input must be less than unity.

10–11. Determine the continuous time solution to the regulator problem considered in Section 10–6. How does the dynamic programming solution compare with the conventional direct approach?

CHAPTER 11

11–1. The Aeronutronic impulsive-response adaptive control system determines the damping of the overall system by measuring the ratio of the positive area to the negative area of the resultant decaying oscillation. Show that the ratio of positive area A_+ to negative area A_- for a second-order system is given by

$$K = \left| \frac{A_+}{A_-} \right| = \exp\left(\frac{\zeta\pi}{\sqrt{1 - \zeta^2}} \right)$$

11–2. The performance criterion for the Aeronutronic impulsive-response adaptive control system has been suggested to be given by $A_+ - KA_-$ where K was defined in Problem 11–1.

(a) Show that

The performance criterion $= P.C. = A_+ - KA_- = \dfrac{1 - K \exp(- \zeta\pi/\sqrt{1 - \zeta^2})}{1 - \exp(- \zeta\pi\sqrt{1 - \zeta^2})}$

(b) Plot the P.C. against the damping factor ζ.
(c) From your result in part (b), notice that the P.C. can be made to change sign at a desired damping factor by a suitable choice of K. The sensitivity of P.C. to sign changes makes it useful as an error signal for adaptive systems. Assuming that a damping factor of 0.8 were desired, what value of K would be designed into the performance computer so that it would be suitable as an error signal in an adaptive control system?

11–3. Assuming that the Aeronutronic adaptive control system is being extended to n output channels, what would be a practical expression for the performance criterion?

11–4. An adaptive feedback control system is shown in Figure P11–4a. The switch remains in position 1 for positive input signals but switches to position 2 for negative input signals.

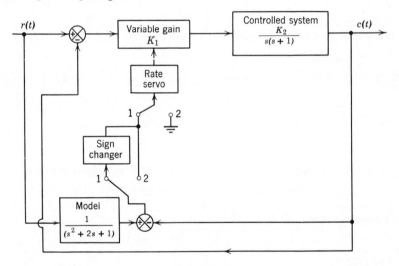

Figure P11–4a

(a) Qualitatively describe the behavior of this system.
(b) In what classification of adaptive control systems would you place it?
(c) Describe the behavior of this system when the input $r(t)$ varies as shown in Figure P11 4b.
(d) What is a reasonable performance criterion to use for this system?
(e) If K_2 should suddenly change value as the input is following a step input, describe the system's behavior.

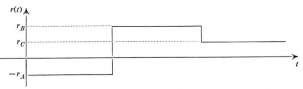

Figure P11–4b

11–5. The system shown in Figure P11–5 illustrates a sampled-data computer controlled adaptive control system. $G_a(z)$ represents the z-transform of the actual controlled system and $G_d(z)$ represents the z-transform of the desired control system.

(a) Qualitatively describe the operation of this system.

(b) What are its advantages and disadvantages?

(c) What effect on system stability and the computer design would a pole of $G_a(z)$, located in the right half plane, have?

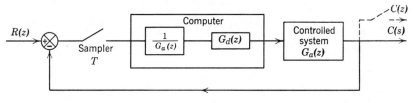

Figure P11–5

11–6. Assume that the Sperry impulsive-response adaptive control system, shown in Figure 11–8, is applied to an aircraft whose poles and zeros in the complex plane are located at

Poles	Zeros
$P_A = -4 \pm j2$	$\omega_1 = -3$
$P_B = -1 \pm j$	$\omega_2 = -2$

The poles due to the actuator are located at

$$P_C = -3 \pm 6j$$

The zero due to the autopilot computer is located at

$$\omega_C = -6$$

(a) Draw the root locus of this system.

(b) Find the velocity constant K_V that will result in a damping factor of 0.8.

INDEX